The New Companion Series
ADVENTURES IN LITERATURE

- Adventures for You, SECOND EDITION
- Adventures Ahead, SECOND EDITION
- Adventures for Today, THIRD EDITION
- Adventures in Living, THIRD EDITION
- Adventures for Americans, THIRD EDITION
- Adventures in Values

CHARLES G. SPIEGLER
Chairman of English
Central Commercial High School
New York City

TRASK H. WILKINSON
Director of English (K-12)
Brookline Public Schools
Brookline, Mass.

JOHN K. M. McCAFFERY
Editor, The American Dream
Author, Ernest Hemingway, The Man and His Work
Television and Radio Newscaster

HARCOURT BRACE JOVANOVICH

New York   Chicago   San Francisco   Atlanta   Dallas   *and*   London

The New
Companion Series:
Adventures in
Literature

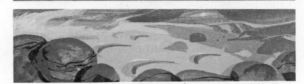

ADVENTURES
FOR AMERICANS

PRINTED IN THE UNITED STATES OF AMERICA

ISBN 0-15-337410-1

ACKNOWLEDGMENTS

For permission to reprint copyrighted material, grateful acknowledgment is made to the following publishers, authors and agents:

American Heritage Publishing Co., Inc.: "The Hanging of John Brown" by David Hunter Strother from *American Heritage*, February 1955. Introduction by Bruce Catton and "The Undelivered Speech" by John F. Kennedy from *Four Days. Ashley Famous Agency, Inc.:* "The Wild, Wild West" by Peter Lyon from *American Heritage*, August 1960, copyright ©1960 by Peter Lyon. *The Belknap Press of Harvard University Press* and *The Trustees of Amherst College:* "As Old as Woe" and "Like Rain It Sounded" from *The Poems of Emily Dickinson*, edited by Thomas H. Johnson, copyright 1951, 1955 by The President and Fellows of Harvard College. *Brandt & Brandt:* From *John Brown's Body* by Stephen Vincent Benét, copyright 1927, 1928 by Stephen Vincent Benét, copyright renewed ©1955, 1956 by Rosemary Carr Benét. "Robert E. Lee" by Rosemary Carr Benét and "Thomas Jefferson" by Stephen Vincent Benét from *A Book of Americans* by Rosemary and Stephen Vincent Benét, copyright 1933 by Rosemary and Stephen Vincent Benét, copyright renewed ©1961 by Rosemary Carr Benét. *Curtis Brown, Ltd.:* "Aches and Pains and Three Batting Titles" by Myron Cope from *Sports Illustrated*, March 7, 1966, copyright ©1966 by Time, Inc. *Marion Danielson Campbell:* "Corporal Hardy" by Richard Ely Danielson, copyright 1938 by Richard Ely Danielson. *The Christian Science Monitor:* From "The Poetry of Amy Lowell" by Robert Frost. *Richard Donovan:* Condensation of "The Fabulous Satchel Paige" by Richard Donovan. First published in *Collier's. Doubleday & Company, Inc.:* "R.M.S. *Titanic*" from *Sea Fights and Shipwrecks* by Hanson W. Baldwin, copyright ©1955 by Hanson W. Baldwin. *E. P. Dutton & Co., Inc.:* "You've Got to Learn" from *The Phantom Setter and Other Stories* by Robert Murphy, copyright ©1966 by Robert Murphy. *James A. Emanuel* and *The New York Times Company:* "After the Record Is Broken" by James A. Emanuel from *The New York Times*, October 22, 1964, ©1964 by The New York Times Company. *Colin Fletcher, Gary Beeman* and *The Reader's Digest:* "Trapped in the Desert" by Gary Beeman as told to Colin Fletcher from *Reader's Digest*, August 1964, copyright ©1964 by The Reader's Digest Association, Inc. *Blanche Gaines:* "The Strike" by Rod Serling. *Lawrence Sargent Hall:* "The Ledge" by Lawrence Sargent Hall, copyright ©1960 by Lawrence Sargent Hall. First published in *The Hudson Review*, Volume XI, No. 4, Winter 1958-59. *Harcourt Brace Jovanovich, Inc.:* "Anywhere and Everywhere People" and "Arithmetic" from *Complete Poems*, copyright 1950 by Carl Sandburg. "Elm Buds" from *Honey and Salt*, ©1963 by Carl Sandburg. "New Hampshire Again" from *Good Morning, America*, copyright 1928, 1956 by Carl Sandburg. "Abe Lincoln Grows Up" from *Abe Lincoln Grows Up* by Carl Sandburg, copyright 1926, 1928 by Harcourt Brace Jovanovich, Inc., renewed 1954, 1956 by Carl Sandburg. "A Tree is Best Measured When It's Down" from *Abraham Lincoln: The War Years*, copyright 1936, 1937, 1938, 1939 by Carl Sandburg, copyright 1939 by Harcourt Brace Jovanovich, Inc. "On the Road" from *Prairie-Town Boy*, copyright 1952, 1953 by Carl Sandburg. P. 451 from *Abraham Lincoln: The Prairie Years* by Carl Sandburg, copyright 1926 by Harcourt Brace Jovanovich, Inc.; renewed 1954 by Carl Sandburg. *Harcourt Brace Jovanovich, Inc.* and *American Museum of Natural History:* "Harmless or Deadly" (Part 1) by Osmond P. Breland from *Design for Good Reading: Level 1* by Melba Schumacher *et al.*, copyright ©1962 by Harcourt Brace Jovanovich, Inc. Adapted from *Natural History Magazine*, November 1953. *Harper & Row, Publishers:* "A Choice of Weapons" from *A Choice of Weapons* by Gordon Parks, copyright ©1965, 1966 by Gordon Parks. Adaptation of "Conversation with Leontyne Price" from *A Little Night-music* by Samuel Chotzinoff, copyright ©1964 by Samuel Chotzinoff. First published in *Holiday Magazine*. "Ex-Basketball Player," copyright ©1957 by John Updike and "Superman," copyright ©1955 by John Updike from *The Carpentered Hen and Other Tame Creatures* by John Updike. "Edmund G. Ross" (retitled "I...Looked Down into My Open Grave") from *Profiles in Courage* by John F. Kennedy, copyright ©1955 by

The authors wish to acknowledge with thanks the assistance given them in the preparation of this book by the following people:

Mr. Alfred Charasz, *student at the City College of the City University (Baruch Center).* Miss Marjorie Kaplan, *student at Brookline High School, Brookline, Mass.,* for permission to use the essay quoted on page 650.

Title Page: ALBERT PUCCI. Contents Art: PORTIA TAKAKJIAN.

ART CREDITS

JOSEPH CELLINI: 122, 124, 130, 340-41; JOE CLEARY: 39, 43, 198, 205, 209, 221, 332, 396, 398, 532, 538; JOSEPH GIORDANO: 3, 61, 100-01, 119, 185, 235, 293, 363, 366, 372, 374, 376, 381, 403, 439, 442, 444, 451, 453, 457, 459, 471, 497, 509, 547; PAUL GRANGER: 33, 35, 325, 328; RICHARD HARVEY: 14, 22, 187, 193, 237, 245; LARRY LASLO: 463, 527, 550, 559; WILSON MC LEAN: 25, 30, 68, 75, 132, 137; GERALD MC CONNELL: 252, 261, 264; JERRY PINKNEY: 102, 280, 283, 303, 310; GEORGE PORTER: 464, 542; ALBERT PUCCI: 80, 83, 112, 115; TOM QUINN: 407, 410, 413, 474, 476, 479, 482, 486, 568; SARAH READER: 5, 11, 415, 419, 520, 573; PHILIP RENAUD: 87, 91, 104, 108, 346, 353, 356, 506, 564; WILLIAM SHIELDS: 46, 54, 57, 93, 97, 146-47, 152, 161, 166, 213; PORTIA TAKAKJIAN: 387, 390, 429, 490, 499.

PICTURE ACKNOWLEDGMENTS

P. 37, Culver Pictures, Inc.; pp. 64, 66, United Press International; p. 78, Harper & Row; p. 86, Library of Congress; p. 91, Bettmann Archive, Inc.; p. 101, Macmillan; p. 103, Peter Simon of Knopt Publishing; p. 121, Mac Whitney; p. 168, Little, Brown and Company; pp. 170, 176, 182, NASA; p. 226, United Press International; p. 229, Courtesy American Museum of Natural History; p. 236, United Press International; p. 250, Bettmann Archive, Inc.; pp. 270, 277, Wide World Photos; p. 284, United Press International; p. 288, Wide World Photos; p. 294, Wayne Miller, Magnum; p. 296, Harper & Row; p. 297, Friedman-Abeles, Inc.; pp. 314, 319, Brown Brothers; p. 324, Bettmann Archive, Inc.; p. 343, Culver Pictures, Inc.; p. 512, lt., Thomas Hollyman, Photo Researchers; rt., Guy Gillette, Photo Researchers; p. 405, Bettmann Archive, Inc.; p. 441, Carew, Monkmeyer; p. 511, Granger Collection; p. 549, Culver Pictures, Inc.; p. 461, Harvard University.

The cover illustration is a photograph of a scale model of the *Seth Parker,* a schooner which once sailed on the Great Lakes. (Model courtesy of Nelson's Folly, New York)

THE AUTHORS

CHARLES G. SPIEGLER was co-author of the second edition of *Adventures For Americans.* In addition to teaching English in a number of New York City high schools and serving as department chairman of one (Central Commercial), he has done experimental work in programed instruction, audio-visual materials, and curriculum development. He is a lecturer in English composition at the City College of New York and has taught reading instruction at Queens College and Hunter College. He is a past president of the Manhattan Chapter of the International Reading Association, and a charter member of its Commission on Lifetime Reading. He is a member of the National Education Committee of the United Nations Association. His work has appeared in the New York *Times* Magazine, the *NEA Journal, Parents' Magazine, Education of the Disadvantaged,* and numerous other periodicals and anthologies, and he is co-author of a guidance book, *If You're Not Going to College.*

TRASK H. WILKINSON has taught English language and literature to students of all ages and backgrounds and is now Director of English for the public school system of Brookline, Massachusetts. He has served as chairman of the English Department of Brookline High School, Secretary-Treasurer of the New England Association of Teachers of English, and Chairman of the School and College Conference on English, and is a member of the National Education Association and of the Massachusetts Teachers Association.

JOHN K. M. MC CAFFERY is familiar to many from his years as newscaster on NBC television and radio and as moderator on "Author Meets the Critics." He was fiction editor of The *American* Magazine and editor of *The American Dream: A Half Century View from American Magazine.* He is the author of *Ernest Hemingway, The Man and His Work.*

CONTENTS

PART ONE
AMERICAN SCENES

UNIT 3 Moments of Decision

UNIT 4 Searchings

UNIT 5 The World of Sports

UNIT 6 Americans Look at Themselves

PART TWO
AMERICAN WRITERS

UNIT 4 Abraham Lincoln, Tragic Hero of the Republic

UNIT 5 The Closed World of Emily Dickinson

UNIT 6 Mark Twain, The Wild Humorist

UNIT 7 Stephen Crane, American Realist

UNIT 8 Frost and Sandburg, Poets of the People

UNIT 9 John Steinbeck: The Dignity of Man

CONTENTS BY TYPE

Fiction

Essays and Articles

Speeches and Quotations

Biography, Autobiography, and Personal Narrative

Poetry

Drama

Letters

PART ONE

The whole world realizes that there is something special about the United States. This is the land where opportunity knocked in a special way, where an uncivilized frontier and unimagined riches of natural resources combined to create a new way of life and a fresh, new-world attitude. This is the nation which was thrust into leadership by World War II and which ever since has poured out its treasures unselfishly to rebuild both its friends and former enemies and to set new nations on their feet. This is the people which John F. Kennedy in his last speech called the "watchmen on the walls of world freedom" and which has sent its young men all over the earth on missions of peace as well as war. This is America. But what is America like? What is special about Americans?

"Literature is people," someone has said. If this is true, you will find in the pages ahead something about the people of America.

There is much to be said about the American people. One aspect that you might notice above all is an attitude toward life. You will read about men, women, and young people who fought against their times, against the elements, against others, against themselves. All of these people knew that life must be faced and that life is always lived with other people. "Life is too strong for you," said one woman in this book; "it takes life to love Life." Another shook her finger in the President's face and cried: "Mr. President, you've got to do better than that for me."

People we meet in life give us ideas, but people we meet in books may give us stronger ideas or strongly enforce the ideas we get in life. Some people think that fictional lives are not worth reading and thinking about. Why should this book present you with anything but the exploits of actual, living people? As you read, you will see for yourself. People created for you in the mind of an author do have reality: fictional characters show attitudes toward the world, toward life and living, which express the viewpoint of

AMERICAN SCENES

the author. More important than these attitudes is the fact that characters in fiction are real people; people who *live* in the way you live and all men and women live who participate in their world. Corporal Hardy, Thief Jones, and Darkcat are people you may remember long after you have forgotten some of your class-mates.

Participating in the world is not all action. America was first a frontier which only strength and vigor could tame, but now our nation has moved into a time in which knowledge is truly power. Like our nation, most of our leaders grew from men of action to men of thought, but they retained in their mature years their youthful capacity for action. Washington and Theodore Roosevelt were noted horsemen and outdoorsmen; Andrew Jackson and Lincoln were men roughhewn by frontier life; ten presidents had been generals in wartime before election to the nation's highest office. Even quiet-seeming Supreme Court justices often have lives packed with action. One you will read about in "Two Boys on a Mountain." Another was Oliver Wendell Holmes, who as a young officer in the Civil War stood on a rooftop with Lincoln when Washington was being attacked. The story goes that Holmes saved the President's life by yelling at him, "Get down, you fool!" Later, of course, Holmes made many famous and more judicious statements, but he never forgot his years in the war. He wrote: "The final test . . . is battle in some form. It is one thing to utter a happy phrase . . . ; another to think under fire—to think for action upon which great interests depend."

In this book you will meet people who have to think under fire, people who find life a struggle. There are people who struggle for a piece of land to call their own, land where they can work and make a living. You will read about President Kennedy's personal cour-age, and also a story he wrote about another man's courage. You will meet American heroes—some real, others imaginary—in

1

action from the bridge at Concord to a town on Mars, from the year 1775 to the year 2001.

There is an entire unit on sports. The courage, endurance, and skill of an athlete are tested every time he steps onto the playing field. He must contend not only with his opponent but also with himself. This conflict is strong in the baseball stories of Satchel Paige and Roberto Clemente. Sometimes a man has only himself to depend on, as Ben Hogan on the golf course, and Jack London's Tom King in the fight ring.

There is a unit on the kind of searches men make: scientists searching for ways to conquer a killing epidemic; two boys searching for a way out of a desert in which they are trapped. There also is a unit on decisions that have to be faced. When is an enemy a friend? Can a boy make that one decision that shows he is becoming an adult? What time is safest to send into space the first American to orbit the earth?

There is an opening unit made up of nothing but action stories. Sprinkled throughout the book are poetry and humor. The poetry represents man's struggle to express himself, to communicate, to open minds and hearts. A poet, like Countee Cullen in "Any Human to Another," displays a unique vision of the world and tries to communicate this vision to you:

> "Your grief and mine
> Must intertwine
> Like sea and river. . . ."

A writer's unique vision is not always expressed in poetry; sometimes it is best handled as humor. You may laugh at the city man taken in by country folks, at the real story of Wyatt Earp, and at John Updike's modern American "Superman." James Thurber makes us laugh at the antics of his family the night the ghost got in, but we are laughing at ourselves as much as at the characters in the story. You may agree with Thurber that humor is a serious thing. He wrote, "I like to think of it as one of our greatest national resources."

There are many other works in Part One of ADVENTURES FOR AMERICANS, but all of them concern American life. These selections represent life as lived by Americans and literature written by Americans. When you finish the book, you should understand America—and perhaps yourself—a little better.

Stories of Action

Americans love adventure. The men who discovered America were adventurers. The colonists who bravely built the first American settlements, the frontiersmen who fought their way across the continent, the miners and mountain men, the hunters and trappers, the cowboys and sod-busting farmers, the hardy immigrants and restless New Englanders—all of these men were adventurers. Sometimes they sought adventure for money; sometimes to find a place to settle their families; sometimes just because they craved adventure.

Of course, every adventure implies excitement. All excitement, however, doesn't come from adventure. Some excitement is just for kicks. Some excitement happens to people not looking for it. In this section you will read about people who either were adventurers or did things just for kicks, or people to whom adventure came unbidden. You will read about an Indian who takes a strange risk while pursued by a posse. You will read about a man and two boys who on a bleak Christmas Day are trapped offshore by a rising tide. You will read the thoughts that run through a man's mind in the moment of his death. In one story you will read about two teen-age boys who find out that hot-rodding carries a little more responsi-

bility to it than they thought. Three of the stories occur in the present; the rest range from Civil War times to the year 2001. The action in these stories covers the country from the Mexican border to the coast of Maine—and even to a little town on the planet Mars. Not too many years ago, stories written about men on Mars were regarded as fantastic imaginings, but now we no longer regard ideas of this kind as fantastic. Space travel is an adventure of the kind that Columbus had when he set out to reach the rich and fabled East by sailing west. When he met Indians for the first time on the island of San Salvador, they must have seemed as strange to him as the Martian does to the hero in Ray Bradbury's story.

There is another kind of excitement in this section, the kind of excitement that also makes you laugh. James Thurber's story about the night the ghost got in is one example.

All of the stories in this section involve some sort of risk. All of us lead lives in which risk is involved—perhaps playing football or driving a car or simply doing a job. Risk is a part of our lives, in some degree. Perhaps this is one reason why we enjoy reading about it in the lives of others, in the real world, and in the world of the imagination.

The Returning

DANIEL DE PAOLA

Darkcat, after fleeing from an Indian reservation and killing one of his pursuers, finds himself at the lonely ranch house of another member of the posse. In the house are the white man's wife and baby, sick and needing help; in the barn is a fresh horse. What should Darkcat do?

It was the only house he had seen in three days; it nestled just at the base of the foothills which led to the Mexican border. For a long time he sat in the brush and wondered whether he should chance it. His throat was so dry he couldn't swallow, his mouth and lips were sore from lack of water, and he felt that if he didn't get some kind of food in his stomach soon, it wouldn't make any difference whether he made the border or not.

He moved closer; from fifty yards away he could see only a few chickens inside the fence; there was no other sign of life, no sounds, no smoke coming from the chimney, though it was nearing sundown. Whoever lived out here in such isolation must be independent and have a mind of his own, he thought. It didn't have to follow that they would suspect him just because he was an Indian. And perhaps they might even give him some food and water.

He went very slowly now; many of these outlying places had dogs to keep a watch. When he was satisfied there was none, he was no more than a score of paces from the fence. At this point he noted that the front door was ajar about a foot or so; this added to the strangeness of the place. The wind blew in gusts and he saw dust in small clouds swirl up on the porch and some of it enter the house. That and the quiet made him see there was something very odd about this place.

In a moment he was up on the porch. After looking at the horizon, he squinted in beyond the door and saw a dust-covered living room, old furniture, and faded walls. There was no one about and he entered; then he heard the heavy breathing, like sighing, from another room. The door on the left was half-open, and when he reached it, he heard the breathing more clearly. He pushed the door back silently and looked into a bedroom; and on the bed was a white woman and a small baby in her arms.

They were very sick, he saw close up; they seemed in a heavy, unnatural sleep, almost like a coma. The woman coughed several times, a harsh, racking cough that left her breathing all the louder. Her face was a deathly white and her eyelids trembled but never opened. The baby was exhaling quickly in a hoarse tone; on closer look he saw the reddish tinge of its throat and neck. Then he felt he knew what was wrong with them.

He looked all over the house quickly until he found a kerosene lamp in the kitchen; he took the top off, dipped a piece of cloth in it, and went back to the bedroom, where he rubbed both their throats with it. With more kerosene-soaked cloths wrapped around their throats, he used one wad at the end of a spoon to coat the insides of their throats with more of the spirit, a device he had seen his own mother use many years ago when he and his sisters had had diphtheria.

After he had a sip of water and munched on a hard piece of bread he found, he began the second phase of his treatment. With a damp towel he washed down both their bodies, then laid the baby out alongside the mother, who still wanted to hold it even in her condition. He then found two heavy blankets and threw them over the two patients. They slept on while he sat near and wondered what else he could do.

He recalled one old uncle saying that sufferers from the throat sickness seemed to get some relief from breathing fumes of gunpowder. Having only a knife, he began another search of the house. But though he could find no weapons or shells about, he did find a can out on the back porch which was half-filled with kerosene; this he brought into the kitchen and placed under the table for use later.

Back in the bedroom he redampened the cloths around their necks and felt their pulses and foreheads. They were still very hot and uneasy, but their breathing didn't sound quite so rough as it had earlier. He placed the chair near the window and gazed out. It was a lonely stretch—a few small trees beyond the small patch of prairie, and then the rocky slope leading up. A woman and baby here meant that there had to be a man about; and for a long time he thought of fleeing before the man returned. But then he saw a cow come into view around back and it made him see how thoughtless he had been.

He got a small fire going in the stove and put a pot of water on; he found some jelled soup in a larder and put that on the stove too to heat up. Then he took another small pan and went out to the cow, which he milked for a long time before she would stand still long enough to give him a small amount. This too he put on the stove. He rechecked his patients and went outside to bring in more wood to get the fire as hot as possible.

While he drank a small bit of the

warm soup, he looked at the needle-work in the dining room and scanned the living room, which had small poems hanging up on the walls. One was en-titled "Bless This Home," and another was a prayer to the Lord to give the oc-cupants fortitude and patience. He stood before a third one a long time, reading "Everyman is me, I am his brother. No man is my enemy. I am Everyman and He is Myself."

Out on the porch he looked back the way he had come. Ten days and one man's life back, he had left the reserva-tion, vowing never to return to that shameful bondage. But no sooner had he set out on his way west than the chief notified the Indian agent, who sent sev-eral deputies to recapture him. He re-called how they had separated and the one had guessed his next move back in the Diablo mountains, surprising him in a narrow rocky pass. He had only wanted to get away; he hadn't wanted to stab the man who had been so careless and heavy-handed as to miss the knife in his pants and to cuss him out for a dumb injun who didn't know when he was well off.

He took the deputy's horse and rode south for three days before it fell to the ground, unable to move any farther or stand. He had gone about a hundred yards away when he turned and saw the buzzards circling in the sky above it. Throwing curses at them as a kind of relief and cover, he went back, drew his knife, and made a cut deep in the horse's neck. He sat near it, glaring up at the black birds while the life of the animal oozed out into the thick sandy stubble around them.

After he had been walking for a long while, he turned and looked back. He saw the birds beginning to glide lower and lower until they landed; and he tried to find some solace in the memory of the tribe elders explaining how buz-zards and other ghouls helped keep the prairies clean. He tried to think of that but it didn't do much good. Just as it had never done any good to think of what the elders had said about their be-ing brought into reservations. The whites *had* grown too numerous and powerful; his own people *had* grown weaker and fewer in number. It was a fact of life they had to accept in the long run. But even so, he did his best not to think about it. Things were bad enough without basking in their defeat.

So when the prospect of undergoing another summer of skimpy planting and harvesting on reservations faced him again, some weeks back, he began to drink all the more to bolster the deci-sion he had made soon after they had been placed on the government land some two years before. And when the chief and several elders warned him two or three times in the past weeks, he knew the time had come. But before he could make a well-planned departure with supplies and a horse, he got into an argument with another man over a squaw and almost killed him in a fight; thus, before the elders could decide on his punishment, he slipped away one night with only the clothes he wore and his knife.

Knowing he had talked many times of heading west if and when he jumped the reservation, he decided to strike south instead, to throw off pursuers sent out by the chief and the agent. But they soon picked up his trail, and for a time he was desperate with the fear of being brought back to his people—not for the punishment they might set up for him, but for the shame he would have to bear, like an unruly hapless prisoner being brought back to his prison. He told him-self many times that he would endure almost anything but that.

It was their passivity that he had found most unbearable back on the reservation. Not only had they become like orphans waiting for the charity of the whites, but the chief and his people seemed satisfied to get less and less of what they were originally promised. More than once, he and several other braves had told the chief it was shameful for them, a tribe once as strong as the Blackfeet, to accept each new insult without so much as a word of complaint. But the chief had always promised to talk to the agent and never did; he knew full well if he dared to complain, another elder would soon be chief and receiving the little favors from the agent.

True, there had often been unrest and talk of deserting the reservation; but it had always occurred when men were drinking or bitter over the agent's shortcomings. Generally, the families accepted the few blankets and cows and horses and said that perhaps they were better off than other lone tribes who starved in bad weather. And when he had tried to argue that other tribes, even if some of them were starving, were still real people and not slaves to the whites, often he had been told that if he felt that way, why did he stay?

All through the night he bathed and rebathed the patients with hot cloths and painted their throats. Once or twice he tried to get some soup down them, but it didn't work. So he kept them warm and continued to watch them when he wasn't out on the porch watching the night. He wondered if he should continue south tomorrow or turn west as he had originally planned. He had heard tales of the opportunities in the Pacific Northwest or even up in the Yukon. Mexico was too close and offered only more land to flee through. He was weary and wanted to stop somewhere.

He dozed off in his chair and woke just before sunup; the woman was awake and saw him. She tried to sit up but was too weak; he moved to her and smiled down at her. "Are you feeling better?"

"Who are you?" Then before he could answer, she turned to her baby and held it close. "Is she going to be all right?"

"She is better," he nodded.

The woman scrutinized the baby for a moment and saw it was true. "Did you take care of her?"

He nodded again.

"Who are you?"

"I was passing and saw you were sick."

She looked over his dark, angular face, his stiff clothes, and the way his odd appearance filled the room. "Are you a doctor?"

"No, but I've seen this sickness before."

She gazed at him. "It was very good of you to stop and help us."

"Is there no one else here? You have a husband?"

"He left a few days ago; he works for the sheriff of the county."

"Will he be back soon?"

"I don't know."

"You have no friends near, to help?"

"Only over in town," she said.

He nodded and told her, "You mustn't talk more. Rest, and I will stay until you are better."

When he had tucked her and the baby in and resumed his seat by the window, he found her eyes on him. "What is your name?" she asked.

"Nachobi," he said, giving the first name which came to him.

She smiled faintly and said, "Well, I'm very grateful to you."

When she slept again, he rose and went outside. Odd how the name of a dead kinsman had come to his lips, one who had been killed in battle and not been like those on the reservation. But then he realized it wasn't so odd after all; when he was a boy, his father had told him all the great names, and he still remembered so many—Nachobi, Pionsomen, Long Face, Diniseau, and Laughing Cat, after whom his father had wanted to name him. His mother had compromised on Darkcat, used as a white man's last name, and had given him the first name of Willis, after an agent she had admired.

He wondered if the woman's husband was on his trail, too. Perhaps not, since the reservation was up in Oklahoma; but he did know that he couldn't afford to remain here much longer. The deputy had to be coming home soon, and he wasn't going to like having Willis here, no matter what he had done for the woman and baby. He told himself that he would leave sometime this day, as soon as the woman was strong enough to get food for her baby. In the meanwhile he could keep checking with her on the location of her husband.

He stood by the window of the bedroom and gazed in on the woman. He wondered if his several women friends in the tribe still spoke of him, although it was probably forbidden by the chief; and he wondered too if his old mother was being shunned by others because of this so-called shame. He pictured the small, bony woman with no teeth, who always watched him with those sad eyes when he grew from a wild boyhood into a bitter manhood; and he could still hear her saying, "You must see that we have to live thinner days now. Our ancestors, if they were alive with us, would be living just as we are." And he would never believe that; he told her more than once when drinking that the ancestors would never accept such a trammeled life; they would erupt like a river over its banks.

He never got over feeling that he had been cursed in the time he was born; his life had spanned the whole decline, and thus the memories he had as a boy led him into an empty maturity. Often when he had been a small boy, he had seen great chiefs and heard of victories over the whites. His father and his uncles had shown him bits of the glory; he had been like an observer of the epoch and didn't know until many years later that the epoch had been closing. If he had been born thirty years later, perhaps he would have listened to his mother's words and not felt quite so much dissatisfaction with himself and his people.

He had often envied the braves who had adapted themselves to the new life; they had taken their wives and plots of land and begun to work as any white would on his homestead. When Willis and other drunken braves gathered late at night, they talked of these "white braves" and scoffed at their methods and outlook. And he joined in with the most scornful tones and sarcastic laugh. But when he was alone, he now and then wondered if perhaps the white braves weren't the wisest of their tribe. Most of the time, however, he tried not to think of them and never had anything to do with them.

If he knew he could never enter into the white braves' mode of life, he knew also that the existence of his cronies was as bad or worse. Night after night of drinking, gaming, and fighting was like letting out the pent-up emotion of his wasting years. Now and again he woke up with a hangover, lying among a bunch of sprawled forms, and felt he was a bigger fool than any of them. He too was becoming old and paunchy and idiotic. But when the others got up and did a little work to get money for more liquor, he sat around staring at the circle of the horizon. That was when his anger would reach its whitest pitch: their ancestors had roamed the continent from one coast to another and here they were confined to a three-hundred-square-mile plot like fishes in a lake.

He found a small bottle later and put some warm milk in it for the baby; the mother woke up and fed it while he watched. The mother seemed stronger now; her fever was down and she didn't cough too often. As the baby drank slowly, she gazed up at Willis.

"Do you have to be moving on?"

"Yes, I do. I was waiting to see if you were better. Does your throat hurt much?"

"A little, but I'm much better, thanks to you."

She gazed down at her baby drinking.

"She looks better too," he said.

"Yes, she does. I don't know what we would've done without you."

He asked her how it had all happened and she told him that she and the baby had been hit almost simultaneously with a sudden fever and sore throat; then coughing and dizziness set in so that she had to take to her bed. He told her he had had diphtheria as a boy and had remembered some of the symptoms and treatments.

She smiled at him and said, "It was divine providence that you happened by."

He asked if her husband often stayed away this long, and she replied he did when his job demanded it, knowing she could take care of herself and the baby. "Until this time," she smiled.

He asked if she could swallow some soup and she said she would try. He brought some in to her and sat at the window as she drank it. She was a fairly young woman, hardy-looking, with a round face and long blonde hair. Between sips she asked where he came from and where he was bound. He made up a story of heading for a job in some Mexican gold fields. She said she wished he would stay long enough to receive the thanks of her husband, who was probably on his way home by now. But that if he didn't, she would understand.

For a moment they were silent; he sat next to the window watching her, and she, between turning to the baby and drinking her soup, was looking over at him. At another time and place he wouldn't have wanted to linger in a room alone with a white woman. He had heard of more than one Indian in such an instance being accused of everything from attempted assault to terrorizing a helpless female. But here and now there was only friendliness between them; it was a kind of kinship he had never felt toward a white before. It made him think of the words he had read in the living room.

He saw that the woman was still weak; he took away the bottle and dish, and told her he would stay a while longer until she got a little more rest. She smiled tiredly and said it was very good of him, she didn't know how to thank him. He resumed his post at the window and took to scanning the northern prairie. He knew he was stretching his luck; if he was smart, he would wait until she dozed off and then leave. But somehow he just couldn't.

The longer he sat, however, the more restive he became. He began to think of the times his people had suffered at the hands of the whites, mainly for trusting the whites too much. One of his uncles had taught him early the saying that an Indian should trust the whites but keep his knife sharp. Perhaps the woman would never hurt him after what he had done for her, but the husband was something else again. He went outside and thought about what he should do.

While he tried to make a plan, he

milked the cow, chopped more wood, fed the chickens, and cleaned the pots he had used. Then he brought several buckets of water in from the well out back; afterward he went into the bedroom to see if she was awake. She was dozing, and he took the chair to wait.

It was almost noon when she woke up. He smiled at her when she glanced over, and he said, "Feeling stronger?"

"Yes, very much so."

"I thought after I got you and the baby a lunch, I would leave."

"Of course; we've kept you far too long already. In fact, I think I can get up now." She started to sit up and he moved to her.

"Not yet," he told her. "Have some more soup and take a few more hours of rest. You will feel much better by evening."

"Maybe you're right." She lay back. "You're the doctor here."

He returned to the kitchen and got the soup ready. While she fed the baby and had some herself, she said she had to pay him in some way for all this help.

He tried to protest but she insisted. "Is your horse rested and fed?" she asked. When he told her he had no horse, she said, "There's the answer; you'll take our spare horse."

"I couldn't do that," he said.

"But you must."

"It's kind of you, generous, but I can't take your horse."

For the next few moments she kept insisting and he kept refusing. He had a pretty good idea of what would happen if he was caught with a white man's horse. Back at the window he noted a puff of dust in the distance. While he listened to her, he saw it grow until he could make out the form of a man on a horse. When she saw him gazing out, she asked, "Is someone coming?"

"Yes," he told her.

"It must be Jim, my husband." Perhaps she guessed his feelings, for she added, "I'm so glad he's come home before you left. I want to tell him all you've done for us."

He listened to her talk about moving closer to town and all the while he kept glancing at the approaching rider. Soon he could hear the hoofs of the horse hitting the ground and presently the rider was coming through the fence up to the house.

"That's him; I can tell by the sound," she said. When they heard steps on the porch, she sat up and called out, "Jim? I'm in here." The man then came into the bedroom.

As he moved to his wife, he grew aware of Willis near the window. He stopped and stared at the Indian.

"This is Mr. Nachobi," the woman told him. "And if he hadn't come along yesterday, I don't know what you would've found here today." While the cowboy regarded the Indian searchingly, she gave him the whole story, laying a special stress on how Willis had worked like a doctor with only crude tools to save both her and the baby. The cowboy was around thirty, tall and lean, with the hard look of a man much in the saddle. He had fair skin and light eyes, which looked hard and soft at the same time. Now they seemed friendly as he said, "I'm much obliged to you; it was a darn fine thing you did here."

Willis nodded and waited.

"I told Mr. Nachobi that he had to take Daisy in payment," the woman went on. "He has no horse of his own and this is the least we can do. Don't you think so?"

"Of course," said the cowboy. "No buts about it, after all he did for us." He bent over his baby, eyed it closely, and then kissed it on the head. He then caressed the woman and looked back at Willis.

"He was just going to leave when you came," the woman told her husband.

"Sure glad you were here for me to thank you," he said to Willis.

"But I think he has to be on his way now," she went on.

The cowboy turned questioningly to Willis, who said this was true.

"Well, then, I'll saddle up Daisy for you."

Willis said good-by to the woman and followed the man out back. He watched the cowboy bring the mare out of the barn and throw a saddle over her. After he had tightened the cinches and patted the horse, he turned and studied the Indian. "You're Darkcat, aren't you?"

Now the blue eyes were cold and challenging. And Willis said it was so.

"I thought so as soon as I saw you." After a pause the cowboy went on. "For what you did, I can never repay you. It was as good as I've ever seen; not many white men would've done it." Another long pause. "We got the word on you last week and we found Jorgensen, the man you killed." Their eyes met and locked. "You know I can't let you go, don't you?" said the cowboy.

"I know," nodded Willis.

"All right. But for saving my wife and baby, I can give you a day."

Willis stared, not understanding.

"I've been in the saddle for five days, so I'm taking a day's rest. By then my wife'll be up and I can leave again. And then I'm coming out after you. Understand?"

"I understand," said Willis.

"She's a good horse." He patted the mare. "She'll give you all she's got; you won't have to drive her much." He put a canteen of water up over the saddle horn and asked Willis if he wanted any food.

Willis refused, and they stood in silence. "Well," said Willis finally, "I'll leave now." He swung up into the saddle and gazed down at the man.

"I'll be starting out tomorrow about this time," said the cowboy.

Willis nodded.

"And make no mistake about it, I mean to get you."

"I understand," Willis repeated.

He moved the mare south toward the hills; he turned once and saw the cowboy still watching him. And he knew he was in for more and now perhaps even harder pursuit.

The farther he rode, the less did he feel the cowboy had been boyish or silly or downright crazy. He saw that even amid the whites, there was still a touch of the old, undying spirit. And he felt he was closer to this blue-eyed white man than to any of his own people. When they finally did meet again over a gun or knife, it would be a more fitting finish for either than anything else that might come their way.

THE FACT IS—

1. What did Darkcat see that made him realize that there was something strange about the white man's home?

2. How did the Indian know what treatment to give his patients?

3. What circumstances made Darkcat rebellious?

4. What does Jim do to repay Darkcat?

EVERYMAN IS ME

1. The Indian saw small poems hanging on the walls of the cowboy's home. One read: "Everyman is me, I am his brother. No man is my enemy. I am Everyman and He is Myself." Discuss the meaning of this quotation. How does Darkcat react to it? Do you know John Donne's meditation "No Man Is an Island"? Look it up to see if Donne would have approved of Darkcat's reaction.

2. Explain how this story gives you insight into the relations between the Indian and the white man at one time in the history of our country. Write one or two paragraphs on this subject.

3. The story ends: "When they finally did meet again over a gun or knife, it would be a more fitting finish for either than anything else that might come their way." Why would it be a "more fitting finish" for Darkcat? Why for Jim? What do you think will happen when—and if—they do meet again?

A WORD TO REMEMBER: scrutinize

The author uses this word in the following context: "The woman scrutinized (SKROO·tih·nyzd) the baby for a moment and saw it was true." *Scrutinize* means "to examine closely."

What part of speech is formed by adding the suffix *–ize*? Name five other words with this suffix.

Terror
on
the
Highway

ALEX GABY

The name of the game is
"Chicken!" This hair-raising
account of reckless driving
ends in a nighttime crash
on a lonely highway.

There was a little, persistent ache in his right shoulder, as there always was now when he was behind the wheel for more than an hour or two, but that was all. Everything else was fine.

Another three hours at this rate, and they would be at Mildred's. That would make it after eleven; the children would all be too tired for roughhouse, and by twelve just the grownups, he, Paula, Mildred, and Frank—they would all have a drink and talk a little, laugh a little, have a nice, quiet good time.

He shifted his weight and the ache went out for a second, like a candle snuffed, but was back again. He changed position, hunched against his door.

"Shoulder bothering you some, dear?" Paula looked at him, the excitement of the trip lifting the corners of her mouth.

He glanced at her and back to the long, straight road. "Same as always. Nothing to worry about, hon."

"Let me rub it, Dad. You want me to?" Ruth, in the back seat, hunched forward and began to knead his shoulder. He saw her earnest, ten-year-old face in the rearview mirror, her dark hair wind-blown, tight curls heaped about her head like a crazy mop. Her eyes were intense, staring down at his shoulder, and the intensity puckered her mouth while her strong little hands kneaded his shoulder. Doing a good job of it too.

"Ruth, please," Paula said quietly. "You know you shouldn't bother your father when he's driving. The way people drive these days, it's bad enough, without all that tugging and pulling."

Ruth stopped the kneading and sat back in her seat. "Gee, how much longer, Dad?" she asked. "I can't wait to see Aunt Mildred and the kids and everything. You know?"

"We'll be in Crockerville in a few minutes," he said. "Then only a hundred and twenty miles to Waco."

Paula leaned closer to him. "Getting tired, dear? Three hours against that sun, I wonder you're not blind. And, Biff, slow it down a little, will you?"

He glanced down at the speedometer. Fifty-five. *Speed creeps up on you on these long, straight stretches*, he thought. But that's Texas—long, straight stretches. "Paula, I'm only doing a little over fifty. Relax. No one more careful behind a wheel than I is—I am—I is. I like 'I is' better."

"'I is' is right," she laughed, and leaned close to him, nuzzling her nose against his cheek.

He looked down and noticed that her face was as shiny as marbles, reddened with the heat and the dust that came in with the wind through her window, loosening her hair, but lovely as always—lovely to him.

He stole a quick look in the rearview mirror at Ruth, and saw her in profile, gazing out her window, whistling something horrible between her teeth, and for one piercing instant he felt so sorry for her, alone, while he and Paula—

The sign for Crockerville came at them, and he slowed down to thirty miles per hour. DON'T HURRY TO KILL OUR CHILDREN. POPULATION 2,196. WE WANT TO KEEP IT THAT WAY! the sign said.

In the center of Crockerville, at the only major intersection in the town, there was a light. It was red, and he stopped. A car pulled up on his right with a squeal of brakes. Glancing across to the car, he saw that it was red—incredibly red—with all the chrome removed, and the whole body lowered so that it nestled over its wheels like a short-legged bug.

"Hot rod," he said, nodding toward the red car. "More and more of them around."

Paula looked at it and wrinkled her nose. "It looks like some kind of a throwback. A hybrid or something. Why do they do that to perfectly good cars?"

He shrugged. "They soup them up to really go. Me, I'll take Steady Nelly here."

"I like Steady Nelly too," Ruth piped up from the back seat. "I'll bet we could beat that old thing, couldn't we, Dad?"

Paula whipped her head around to glare at Ruth, "You can just make up your mind, young lady, we're not going to try!" she snapped. "That's just the kind of thing you read about, all this racing on the highways!"

He laughed and hunched over the wheel. He tapped the accelerator and gunned the motor several times.

She turned on him. "Biff! What's wrong with both of you? You're not going to race that idiotic thing!" No matter how many times he threatened to do something spectacular in the car—and never did—she always reacted. It was a private little joke with him.

The light changed. "Watch this!" he hissed through clenched teeth. "That underslung meat wagon, we'll take 'em!"

He stepped down hard on the accelerator and the car lurched ahead. Suddenly there was a peculiar, staccato snort on his right, and the red car was up to him, inching past him, and they were racing. There was a car parked in the path of the red car, not two hundred feet ahead, with people getting out of it at the curb, but the snorting grew louder and the red car did not slow down. A hundred feet, less than a hundred feet, so close now that he stamped his foot on the brake and twisted hard to the left on his wheel, just time enough so that the red car whipped between him and the car parked at the curb, roaring with the staccato bursts down the street. *They knew I'd do that. They knew it.* He was terribly angry and yanked the car back into the right lane.

"Did you see that?" Paula gasped. "Biff, did you see that? Those people— they might have been killed!"

"I saw it," he said. "Blamed fools. I'd like to knock their heads together. They knew I'd pull out, Paula. The blamed fools knew I would. Can you tie that?"

"You could have beat 'em, Dad," Ruth said contentedly from the back seat, her excitement subsiding. "You just didn't want to with me and Mommy in the car."

They stopped on the main street and had soda and a hot dog at a curbside stand, and when they started again, it was getting quite dark, with the sun finally extinguished against the flat edge of the land. He settled back in his seat and made himself comfortable, not quite so happy as he had been before

the red car; angry with the red car for knowing he would pull out. They were near the edge of town now, with the main street becoming road again, and there were the signs up at the gas stations: LAST CHANCE, FILL 'ER UP. NEXT GAS STATION 60 MILES.

There was the red car, sitting like a sleek worm on the apron of the last gas station on the edge of town on his right, glowing with the color of bright blood under the arc lights of the station. The driver had a soft-drink bottle in his hand, hanging out the window, his arm limp, as if the bottle were unbearably heavy.

Without the slightest hesitation, Biff pulled off the road and slid to a stop near the red car. He could see their white shirts gleaming inside the low coupe.

"Hey, you, in there," he said sharply. "If you can't drive that jalopy properly, stay off the road! You hear me?" He was yelling so loud that it surprised him.

Ruth was hopping up and down in the back, also yelling. "We could beat you any day, so there! Nya-a-a-a-a-nya-a-a!"

"Biff . . . Ruth! Stop it!" Paula was pushing at his shoulder.

He subsided and started the car moving. Suddenly there was a laugh from the red car, clear and sharp, and a piercing rebel yell—the kind you hear in Western movies or in pictures about the Civil War.

They drove on, and now the darkness came in completely to scoop away the land on either side of the road, and all he could see of the road itself was the part in his headlights, skimming into him easily, smoothly. He relaxed, switched on his far beams, and loosened his grip on the wheel, yearning to be at Mildred's. He sighed and stepped on the gas a little too hard.

"Biff, slow down a little," Paula said and closed her window. The wind had chilled quickly as the darkness came.

"Sure, hon," he said, and glanced in the mirror at Ruth in the back seat. She was already asleep.

There had been no car besides his on the road. It was the old road, and everyone else used the new superhighway about ten miles north. But this road was a little shorter, and he knew it well. He wished there were a few cars on the road. It would be a friendly thing to do—dipping headlights to an oncoming car, sort of a friendly bow.

And then the red car drew up behind him. First there had been a glow in his rearview mirror, and then there was the red car. He knew it was that car because its headlights were so low, hugging the road. A cold finger touched his spine, and he glanced quickly at Paula; she was dozing, and for that he was suddenly grateful.

He speeded up a little and the lights of the red car receded, but then drew up again behind him, making him feel that it was about to crawl up his neck, like some monster insect.

For at least ten minutes more the red car followed him so closely that if he stepped on his brakes, it would ram him, but he knew they were sure he would not do that, just as they were sure back there in Crockerville that he would yank his wheel to the left so that they could careen in between him and the car at the curb.

He thought how foolish it had been to stop at that gasoline station to yell at them that way. He should have remembered it was Saturday night; not much for people in places like Crockerville, on a by-passed road, to do on Saturday nights, and when a couple of them have one of those souped-up-jalopies— He shook his head and made up his mind to stop worrying about the red car. Sooner or later it would turn around and go back; he'd be hanged if he'd

speed up more than the sixty he was doing. Let them eat his dust if they wanted it that way, but all the time he knew it would not stay that way, not for long. This was not what they wanted.

It came quickly. There was that peculiar sputtering snort behind him, and suddenly it was beside him. He could have reached out his hand and touched it, but in another instant it was in front of him, staying just a few feet in front. Then he smelled the exhaust fumes coming in through his air vents. The smell grew quickly very strong.

Paula was awake. "What was that?" she said, shaking her head sharply. "Oh, Biff! That car—what's he doing here? When—?" Her hand flew to her throat, and when he saw that, besides everything else he felt, he could feel the anger rising in him too.

"Relax, honey," he said quietly, his voice tight with the effort to sound normal. "You'll wake Ruth. They just want to play a little, but I'm not having any. They'll get tired of playing games in a little while, and then they'll go back. Just take it easy."

In a few minutes the red car began to slow down, and he was forced to use his brake several times to keep from riding up their two inadequate little bumpers. Finally they were going thirty miles an hour. His hands clenched, impatience battling with the anger in him, anger not quite covering the cold finger on his spine.

"What do they want?" Paula asked wildly.

He tried to grin at her. "They're getting even for that hiding I gave them back there. It's nothing. They'll quit soon, Paula. Just relax, now." *They've got to quit.*

"I tried to stop you back there," she said. "You and Ruth, yammering away at them—those— Biff! What does he want?"

She had seen the driver of the red car put his arm out of his window and motion them forward, an indolent, graceful movement of the white-shirted arm, inviting them ahead.

The coldness went out of his spine. Now he knew what they wanted, and the knowledge was a relief softening his grip on the wheel. "They wanted to race, honey, that's all," he said. "We'll give them their little race, and that will be that. Really got under their skin back in Crockerville. Those hot-rodders have a certain kind of pride."

"Biff, don't race them!" she gasped. "It's dangerous!"

"It's more dangerous not to," he said. "They're going to have their little race or else. Well, here goes."

He stepped hard on the accelerator, drew out abreast of the red car, and then put the accelerator all the way down to the floor. The car leaped ahead and for an instant it seemed he would pass them. He threw a quick sideward glance at the red car, and in that instant when he thought he would pass them, he felt a surge of exhilaration flood up through his chest into his head, and thought, *Good old Nelly, still more than a match for a jalopy.*

"Biff! For heaven's sake!"

He laughed, his eyes eager and happy. "We'll take 'em, honey! That race they wanted, they got it!"

The staccato snorting grew high-pitched and violent. Before he could pass, the red car was up to him, abreast of him again. He stepped harder on the accelerator, trying to push it through the floor, but his motor was whining now, complaining, and when he flicked his eyes down to the speedometer, he saw the needle wavering uncertainly at eighty-seven, where he had never seen it before. He felt the hesitations and skipping of the motor, and knew it had reached its limit. The red car skimmed ahead, snorting, went ahead easily, with the white arm hanging out the window, its fingers tapping the red door in some kind of lazy rhythm, and in seconds the red car was ahead of them on the road. The white arm lifted an indolent wave, and then the hand, bathed in his lights, clenched itself into a fist with the thumb extended stiffly, pointed down.

He inched the car back to the right lane while the exhilaration drained out of him. It had been no race, he knew. There had been no chance to win, as in a race; there never had been a chance.

"Slow down! Biff, for heaven's sake, slow down!" Paula was leaning toward him, shouting in his ear. *How long had she been shouting?* he wondered, and felt a cramp in his right leg, surprised to find his foot still jamming the accelerator against the floor. His fingers were clamped around the wheel as if tightened there with steel bands. It took an actual effort to lift his foot, and they slowed down quickly—seventy, sixty, fifty, forty-five. Forty-five seemed slow, and the wind had stopped yowling at their windows.

"Don't you ever do a thing like that again!" Paula panted, glaring at him. "Never again, you hear me? Never again!"

He glanced back over his shoulder at Ruth. She was awake, sitting rigidly, her hands dug into the seat on both sides of her. Her eyes were wide, frightened.

The red car had slowed down, too, slowing more, coming closer again to them. Lazily, it drifted back almost on top of them, and they were back to thirty miles an hour. Again, gracefully, the white arm came out, waving them ahead.

"Biff!"

"Don't worry," he muttered. "The race is over." Why didn't they go away? Why didn't they just go away? And now he thought of the red car as his enemy; no longer a playful nuisance, but an enemy hounding him, forcing him to drive thirty miles an hour on this empty, straight road.

"Biff," Paula said in a few moments, "let's just stop for a little while. Why not pull off the road and stop? They'll just go away if we stop. I'm—well, I'm afraid, Biff."

"Not on your life," he snapped. "Who do they think they are? I'm not a child to be pushed around like this." He looked at her and saw her biting her lip nervously, staring hard at the red car so close ahead. "Oh, honey!" He reached over and patted her shoulder. "Sorry I snapped at you like that. But look—as long as we keep going, it's going to be all right. They'll get bored. They'll look for somebody else to race, the fools. Just relax, honey. We'll get there a little later, that's all."

Ruth piped up from the back seat. She was fine again. "Why'n't you just beat 'em, Dad?" she said. "Gee, they're going so slow, you could beat 'em. I know—"

"Ruth, please be quiet. Let Daddy alone." Paula reached back and patted Ruth's knee, but not for a second did she take her eyes off the red car. The white arm was still waving them on, indolently.

A flash of anger hit him and he hooked his thumb over the horn ring and blew his horn, a long blast, and was immediately sorry he had done that. A horn on this road, like a wail in a vacuum. What good was his horn?

But the horn actually broke the spell somehow, and there were sparks from the twin exhausts, sputtering the red car into sudden life. It shot ahead swiftly, leaving the road dark and deserted ahead of him.

Wonder what those maniacs put under that hood? he thought, and said,

"Could be they're tired of us slowpokes. Maybe we've seen the last of them."

"I hope so, Biff. Lord, I hope so!" Paula answered, and after a few more minutes, as the road stayed dark and deserted ahead, she settled back in her seat.

He increased his speed to forty-five, and drove tensely ahead, watching the road as if that, too, had suddenly become an enemy. There was nothing up ahead, nothing one instant, and the next instant the two taillights flashed on not two hundred feet in front of him on the road, bright and red, like a monster's eyes. The red car had been sitting on the road without lights, waiting for him. He jammed on the brake and the nose of his car dipped hard with a squeal coming from his tires, but there had been no need for him to do that, because the red car's rear wheels tore against the concrete of the road and accelerated so quickly that he could not have hit it if he had wanted to. They knew he would hit his brake just like that; just as they had known what he would do in Crockerville and since Crockerville. That was the thing he thought of as the red car shot forward, fast, sputtering ahead, quickly losing itself in distance.

He sucked in his breath as if coming up from a fall into cold water, and then he heard the crying from the back seat. He looked back to see Ruth piled up into a ball on the floor, wailing.

"She's hurt, Biff! Stop the car!" Paula had her door open even before he had the car stopped on the shoulder of the road, and she jumped out to reach for Ruth. He got out on his side and ran around the car. Ruth was standing on the hard-packed dirt of the shoulder, her face buried in Paula's waist.

He took Ruth to the front of the car and they examined her in the light. There was nothing wrong except for a scrape on her elbows and a skinned knee, and in a moment the girl stopped crying.

"Why'd you do that?" she glared at him, hiccuping. "That was a dumb thing to do, all right!"

"I won't do it again, rabbit," he said slowly. "Come on. Everything's fine now. Get in the car."

He saw Paula looking at him, her eyes enormous, frightened. She helped Ruth into the car and slid in herself.

"Biff, do you think we ought to go back to Crockerville?" Paula said, her voice pinched and dreadful. "Didn't you say something about—about having the car checked or something?"

Ruth's face twisted up at him quickly. "You promised we'd be at Aunt Mildred's tonight," she accused. "The kids'll be waiting up; you know that, Dad! We got to go to Waco tonight; you said we would."

"Look, Paula," he said finally. "We're over twenty miles out of Crockerville. It really doesn't make any difference which way we go, you understand? Either they're—I mean, either we've had the last of the trouble or, if we have any more, we can stop somewhere up ahead—call in from a ranch house, you know?"

He got out, went around to the trunk and got out the long jack handle, and then went back to his seat, placing the jack handle on the floor of the car in the back.

Paula was near to tears. "Why not just stay here until morning?" she said, quavering, not sure of herself at all. "By then the trouble will be gone. Biff? Biff? Why not? It's not cold."

"No!" She should know that much about him. There were limits. That she should know after eleven years of marriage. He felt a small flash of anger directed at her—that she should think it was in him to sit parked on the side of the road all night because of that red car.

He drove out on the road, peering ahead. The road was empty, dark ahead of his lights. But as he drove he began to think of the signs back there in Crockerville—sixty miles to the next town. What was it now? Terrence? That was it. Terrence. A few gasoline stations, a store or two, a motel.

Forty miles to go to Terrence, along this familiar, well-remembered road, straight, with no turns, with nothing on it but him and that red car, making the road an enemy for the first time. When he thought of that—just him and that red car—he lost his anger at Paula, and considered for an instant turning around to rush back to Crockerville. But that would do no good, the road was an enemy that way too; and he then considered doing as she suggested—pulling off the road to wait for morning. . . . No!

Then there was a faint glow on the road far ahead. A car coming, coming so fast that he knew it was the red car coming, maybe going home, back to Crockerville at last. He gripped the wheel hard, waiting for the red car to pass them, eager for it to pass, and still worried about the red car coming.

But the red car was coming down his lane, on the wrong side of the road. He felt his chest freeze and blinked his eyes, not believing such a thing was happening, and then opened them wide, almost in fascination as the red car kept coming down his lane, its lights blinding, piercing, hurtling straight at them. The breath stopped in his throat.

Paula and Ruth shrieked together, and still he was frozen, unable to breathe or move, until the lights were leaping at him, almost on him, and at last he convulsively jerked on his wheel to his left and drove his car off the road on the shoulder on the other side, into the dirt.

"Chicken!" He heard the yell from the red car clearly as it slammed by the place where his car had been, and he watched the red car careen around behind him, deftly making a screeching turn, and then it was back again, going back up the road again to Terrence.

He set the hand brake, his hands so slippery and wet he had to fumble with the brake several times before it could be done. The yell "Chicken!" still rang in his ears and, for a moment, almost idly, he wondered what it meant, and then remembered a television program they had seen late one night—races, where two drunks got into their cars and raced at each other to see which would be the one to get out of the way. He remembered saying to Paula that such drivers deserved to be killed, and she had said she didn't believe they did such things, even drunks—a "chicken race" they had called it.

Paula had her arms around Ruth and both of them were crying. "They're going to kill us!" Paula choked, tears draining down her cheeks. "Get us out of here!"

He wiped his wet hands on his trousers and stared at them, his wife and his child; all of them in his car, which was paid for; on a road which his taxes helped pay for—he stared at them until his eyes smarted.

"Chicken!" The red car would do it again. It had to. It was a ballet of some kind, a ballet in a nightmare where these things had to be played out, danced out, until the dance was ended, and the dance was not ended, that he knew.

"Chicken!" He could hear it yelling in his ears, and he could hear his wife and child sobbing, afraid and in danger of the red car, his partner in this dance —a red car, or the enemy in France during World War II coming over a ridge at him, or a fighter plane coming in low over the trees at him—the same danger, the same thing—and not to him

alone, but also now to Paula and his child—and then, as it had been before with him, it was suddenly all right, and the coldness went out of his chest and went, instead up his head, where it could help him, as it did before.

He got out and held the door open. "Get out, Paula. Quick, now. Take Ruth and get out."

She slithered across the seat, taking Ruth with her, and stood in the dirt, still crying, looking up at him.

"Biff, please," she said, holding Ruth against her.

"Don't ask questions!" he snapped. "Take Ruth and get into that field. Don't stand there! Get going, Paula!"

He started the car slowly, back on his own side of the road, creeping ahead, alone now in the car, squinting across his lights at the sides of the road, knowing there had to be one near here. It was time for one on this road, where there were so many because the land was flat and needed drainage.

There it was, just ahead, a short concrete culvert over a drainage ditch, not a quarter of a mile from where he had left Paula and Ruth. It was like a tiny bridge with short, heavy concrete balustrades on each side of it, the bridge just wide enough for two cars, and beneath it the ditch, dry now, crossing under the road. He drove the car beyond the bridge and stopped it about fifteen feet beyond, on the right side of the road, but a little over the center stripe, too, and checked to make sure his far beams were on. Then he reached into the glove compartment and got out a wrench he kept there and placed it on the accelerator, so that the motor raced a little. That was important; he had to get as much brightness to his lights as possible.

There was a flashlight in his pocket, also from the glove compartment, and then he jumped out of the car, slammed

the door shut, and ran down the road a little, turned back and looked at his car. His headlights blinded him so that he could not see the bridge at all. Good. He ran back to the bridge and stared up the road, remembered the jack handle, ran to the car, got it out, and stared up the road again. It had to come. The ballet was not over yet. It had to come.

And come it did. First, there was a glow on the road, far ahead, and then the glow turned into two focal points of light, coming with great speed at him on the wrong side of the road.

A vast exultation shook him, and almost too late he jumped over the balustrade and crouched in the culvert. He wanted terribly to watch the red car kill itself, and in his mind he did see it, very accurately as the red car hurtled down the wrong side of the road, knowing he would turn away at the last instant, knowing that about him, as the red car knew it before—but not this time. A flashing realization—too late—that he was not going to turn away this time, a wild turn of the wheel—a balustrade sharply etched in the lights, not supposed to be there, a shriek and a wilder turn at the wheel, and then noise —a tremendous amount of noise.... Chicken!

The red car finally came to a stop, upright, a hundred yards into the field to the right of the road it had come racing down whole and intact a few seconds before. It had cleared the ditch as if on wings, and had buried its nose in the field, plunging on like a wild plow making an insane furrow; at last shuddering to a stop with its front wheels crumpled and its lights still glowing, one pointed at right angles to the car and the other sending a beacon into the sky.

He had never covered a hundred yards faster in his life. The driver's door was open, sagging like a broken wing. He saw the white shirts inside, and flashed his light at them. They had their hands over their faces, and the one that was not the driver was being violently, convulsively sick, spoiling his white shirt. There was no broken glass and no blood, and he could see, from the way they were sitting, that they were not badly hurt, if at all.

A wild anger at them made him grunt like an animal, and swearing at them through this spouting well of anger, he pulled first the driver, and then the other one, out of the red car onto the field, where they sagged against the side of the car, still holding their faces in their hands. Digging his fists into each of the white shirts, he dragged them like bags of wheat to the headlight that was not pointed at the sky and stood them there, pulling their hands violently away from their faces, and raised the jack handle, ready and wanting to use it.

They were children. The faces of children stared up at him, blinking their staring, children's eyes at him, whimpering like children; and when they saw the jack handle, they raised their arms over their heads, like children, and began to yammer. The driver could not have been eighteen, and the other even younger. He looked down at them and much of the anger left him, but not all.

Something had to be done to get the rest out, he knew. Children! All the way from Crockerville—Ruth terrified and sobbing; Paula hysterical in a field alone in the dark—children in a red car.

The red car. He saw that the hood of it was wrenched loose, and he yanked it open. There it was—the bright chrome of the air scoops, the special milled head, the four-barrel carburetors—all of it that gave the red car its special life. He began to hammer at these things with the jack handle until it was a jagged, broken mess under the hood, and the jack handle was bent in his hand, and then the rest of the anger left him.

The two boys were gaping at him, and then at the red car, and he realized that when the life went out of the red car, when the power of the red car died, much of them died, too, and they were left nothing, alone and powerless with their dead car in the field.

He started to walk back to the road, but when he looked back, he saw the boys standing where he had left them.

"OK, come on, you two!" he said, not too roughly. "I'll take you into Terrence with us. Call the sheriff from there." And then the three of them went back to the road, where they found Paula and Ruth waiting by his car, waiting for him.

THE FACT IS—

1. The author indicates early in the story that Biff is tired and nervous. Select several phrases that support this statement.

2. Ruth encourages her father to become involved in a race with the red car. Explain how he reacts and why.

3. Biff eventually realizes the seriousness of their situation. When?

4. Biff, looking back upon the wreck of the red car, changes his attitude toward the boys. Why?

ON THE ROAD

1. The boys' car is repeatedly described as "the red car"; the redness becomes a symbol. What does the color red suggest to you? Why? Write a short paper telling what red may suggest to different people. In your paper, discuss the use of red as a symbol.

2. The road becomes an enemy to Biff. Explain what the author means by this comparison.

3. The word "Chicken!" occurs several times. How does the repetition of this word contribute to the climax of the story?

4. The casual reader might think that the author is condemning all teen-age drivers. Do you think so? Be prepared to argue this statement.

A WORD TO REMEMBER: indolent

One word appears three times in the story: for example, "an indolent, graceful movement." The word *indolent* (IN·do·lent) means "avoiding exertion, lazy." Find other examples of this word in this story. Use *indolent* in an original sentence.

An Occurrence at Owl Creek Bridge

AMBROSE BIERCE

So long as there are men dedicated to a belief, events of this sort could happen in any country torn by civil war. You will have to read this story carefully to separate the real happenings from those imagined.

A man stood upon a railroad bridge in northern Alabama, looking down into the swift water twenty feet below. The man's hands were behind his back, the wrists bound with a cord. A rope closely encircled his neck. It was attached to a stout cross-timber above his head and the slack fell to the level of his knees. Some loose boards laid upon the sleepers supporting the metals of the railway supplied a footing for him and his executioners—two private soldiers of the Federal army, directed by a sergeant who in civil life may have been a deputy sheriff. At a short remove upon the same temporary platform was an officer in the uniform of his rank, armed. He was a captain. A sentinel at each end of the bridge stood with his rifle in the position known as "support," that is to say, vertical in front of the left shoulder, the hammer resting on the forearm thrown straight across the chest—a formal and unnatural position, enforcing an erect carriage of the body. It did not appear to be the duty of these two men to know what was occurring at the center of the bridge; they merely blockaded the two ends of the foot planking that traversed it.

Beyond one of the sentinels, nobody was in sight; the railroad ran straight away into a forest for a hundred yards, then, curving, was lost to view. Doubtless there was an outpost farther along. The other bank of the stream was open ground—a gentle acclivity topped with a stockade of vertical tree trunks, loopholed for rifles, with a single embrasure through which protruded the muzzle of a brass cannon commanding the bridge. Midway of the slope between bridge and fort were the spectators—a single company of infantry in line, at "parade rest," the butts of the rifles on the ground, the barrels inclining slightly backward against the right shoulder, the hands crossed upon the stock. A lieutenant stood at the right of the line, the point of his sword upon the ground, his left hand resting upon his right. Excepting the group of four at the center of the bridge, not a man moved. The company faced the bridge, staring stonily, motionless. The sentinels, facing the banks of the stream, might have been statues to adorn the bridge. The captain stood with folded arms, silent, observing the work of his subordinates, but making no sign. Death is a dignitary who, when he comes announced, is to be received with formal manifestations of respect, even by those most familiar with him. In the code of military etiquette, silence and fixity are forms of deference.

The man who was engaged in being hanged was apparently about thirty-five years of age. He was a civilian, if one might judge from his habit, which was that of a planter. His features were good—a straight nose, firm mouth, broad forehead, from which his long dark hair

was combed straight back, falling behind his ears to the collar of his well-fitting frock-coat. He wore a mustache and pointed beard, but no whiskers; his eyes were large and dark gray, and had a kindly expression which one would hardly have expected in one whose neck was in the hemp. Evidently this was no vulgar assassin. The liberal military code makes provision for hanging many kinds of persons, and gentlemen are not excluded.

The preparations being complete, the two private soldiers stepped aside and each drew away the plank upon which he had been standing. The sergeant turned to the captain, saluted, and placed himself immediately behind that officer, who in turn moved apart one pace. These movements left the condemned man and the sergeant standing on the two ends of the same plank, which spanned three of the crossties of the bridge. The end upon which the civilian stood almost, but not quite, reached a fourth. This plank had been held in place by the weight of the captain; it was now held by that of the sergeant. At a signal from the former, the latter would step aside, the plank would tilt, and the condemned man go down between two ties. The arrangement commended itself to his judgment as simple and effective. His face had not been covered nor his eyes bandaged. He looked a moment at his "unsteadfast footing," then let his gaze wander to the swirling water of the stream racing madly beneath his feet. A piece of dancing driftwood caught his attention and his eyes followed it down the current. How slowly it appeared to move! What a sluggish stream!

He closed his eyes in order to fix his last thoughts upon his wife and children. The water, touched to gold by the early sun, the brooding mists under the banks at some distance down the stream, the fort, the soldiers, the piece of drift—all had distracted him. And now he became conscious of a new disturbance. Striking through the thought of his dear ones was a sound which he could neither ignore nor understand, a sharp, distinct, metallic percussion like the stroke of a blacksmith's hammer upon the anvil; it had the same ringing quality. He wondered what it was, and whether immeasurably distant or nearby—it seemed both. Its recurrence was regular, but as slow as the tolling of a death knell. He awaited each stroke with impatience and—he knew not why—apprehension. The intervals of silence grew progressively longer; the delays became maddening. With their greater infrequency the sounds increased in strength and sharpness. They hurt his ear like the thrust of a knife; he feared he would shriek. What he heard was the ticking of his watch.

He unclosed his eyes and saw again the water below him. "If I could free my hands," he thought, "I might throw off the noose and spring into the stream. By diving I could evade the bullets and, swimming vigorously, reach the bank, take to the woods, and get away home. My home, thank God, is as yet outside their lines; my wife and little ones are still beyond the invader's farthest advance."

As these thoughts, which have here to be set down in words, were flashed into the doomed man's brain rather than evolved from it, the captain nodded to the sergeant. The sergeant stepped aside.

Peyton Farquhar was a well-to-do planter, of an old and highly respected Alabama family. Being a slave owner and like other slave owners a politician, he was naturally an original secessionist and ardently devoted to the Southern cause. Circumstances of an imperious nature, which it is unnecessary to relate here, had prevented him from taking service with the gallant army that had fought the disastrous campaigns ending with the fall of Corinth, and he chafed under the inglorious restraint, longing for the release of his energies, the larger life of the soldier, the opportunity for distinction. That opportunity, he felt, would come, as it comes to all in wartime. Meanwhile he did what he could. No service was too humble for him to perform in aid of the South, no adventure too perilous for him to undertake if consistent with the character of a civilian who was at heart a soldier, and who in good faith and without too much qualification assented to at least a part of the frankly villainous dictum that all is fair in love and war.

One evening while Farquhar and his wife were sitting on a rustic bench near the entrance to his grounds, a gray-clad soldier rode up to the gate and asked for a drink of water. Mrs. Farquhar was only too happy to serve him with her own white hands. While she was fetching the water, her husband approached the dusty horseman and inquired eagerly for news from the front.

"The Yanks are repairing the railroads," said the man, "and are getting ready for another advance. They have reached the Owl Creek bridge, put it in order, and built a stockade on the north bank. The commandant has issued an order, which is posted everywhere, declaring that any civilian caught interfering with the railroad, its bridges, tunnels, or trains will be summarily hanged. I saw the order."

"How far is it to the Owl Creek bridge?" Farquhar asked.

"About thirty miles."

"Is there no force on this side the creek?"

"Only a picket post half a mile out,

on the railroad, and a single sentinel at this end of the bridge."

"Suppose a man—a civilian and student of hanging—should elude the picket post and perhaps get the better of the sentinel," said Farquhar, smiling. "What could he accomplish?"

The soldier reflected. "I was there a month ago," he replied. "I observed that the flood of last winter had lodged a great quantity of driftwood against the wooden pier at this end of the bridge. It is now dry and would burn like tow."

The lady had now brought the water, which the soldier drank. He thanked her ceremoniously, bowed to her husband, and rode away. An hour later, after nightfall, he repassed the plantation, going northward in the direction from which he had come. He was a Federal scout.

As Peyton Farquhar fell straight downward through the bridge, he lost consciousness and was as one already dead. From this state he was awakened —ages later, it seemed to him—by the pain of a sharp pressure upon his throat, followed by a sense of suffocation. Keen, poignant agonies seemed to shoot from his neck downward through every fiber of his body and limbs. These pains seemed to branch out along definite lines and to beat with an inconceivably rapid periodicity. They seemed like streams of pulsating fire heating him to an intolerable temperature. As to his head, he was conscious of nothing but a feeling of fullness—of congestion. These sensations were unaccompanied by thought. The intellectual part of his nature was already effaced; he had power only to feel, and feeling was torment. He was conscious of motion. Encompassed in a luminous cloud, of which he was now merely the fiery heart, without material substance, he swung through unthinkable arcs of oscillation, like a vast pendulum. Then all at once, with terrible suddenness, the light about him shot upward with the noise of a loud plash; a frightful roaring was in his ears, and all was cold and dark. The power of thought was restored; he knew that the rope had broken and he had fallen into the stream. There was no additional strangulation; the noose about his neck was already suffocating him and kept the water from his lungs. To die of hanging at the bottom of a river!—the idea seemed to him ludicrous. He opened his eyes in the darkness and saw above him a gleam of light, but how distant, how inaccessible! He was still sinking, for the light became fainter and fainter until it was a mere glimmer. Then it began to grow and brighten, and he knew that he was rising toward the surface—knew it with reluctance, for he was now very comfortable. "To be hanged and drowned," he thought, "that is not so bad; but I do not wish to be shot. No, I will not be shot; that is not fair."

He was not conscious of an effort, but a sharp pain in his wrist apprised him that he was trying to free his hands. He gave the struggle his attention, as an idler might observe the feat of a juggler, without interest in the outcome. What splendid effort!—what magnificent, what superhuman strength! Ah, that was a fine endeavor! Bravo! The cord fell away; his arms parted and floated upward, the hands dimly seen on each side in the growing light. He watched them with a new interest as first one and then the other pounced upon the noose at his neck. They tore it away and thrust it fiercely aside, its undulations resembling those of a water snake. "Put it back, put it back!" He thought he shouted these words to his hands, for the undoing of the noose had been succeeded by the direst pang that he had yet experienced. His neck ached horribly; his brain was on fire; his heart, which had been fluttering faintly, gave a great leap, trying to force itself out at his mouth. His whole body was racked and wrenched with an insupportable anguish! But his disobedient hands gave no heed to the command. They beat the water vigorously with quick, downward strokes, forcing him to the surface. He felt his head emerge; his eyes were blinded by the sunlight; his chest expanded convulsively, and with a supreme and crowning agony his lungs engulfed a great draft of air, which instantly he expelled in a shriek!

He was now in full possession of his physical senses. They were, indeed, preternaturally keen and alert. Something in the awful disturbance of his organic system had so exalted and refined them that they made record of things never before perceived. He felt the ripples upon his face and heard their separate sounds as they struck. He looked at the forest on the bank of the stream, saw the individual trees, the leaves, and the veining of each leaf—saw the very insects upon them: the locusts, the brilliant-bodied flies, the gray spiders stretching their webs from twig to twig. He noted the prismatic colors in all the dewdrops upon a million blades of grass. The humming of the gnats that danced above the eddies of the stream, the beating of the dragon-flies' wings, the strokes of the water-spiders' legs, like oars which had lifted their boat—all these made audible music. A fish slid along beneath his eyes and he heard the rush of its body parting the water.

He had come to the surface facing down the stream; in a moment the visible world seemed to wheel slowly round, himself the pivotal point, and he saw the bridge, the fort, the soldiers upon the bridge, the captain, the sergeant, the two privates, his executioners. They were in silhouette against the blue sky. They shouted and gesticulated, pointing at him. The captain had drawn his pistol, but did not fire; the others were unarmed. Their movements were grotesque and horrible, their forms gigantic.

Suddenly he heard a sharp report and something struck the water smartly within a few inches of his head, spattering his face with spray. He heard a second report, and saw one of the sentinels with his rifle at his shoulder, a light cloud of blue smoke rising from the muzzle. The man in the water saw the eye of the man on the bridge gazing into his own through the sights of the rifle. He observed that it was a gray eye and remembered having read that gray eyes were keenest, and that all famous marksmen had them. Nevertheless, this one had missed.

A counterswirl had caught Farquhar and turned him half round; he was again looking into the forest on the bank opposite the fort. The sound of a clear, high voice in a monotonous singsong now rang out behind him and came across the water with a distinctness that pierced and subdued all other sounds, even the beating of the ripples in his ears. Although no soldier, he had frequented camps enough to know the dread significance of that deliberate, drawling chant; the lieutenant on shore was taking a part in the morning's work. How coldly and pitilessly—in what an even, calm voice, foretelling, and enforcing quiet among the men—with what accurately measured intervals fell those cruel words:

"Attention, company! . . . Shoulder arms! . . . Ready! . . . Aim! . . . Fire!"

Farquhar dived—dived as deeply as he could. The water roared in his ears like the voice of Niagara, yet he heard the dulled thunder of the volley and, rising again toward the surface, met shining bits of metal, singularly flattened, oscillating slowly downward. Some of them touched him on the face and hands, then fell away, continuing their descent. One lodged between his collar and neck; it was comfortably warm and he snatched it out.

As he rose to the surface, gasping for breath, he saw that he had been a long time underwater; he was perceptibly farther downstream—nearer to safety. The soldiers had almost finished reloading; the metal ramrods flashed all at once in the sunshine as they were drawn from the barrels, turned in the air, and thrust into their sockets. The two sentinels fired again, independently and ineffectually.

The hunted man saw all this over his shoulder; he was now swimming vigorously with the current. His brain was as energetic as his arms and legs; he thought with the rapidity of lightning.

"The officer," he reasoned, "will not make that martinet's error a second time. It is as easy to dodge a volley as a single shot. He has probably already given the command to fire at will. God help me, I cannot dodge them all!"

An appalling plash within two yards of him was followed by a loud, rushing sound, diminuendo, which seemed to travel back through the air to the fort and died in an explosion which stirred the very river to its deeps! A rising sheet of water curved over him, fell down upon him, blinded him, strangled him! The cannon had taken a hand in the game. As he shook his head free from the agitation of the water, he heard the deflected shot humming through the air ahead, and in an instant it was cracking and smashing the branches in the forest beyond.

"They will not do that again," he

thought; "the next time they will use a charge of grape. I must keep my eye upon the gun; the smoke will apprise me—the report arrives too late; it lags behind the missile. That is a good gun."

Suddenly he felt himself whirled round and round—spinning like a top. The water, the banks, the forests, the now distant bridge, fort, and men—all were commingled and blurred. Objects were represented by their colors only; circular horizontal streaks of color— that was all he saw. He had been caught in a vortex and was being whirled on with a velocity of advance and gyration that made him giddy and sick. In a few moments he was flung upon the gravel at the foot of the left bank of the stream —the southern bank—and behind a projecting point which concealed him from his enemies. The sudden arrest of his motion, the abrasion of one of his hands on the gravel, restored him, and he wept with delight. He dug his fingers into the sand, threw it over himself in handfuls, and audibly blessed it. It looked like diamonds, rubies, emeralds; he could think of nothing beautiful which it did not resemble. The trees upon the bank were giant garden plants; he noted a definite order in their arrangement, inhaled the fragrance of their blooms. A strange, roseate light shone through the spaces among their trunks, and the wind made in their branches the music of aeolian harps. He had no wish to perfect his escape—was content to remain in that enchanting spot until retaken.

A whiz and rattle of grapeshot among the branches high above his head roused him from his dream. The baffled cannoneer had fired him a random farewell. He sprang to his feet, rushed up the sloping bank, and plunged into the forest.

All that day he traveled, laying his course by the rounding sun. The forest seemed interminable; nowhere did he discover a break in it, not even a woodman's road. He had not known that he lived in so wild a region. There was something uncanny in the revelation.

By nightfall he was fatigued, footsore, famishing. The thought of his wife and children urged him on. At last he found a road which led him in what he knew to be the right direction. It was as wide and straight as a city street, yet it seemed untraveled. No fields bordered it, no dwelling anywhere. Not so much as the barking of a dog suggested human habitation. The black bodies of the trees formed a straight wall on both sides, terminating on the horizon in a point. Overhead, as he looked up through this rift in the wood, shone great golden stars looking unfamiliar and grouped in strange constellations. He was sure they were arranged in some order which had a secret and malign significance. The wood on either side was full of singular noises, among which—once, twice, and again—he distinctly heard whispers in an unknown tongue.

His neck was in pain and, lifting his hand to it, he found it horribly swollen. He knew that it had a circle of black where the rope had bruised it. His eyes felt congested; he could no longer close them. His tongue was swollen with thirst; he relieved its fever by thrusting it forward from between his teeth into the cold air. How softly the turf had carpeted the untraveled avenue —he could no longer feel the roadway beneath his feet!

Doubtless, despite his suffering, he had fallen asleep while walking, for now he sees another scene—perhaps he has merely recovered from a delirium. He stands at the gate of his own home. All is as he left it, and all bright and beautiful in the morning sunshine. He must have traveled the entire night. As he pushes open the gate and passes up the wide white walk, he sees a flutter of female garments; his wife, looking fresh and cool and sweet, steps down from the veranda to meet him. At the bottom of the steps, she stands waiting, with a smile of ineffable joy, an attitude of matchless grace and dignity. Ah, how beautiful she is! He springs forward with extended arms. As he is about to clasp her, he feels a stunning blow upon the back of the neck; a blinding white light blazes all about him with a sound like the shock of a cannon —then all is darkness and silence!

Peyton Farquhar was dead; his body with a broken neck, swung gently from side to side beneath the timbers of the Owl Creek bridge.

THE FACT IS—

1. Section I (pages 25–27) establishes the setting and the act with which this part concludes. Does the author arouse your sympathy for the condemned man? If so, how?

2. Section II (pages 27–28) presents a flashback to explain how Peyton Farquhar became involved in a hanging. How does his being tricked by a Federal scout influence your feelings and your thinking?

3. Section III (pages 28–31) offers a dream sequence. In the seconds before his death, the hanged man is represented, in his agony, as struggling to live even as he imagines seeing his loving wife. Is this description of a dying man convincing?

THIS SIDE OF DEATH

1. During Farquhar's death struggle he thinks, "To be hanged and drowned, that is not so bad. . . . No, I will not be shot; that is not fair." Do you sympathize with his feelings? Why?

2. If you accept this description of a dying man's last thoughts, write a paragraph in which you explain how the author gets this idea across to you. If you do not accept it, tell what you think is wrong with the description.

3. During the next-to-last paragraph, the verb tenses suddenly shift from past to present. What effect is gained by this change? Can you explain it?

WORDS AND THEIR DERIVATIONS

Some words are derived from the names of people. In this story the following sentence appears: "The officer will not make that martinet's error a second time." General Martinet, a stern French drillmaster, invented a system of drill which won him the reputation of being a stickler for strict discipline; hence, a *martinet* is any rigid disciplinarian.

macadam. John Loudon McAdam, a Scottish engineer, created a roadway from material recommended by him; hence, a macadam road.

pasteurize. Louis Pasteur, a French scientist, invented a method of sterilization to prevent fermentation in milk, wine, and so forth; hence, to sterilize by Pasteur's method is to pasteurize.

Look up the derivations and meanings of the following words: *volt, zeppelin, mackintosh, cardigan, pompadour, sideburns.*

The Night the Ghost Got In

JAMES THURBER

When a well-known American humorist writes a ghost story, strange things happen, but the weirdest of all is Grandfather's shooting a policeman.

The ghost that got into our house on the night of November 17, 1915, raised such a hullabaloo of misunderstanding that I am sorry I didn't just let it keep on walking, and go to bed. Its advent caused my mother to throw a shoe through a window of the house next door and ended up with my grandfather shooting a patrolman. I am sorry, therefore, as I have said, that I ever paid any attention to the footsteps.

They began about a quarter past one o'clock in the morning, a rhythmic, quick-cadenced walking around the dining-room table. My mother was asleep in one room upstairs, my brother Herman in another; Grandfather was in the attic, in the old walnut bed which once fell on my father. I had just stepped out of the bathtub and was busily rubbing myself with a towel when I heard the steps. They were the steps of a man walking rapidly around the dining-room table downstairs. The light from the bathroom shone down the back steps, which dropped directly into the dining room; I could see the faint shine of plates on the plate rail; I couldn't see the table. The steps kept going round and round the table; at regular intervals a board creaked, when it was trod upon. I supposed at first that it was my father or my brother Roy, who had gone to Indianapolis but were expected home at any time. I suspected next that it was a burglar. It did not enter my mind until later that it was a ghost.

After the walking had gone on for perhaps three minutes, I tiptoed to Herman's room. "Psst!" I hissed in the dark, shaking him. "Awp," he said, in the low, hopeless tone of a despondent beagle— he always half-suspected that something would "get him" in the night. I told him who I was. "There's something downstairs!" I said. He got up and followed me to the head of the back staircase. We listened together. There was no sound. The steps had ceased. Herman looked at me in some alarm—I had only the bath towel around my waist. He wanted to go back to bed, but I gripped his arm. "There's something down there!" I said. Instantly the steps began again, circled the dining-room table like a man running, and started up the stairs toward us, heavily, two at a time. The light still shone palely down the stairs; we saw nothing coming; we only heard the steps. Herman rushed to his room and slammed the door. I slammed shut the door at the stairs' top and held my knee against it. After a long minute I slowly opened it again. There was nothing there. There

was no sound. None of us ever heard the ghost again.

The slamming of the doors had aroused Mother; she peered out of her room. "What on earth are you boys doing?" she demanded. Herman ventured out of his room. "Nothing," he said gruffly, but he was, in color, a light green. "What was all that running around downstairs?" said Mother. So she had heard the steps, too! We just looked at her. "Burglars!" she shouted intuitively. I tried to quiet her by starting lightly downstairs.

"Come on, Herman," I said.

"I'll stay with Mother," he said. "She's all excited."

I stepped back onto the landing.

"Don't either of you go a step," said Mother. "We'll call the police." Since the phone was downstairs, I didn't see how we were going to call the police— nor did I want the police—but Mother made one of her quick, incomparable decisions. She flung up a window of her bedroom which faced the bedroom windows of the house of a neighbor, picked up a shoe, and whammed it through a pane of glass across the narrow space that separated the two houses. Glass tinkled into the bedroom occupied by a retired engraver named Bodwell and his wife. Bodwell had been for some years in rather a bad way and was subject to mild "attacks." Most everybody we knew or lived near had *some* kind of attacks.

It was now about two o'clock of a moonless night; clouds hung black and low. Bodwell was at the window in a minute, shouting, frothing a little, shaking his fist. "We'll sell the house and go back to Peoria," we could hear Mrs. Bodwell saying. It was some time before Mother "got through" to Bodwell. "Burglars!" she shouted. "Burglars in the house!" Herman and I hadn't dared to tell her that it was not burglars but ghosts, for she was even more afraid of ghosts than of burglars. Bodwell at first thought that she meant there were burglars in his house, but finally he quieted down and called the police for us over an extension phone by his bed. After he had disappeared from the window, Mother suddenly made as if to throw another shoe, not because there was further need of it but, as she later explained, because the thrill of heaving a shoe through a window glass had enormously taken her fancy. I prevented her.

The police were on hand in a commendably short time—a Ford sedan full of them, two on motorcycles, and a patrol wagon with about eight in it and a few reporters. They began banging at our front door. Flashlights shot streaks of gleam up and down the walls, across the yard, down the walk between our house and Bodwell's. "Open up!" cried a hoarse voice. "We're men from headquarters!" I wanted to go down and let them in, since there they were; but Mother wouldn't hear of it. "You haven't a stitch on," she pointed out. "You'd catch your death." I wound the towel around me again. Finally the cops put their shoulders to our big heavy front door with its thick beveled glass and broke it in; I could hear a rending of wood and a splash of glass on the floor of the hall. Their lights played all over the living room and crisscrossed nervously in the dining room, stabbed into hallways, shot up the front stairs and finally up the back. They caught me standing in my towel at the top. A heavy policeman bounded up the steps. "Who are you?" he demanded. "I live here," I

THE NIGHT THE GHOST GOT IN　　　**35**

said. "Well, whattsa matta, ya hot?" he asked. It was, as a matter of fact, cold; I went to my room and pulled on some trousers. On my way out, a cop stuck a gun into my ribs. "Whatta you doin' here?" he demanded. "I live here," I said.

The officer in charge reported to Mother. "No sign of nobody, lady," he said. "Musta got away. Whatt'd he look like?"

"There were two or three of them," Mother said, "whooping and carrying on and slamming doors."

"Funny," said the cop. "All ya windows and doors was locked on the inside tight as a tick."

Downstairs we could hear the tromping of the other police. Police were all over the place—doors were yanked open; drawers were yanked open; windows were shot up and pulled down; furniture fell with dull thumps. A half-dozen policemen emerged out of the darkness of the front hallway upstairs. They began to ransack the floor— pulled beds away from walls, tore clothes off hooks in the closets, pulled suitcases and boxes off shelves. One of them found an old zither that Roy had won in a pool tournament. "Looky here, Joe," he said, strumming it with a big paw. The cop named Joe took it and turned it over. "What is it?" he asked me. "It's an old zither our guinea pig used to sleep on," I said. It was true that a pet guinea pig we once had would never sleep anywhere except on the zither, but I should never have said so. Joe and the other cop looked at me a long time. They put the zither back on a shelf.

"No sign o' nuthin'," said the cop who had first spoken to Mother. "This guy," he explained to the others, jerking a thumb at me, "was nekked. The lady seems historical." They all nodded, but said nothing—just looked at me. In the small silence we all heard a creaking in the attic. Grandfather was turning over in bed. "What's 'at?" snapped Joe. Five or six cops sprang for the attic door before I could intervene or explain. I realized that it would be bad if they burst in on Grandfather unannounced, or even announced. He was going through a phase in which he believed that General Meade's men, under steady hammering by Stonewall Jackson,[1] were beginning to retreat and even desert.

When I got to the attic, things were pretty confused. Grandfather had evidently jumped to the conclusion that the police were deserters from Meade's army, trying to hide away in his attic. He bounded out of bed wearing a long flannel nightgown over long woolen underwear, a nightcap, and a leather jacket around his chest. The cops must have realized at once that the indignant white-haired old man belonged in the house, but they had no chance to say so. "Back, ye cowardly dogs!" roared Grandfather. "Back t' the lines, ye lily-livered cattle!" With that he fetched the officer who found the zither a flat-handed smack alongside his head that sent him sprawling. The others beat a retreat, but not fast enough; Grandfather grabbed Zither's gun from its holster and let fly. The report seemed to crack the rafters; smoke filled the attic. A cop cursed and shot his hand to his shoulder. Somehow we all finally got downstairs again and locked the door against the old gentleman. He fired once or twice more in the darkness and then went back to bed.

"That was Grandfather," I explained to Joe, out of breath. "He thinks you're deserters."

[1] **Meade** was a Union general in the Civil War; **Jackson** was a Confederate general.

"I'll say he does," said Joe.

The cops were reluctant to leave without getting their hands on somebody besides Grandfather; the night had been distinctly a defeat for them. Furthermore they obviously didn't like the "layout"; something looked—and I can see their viewpoint—phony. They began to poke into things again. A reporter, a thin-faced, wispy man, came up to me. I had put on one of Mother's blouses, not being able to find anything else. The reporter looked at me with mingled suspicion and interest. "Just what is the real lowdown here, bud?" he asked. I decided to be frank with him. "We had ghosts," I said. He gazed at me a long time as if I were a slot machine into which he had, without results, dropped a nickel. Then he walked away. The cops followed him, the one Grandfather shot holding his now-bandaged arm, cursing and blaspheming. "I'm gonna get my gun back from that old bird," said the zither-cop. "Yeh," said Joe. "You—and who else?" I told them I would bring it to the station house the next day.

"What was the matter with that one policeman?" Mother asked after they had gone. "Grandfather shot him," I said. "What for?" she demanded. I told her he was a deserter. "Of all things!" said Mother. "He was such a nice-looking young man."

Grandfather was fresh as a daisy and full of jokes at breakfast next morning. We thought at first he had forgotten all about what had happened, but he hadn't. Over his third cup of coffee, he glared at Herman and me. "What was the idee of all them cops tarryhootin' round the house last night?" he demanded. He had us there.

JAMES THURBER (1894–1961).

"A professor of mine once said that if a thing cannot stand laughter, it is not a good thing; and we must not lose in this country the uses of laughter."

James Thurber found very little in life that could not stand laughter. Born in Columbus, Ohio, of an exceptionally lively family, he drew almost inexhaustibly upon his boyhood and youth to write the appealing and often outrageously funny stories which were half his trademark. I say "half," for Thurber was more than a writer. He was a cartoonist whose childlike drawings contrasted with his sharp, mature humor. Anyone who has ever seen a Thurber dog knows that it is a *Thurber Dog*. His drawing was severely handicapped by progressive blindness: he had to draw his cartoons on larger and larger sheets of paper until he finally couldn't see or draw at all. In addition to his cartoons and short stories, he wrote many essays and (with Elliot Nugent) a successful Broadway play, **The Male Animal.** His short stories and even his humorous work are pervaded by a steely quality and a quality of sadness. He said of his stories, "The little wheels of their invention are set in motion by the damp hand of melancholy." Gay and glad or sad and melancholy, James Thurber struck a native vein of American life.

THE FACT IS—

1. A ghost started all the excitement in the narrator's home. Who discovered it, and how?

2. Mother, thinking burglars were downstairs, got word to the police. How did she manage to reach them?

3. The reporter was suspicious of the narrator. Why?

4. One policeman was shot. How did this accident occur?

5. Joe's partner was called "the zither-cop." How did he get this name?

A GUINEA PIG ON A ZITHER?

1. Much of the fun in reading humorous stories comes from noticing unexpected combinations of words and ideas. For instance, who but a humorist would think of a guinea pig sleeping on a zither? Look through this selection again and find four or five phrases or sentences that are funny to you. Explain why they made you laugh.

2. Have you ever visited a "haunted" house or a cemetery at night? Or have you imagined burglars in the house and aroused everybody? Try writing your experience in a humorous way. Exaggeration helps to make a story funny.

WORD TO REMEMBER: commendably

This word comes from the verb *to commend* (ka·MEND), which means "to praise" or "to express approval of." Variations include *commendation* (kom·men·DAY·shun), the noun, *commendable* (ka·MEN·da·b'l), the adjective, and *commendably* (ka·MEN·da·blee), the adverb. All these words mean "expressing approval." Hence, "The police were on hand in a commendably short time." Is *commend* more closely related to *comment* or *command?* You may need to consult your dictionary to find out. Use each of these three words in an original sentence.

Night Meeting

RAY BRADBURY

Ray Bradbury is well known for his science fiction stories. Here is one of his best, an interplanetary ghost story with interchangeable ghosts.

Before going on up into the blue hills, Tomás Gomez stopped for gasoline at the lonely station.

"Kind of alone out here, aren't you, Pop?" said Tomás.

The old man wiped off the windshield of the small truck. "Not bad."

"How do you like Mars, Pop?"

"Fine. Always something new. I made up my mind when I came here last year I wouldn't expect nothing, nor ask nothing, nor be surprised at nothing. We've got to forget Earth and how things were. We've got to look at what we're in here, and how *different* it is. I get a lot of fun out of just the weather here. It's *Martian* weather. Hot as hell daytimes, cold as hell nights. I get a big kick out of the different flowers and different rain. I came to Mars to retire and I wanted to retire in a place where everything is different. An old man needs to have things different. Young people don't want to talk to him, other old people bore him. So I thought the best thing for me is a place so different that all you got to do is open your eyes and you're entertained. I got this gas station. If business picks up too much, I'll move on back to some other old highway that's not so busy, where I can earn just enough to live on and still have time to feel the *different* things here."

"You got the right idea, Pop," said Tomás, his brown hands idly on the wheel. He was feeling good. He had been working in one of the new colonies for ten days straight and now he had two days off and was on his way to a party.

"I'm not surprised at anything any more," said the old man. "I'm just looking. I'm just experiencing. If you can't take Mars for what she is, you might as well go back to Earth. Everything's crazy up here, the soil, the air, the canals, the natives (I never saw any yet, but I hear they're around), the clocks. Even my clock acts funny. Even *time* is crazy up here. Sometimes I feel I'm here all by myself, no one else on the whole darn planet. I'd take bets on it. Sometimes I feel about eight years old, my body squeezed up and everything else tall. It's just the place for an old man. Keeps me alert and keeps me happy. You know what Mars is? It's like a thing I got for Christmas seventy years ago—don't know if you ever had one—they called them kaleidoscopes, bits of crystal and cloth and beads and pretty junk. You held it up to the sunlight and looked in through at it, and it took your breath away. All the patterns! Well, that's Mars. Enjoy it. Don't ask it to be nothing else but what it is. You know that highway right there, built by the Martians, is over sixteen centuries old and still in good condition? That's one dollar and fifty cents. Thanks and good night."

Tomás drove off down the ancient highway, laughing quietly.

It was a long road going into darkness and hills and he held to the wheel, now and again reaching into his lunch bucket and taking out a piece of candy. He had been driving steadily for an hour, with no other car on the road, no light, just the road going under, the hum, the roar, and Mars out there, so quiet. Mars was always quiet, but quieter tonight than any other. The deserts and empty seas swung by him, and the mountains against the stars.

There was a smell of Time in the air tonight. He smiled and turned the fancy in his mind. There was a thought. What did Time smell like? Like dust and clocks and people. And if you wondered what Time sounded like, it sounded like water running in a dark cave and voices crying and dirt dropping down upon hollow box lids, and rain. And, going further, what did Time *look* like? Time looked like snow dropping silently into a black room or it looked like a silent film in an ancient theater, one hundred billion faces falling like those New Year balloons, down and down into nothing. That was how Time smelled and looked and sounded. And tonight—Tomás shoved a hand into the wind outside the truck—tonight you could almost *touch* Time.

He drove the truck between hills of Time. His neck prickled and he sat up, watching ahead.

He pulled into a little dead Martian town, stopped the engine, and let the silence come in around him. He sat, not breathing, looking out at the white buildings in the moonlight. Uninhabited for centuries. Perfect, faultless, in ruins, yes, but perfect, nevertheless.

He started the engine and drove on another mile or more before stopping again, climbing out, carrying his lunch bucket, and walking to a little promontory where he could look back at that dusty city. He opened his thermos and poured himself a cup of coffee. A night bird flew by. He felt very good, very much at peace.

Perhaps five minutes later there was a sound. Off in the hills, where the ancient highway curved, there was a motion, a dim light, and then a murmur.

Tomás turned slowly with the coffee cup in his hand.

And out of the hills came a strange thing.

It was a machine like a jade-green insect, a praying mantis, delicately rushing through the cold air, indistinct, countless green diamonds winking over its body, and red jewels that glittered with multifaceted eyes. Its six legs fell upon the ancient highway with the sounds of a sparse rain which dwindled away, and from the back of the machine a Martian with melted gold for eyes looked down at Tomás as if he were looking into a well.

Tomás raised his hand and thought *Hello!* automatically but did not move his lips, for this *was* a Martian. But Tomás had swum in blue rivers on Earth, with strangers passing on the road, and eaten in strange houses with strange people, and his weapon had always been his smile. He did not carry a gun. And he did not feel the need of one now, even with the little fear that gathered about his heart at this moment.

The Martian's hands were empty too. For a moment they looked across the cool air at each other.

It was Tomás who moved first.

"Hello!" he called.

"Hello!" called the Martian in his own language.

They did not understand each other.

"Did you say hello?" they both asked.

"What did you say?" they said, each in a different tongue.

They scowled.

"Who are you?" said Tomás in English.

"What are you doing here?" in Martian; the stranger's lips moved.

"Where are you going?" they said, and looked bewildered.

"I'm Tomás Gomez."

"I'm Muhe Ca."

Neither understood, but they tapped their chests with the words and then it became clear.

And then the Martian laughed. "Wait!" Tomás felt his head touched, but no hand had touched him. "There!" said the Martian in English. "That is better!"

"You learned my language, so quick!"

"Nothing at all!"

They looked, embarrassed with a new silence, at the steaming coffee he had in one hand.

"Something different?" said the Martian, eying him and the coffee, referring to them both, perhaps.

"May I offer you a drink?" said Tomás.

The Martian slid down from his machine.

A second cup was produced and filled, steaming. Tomás held it out.

Their hands met and—like mist—fell through each other.

"Good Heavens!" cried Tomás, and dropped the cup.

"Name of the Gods!" said the Martian in his own tongue.

"Did you see what happened?" they both whispered.

They were very cold and terrified.

The Martian bent to touch the cup but could not touch it.

"Caramba!" said Tomás.

"Indeed." The Martian tried again and again to get hold of the cup, but could not. He stood up and thought for a moment, then took a knife from his belt. "Hey!" cried Tomás. "You misunderstand. Catch!" said the Martian, and tossed it. Tomás cupped his hands. The knife fell through his flesh. It hit the ground. Tomás bent to pick it up but could not touch it, and he recoiled, shivering.

Now he looked at the Martian against the sky.

"The stars!" he said.

"The stars!" said the Martian, looking, in turn, at Tomás.

The stars were white and sharp beyond the flesh of the Martian, and he seemed to see them glowing as through a jellyfish. You could see stars flickering like violet eyes in the Martian's stomach and chest, and through his wrists, like jewelry.

"I can see through you!" said Tomás.

"And I through you!" said the Martian, stepping back.

Tomás felt of his own body and, feeling the warmth, was reassured. *I am real,* he thought.

The Martian touched his own nose and lips. "*I have flesh,*" he said, half aloud. "*I am alive.*"

Tomás stared at the stranger. "And if *I* am real, then, *you* must be dead."

"No, you!"

"A ghost!"

"A phantom!"

They pointed at each other, with starlight burning in their limbs like daggers and icicles and fireflies, and then fell to judging their limbs again, each finding himself intact, hot, excited, stunned, awed, and the other, ah, yes, that other over there, unreal, a ghostly prism flashing the accumulated light of distant worlds.

I'm drunk, thought Tomás. *I won't tell anyone of this tomorrow, no, no.*

They stood there on the ancient highway, neither of them moving.

"Where are you from?" asked the Martian at last.

"Earth."

"What is that?"

"There." Tomás nodded to the sky.

"When?"

"We landed over a year ago, remember?"

"No."

"And all of you were dead, all but a few. You're rare, don't you *know* that?"

"That's not true."

"Yes, dead. I saw the bodies. Black, in the rooms, in the houses, dead. Thousands of them."

"That's ridiculous. We're *alive!*"

"Mister, you're invaded, only you don't know it. You must have escaped."

"I haven't escaped; there was nothing to escape. What do you mean? I'm on my way to a festival now at the canal, near the Eniall Mountains. I was there last night. Don't you see the city there?" The Martian pointed.

Tomás looked and saw the ruins. "Why, that city's been dead thousands of years."

The Martian laughed. "Dead? I slept there yesterday!"

"And I was in it a week ago and the week before that, and I just drove through it now, and it's a heap. See the broken pillars?"

"Broken? Why, I see them perfectly. The moonlight helps. And the pillars are upright."

"There's dust in the streets," said Tomás.

"The streets are clean!"

"The canals are empty right there."

"The canals are full of lavender wine!"

"It's dead."

"It's alive!" protested the Martian, laughing more now. "Oh, you're quite wrong. See all the carnival lights? There are beautiful boats as slim as women, beautiful women as slim as boats, women the color of sand, women with fire flowers in their hands. I can see them, small, running in the streets there. That's where I'm going now, to the festival; we'll float on the waters all night long; we'll sing, we'll drink, we'll make love. Can't you see it?"

"Mister, that city is dead as a dried lizard. Ask any of our party. Me, I'm on my way to Green City tonight; that's the new colony we just raised over near Illinois Highway. You're mixed up. We

brought in a million board feet of Oregon lumber and a couple dozen tons of good steel nails and hammered together two of the nicest little villages you ever saw. Tonight we're warming one of them. A couple rockets are coming in from Earth, bringing our wives and girl friends. There'll be barn dances and whiskey——"

The Martian was now disquieted. "You say it is over *that* way?"

"There are the rockets." Tomás walked him to the edge of the hill and pointed down. "See?"

"No."

"Damn it, there they *are!* Those long silver things."

"No."

Now Tomás laughed. "You're blind!"

"I see very well. You are the one who does not see."

"But you see the new *town*, don't you?"

"I see nothing but an ocean, and water at low tide."

"Mister, that water's been evaporated for forty centuries."

"Ah, now, now, that *is* enough."

"It's true, I tell you."

The Martian grew very serious. "Tell me again. You do not see the city the way I describe it? The pillars very white, the boats very slender, the festival lights—oh, I see them *clearly!* And listen! I can hear them singing. It's no space away at all."

Tomás listened and shook his head. "No."

"And I, on the other hand," said the

Martian, "cannot see what you describe. Well."

Again they were cold. An ice was in their flesh.

"Can it be . . . ?"

"What?"

"You say 'from the sky'?"

"Earth."

"Earth, a name, nothing," said the Martian. "*But* . . . as I came up the pass an hour ago . . ." He touched the back of his neck. "I felt . . ."

"Cold?"

"Yes."

"And now?"

"Cold again. Oddly. There was a thing to the light, to the hills, the road," said the Martian. "I felt the strangeness, the road, the light, and for a moment I felt as if I were the last man alive on this world. . . ."

"So did I!" said Tomás, and it was like talking to an old and dear friend, confiding, growing warm with the topic.

The Martian closed his eyes and opened them again. "This can only mean one thing. It has to do with Time. Yes. You are a figment of the Past!"

"No, you are from the Past," said the Earth Man, having had time to think of it now.

"You are so *certain*. How can you prove who is from the Past, who from the Future? What year is it?"

"Two thousand and one!"

"What does that mean to *me*?"

Tomás considered and shrugged. "Nothing."

"It is as if I told you that it is the year 4462853 s.e.c. It is nothing and more than nothing! Where is the clock to show us how the stars stand?"

"But the ruins prove it! They prove that *I* am the Future, *I* am alive, *you* are dead!"

"Everything in me denies this. My heart beats, my stomach hungers, my mouth thirsts. No, no, not dead, not

alive, either of us. More alive than anything else. Caught between is more like it. Two strangers passing in the night, that is it. Two strangers passing. Ruins, you say?"

"Yes. You're afraid?"

"Who wants to see the Future, who *ever* does? A man can face the Past, but to think—the pillars *crumbled*, you say? And the sea empty, and the canals dry, and the maidens dead, and the flowers withered?" The Martian was silent, but then he looked on ahead. "But there they *are*. I *see* them. Isn't that enough for me? They wait for me now, no matter *what* you say."

And for Tomás the rockets, far away, waiting for *him*, and the town and the women from Earth. "We can never agree," he said.

"Let us agree to disagree," said the Martian. "What does it matter who is Past or Future, if we are both alive, for what follows will follow, tomorrow or in ten thousand years. How do you know that those temples are not the temples of your own civilization one hundred centuries from now, tumbled and broken? You do not know. Then don't ask. But the night is very short. There go the festival fires in the sky, and the birds."

Tomás put out his hand. The Martian did likewise in imitation.

Their hands did not touch; they melted through each other.

"Will we meet again?"

"Who knows? Perhaps some other night."

"I'd like to go with you to that festival."

"And I wish I might come to your new town, to see this ship you speak of, to see these men, to hear all that has happened."

"Good-by," said Tomás.

"Good night."

The Martian rode his green metal

vehicle quietly away into the hills. The Earth Man turned his truck and drove it silently in the opposite direction.

"What a dream that was," sighed Tomás, his hands on the wheel, thinking of the rockets, the women, the raw whiskey, the Virginia reels, the party.

How strange a vision was that, thought the Martian, rushing on, thinking of the festival, the canals, the boats, the women with golden eyes, and the songs.

The night was dark. The moons had gone down. Starlight twinkled on the empty highway where now there was not a sound, no car, no person, nothing. And it remained that way all the rest of the cool dark night.

QUESTIONS TO PONDER

1. Why did the author open his story with a meeting between two Earth Men?

2. The old man described Mars as something you see through a kaleidoscope. What did his first impression of the place add? (Consult a dictionary if you need to.)

3. "And out of the hills came a strange thing"! What did it look like? Was it an appropriate means of transportation for the Martian? Why?

4. The Martian learned English very quickly. How? What might this indicate about him and his civilization?

5. Both the Martian and Tomás argued that they were from the Future, not the Past. Why should they reject the Past? Was one more convincing in his argument than the other?

6. The Martian finally said, "Let us agree to disagree." Explain this statement. Was it an appropriate conclusion to their conversation?

7. At no time did these two *touch* each other. Why?

8. As they parted friends, Tomás sighed, "What a dream that was," and the Martian thought, *How strange a vision was that.* What final impression regarding this story do you have? How did the author indicate that both men may be from the Past? What is the special meaning of "Night Meeting"?

A WORD TO REMEMBER: sparse

This word appears in the following sentence: "Its six legs fell upon the ancient highway with the sounds of a sparse rain which dwindled away." *Sparse* means "thinly scattered, scanty."

The word also means "not thickly grown," as in the following sentence: "A sparse growth of hair on his head suggested that he might become prematurely bald." From which Latin word is *sparse* derived? What does the Latin word mean?

The Ledge

LAWRENCE SARGENT HALL

A gruff but loving father, two teen-age boys, and a devoted dog—these are the principal characters in this story of the sea. Can you imagine being caught two miles offshore, clinging desperately to a slippery ledge on a cold Christmas morning?

On Christmas morning before sunup, the fisherman embraced his warm wife and left his close bed. She did not want him to go. It was Christmas morning. He was a big, raw man, with too much strength, whose delight in winter was to hunt the sea ducks that flew in to feed by the outer ledges, bare at low tide.

As his bare feet touched the cold floor and the frosty air struck his nude flesh, he might have changed his mind in the dark of this special day. It was a home day, which made it seem natural to think of the outer ledges merely as someplace he had shot ducks in the past. But he had promised his son, thirteen, and his nephew, fifteen, who came from inland. That was why he had given them his present of an automatic shotgun each the night before, on Christmas Eve. Rough man though he was known to be, and no spoiler of boys, he kept his promises when he understood what they meant. And to the boys, as to him, home meant where you came for rest after you had had your Christmas fill of action and excitement.

His legs astride, his arms raised, the fisherman stretched as high as he could in the dim privacy of his bedroom. Above the snug murmur of his wife's protest, he heard the wind in the pines and knew it was easterly as the boys had hoped and he had surmised the night before. Conditions would be ideal, and when they were, anybody ought to take advantage of them. The birds would be flying. The boys would get a man's sport their first time outside on the ledges.

His son at thirteen, small but steady and experienced, was fierce to grow up in hunting, to graduate from sheltered waters and the blinds along the shores of the inner bay. His nephew at fifteen, an overgrown farm boy, had a farm boy's love of the sea, though he could not swim a stroke and was often sick in choppy weather. That was the reason his father, the fisherman's brother, was a farmer and chose to sleep in on the holiday morning at his brother's house. Many of the ones the farmer had grown up with were regularly seasick and could not swim, but they were unafraid of the water. They could not have dreamed of being anything but fishermen. The fisherman himself could swim like a seal and was never sick, and he would sooner die than be anything else.

He dressed in the cold and dark, and woke the boys gruffly. They tumbled out of bed, their instincts instantly awake while their thoughts still fumbled slumberously. The fisherman's wife in the adjacent bedroom heard them apparently trying to find their clothes, mumbling sleepily and happily to each other, while her husband went down to the hot kitchen to fry eggs—sunnyside up, she knew, because that was how they all liked them.

Always in winter she hated to have them go outside, the weather was so treacherous and there were so few others out in case of trouble. To the fisherman these were no more than woman's fears, to be taken for granted and laughed off. When they were first married, they fought miserably every fall because she was after him constantly to put his boat up until spring. The fishing was all outside in winter, and though prices were high, the storms made the rate of attrition high on gear. Nevertheless he did well. So she could do nothing with him.

People thought him a hard man, and gave him the reputation of being all out for himself because he was inclined to brag and be disdainful. If it was true, and his own brother was one of those who strongly felt it was, they lived better than others, and his brother had small right to criticize. There had been times when in her loneliness she had yearned to leave him for another man. But it would have been dangerous. So over the years she had learned to shut her mind to his hard-driving, and take what comfort she might from his unsympathetic competence. Only once or twice, perhaps, had she gone so far as to dwell guiltily on what it would be like to be a widow.

The thought that her boy, possibly because he was small, would not be insensitive like his father, and the rattle of dishes and smell of frying bacon downstairs in the kitchen shut off from the rest of the chilly house, restored the cozy feeling she had had before she was alone in bed. She heard them after a while go out and shut the back door.

Under her window she heard the snow grind dryly beneath their boots, and her husband's sharp, exasperated commands to the boys. She shivered slightly in the envelope of her own warmth. She listened to the noise of her son and nephew talking elatedly. Twice she caught the glimmer of their lights on the white ceiling above the window as they went down the path to the shore. There would be frost on the skiff and freezing suds at the water's edge. She herself used to go gunning when she was younger; now, it seemed to her, anyone going out like that on Christmas morning had to be incurably male. They would none of them think about her until they returned and piled the birds they had shot on top of the sink for her to dress.

Ripping into the quiet predawn cold she heard the hot snarl of the outboard taking them out to the boat. It died as abruptly as it had burst into life. Two or three or four or five minutes later the big engine broke into a warm reassuring roar. He had the best of equipment, and he kept it in the best of condition. She closed her eyes. It would not be too long before the others would be up for Christmas. The summer drone of the exhaust deepened. Then gradually it faded in the wind until it was lost at sea, or she slept.

The engine had started immediately in spite of the temperature. This put the fisherman in a good mood. He was proud of his boat. Together he and the two boys heaved the skiff and outboard onto the stern and secured it athwartships. His son went forward along the deck, iridescent in the ray of the light the nephew shone through the windshield, and cast the mooring pennant loose into darkness. The fisherman swung to starboard, glanced at his compass, and headed seaward down the obscure bay.

There would be just enough visibility by the time they reached the headland to navigate the crooked channel between the islands. It was the only nasty stretch of water. The fisherman had done it often in fog or at night—he always swore he could go anywhere in the bay blindfolded—but there was no sense in taking chances if you didn't have to. From the mouth of the channel, he could lay a straight course for Brown Cow Island, anchor the boat out of sight behind it, and from the skiff set their tollers off Devil's Hump three hundred yards to seaward. By then the tide would be clearing the ledge and they could land and be ready to shoot around half-tide.

It was early, it was Christmas, and it was farther out than most hunters cared to go in this season of the closing year, so that he felt sure no one would be taking possession ahead of them. He had shot thousands of ducks there in his day. The Hump was by far the best hunting. Only thing was you had to plan for the right conditions because you didn't have too much time. About four hours was all, and you had to get it before three in the afternoon when the birds left and went out to sea ahead of nightfall.

They had it figured exactly right for today. The ledge would not be going under until after the gunning was over, and they would be home for supper in good season. With a little luck the boys would have a skiffload of birds to show for their first time outside. Well beyond the legal limit, which was no matter. You took what you could get in this life, or the next man made out and you didn't.

The fisherman had never failed to make out gunning from Devil's Hump. And this trip, he had a hunch, would be above ordinary. The easterly wind would come up just stiff enough, the tide was right, and it was going to storm by tomorrow morning so the birds would be moving. Things were perfect.

The old fierceness was in his bones. Keeping a weather eye to the murk out front and a hand on the wheel, he reached over and cuffed both boys playfully as they stood together close to the heat of the exhaust pipe running up through the center of the house. They poked back at him and shouted above the drumming engine, making bets as they always did on who would shoot the most birds. This trip they had the thrill of new guns, the best money could buy, and a man's hunting ground. The black retriever wagged at them and barked. He was too old and arthritic to be allowed in December water, but he was jaunty anyway at being brought along.

Groping in his pocket for his pipe, the fisherman suddenly had his high spirits rocked by the discovery that he had left his tobacco at home. He swore. Anticipation of a day out with nothing to smoke made him incredulous. He searched his clothes, and then he searched them again, unable to believe the tobacco was not somewhere. When the boys inquired what was wrong, he spoke angrily to them, blaming them for being in some devious way at fault. They were instantly crestfallen and willing to put back after the tobacco, though they could appreciate what it meant only through his irritation. But he bitterly refused. That would throw everything out of phase. He was a man who did things the way he set out to do.

He clamped his pipe between his teeth, and twice more during the next few minutes he ransacked his clothes in disbelief. He was no stoic. For one relaxed moment he considered putting about and gunning somewhere nearer home. Instead he held his course and sucked the empty pipe, consoling himself with the reflection that at least he had whiskey enough if it got too uncomfortable on the ledge. Peremptorily he made the boys check to make certain the bottle was really in the knapsack with the lunches where he thought he had taken care to put it. When they re-

assured him, he despised his fate a little less.

The fisherman's judgment was as usual accurate. By the time they were abreast of the headland, there was sufficient light so that he could wind his way among the reefs without slackening speed. At last he turned his bows toward open ocean, and as the winter dawn filtered upward through long layers of smoky cloud on the eastern rim, his spirits rose again with it.

He opened the throttle, steadied on his course, and settled down to the two-hour run. The wind was stronger but seemed less cold coming from the sea. The boys had withdrawn from the fisherman and were talking together while they watched the sky through the windows. The boat churned solidly through a light chop, flinging spray off her flaring bows. Astern the headland thinned rapidly till it lay like a blackened sill on the gray water. No other boats were abroad.

The boys fondled their new guns, sighted along the barrels, worked the mechanisms, compared notes, boasted, and gave each other contradictory advice. The fisherman got their attention once and pointed at the horizon. They peered through the windows and saw what looked like a black scum floating on top of gently agitated water. It wheeled and tilted, rippled, curled, then rose, strung itself out, and became a huge raft of ducks escaping over the sea. A good sign.

The boys rushed out and leaned over the washboards in the wind and spray to see the flock curl below the horizon. Then they went and hovered around the hot engine, bewailing their lot. If only they had been already set out and waiting. Maybe these ducks would be crazy enough to return later and be slaughtered. Ducks were known to be foolish.

In due course and right on schedule,

they anchored at midmorning in the lee of Brown Cow Island. They put the skiff overboard and loaded it with guns, knapsacks, and tollers. The boys showed their eagerness by being clumsy. The fisherman showed his in bad temper and abuse which they silently accepted in the absorbed tolerance of being boys. No doubt they laid it to lack of tobacco.

By outboard they rounded the island and pointed due east in the direction of a ridge of foam which could be seen whitening the surface three hundred yards away. They set the decoys in a broad, straddling vee opening wide into the ocean. The fisherman warned them not to get their hands wet, and when they did, he made them carry on with red and painful fingers, in order to teach them. Once the last toller was bobbing among his fellows, brisk and alluring, they got their numbed fingers inside their oilskins. In the meantime the fisherman had turned the skiff toward the patch of foam where as if by magic, like a black glossy rib of earth, the ledge had broken through the belly of the sea.

Carefully they inhabited their slippery nub of the North American continent, while the unresting Atlantic swelled and swirled as it had for eons round the indomitable edges. They hauled the skiff after them, established themselves as comfortably as they could in a shallow sump on top, lay on their sides a foot or so above the water, and waited, guns in hand.

In time the fisherman took a thermos bottle from the knapsack and they drank steaming coffee, and waited for the nodding decoys to lure in the first flight to the rock. Eventually the boys got hungry and restless. The fisherman let them open the picnic lunch and eat one sandwich apiece, which they both shared with the dog. Having no tobacco, the fisherman himself would not eat.

Actually the day was relatively mild, and they were warm enough at present in their woolen clothes and socks underneath oilskins and hip boots. After a while, however, the boys began to feel cramped. Their nerves were agonized by inactivity. The nephew complained and was severely told by the fisherman—who pointed to the dog, crouched unmoving except for his white-rimmed eyes—that part of doing a man's hunting was learning how to wait. But he was beginning to have misgivings of his own. This could be one of those days where all the right conditions masked an incalculable flaw.

If the fisherman had been alone, as he often was, stopping off when the necessary coincidence of tide and time occurred on his way home from hauling trawls, and had plenty of tobacco, he would not have fidgeted. The boys' being nervous made him nervous. He growled at them again. When it came, it was likely to come all at once, and then in a few moments be over. He warned them not to slack off, never to slack off, to be always ready. Under his rebuke they kept their tortured peace, though they could not help shifting and twisting until he lost what patience he had left and bullied them into lying still. A duck could see an eyelid twitch. If the dog could go without moving, so could they.

"Here it comes!" the fisherman said tersely at last.

The boys quivered with quick relief. The flock came in downwind, quartering slightly, myriad, black, and swift.

"Beautiful—" breathed the fisherman's son.

"All right," said the fisherman, intense and precise. "Aim at singles in the thickest part of the flock. Wait for me to fire and then don't stop shooting till your gun's empty." He rolled up onto his left elbow and spread his legs to brace himself. The flock bore down, arrowy and vibrant, then a hundred yards beyond the decoys it veered off.

"They're going away!" the boys cried, sighting in.

"Not yet!" snapped the fisherman. "They're coming round."

The flock changed shape, folded over itself, and drove into the wind in a tight arc. "Thousands—" the boys hissed through their teeth. All at once a whistling storm of black and white broke over the decoys.

"Now!" the fisherman shouted. "Perfect!" And he opened fire at the flock just as it hung suspended in momentary chaos above the tollers. The three pulled at their triggers and the birds splashed into the water, until the last report went off unheard, the last smoking shell flew unheeded over their shoulders, and the last of the routed flock scattered diminishing, diminishing, diminishing in every direction.

Exultantly the boys dropped their guns, jumped up, and scrambled for the skiff.

"I'll handle that skiff!" the fisherman shouted at them. They stopped. Gripping the painter and balancing himself, he eased the skiff into the water stern first and held the bow hard against the side of the rock shelf the skiff had rested on. "You stay here," he said to his nephew. "No sense in all three of us going in the boat."

The boy on the reef gazed at the gray water rising and falling hypnotically along the glistening edge. It had dropped about a foot since their arrival. "I want to go with you," he said in a sullen tone, his eyes on the streaming eddies.

"You want to do what I tell you if you want to gun with me," answered the fisherman harshly. The boy couldn't swim, and he wasn't going to have him climbing in and out of the skiff any more

than necessary. Besides he was too big.

The fisherman took his son in the skiff and cruised round and round among the decoys picking up dead birds. Meanwhile the other boy stared unmoving after them from the highest part of the ledge. Before they had quite finished gathering the dead birds, the fisherman cut the outboard and dropped to his knees in the skiff. "Down!" he yelled. "Get down!" About a dozen birds came tolling in. "Shoot—shoot!" his son hollered from the bottom of the boat to the boy on the ledge.

The dog, who had been running back and forth whining, sank to his belly, his muzzle on his forepaws. But the boy on the ledge never stirred. The ducks took late alarm at the skiff, swerved aside and into the air, passing with a whirr no more than fifty feet over the head of the boy, who remained on the ledge like a statue, without his gun, watching the two crouching in the boat.

The fisherman's son climbed onto the ledge and held the painter. The bottom of the skiff was covered with feathery black and white bodies with feet upturned and necks lolling. He was jubilant. "We got twenty-seven!" he told his cousin. "How's that? Nine apiece. Boy—" he added, "what a cool Christmas!"

The fisherman pulled the skiff onto its shelf and all three went and lay down again in anticipation of the next flight. The son, reloading, patted his shotgun affectionately. "I'm going to get me ten next time," he said. Then he asked his cousin, "Whatsamatter— didn't you see the strays?"

"Yeah," the boy said.

"How come you didn't shoot at 'em?"

"Didn't feel like it," replied the boy, still with a trace of sullenness.

"You stupid or something?" The fisherman's son was astounded. "What a highlander!" But the fisherman, though he said nothing, knew that the older boy had had an attack of ledge fever.

"Cripes!" His son kept at it. "I'd at least of tried."

"Shut up," the fisherman finally told him, "and leave him be."

At slack water three more flocks came in, one right after the other, and when it was over, the skiff was half-full of clean, dead birds. During the subsequent lull they broke out the lunch and ate it all and finished the hot coffee. For a while the fisherman sucked away on his cold pipe. Then he had himself a swig of whiskey.

The boys passed the time contentedly jabbering about who shot the most —there were ninety-two all told—which of their friends they would show the biggest ones to, how many each could eat at a meal provided they didn't have to eat any vegetables. Now and then they heard sporadic distant gunfire on the mainland, at its nearest point about two miles to the north. Once far off they saw a fishing boat making in the direction of home.

At length the fisherman got a hand inside his oilskins and produced his watch.

"Do we have to go now?" asked his son.

"Not just yet," he replied. "Pretty soon." Everything had been perfect. As good as he had ever had it. Because he was getting tired of the boys' chatter, he got up, heavily in his hip boots, and stretched. The tide had turned and was coming in, the sky was more ashen, and the wind had freshened enough so that whitecaps were beginning to blossom. It would be a good hour before they had to leave the ledge and pick up the tollers. However, he guessed they would leave a little early. On account of the rising wind, he doubted there would be much more shooting. He stepped carefully along the back of the ledge, to work his kinks out. It was also getting a little colder.

The whiskey had begun to warm him, but he was unprepared for the sudden blaze that flashed upward inside him from belly to head. He was standing looking at the shelf where the skiff was. Only the foolish skiff was not there!

For the second time that day the fisherman felt the deep vacuity of disbelief. He gaped, seeing nothing but the flat shelf of rock. He whirled, started toward the boys, slipped, recovered himself, fetched a complete circle, and stared at the unimaginably empty shelf. Its emptiness made him feel as if everything he had done that day so far, his life, he had dreamed. What could have happened? The tide was still nearly a foot below. There had been no sea to speak of. The skiff could hardly have slid off by itself. For the life of him, consciously careful as he inveterately was, he could not now remember hauling it up the last time. Perhaps in the heat of hunting, he had left it to the boy. Perhaps he could not remember which was the last time.

He exclaimed loudly, without realizing it because he was so entranced by the invisible event.

"What's wrong, Dad?" asked his son, getting to his feet.

The fisherman went blind with uncontainable rage. "Get back down there where you belong!" he screamed. He scarcely noticed the boy sink back in amazement. In a frenzy he ran along the ledge thinking the skiff might have been drawn up at another place, though he knew better. There was no other place.

He stumbled, half-falling, back to the boys who were gawking at him in consternation, as though he had gone insane. "Damn it!" he yelled savagely, grabbing both of them and yanking them to their knees. "Get on your feet!"

"What's wrong?" his son repeated in a stifled voice.

"Never mind what's wrong," he snarled. "Look for the skiff—it's adrift!" When they peered around, he gripped their shoulders, brutally facing them about. "Downwind—" He slammed his fist against his thigh.

At last he sighted the skiff himself, magically bobbing along the grim sea like a toller, a quarter of a mile to leeward on a direct course for home. The impulse to strip himself naked was succeeded instantly by a queer calm. He simply sat down on the ledge and forgot everything except the marvelous mystery.

As his awareness partially returned, he glanced toward the boys. They were still observing the skiff speechlessly. Then he was gazing into the clear young eyes of his son.

"Dad," asked the boy steadily, "what do we do now?"

That brought the fisherman upright. "The first thing we have to do," he heard himself saying with infinite tenderness as if he were making love, "is think."

"Could you swim it?" asked his son.

He shook his head and smiled at them. They smiled quickly back, too quickly. "A hundred yards maybe, in this water. I wish I could," he added. It was the most intimate and pitiful thing he had ever said. He walked in circles round them, trying to break the stall his mind was left in.

He gauged the level of the water. To the eye it was quite stationary, six inches from the shelf at this second. The fisherman did not have to mark it on the side of the rock against the passing of time to prove to his reason that it was rising, always rising. Already it was over the brink of reason, beyond the margins of thought—a senseless measurement. No sense to it.

All his life the fisherman had tried to lick the element of time, by getting up earlier and going to bed later, owning a faster boat, planning more than the day would hold, and tackling just one other job before the deadline fell. If, as on rare occasions he had the grand illusion, he ever really had beaten the game, he would need to call on all his reserves of practice and cunning now.

He sized up the scant but unforgivable three hundred yards to Brown Cow Island. Another hundred yards behind it his boat rode at anchor, where, had he been aboard, he could have used the ship-to-shore radio on which in a very short time he would have heard his wife's voice talking to him over the air about homecoming.

"Couldn't we wave something so somebody would see us?" his nephew suggested.

The fisherman spun round. "Load your guns!" he ordered. They loaded as if the air had suddenly gone frantic with birds. "I'll fire once and count to five. Then you fire. Count to five. That way they won't just think it's only somebody gunning ducks. We'll keep doing that."

"We've only got just two-and-a-half boxes left," said his son.

The fisherman nodded, understanding that from beginning to end their situation was purely mathematical, like the ticking of the alarm clock in his silent bedroom. Then he fired. The dog, who had been keeping watch over the decoys, leaped forward and yelped in confusion. They all counted off, fired the first five rounds by threes and reloaded. The fisherman scanned first the horizon, then the contracting borders of the ledge, which was the sole place the water appeared to be climbing. Soon it would be over the shelf.

They counted off and fired the second five rounds. "We'll hold off a while on the last one," the fisherman told the

boys. He sat down and pondered what a trivial thing was a skiff. This one he and the boy had knocked together in a day. Was a gun, manufactured for killing.

His son tallied up the remaining shells, grouping them symmetrically in threes on the rock when the wet box fell apart. "Two short," he announced. They reloaded and laid the guns on their knees.

Behind thickening clouds they could not see the sun going down. The water, coming up, was growing blacker. The fisherman thought he might have told his wife they would be home before dark since it was Christmas Day. He realized he had forgotten about its being any particular day. The tide would not be high until two hours after sunset. When they did not get in by nightfall, and could not be raised by radio, she might send somebody to hunt for them right away. He rejected this arithmetic immediately, with a sickening shock, recollecting it was a two-and-a-half-hour run at best. Then it occurred to him that she might send somebody on the mainland who was nearer. She would think he had engine trouble.

He rose and searched the shoreline, barely visible. Then his glance dropped to the toy shoreline at the edges of the reef. The shrinking ledge, so sinister from a boat, grew dearer minute by minute as though the whole wide world he gazed on from horizon to horizon balanced on its contracting rim. He checked the water level and found the shelf awash.

Some of what went through his mind the fisherman told to the boys. They accepted it without comment. If he caught their eyes, they looked away to spare him or because they were not yet old enough to face what they saw. Mostly they watched the rising water. The fisherman was unable to initiate a word of encouragement. He wanted one of them to ask him whether somebody would reach them ahead of the tide. He would have found it possible to say yes. But they did not inquire.

The fisherman was not sure how much, at their age, they were able to imagine. Both of them had seen from the docks drowned bodies put ashore out of boats. Sometimes they grasped things, and sometimes not. He supposed they might be longing for the comfort of their mothers, and was astonished, as much as he was capable of any astonishment except the supreme one, to discover himself wishing he had not left his wife's dark, close, naked bed that morning.

"Is it time to shoot now?" asked his nephew.

"Pretty soon," he said, as if he were putting off making good on a promise. "Not yet."

His own boy cried softly for a brief moment, like a man, his face averted in an effort neither to give or show pain.

"Before school starts," the fisherman said, wonderfully detached, "we'll go to town and I'll buy you boys anything you want."

With great difficulty, in a dull tone as though he did not in the least desire it, his son said after a pause, "I'd like one of those new thirty-horse outboards."

"All right," said the fisherman. And to his nephew, "How about you?"

The nephew shook his head desolately. "I don't want anything," he said.

After another pause the fisherman's son said, "Yes, he does, Dad. He wants one too."

"All right—" the fisherman said again, and said no more.

The dog whined in uncertainty and licked the boys' faces where they sat together. Each threw an arm over his back and hugged him. Three strays flew in and sat companionably down among the stiff-necked decoys. The dog crouched, obedient to his training. The boys observed them listlessly. Presently, sensing something untoward, the ducks took off, splashing the wave tops with feet and wingtips, into the dusky waste.

The sea began to make up in the mounting wind, and the wind bore a new and deathly chill. The fisherman, scouring the somber, dwindling shadow of the mainland for a sign, hoped it would not snow. But it did. First a few flakes, then a flurry, then storming past horizontally. The fisherman took one long, bewildered look at Brown Cow Island three hundred yards dead to leeward, and got to his feet.

Then it shut in, as if what was happening on the ledge was too private even for the last wan light of the expiring day.

"Last round," the fisherman said austerely.

The boys rose and shouldered their tacit guns. The fisherman fired into the flying snow. He counted methodically to five. His son fired and counted. His nephew. All three fired and counted. Four rounds.

"You've got one left, Dad," his son said.

The fisherman hesitated another second, then he fired the final shell. Its pathetic report, like the spat of a popgun, whipped away on the wind and was instantly blanketed in falling snow.

Night fell all in a moment to meet the ascending sea. They were now barely able to make one another out through driving snowflakes, dim as ghosts in their yellow oilskins. The fisherman heard a sea break and glanced down where his feet were. They seemed to be wound in a snowy sheet. Gently he took the boys by the shoulders and pushed them in front of him, feeling with his feet along the shallow sump to the place where it triangulated into a sharp crevice at the highest point of the ledge. "Face ahead," he told them. "Put the guns down."

"I'd like to hold mine, Dad," begged his son.

"Put it down," said the fisherman. "The tide won't hurt it. Now brace your feet against both sides and stay there."

They felt the dog, who was pitch black, running up and down in perplexity between their straddled legs. "Dad," said his son, "what about the pooch?"

If he had called the dog by name, it would have been too personal. The fisherman would have wept. As it was, he had all he could do to keep from laughing. He bent his knees, and when he touched the dog hoisted him under one arm. The dog's belly was soaking wet.

So they waited, marooned in their consciousness, surrounded by a monstrous tidal space which was slowly, slowly closing them out. In this space the periwinkle beneath the fisherman's boots was king. While hovering airborne in his mind, he had an inward glimpse of his house as curiously separate, like a June mirage.

Snow, rocks, seas, wind the fisherman had lived by all his life. Now he thought he had never comprehended what they were, and he hated them. Though they had not changed. He was deadly chilled. He set out to ask the boys if they were cold. There was no sense. He thought of the whiskey, and sidled backward, still holding the awkward dog, till he located the bottle under water with his toe. He picked it up squeamishly as though afraid of getting his sleeve wet, worked his way forward, and bent over his son. "Drink it," he said, holding the bottle against the boy's ribs. The boy tipped his head back, drank, coughed hotly, then vomited.

"I can't," he told his father wretchedly.

"Try—try—" the fisherman pleaded, as if it meant the difference between life and death.

The boy obediently drank, and again he vomited hotly. He shook his head against his father's chest and passed the bottle forward to his cousin, who drank and vomited also. Passing the bottle back, the boys dropped it in the frigid water between them.

When the waves reached his knees, the fisherman set the warm dog loose and said to his son, "Turn around and get up on my shoulders." The boy obeyed. The fisherman opened his oilskin jacket and twisted his hands behind him through his suspenders, clamping the boy's booted ankles with his elbows.

"What about the dog?" the boy asked.

"He'll make his own way all right," the fisherman said. "He can take the cold water." His knees were trembling. Every instinct shrieked for gymnastics. He ground his teeth and braced like a colossus against the sides of the submerged crevice.

The dog, having lived faithfully as though one of them for eleven years, swam a few minutes in and out around the fisherman's legs, not knowing what was happening, and left them without a whimper. He would swim and swim at random by himself, round and round in the blinding night, and when he had swum routinely through the paralyzing water all he could, he would simply, in one incomprehensible moment, drown. Almost, the fisherman, waiting out infinity, envied him his pattern.

Freezing seas swept by, flooding inexorably up and up as the earth sank away imperceptibly beneath them. The boy called out once to his cousin. There was no answer. The fisherman, marveling on a terror without voice, was dumbly glad when the boy did not call again. His own boots were long full of water. With no sensation left in his straddling legs, he dared not move them. So long as the seas came sidewise against his hips, and then sidewise against his shoulders, he might balance—no telling how long. The upper half of him was what felt frozen. His legs, disengaged from his nerves and his will, he came to regard quite scientifically. They were the absurd, precarious axis around which reeled and surged universal tumult. The waves would come on and on; he could not visualize how many tossing reinforcements lurked in the night beyond—inexhaustible numbers, and he wept in supernatural fury at each because it was higher, till he transcended hate and took them, swaying like a convert, one by one as they lunged against him and away aimlessly into their own undisputed, wild realm.

From his hips upward the fisherman stretched to his utmost as a man does whose spirit reaches out of dead sleep. The boy's head, none too high, must be at least seven feet above the ledge. Though growing larger every minute, it was a small, light life. The fisherman meant to hold it there, if need be, through a thousand tides.

By and by the boy, slumped on the head of his father, asked, "Is it over your boots, Dad?"

"Not yet," the fisherman said. Then through his teeth he added, "If I fall—kick your boots off—swim for it—downwind—to the island. . . ."

"You . . .?" the boy finally asked.

The fisherman nodded against the boy's belly. "—Won't see each other," he said.

The boy did for the fisherman the greatest thing that can be done. He may have been too young for perfect terror, but he was old enough to know there were things beyond the power of any man. All he could do he did, by trusting his father to do all he could; and asking nothing more.

The fisherman, rocked to his soul by a sea, held his eyes shut upon the interminable night.

"Is it time now?" the boy said.

The fisherman could hardly speak. "Not yet," he said. "Not just yet. . . ."

As the land mass pivoted toward sunlight the day after Christmas, a tiny fleet of small craft converged offshore like iron filings to a magnet. At daybreak they found the skiff floating unscathed off the headland, half-full of ducks and snow. The shooting *had* been good, as someone hearing on the nearby mainland the previous afternoon had supposed. Two hours afterward they found the unharmed boat adrift five miles at sea. At high noon they found the fisherman at ebb tide, his right foot jammed cruelly into a glacial crevice of the ledge beside three shotguns, his hands tangled behind him in his suspenders, and under his right elbow a rubber boot with a sock and a live starfish in it. After dragging unlit depths all day for the boys, they towed the fisherman home in his own boat at sundown, and in the frost of evening, mute with discovering purgatory, laid him on his wharf for his wife to see.

She, somehow, standing on the dock as in her frequent dream, gazing at the fisherman pure as crystal on the icy boards, a small rubber boot still frozen under one clenched arm, saw him exaggerated beyond remorse or grief, absolved of his mortality.

THE FACT IS—

1. The author anticipates the conclusion of this story in the first few pages by using the word *outside*. Explain.

2. The fisherman's determination to "think" in the face of disaster reveals one side of his character. Explain.

3. The father and his son offer a picture of mutual trust just before they die. How do they show their trust in each other?

DEATH ON THE LEDGE

1. The characters in this story have no names. Do you think this device adds to the effectiveness of the tragedy?

2. Can you select the exact time of climax, the moment of action that determines the outcome? Justify your choice by explaining it in relation to other events.

3. Does the mother seem worried about her husband's safety? Find several references in the story to support your opinion. Does her attitude lead us to a better understanding of the fisherman? Explain.

4. Would you choose the mother or the father as the most sympathetic character in this story—from the reader's point of view? Defend your opinion.

A WORD TO REMEMBER: diminishing

As the flock of birds scatter, they are described as "diminishing, diminishing, diminishing in every direction." The word *diminish* (di·MIN·ish) means "to lessen, decrease."

"He who allows his efforts to diminish courts failure." Use *diminish* in a good sentence of your own.

THINKING ABOUT STORIES OF ACTION

FASCINATION OF ACTION STORIES

1. Which three stories in this unit did you find most exciting? Why? Compare any two from this viewpoint.

2. In three of these stories, a man's concern for members of his family leads him to perform acts he would not ordinarily perform. Which are the stories and what are the uncharacteristic actions?

3. Three of the stories revolve around events that—as far as the reader can tell—never happened. Which are the stories and what are the events?

4. Americans like to race and to read about races. In one story in this unit, a man loses a race because of a moment of forgetfulness; in another a man avoids a kind of race by a desperate act; in another the final stage of the race begins as the story ends. Tell which three stories these are and explain how each description fits the story.

5. Climax in action stories adds to the thrill of reading them. Select two of these stories in which authors *emphasize* climax with special effectiveness, and show just where it occurs in each case.

6. Several of these stories have serious ideas behind the action. Choose at least two such stories and state the ideas in your own words.

DO YOU REMEMBER THESE WORDS?

Give the meaning of each of the italicized words in the following sentences; then try using each word in a substantial, original sentence.

1. The critics *scrutinized* each painting in the exhibit before awarding prizes.

2. Frequently army sergeants on TV programs are represented as *martinets*.

3. The *diminishing* supply of records caused alarm among the students who were planning an informal dance.

4. An *indolent* attitude toward any kind of work will get you nowhere.

5. The early settlers often went hungry during the winter because of *sparse* crops.

6. The *ravenous* appetite of a miser for money may bring him temporary satisfaction, but it won't win him friends.

7. Kind words of *commendation* generally lead people to perform better.

Americans
Worth
Remembering

"And so, my fellow Americans, ask not what your country can do for you—ask what you can do for your country."

These words, spoken by John F. Kennedy in his Inaugural Address, struck a responsive chord in the hearts of many Americans, partly because they knew that John F. Kennedy had given of himself for his country. In World War II his heroic action after the sinking of his boat—PT–109—aggravated an old football injury to his back. One crewman told a reporter: "He swam in that water for hours. He rescued two men on his own, then he rescued us all." As the years passed, the injury put him out of action for weeks at a time. In a hospital in 1954, he conceived the idea of a book which he called *Profiles in Courage,* a series of memorable biographies about American political figures who had shown exceptional moral courage. One of the biographies appears in this unit.

Here also you will meet another remarkable man, a man who lived with the Cherokee Indians, who served as Governor of one state and President of another, as a United States Senator, and as the "commander in chief of the armies of the independent Republic of Texas," General Sam Houston. Houston, who had proven his courage as a frontiersman and as a soldier, when faced with a moral decision, chose the United States and fell into disgrace in the state he had freed.

Throughout this unit you will also find selections that provide glimpses of other unusual Americans: Thomas Jefferson, author of the Declaration of Independence; Robert E. Lee, who favored the Union but fought in defense of his native Virginia; John Paul Jones, the first great hero of the American Navy and captain of the *Bonhomme Richard,* the famous ship that sank in victory. You will meet Mary McLeod Bethune, daughter of South Carolina slaves, crusader for women's rights and for civil rights, and founder of a Florida college. In Edgar Lee Masters' poem of a Midwestern town, you will read about Lucinda Matlock, a strong pioneer woman who scorns and scolds the weaker spirits who live after her time.

Over and over again in these stories, you will meet Americans who do more for their country than they expect their country to do for them. This ideal is summed up in Ralph Waldo Emerson's "Concord Hymn," a poem praising the heroes of the first battle of the American Revolution.

But American life is not all sacrifice and patriotism. You will also meet playwright Moss Hart, who has dramatized the lighter side of American life. And you will find a poem about the average American who experiences life in terms of supermarkets, super highways, and the other "supers" of American merchandising and technology. He is not to be forgotten when we consider Americans Worth Remembering.

Memories of
John F. Kennedy

The assassination of President John F. Kennedy on November 22, 1963, shocked the nation and set into motion a chain reaction of events and publications. One of the best books on the death of the young President was *Four Days,* introduced in lively yet thoughtful fashion by noted historian Bruce Catton. *Four Days* closes with the final paragraphs of the speech President Kennedy wrote but never delivered. This speech—with its strength, verbal harmony, and Biblical allusions—makes an interesting comparison to the Gettysburg Address of Abraham Lincoln.

Kennedy's assassination and solemn state funeral brought forth many other comparisons with Lincoln. Some reveal the nation's hysteria by their employment of extreme, meaningless coincidences: both assassinated presidents had a last name of seven letters including two *n's* and two vowels. Both were killed with a gun from behind, and in both cases there is considerable doubt, confusion, and controversy as to the motives and identity of the killer. Both presumed assassins—John Wilkes Booth and Lee Harvey Oswald—were themselves assassinated. One of the more striking coincidences is the fact that both Kennedy and Lincoln were succeeded by vice presidents named Johnson. After Catton's introduction and "The Undelivered Speech," you will read the chapter of Kennedy's *Profiles in Courage* telling the story of the man who saved the earlier Johnson and probably even the office of President.

Introduction to *Four Days*

BRUCE CATTON

hat John F. Kennedy left us was most of all an attitude. To put it in the simplest terms, he looked ahead. He knew no more than anyone else what the future was going to be like, but he did know that that was where we ought to be looking. Only to a limited extent are we prisoners of the past. The future sets us free. It is our escape hatch. We can shape it to our liking, and we had better start thinking about how we would like it.

It was time for us to take that attitude, because we thought we were growing old. We had lived through hard experiences and we were tired, and out of our weariness came caution, suspicion, and the crippling desire to play it safe. We became so worried about what we had to lose that we never

began to think about what was still to be gained, and sometimes it looked as if we were becoming a nation of fuddy-duddies. The world was moving faster than ever before, and we were beginning to regret that it was moving at all because we were afraid where it might take us.

But President Kennedy personified youth and vigor—and perhaps it was symbolic that both his friends and his foes picked up his Boston accent and began to say "vigah." He went about hatless, he liked to mingle with crowds and shake the hands of all and sundry; for recreation he played touch football, and for rest he sat in an old-fashioned rocking chair as if in sly mockery of his own exuberance. He seemed to think that things like music and painting and literature were essential parts of American life and that it was worthwhile to know what the musicians and artists and writers were doing. Whatever he did was done with zest, as if youth were for the first time touching life and finding it exciting.

With all of this, there was a cool maturity of outlook. By itself, vigor is not enough. Courage is needed also, and when youth has courage, it acquires composure. In the most perilous moments President Kennedy kept his poise. He challenged the power of darkness at least once, and during the hours when his hand had to stay close to the fateful trigger, he was composed and unafraid. Once in a great while a nation, like a man, has to be ready to spend itself utterly for some value that means more than survival itself means. President Kennedy led us through such a time, and we began to see that the power of darkness is perhaps not quite as strong as we had supposed—and that even if it were, there is something else that matters much more.

It was his attitude that made the difference. Performance can be adjudged in various ways, and we have plenty of time to appraise the value or the lack of value of the concrete achievements of the Kennedy Administration. The President who called on us to stop thinking about what our country could do for us and to think instead about what we could do for our country may or may not have given us specific programs that would embody that ideal in actual practice; the point is that he wrenched us out of ourselves and compelled us to meditate about the whole that is greater than the sum of its parts. From the beginning, the whole of our American experiment has been made up of an infinite number of aspirations and unremembered bits of heroism, devotion, and hope, lodged in the hearts of innumer-

able separate Americans. When all of these are brought together, the nation goes forward.

That, in the last analysis, is the faith America has wanted to live by. We are always uneasy when we find ourselves keeping our noblest ideals in mothballs, carefully shielded from contact with the workaday world; deep in our hearts we know that we are supposed to take them out and work for them even if contact with harsh reality occasionally knocks chips off them here and there. Whether this man knew the best ways to put our ideals into practical use is a secondary consideration now. He did think that we ought to try our best to do something about them, and that belief his death did not take away from us, because we came to share in it.

We turned some sort of corner in the last few years. Almost without our knowing it, one era came to an end and a new one began. The change had little to do with formal acts of government—with specific programs, bits of legislation, or exercises of presidential power. It reflected a change in the times themselves. For a whole generation we had had to face terrible immediate problems—depression, war, cold war, the infinite destructive power of the nuclear mystery that we knew how to release but did not quite know how to control. Then came a breathing spell, a faint but definite easing of the tensions. Almost for the first moment in our lifetimes, we began to look ahead once more and to realize that it was not only possible but imperative to think about the limitless future rather than about the mere problem of warding off disaster.

President Kennedy came to symbolize that moment of change, not because he caused it but because he fitted into it; not because of what he did but simply because of what he was.

The Undelivered Speech

JOHN F. KENNEDY

America today is stronger than ever before. Our adversaries have not abandoned their ambitions—our dangers have not diminished—our vigilance cannot be relaxed. But now we have the military, the scientific, and the economic strength to do whatever must be done for the preservation and promotion of freedom.

That strength will never be used in pursuit of aggressive ambitions—it will always be used in pursuit of peace. It will never be used to promote provocations—it will always be used to promote the peaceful settlement of disputes.

We in this country, in this generation, are—by destiny rather than choice—the watchmen on the walls of world freedom. We ask, therefore, that we may be worthy of our power and responsibility—that we may exercise our strength with wisdom and restraint—and that we may achieve in our time and for all time the ancient vision of peace on earth, good will toward men. That must always be our goal—and the righteousness of our cause must always underlie our strength. For as was written long ago: "Except the Lord keep the city, the watchman waketh but in vain."

THE FACT IS—

1. President Kennedy's Boston accent was imitated by various people: i.e., "vigah" for *vigor*. What prompted them to do this?

2. What was it that "made the difference" in the nation's attitude toward the perilous world situation in the early '60's? How can you explain this difference?

3. What is "the faith America has wanted to live by"?

4. In "The Undelivered Speech," Kennedy wrote that we are "the watchmen on the walls of world freedom." What did he mean by this phrase?

A MAN'S DREAM

1. President Kennedy "challenged the power of darkness at least once." Explain the circumstances. What qualities of character did he reveal?

2. Mr. Kennedy "compelled us to meditate about the whole that is greater than the sum of its parts." What does this statement mean? In one or two sentences, show your understanding by an example.

3. What was his attitude toward the past? the present? the future? What was his dream?

4. "The Undelivered Speech" closes with this quotation: "Except the Lord keep the city, the watchman waketh but in vain." In a careful paragraph, interpret this quotation.

A WORD TO REMEMBER: adversaries

President Kennedy said in his last official words, "Our adversaries have not abandoned their ambitions." An *adversary* is an enemy, foe, or opponent. Your *adversaries* in any contest are those who oppose or resist you. What is an antonym for this word? Use *adversary* in an original sentence.

I...Looked Down into My Open Grave

JOHN F. KENNEDY

Do you know men who have risked everything for a firm

conviction? Such basic honesty reflects great courage.

In a lonely grave, forgotten and unknown, lies "the man who saved a President," and who as a result may well have preserved for ourselves and posterity constitutional government in the United States—the man who performed in 1868 what one historian has called "the most heroic act in American history, incomparably more difficult than any deed of valor upon the field of battle"—but a United States Senator whose name no one recalls: Edmund G. Ross of Kansas.

The impeachment of President Andrew Johnson, the event in which the obscure Ross was to play such a dramatic role, was the sensational climax to the bitter struggle between the President, determined to carry out Abraham Lincoln's policies of reconciliation with the defeated South, and the more radical Republican leaders in Congress, who sought to administer the downtrodden Southern states as conquered provinces which had forfeited their rights under the Constitution. It was, moreover, a struggle between Executive and Legislative authority. Andrew Johnson, the courageous if untactful Tennessean who had been the only Southern Member of Congress to refuse to secede with his state, had committed himself to the policies of the Great Emancipator to whose high station he had succeeded only by the course of an assassin's bullet. He knew that Lincoln prior to his death had already clashed with the extremists in Congress, who had opposed his approach to reconstruction in a constitutional and charitable manner and sought to make the Legislative branch of the government supreme. And his own belligerent temperament soon destroyed any hope that Congress might now join hands in carrying out Lincoln's policies of permitting the South to resume its place in the Union with as little delay and controversy as possible.

By 1866, when Edmund Ross first came to the Senate, the two branches of the government were already at each other's throats, snarling and bristling with anger. Bill after bill was vetoed by the President on the grounds that it was unconstitutional, too harsh in its treatment of the South, an unnecessary prolongation of military rule in peacetime, or undue interference with the authority of the Executive branch. And for the first time in our nation's history, important public measures were passed over a President's veto and became law without his support.

But not all of Andrew Johnson's vetoes were overturned; and the "Radical" Republicans of the Congress promptly realized that one final step was necessary before they could crush their despised foe (and in the heat of political battle, their vengeance was turned upon their President far more than their former military enemies of the South). That one remaining step was the assurance of a two-thirds majority in the Senate—for under the Constitution, such a majority was necessary to override a Presidential veto. And more important, such a majority was constitutionally required to accomplish their

major ambition, now an ill-kept secret, conviction of the President under an impeachment and his dismissal from office!

The temporary and unstable two-thirds majority which had enabled the Senate Radical Republicans on several occasions to enact legislation over the President's veto was, they knew, insufficiently reliable for an impeachment conviction. To solidify this bloc became the paramount goal of Congress, expressly or impliedly governing its decisions on other issues—particularly the admission of new states, the readmission of Southern states, and the determination of senatorial credentials. By extremely dubious methods a pro-Johnson Senator was denied his seat. Over the President's veto Nebraska was admitted to the Union, seating two more anti-administration Senators. Although last-minute maneuvers failed to admit Colorado over the President's veto (sparsely populated Colorado had rejected statehood in a referendum), an unexpected tragedy brought false tears and fresh hopes for a new vote, in Kansas.

Senator Jim Lane of Kansas had been a "conservative" Republican sympathetic to Johnson's plans to carry out Lincoln's reconstruction policies. But his frontier state was one of the most "radical" in the Union. When Lane voted to uphold Johnson's veto of the Civil Rights Bill of 1866 and introduced the administration's bill for recognition of the new state government of Arkansas, Kansas had arisen in outraged heat. A mass meeting at Lawrence had vilified the Senator and speedily reported resolutions sharply condemning his position. Humiliated, mentally ailing, broken in health, and laboring under charges of financial irregularities, Jim Lane took his own life on July 1, 1866.

With this thorn in their side removed, the Radical Republicans in

Washington looked anxiously toward Kansas and the selection of Lane's successor. Their fondest hopes were realized, for the new Senator from Kansas turned out to be Edmund G. Ross, the very man who had introduced the resolutions attacking Lane at Lawrence.

There could be no doubt as to where Ross's sympathies lay, for his entire career was one of determined opposition to the slave states of the South, their practices and their friends. In 1854, when only twenty-eight, he had taken part in the mob rescue of a fugitive slave in Milwaukee. In 1856 he had joined that flood of antislavery immigrants to "bleeding" Kansas who intended to keep it a free territory. Disgusted with the Democratic party of his youth, he had left that party, and volunteered in the Kansas Free State Army to drive back a force of proslavery men invading the territory. In 1862 he had given up his newspaper work to enlist in the Union Army, from which he emerged a Major. His leading role in the condemnation of Lane at Lawrence convinced the Radical Republican leaders in Congress that in Edmund G. Ross they had a solid member of that vital two-thirds.

The stage was now set for the final scene—the removal of Johnson. Early in 1867, Congress enacted over the President's veto the Tenure-of-Office Bill which prevented the President from removing without the consent of the Senate all new officeholders whose appointment required confirmation by that body. At the time nothing more than the cry for more patronage was involved, Cabinet Members having originally been specifically exempt.

On August 5, 1867, President Johnson—convinced that the Secretary of War, whom he had inherited from Lincoln, Edwin M. Stanton, was the surreptitious tool of the Radical Republicans and was seeking to become the almighty dictator of the conquered South—asked for his immediate resignation; and Stanton arrogantly fired back the reply that he declined to resign before the next meeting of Congress. Not one to cower before this kind of effrontery, the President one week later suspended Stanton, and appointed in his place the one man whom Stanton did not dare resist, General Grant. On January 13, 1868, an angry Senate notified the President and Grant that it did not concur in the suspension of Stanton, and Grant vacated the office upon Stanton's return. But the situation was intolerable. The Secretary of War was unable to attend Cabinet meetings or associate with his colleagues in the administration; and on February 21, President Johnson, anxious to obtain a court test of the act he believed obviously unconstitutional, again notified Stanton that he had been summarily removed from the office of Secretary of War.

While Stanton, refusing to yield possession, barricaded himself in his office, public opinion in the nation ran heavily against the President. He had intentionally broken the law and dictatorially thwarted the will of Congress! Although previous resolutions of impeachment had been defeated in the House, both in committee and on the floor, a new resolution was swiftly reported and adopted on February 24 by a tremendous vote. Every single Republican voted in the affirmative, and Thaddeus Stevens of Pennsylvania—the crippled, fanatical personification of the extremes of the Radical Republican movement, master of the House of Representatives, with a mouth like the thin edge of an ax—warned both Houses of the Congress coldly: "Let me see the recreant who would vote to let such a criminal escape. Point me to one who will dare do it and I will show you one who will dare the infamy of posterity."

With the President impeached—in effect, indicted—by the House, the frenzied trial for his conviction or acquittal under the Articles of Impeachment began on March 5 in the Senate, presided over by the Chief Justice. It was a trial to rank with all the great trials in history—Charles I before the High Court of Justice, Louis XVI before the French Convention, and Warren Hastings before the House of Lords.[1] Two great elements of drama were missing: the actual cause for which the President was being tried was not fundamental to the welfare of the nation; and the defendant himself was at all times absent.

But every other element of the highest courtroom drama was present. To each Senator, the Chief Justice administered an oath "to do impartial justice" (including even the hot-headed Radical Senator from Ohio, Benjamin Wade, who as President Pro Tempore of the Senate was next in line for the Presidency). The chief prosecutor for the House was General Benjamin F. Butler, the "butcher of New Orleans," a talented but coarse and demagogic Congressman from Massachusetts. (When he lost his seat in 1874, he was so hated by his own party as well as his opponents that one Republican wired concerning the Democratic sweep, "Butler defeated, everything else lost.") Some one thousand tickets were printed

for admission to the Senate galleries during the trial, and every conceivable device was used to obtain one of the four tickets allotted each Senator.

From the fifth of March to the sixteenth of May, the drama continued. Of the eleven Articles of Impeachment adopted by the House, the first eight were based upon the removal of Stanton and the appointment of a new Secretary of War in violation of the Tenure-of-Office Act; the ninth related to Johnson's conversation with a general which was said to induce violations of the Army Appropriations Act; the tenth recited that Johnson had delivered "intemperate, inflammatory, and scandalous harangues . . . as well against Congress as the laws of the United States"; and the eleventh was a deliberately obscure conglomeration of all the charges in the preceding articles, which had been designed by Thaddeus Stevens to furnish a common ground for those who favored conviction but were unwilling to identify themselves on basic issues. In opposition to Butler's inflammatory arguments in support of this hastily drawn indictment, Johnson's able and learned counsel replied with considerable effectiveness. They insisted that the Tenure-of-Office Act was null and void as a clear violation of the Constitution; that even if it were valid, it would not apply to Stanton, for the reasons previously mentioned; and that the only way that a judicial test of the law could be obtained was for Stanton to be dismissed and sue for his rights in the courts.

But as the trial progressed, it became increasingly apparent that the impatient Republicans did not intend to give the President a fair trial on the formal issues upon which the impeachment was drawn, but intended instead to depose him from the White House on any grounds, real or imagined, for refusing to accept their policies. Telling

---

[1] Charles I before the High Court of Justice: The king of Great Britain who was tried for treason and executed. Louis XVI before the French Convention: King of France who was tried for treason during the French Revolution and sent to the guillotine in 1793. Warren Hastings before the House of Lords: A British soldier and statesman, who was charged with cruelty and dishonesty in his post as the first governor-general of India, brought to trial in 1788, and, after seven years, found "Not guilty" by the House of Lords.

evidence in the President's favor was arbitrarily excluded. Prejudgment on the part of most Senators was brazenly announced. Attempted bribery and other forms of pressure were rampant. The chief interest was not in the trial or the evidence, but in the tallying of votes necessary for conviction.

Twenty-seven states (excluding the unrecognized Southern states) in the Union meant fifty-four members of the Senate, and thirty-six votes were required to constitute the two-thirds majority necessary for conviction. All twelve Democratic votes were obviously lost, and the forty-two Republicans knew that they could afford to lose only six of their own members if Johnson were to be ousted. To their dismay, at a preliminary Republican caucus, six courageous Republicans indicated that the evidence so far introduced was not in their opinion sufficient to convict Johnson under the Articles of Impeachment. "Infamy!" cried the Philadelphia *Press*. The Republic has "been betrayed in the house of its friends!"

But if the remaining thirty-six Republicans would hold, there would be no doubt as to the outcome. All must stand together! But one Republican Senator would not announce his verdict in the preliminary poll—Edmund G. Ross of Kansas. The Radicals were outraged that a Senator from such an anti-Johnson stronghold as Kansas could be doubtful. "It was a very clear case," Senator Sumner of Massachusetts fumed, "especially for a Kansas man. I did not think that a Kansas man could quibble against his country."

From the very time Ross had taken his seat, the Radical leaders had been confident of his vote. His entire background, as already indicated, was one of firm support of their cause. One of his first acts in the Senate had been to read a declaration of his adherence to Radical Republican policy, and he had silently voted for all of their measures. He had made it clear that he was not in sympathy with Andrew Johnson personally or politically; and after the removal of Stanton, he had voted with the majority in adopting a resolution declaring such removal unlawful. His colleague from Kansas, Senator Pomeroy, was one of the most Radical leaders of the anti-Johnson group. The Republicans insisted that Ross's crucial vote was rightfully theirs, and they were determined to get it by whatever means available. As stated by De Witt in his memorable *Impeachment of Andrew Johnson*, "The full brunt of the struggle turned at last on the one remaining doubtful Senator, Edmund G. Ross."

When the impeachment resolution had passed the House, Senator Ross had casually remarked to Senator Sprague of Rhode Island, "Well, Sprague, the thing is here; and, so far as I am concerned, though a Republican and opposed to Mr. Johnson and his policy, he shall have as fair a trial as an accused man ever had on this earth." Immediately the word spread that "Ross was shaky." "From that hour," he later wrote, "not a day passed that did not bring me, by mail and telegraph and in personal intercourse, appeals to stand fast for impeachment, and not a few were the admonitions of condign visitations upon any indication even of lukewarmness."

Throughout the country, and in all walks of life, as indicated by the correspondence of Members of the Senate, the condition of the public mind was not unlike that preceding a great battle. The dominant party of the nation seemed to occupy the position of public prosecutor, and it was scarcely in the mood to brook delay for trial or to hear defense. Washington had become during the trial the central point of the politically dissatisfied and swarmed with representatives of every state of the Union, demanding in a practically united voice the deposition of the President. The footsteps of the anti-impeaching Republicans were dogged from the day's beginning to its end and far into the night, with entreaties, considerations, and threats. The newspapers came daily filled with not a few threats of violence upon their return to their constituents.

Ross and his fellow doubtful Republicans were daily pestered, spied upon, and subjected to every form of pressure. Their residences were carefully watched, their social circles suspiciously scrutinized, and their every move and companions secretly marked in special notebooks. They were warned in the party press, harangued by their constituents, and sent dire warnings threatening political ostracism and even assassination. Stanton himself, from his barricaded headquarters in the War Department, worked day and night to bring to bear upon the doubtful Senators all the weight of his impressive military associations. The Philadelphia *Press* reported "a fearful avalanche of telegrams from every section of the country," a great surge of public opinion from the "common people" who had given their money and lives to the country and would not "willingly or unavenged see their great sacrifice made naught."

The New York *Tribune* reported that Edmund Ross in particular was "mercilessly dragged this way and that by both sides, hunted like a fox night and day, and badgered by his own colleagues, like the bridge at Arcola [1] now trod upon by one army and now trampled by the other." His background and life were investigated from top to bottom, and his constituents and colleagues pursued him throughout Washington to gain

[1] **Arcola:** a village (now Arcole) in Italy on the Adige River. Here in a three-day, seesawing battle in 1796, Napoleon defeated the Austrians.

some inkling of his opinion. He was the target of every eye, his name was on every mouth, and his intentions were discussed in every newspaper. Although there is evidence that he gave some hint of agreement to each side, and each attempted to claim him publicly, he actually kept both sides in a state of complete suspense by his judicial silence.

But with no experience in political turmoil, no reputation in the Senate, no independent income, and the most radical state in the Union to deal with, Ross was judged to be the most sensitive to criticism and the most certain to be swayed by expert tactics. A committee of Congressmen and Senators sent to Kansas, and to the states of the other doubtful Republicans, this telegram: "Great danger to the peace of the country and the Republican cause if impeachment fails. Send to your Senators public opinion by resolutions, letters, and delegations." A member of the Kansas Legislature called upon Ross at the Capitol. A general urged on by Stanton remained at his lodge until four o'clock in the morning determined to see him. His brother received a letter offering $20,000 for revelation of the Senator's intentions. Gruff Ben Butler exclaimed of Ross, "There is a bushel of money! How much does the damned scoundrel want?" The night before the Senate was to take its first vote for the conviction or acquittal of Johnson, Ross received this telegram from home:

Kansas has heard the evidence and demands the conviction of the President. (*signed*) D. R. ANTHONY AND 1,000 OTHERS

And on that fateful morning of May 16, Ross replied:

To D. R. Anthony and 1,000 Others: I do not recognize your right to demand that I vote either for or against conviction. I have taken an oath to do impartial justice according to the Constitution and laws, and trust that I shall have the courage to vote according to the dictates of my judgment and for the highest good of the country.

(signed) E. G. Ross

That morning spies traced Ross to his breakfast; and ten minutes before the vote was taken, his Kansas colleague warned him in the presence of Thaddeus Stevens that a vote for acquittal would mean trumped-up charges and his political death.

But now the fateful hour was at hand. Neither escape, delay, nor indecision was possible. As Ross himself later described it: "The galleries were packed. Tickets of admission were at an enormous premium. The House had adjourned and all of its members were in the Senate chamber. Every chair on the Senate floor was filled with a Senator, a Cabinet Officer, a member of the President's counsel, or a member of the House." Every Senator was in his seat, the desperately ill Grimes of Iowa being literally carried in.

It had been decided to take the first vote under that broad Eleventh Article of Impeachment, believed to command the widest support. As the Chief Justice announced the voting would begin, he reminded "the citizens and strangers in the galleries that absolute silence and perfect order are required." But already a deathlike stillness enveloped the Senate chamber. A Congressman later recalled that "Some of the members of the House near me grew pale and sick under the burden of suspense"; and Ross noted that there was even "a subsidence of the shuffling of feet, the rustling of silks, the fluttering of fans, and of conversation."

The voting tensely commenced. By the time the Chief Justice reached the name of Edmund Ross, twenty-four "guilties" had been pronounced. Ten more were certain and one other practically certain. Only Ross's vote was needed to obtain the thirty-six votes necessary to convict the President. But not a single person in the room knew how this young Kansan would vote. Unable to conceal the suspense and emotion in his voice, the Chief Justice put the question to him: "Mr. Senator Ross, how say you? Is the respondent Andrew Johnson guilty or not guilty of a high misdemeanor as charged in this Article?" Every voice was still; every eye was upon the freshman Senator from Kansas. The hopes and fears, the hatred and bitterness of past decades were centered upon this one man.

As Ross himself later described it, his "powers of hearing and seeing seemed developed in an abnormal degree."

Every individual in that great audience seemed distinctly visible, some with lips apart and bending forward in anxious expectancy, others with hand uplifted as if to ward off an apprehended blow . . . and each peering with an intensity that was almost tragic upon the face of him who was about to cast the fateful vote. . . . Every fan was folded, not a foot moved, not the rustle of a garment, not a whisper was heard. . . . Hope and fear seemed blended in every face, instantaneously alternating, some with revengeful hate . . . others lighted with hope. . . . The Senators in their seats leaned over their desks, many with hand to ear. . . . It was a tremendous responsibility, and it was not strange that he upon whom it had been imposed by a fateful combination of conditions should have sought to avoid it, to put it away from him as one shuns, or tries to fight off, a nightmare. . . . I almost literally looked down into my open grave. Friendships, position, fortune, everything that makes life desirable to an ambitious man were about to be swept away by the breath of my mouth, perhaps forever. It is not strange that my answer was carried waveringly over the air and failed to reach the limits of the audience, or that repetition was called for by distant Senators on the opposite side of the Chamber.

Then came the answer again in a voice that could not be misunderstood —full, final, definite, unhesitating, and unmistakable: "Not guilty." The deed was done, the President saved, the trial as good as over, and the conviction lost. The remainder of the roll call was unimportant; conviction had failed by the margin of a single vote, and a general rumbling filled the chamber until the Chief Justice proclaimed that "on this Article thirty-five Senators having voted guilty and nineteen not guilty, a two-thirds majority not having voted for conviction, the President is, therefore, acquitted under this Article."

A ten-day recess followed, ten turbulent days to change votes on the remaining Articles. An attempt was made to rush through bills to readmit six Southern states, whose twelve Senators were guaranteed to vote for conviction. But this could not be accomplished in time. Again Ross was the only one uncommitted on the other Articles, the only one whose vote could not be predicted in advance. And again he was subjected to terrible pressure. From "D. R. Anthony and Others," he received a wire informing him that "Kansas repudiates you as she does all perjurers and skunks." Every incident in his life was examined and distorted. Professional witnesses were found by Senator Pomeroy to testify before a special House committee that Ross had indicated a willingness to change his vote for a consideration. (Unfortunately this witness was so delighted in his exciting role that he also swore that Senator Pomeroy had made an offer to produce three votes for acquittal for $40,000.) When Ross, in his capacity as a Committee Chairman, took several bills to the President, James G. Blaine remarked: "There goes the rascal to get his pay." (Long afterward Blaine was to admit: "In the exaggerated denunciation caused by the anger and chagrin of the moment, great injustice was done to statesmen of spotless character.")

Again the wild rumors spread that Ross had been won over on the remaining Articles of Impeachment. As the Senate reassembled, he was the only one of the seven "renegade" Republicans to vote with the majority on preliminary procedural matters. But when the second and third Articles of Impeachment were read, and the name of Ross was reached again with the same intense suspense of ten days earlier, again came the calm answer "Not guilty."

Why did Ross, whose dislike for Johnson continued, vote "Not guilty"? His motives appear clearly from his own writings on the subject years later in articles contributed to *Scribner's* and *Forum* magazines:

In a large sense, the independence of the executive office as a coordinate branch of the government was on trial.... If ... the President must step down ... a disgraced man and a political outcast ... upon insufficient proofs and from partisan considerations, the office of President would be degraded, cease to be a coordinate branch of the government, and ever after subordinated to the legislative will. It would practically have revolutionized our splendid political fabric into a partisan Congressional autocracy.... This government had never faced so insidious a danger ... control by the worst element of American politics.... If Andrew Johnson were acquitted by a nonpartisan vote ... America would pass the danger point of partisan rule and that intolerance which so often characterizes the sway of great majorities and makes them dangerous.

The "open grave" which Edmund Ross had foreseen was hardly an exaggeration. A Justice of the Kansas Supreme Court telegraphed him that "the rope with which Judas Iscariot hanged himself is lost, but Jim Lane's pistol is at your service." An editorial in a Kansas newspaper screamed:

On Saturday last Edmund G. Ross, United States Senator from Kansas, sold himself, and betrayed his constituents; stultified his own record, basely lied to his friends, shamefully violated his solemn pledge . . . and to the utmost of his poor ability signed the death warrant of his country's liberty. This act was done deliberately, because the traitor, like Benedict Arnold, loved money better than he did principle, friends, honor, and his country, all combined. Poor, pitiful, shriveled wretch, with a soul so small that a little pelf would outweigh all things else that dignify or ennoble manhood.

Ross's political career was ended. To the New York *Tribune*, he was nothing but "a miserable poltroon and traitor." The Philadelphia *Press* said that in Ross "littleness" had "simply borne its legitimate fruit," and that he and his fellow recalcitrant Republicans had "plunged from a precipice of fame into the groveling depths of infamy and death." The Philadelphia *Inquirer* said that "They had tried, convicted, and sentenced themselves." For them there could be "no allowance, no clemency."

Comparative peace returned to Washington as Stanton relinquished his office and Johnson served out the rest of his term, later—unlike his Republican defenders—to return triumphantly to the Senate as Senator from Tennessee. But no one paid attention when Ross tried unsuccessfully to explain his vote, and denounced the falsehoods of Ben Butler's investigating committee, recalling that the General's "well-known groveling instincts and proneness to slime and uncleanness" had led "the public to insult the brute creation by dubbing him 'the beast.'" He clung unhappily to his seat in the Senate until the expiration of his term, frequently referred to as "the traitor Ross," and complaining that his fellow Congressmen, as well as citizens on the street, considered association with him "disreputable and scandalous," and passed him by as if he were "a leper, with averted face and every indication of hatred and disgust."

Neither Ross nor any other Republican who had voted for the acquittal of Johnson was ever reelected to the Senate, not a one of them retaining the support of their party's organization. When he returned to Kansas in 1871, he and his family suffered social ostracism, physical attack, and near poverty.

Who was Edmund G. Ross? Practically nobody. Not a single public law bears his name, not a single history book includes his picture, not a single list of Senate "greats" mentions his service. His one heroic deed has been all but forgotten. But who might Edmund G. Ross have been? That is the question—for Ross, a man with an excellent command of words, an excellent background for politics, and an excellent future in the Senate, might well have outstripped his colleagues in prestige and power throughout a long Senate career. Instead, he chose to throw all of this away for one act of conscience.

But the twisting course of human events eventually upheld the faith he expressed to his wife shortly after the trial: "Millions of men cursing me today will bless me tomorrow for having saved the country from the greatest peril through which it has ever passed, though none but God can ever know the struggle it has cost me." For twenty years later Congress repealed the Tenure-of-Office Act, to which every President after Johnson, regardless of party, had objected; and still later the Supreme Court, referring to "the extremes of that episode in our government," held it to be unconstitutional. Ross moved to New Mexico, where in his later years he was to be appointed Territorial Governor. Just prior to his death, when he was awarded a special pension by Congress for his service in the Civil War, the press and the country took the opportunity to pay tribute to his fidelity to principle in a trying hour and his courage in saving his government from a devastating reign of terror. They now agreed with Ross's earlier judgment that his vote had "saved the country from . . . a strain that would have wrecked any other form of government." Those Kansas newspapers and political leaders who had bitterly denounced him in earlier years praised Ross for his stand against legislative mob rule: "By the firmness and courage of Senator Ross," it was said, "the country was saved from calamity greater than war, while it consigned him to a political martyrdom, the most cruel in our history. . . . Ross was the victim of a wild flame of intolerance which swept everything before it. He did his duty knowing that it meant his political death. . . . It was a brave thing for Ross to do, but Ross did it. He acted for his conscience and with a lofty patriotism, regardless of what he knew must be the ruinous consequences to himself. He acted right."

JOHN F. KENNEDY (1917–1963).

"I think continually of those who were truly great.

. . . . .

The names of those who in their lives fought for life,
Who were at their hearts the fire's center.
Born of the sun they traveled a short while toward the sun,
And left the vivid air signed with their honor."
— STEPHEN SPENDER

The triumph and tragedy of John F. Kennedy are close to the hearts and memories of all the people of this generation. We all know that he was born the son of a wealthy Boston financier, that he played football at Harvard and graduated with distinction, that in his early twenties he published a significant book on England's unreadiness for World War II, that he was a wounded PT-boat hero during that war. We know his meteoric rise through the Congress to the Presidency. We know, too, that he was to young people all over the world a symbol of hope and enthusiasm. No one could sum up John F. Kennedy's attitude better than he did himself in his Inauguration Address:

"And so, my fellow Americans, ask not what your country can do for you; ask what you can do for your country.

"My fellow citizens of the world, ask not what America will do for you, but what together we can do for the freedom of man.

"Finally, whether you are citizens of America or citizens of the world, ask of us here the same high standards of strength and sacrifice which we ask of you. With a good conscience our only sure reward, with history the final judge of our deeds, let us go forth to lead the land we love, asking His blessing and His help, but knowing that here on earth God's work must truly be our own."

THE FACT IS—

1. What policies after the Civil War was President Andrew Johnson trying to carry out?

2. How great a majority in the Senate was necessary to override a Presidential veto?

3. What was the importance of Senator Jim Lane's death?

4. How many Republican votes were considered doubtful?

5. How was Ross treated immediately after the acquittal of President Johnson?

A MOST HEROIC ACT

1. Who was the "Great Emancipator" mentioned on page 69?

2. What bill paved the way for the impeachment proceedings against President Johnson? What was Johnson's reaction to it? What was the result?

3. At the trial of Johnson, the Chief Justice administered to each Senator an oath "to do impartial justice." Explain the irony.

4. Why were the Radical Republican leaders confident of Ross's vote? Did he let them down? Explain why, or why not.

5. Do you think the "open grave" for Edmund Ross after Johnson's acquittal was an exaggeration? In a well-developed paragraph, summarize in your own words the immediate aftereffects of the trial.

6. Ross "acted for his conscience and with a lofty patriotism. . . . He acted right." Name one or two other men in history who have acted in a similar manner, even though in your opinion they may not have been "right." Explain the circumstances.

A WORD TO REMEMBER: belligerent

President Andrew Johnson's temperament is described as *belligerent* (page 69). This word is derived from the Latin: *bellum,* "war," and *gerere* "to wage"; hence, literally, "to wage war." Synonyms are *hostile, pugnacious, quarrelsome.* Which one of the three would be most appropriate for *belligerent* as used here?

John
Paul
Jones

From what simple beginnings did our present-day great Navy spring? See what World War II Admiral Dan Gallery says in his introduction to Samuel Eliot Morison's Pulitzer-Prize-winning biography of our first naval hero, John Paul Jones.

DANIEL V. GALLERY

The U.S. Navy has good reason to be proud of and grateful to the hero whose body lies enshrined in the Academy chapel at Annapolis. Thanks to John Paul Jones, the Navy can claim the greatest hero of the Revolution next to George Washington. Aside from Jones, the Navy didn't do much in the Revolution. Both the Navy's debt to Jones and its troubles in fighting its first war

Daniel V. Gallery's Introduction appears in the *Time* Reading Program Edition of *John Paul Jones* and is reprinted with the express permission of Time-Life Books, New York, New York.

emerge sharply in Samuel Eliot Morison's *John Paul Jones*. Professor Morison does not go out of his way to make the Continental Navy look bad. He just couldn't tell Jones's story truthfully without doing so.

Sea power did play a vital role in the Revolution, but for the most part it was not official American sea power. Privateers—armed private vessels which fought for plunder—did most of the fighting in American waters. There were nearly five hundred of them, freebooters who were little better than pirates by present-day standards. They harassed British commerce, captured much-needed supplies for the American armies—and made fortunes for themselves. But their overall effect on the war was small, except to infuriate the British Crown. It was French sea power, not American, which finally turned the tide with a battle fleet that bottled up Cornwallis at Yorktown.[1]

Throughout the Revolution, the Continental Navy was steeped in politics and torn by internal jealousy and vicious intrigue. It accomplished little except to dissipate the new nation's meager resources on ships that never got to sea or that were destroyed or captured as soon as they did. The great exception was John Paul Jones. He got to sea, accomplished a great deal—and the British never laid hands on him, although he gave them plenty of opportunity.

The main reason why the United States couldn't have a proper navy in those days was something that also plagued the Royal Navy: prize money. The whole crew of a privateer shared in the loot taken at sea, and privateers took on only lightly armed merchant ships. Navy ships got prize money too,

---

[1] **Yorktown:** a Virginia town where Cornwallis surrendered to Washington.

but a smaller share than the privateers. And their main job was to fight; prizes were supposed to be incidental. Few patriots were willing to go to sea in naval ships and fight for glory when they could ship in privateers, fight less, and make much more money.

Although Jones was more than willing to fight, even he (quite rightly) insisted on his share of the prize money when he did happen to capture merchant ships. In fact, as Morison relates, he spent a large part of his time ashore trying to collect what was coming to him and his crew. Usually it took him a long time to get it. Histories of the Continental Navy are full of disputes over prize money, which was the main motivating force for seafaring men in those days.

But prize money was incidental to Jones. He thought in terms of high strategy and thoroughly understood how huge naval forces could be tied up by a lone, bold raider on the loose near the enemy homeland. Jones carried the war across the Atlantic and dumped it right on England's doorstep. In *Ranger* he cruised through the Irish Sea as if he owned it. In *Bonhomme Richard,* accompanied by a small, makeshift task force, he circled Ireland and Scotland and nearly got to the Thames, capturing merchant ships and men-of-war within sight of British shores. He sailed into the Bay of Belfast, the Firth of Clyde, Solway Firth, and Firth of Forth, and twice he actually led armed parties ashore in Scotland. Then, in the famous battle off Flamborough Head, he boarded and captured the far-superior H.M.S. *Serapis,* only 150 miles from London.

The material damage which Jones did to the British Empire was insignificant. But the impact of his operations on morale was like an atom bomb. While he was in British waters, every coastal city in the British Isles howled for a squadron of naval ships as protection against the American "pirate." Their Lordships of the Admiralty had an unhappy time.

It seems incredible that the great Navy we have today sprang from the beginnings described in this book. The Continental Navy consisted for the most part of a ragtag, undisciplined bunch of scalawags. Mutiny was commonplace. When it occurred, it seems to have been customary for the captain to appease the mutineers as best he could and then sweep the whole thing into the lee scuppers and forget it. As Morison relates, Jones did this several times. But when the crew of his gig got drunk ashore and couldn't row him back to the ship, he triced them up in the rigging and flogged them. Several times during my naval career I have had occasion to think we were perhaps a bit premature in abolishing the old Navy custom of flogging. But never in my forty-four years of active duty did I see anything in the U.S. Navy even remotely resembling a mutiny.

One interesting slant on life at sea in those days is given by Morison's list of the stores Jones put aboard the sloop *Providence,* which went with him on a raiding voyage. It includes 583 gallons of rum, intended to last a crew of some seventy for two months. This works out to be just about a pint of rum per man per day. Of course, a pint of rum isn't going to get a two-fisted seafaring man drunk. But I certainly wouldn't want to try to furl sail on a heaving yardarm with a gale of wind blowing and a pint of rum under my belt. Maybe it was the rum that gave the oldtimers the nerve to do it!

The utter lack of discipline in those days is shown by the conduct of Captain Pierre Landais, U.S.N., during the battle between *Bonhomme Richard* and

Serapis. Theoretically, Jones had two other frigates under his command besides *Bonhomme Richard. Pallas,* a French ship flying U.S. colors, behaved well enough in the battle and captured H.M.S. *Countess of Scarborough.* The other ship was *Alliance,* a fine American-built frigate better in every material way than the *Richard.* Landais, her commander, was an ex-French naval officer who had been commissioned captain in the U.S.N.

Serapis was a much more powerful ship than the *Bonhomme Richard.* But *Richard* and *Alliance* against *Serapis* would have had a pushover. As things turned out, it was *Richard* against both *Serapis* and *Alliance!*

Landais hated Jones and resented serving under him. Throughout the cruise leading up to the battle, he refused to obey Jones's orders and operated independently whenever he felt like it, doing his best meanwhile to discredit and undermine Jones. Early in the battle he fired one broadside which raked *Bonhomme Richard* and then hauled clear, making no move to help Jones fight his much bigger enemy. At the crucial point in the battle, after Jones lashed his battered ship alongside *Serapis,* Landais sailed up close aboard and deliberately let *Richard* have his full broadside. Then he came about and let her have another, inflicting more damage on Jones's ship than the British had done.

If I had been in Jones's shoes, I think that right after the battle I would have hanged this sneaking rat from his own yardarm, even though I might have swung for it myself later. As it was, Landais eventually was court-martialed and cashiered from the Navy, although not for his dastardly conduct in this battle. He later collected $4,000 as his share of the prize money taken during that cruise. Even a traitor's right to his

prize money was sacred in those days.

Jones's feat in capturing *Serapis* was so remarkable that even the British gave him credit for it, in a sort of left-handed way: they made Richard Pearson, the defeated captain, a knight. (The old British custom of easing the sting of a defeat by honoring the beaten commander has persisted to modern times. After the inferior German High Seas Fleet gave the British Grand Fleet a sound tactical beating at Jutland, the British made their top commander at Jutland, Admiral John Jellicoe, a viscount, and his second-in-command, Admiral David Beatty, an earl.) Morison quotes a priceless comment from Jones upon hearing that Pearson had been knighted: "Let me fight him again . . . and I'll make him a Lord!"

Jones was a great captain by any standard. In single-ship actions he was superb. He was cut from the same canvas as Horatio Nelson,[1] and he had the makings of a great admiral. But we will never know about that. The United States did not see fit to give him flag rank, and he never commanded a proper squadron. He *was* given flag rank when he fought for Catherine the Great (with U.S. permission). The result was a fiasco, but that proves nothing except that the Russians were just as hard to get along with then as they are now. Jones never really had a chance to show his naval genius in Russia. He stepped in near the top of a foreign navy riddled with court politics and international intrigue. He had no part in training the outfit which he commanded and didn't even speak their language. It's no wonder he didn't do much with the strange forces placed under him.

Morison tells Jones's story saltily and well, without trying to make a plaster saint out of him. In fact, he seems to have great fun doing the opposite. He devotes as much attention to Jones's conquests ashore as he does to those afloat—just as Jones himself did. Although the captain's favorite occupation was fighting against heavy odds at sea, he didn't get to do this often; between battles ashore he indulged in his next

---

[1] **Horatio Nelson:** noted British admiral.

favorite pastime: courting the ladies, which is still popular among seafaring men. He was quite successful in that field too.

Morison has given us an authoritative account of our great naval hero to hand down to posterity. Such an account is especially useful in this era of change. The advent of radio has made it impossible for individual ship captains to operate on their own as Jones did. Current improvements in communications—coupled with the invasion of the Pentagon by mechanical brains and Whiz Kids—may even end the era of more modern individualists like Admirals King, Nimitz, and Halsey.

Meantime the stature of John Paul Jones as a naval commander grows, and this Pulitzer Prize book has helped the process. It is fascinating reading for anybody.

THE FACT IS—

1. Why does Admiral Gallery rate John Paul Jones as "the greatest hero of the Revolution next to George Washington"?

2. The sea power of what country finally "turned the tide" of battle at Yorktown?

3. Who or what were *Bonhomme Richard, Pallas,* and *Alliance?*

4. What was the highest rank ever given to John Paul Jones?

FOR COUNTRY AND FOR GLORY

1. Privateers played an important part in winning the American Revolution. Explain their role on the high seas. What was their overall effect?

2. "Prize money was incidental to Jones" (page 81). What was most important to him and how did he contribute most effectively? Write a paragraph summarizing your ideas.

3. In this essay there are moments of humor. Select two or three sentences which illustrate this statement and explain the humor.

A WORD TO REMEMBER: stature

John Paul Jones is described as a man growing in stature (page 84). This word refers literally to the "natural height of a man." It is derived from the Latin *statura,* meaning originally "an upright posture." A man of stature is one of good name and reputation. *Statue, statute, stature,* and *status* are easily confused. Define each one of the four. Which two of the four are most closely related?

Concord Hymn

RALPH WALDO EMERSON

By the rude bridge that arched the flood,
   Their flag to April's breeze unfurled,
Here once the embattled farmers stood
   And fired the shot heard round the world.

The foe long since in silence slept;   5
   Alike the conqueror silent sleeps;
And Time the ruined bridge has swept
   Down the dark stream which seaward creeps.

On this green bank, by this soft stream,
   We set today a votive stone;   10
That memory may their deed redeem,
   When, like our sires, our sons are gone.

Spirit, that made those heroes dare
   To die, and leave their children free,
Bid Time and Nature gently spare   15
   The shaft we raise to them and thee.

RALPH WALDO EMERSON (1803–1882).

Ralph Waldo Emerson is often called "The Sage of Concord." Although he was born in and worked for some time in Boston, his most fruitful years were spent in this tiny Massachusetts village which saw the first battle of the Revolutionary War. He celebrates that event in the poem you have before you. Actually, the picture of Emerson as sage, or great wise man, did not emerge until rather late in his life. He was a poor student at college; Harvard people of his day put quotation marks around the word "educated" when speaking of Emerson's being educated there. Although he taught school and preached for a while in Boston, he was glad to move out to Concord, where he felt closer to nature. Emerson had a small piece of property on Walden Pond where he would bathe or lie for hours in solitary thought. (It was on Emerson's property that Henry David Thoreau built the cabin he wrote about in his famous book, **Walden.**) He often read books there but most of the time just dreamed. At one stage Emerson's life seemed a hopeless jumble. Saddened by the death of his first wife, he reached a turning point in his career when, on a tour of Europe, he met and made friends with many of the great writers and thinkers of the time. He made a particular friend of Thomas Carlyle, who called Emerson the only person who could listen to him and then reply simply and naturally like a human being. When Emerson returned to Concord, his thought and aims in life became cohesive. He became the center of an intellectual circle and the chief figure of Transcendentalism, a movement which attracted many of the finest minds in New England. He was extremely popular as a lecturer; his essays and a few of his poems were acclaimed both here and abroad. His life can best be summed up in his own words:

> Nothing can bring you peace but
> yourself. Nothing can bring you
> peace but the triumph of principles.

IN MEMORIAM

1. Why did the descendants of the minutemen set "a votive stone"? (See line 10.)

2. Lines 15 and 16 reveal the final meaning of the poem. Why are "Time" and "Nature" capitalized? Who are "them" and "thee"? In one sentence, state your understanding of these lines.

3. Do you think this shot for independence is still echoing? If so, give examples to support your opinion.

4. This poem is called a "hymn." Is the word appropriate? (Consult a dictionary.) Why, or why not? Write a carefully planned paragraph to explain your answer.

Thomas Jefferson

ROSEMARY CARR
STEPHEN VINCENT BENÉT

Thomas Jefferson,
What do you say
Under the gravestone
Hidden away?

"I was a giver, 5
I was a molder,
I was a builder
With a strong shoulder."

Six feet and over,
Large-boned and ruddy, 10
The eyes gray-hazel
But bright with study.

The big hands clever
With pen and fiddle
And ready, ever, 15
For any riddle,

From buying empires
To planting 'taters,
From Declarations
To trick dumb-waiters.   20

"I liked the people,
The sweat and crowd of them,
Trusted them always
And spoke aloud of them.

"I liked all learning   25
And wished to share it
Abroad like pollen
For all who merit.

"I liked fine houses
With Greek pilasters,   30
And built them surely,
My touch a master's.

"I liked queer gadgets
And secret shelves,
And helping nations   35
To rule themselves.

"Jealous of others?
Not always candid?
But huge of vision
And open-handed.   40

"A wild-goose-chaser?
Now and again;
Build Monticello,
You little men!

"Design my plow, sirs—   45
They use it still—
Or found my college
At Charlottesville.°

"And still go questing
New things and thinkers.   50
And keep as busy
As twenty tinkers.

"While always guarding
The people's freedom—
You need more hands, sir?   55
I didn't need 'em.

"They call you rascal?
They called me worse.
You'd do grand things, sir,
But lack the purse?   60

"I got no riches.
I died a debtor.
I died free-hearted
And that was better.

"For life was freakish   65
But life was fervent,
And I was always
Life's willing servant.

"Life, life's too weighty?
Too long a haul, sir?   70
I lived past eighty.
I liked it all, sir."

48. **College at Charlottesville:** now the University of Virginia.

HOW ABOUT HUMAN NATURE?

1. What phrases and sentences in this poem suggest this man's varying abilities? List at least three.

2. Explain the historical references in the following lines:

    a. Line 17—"From buying empires"

    b. Line 19—"From Declarations"

3. In verse 7 there is a simile (a comparison of unlike things). Explain how it emphasizes the idea.

4. In verse 9 (lines 33–36 inclusive) how does the use of contrast emphasize the subject matter? Where else does contrast occur?

5. In verse 11, Monticello is mentioned. What is it? Consult an encyclopedia or your American history book, if necessary. What did it mean to Jefferson?

6. Reread the last verse. What particular quality of this man's character is stressed?

7. This poem has been called "half-humorous, half-serious." Write a paragraph explaining this statement.

A WORD TO REMEMBER: candid

The question is raised whether or not Jefferson was always candid. The word *candid* has several meanings: "free from undue bias; frank; straightforward." What does *bias* mean? Note that the line "Not always candid?" ends with a question mark. Are the authors flattering Jefferson?

Robert E. Lee

ROSEMARY CARR
STEPHEN VINCENT BENÉT

This is Lee of the battles,
  Virginia's bright star,
The sword of the South,
  Through the long Civil War.

Of family noted   5
  And most F.F.V.,°
A dauntless and chivalrous
  Leader was he.

He vanquished McClellan°
  And Hooker and Pope.   10
He trimmed poor old Burnside
  Of whiskers and hope.

The pride of the armies
  Who strove for the gray,
He was never defeated   15
  Till Gettysburg's day.

But Meade was the horseshoe
  He didn't quite bend—
And then came Ulysses
  S. Grant—and the end.   20

The end of the war
  And the fall of the South

And wild, bitter counsels
  From many a mouth.

They looked to Marse Robert   25
  To see what he'd say.
He looked at his sword
  And he put it away.

He said, "We have fought.
  We have lost. Let it stand.   30
Forget the old rancors
  And work for your land.

"Put your heart to the task
  And your hand to the plow.
The war days are over.   35
  We're one country, now."

And he spent the last years
  Of his life as the head
Of Washington College°
  And taught for his bread.   40

While, all through the South,
  The quick whispering ran,
"If Marse Robert does it,
  I reckon we can."

6. **F.F.V.:** First Families of Virginia.
9–20. **George McClellan, Joseph Hooker, John Pope, Ambrose Burnside, George Meade, Ulysses S. Grant:** generals in the Union Army.

39. **Washington College:** located at Lexington, Virginia. Its name was later changed to Washington and Lee.

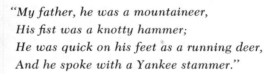

STEPHEN VINCENT BENÉT (1898–1943).

"My father, he was a mountaineer,
His fist was a knotty hammer;
He was quick on his feet as a running deer,
And he spoke with a Yankee stammer."

As these lines from **The Ballad of William Sycamore** illustrate, Stephen Vincent Benét, like so many American writers, found his inspiration in the American past and its relationship to his own time. With his wife, Rosemary Carr Benét, he wrote **A Book of Americans,** a collection of verses including "Thomas Jefferson" and "Robert E. Lee." Benét graduated from Yale in 1919 and wrote short stories, novels, and poetry which sold well but were somewhat imitative. Then came a time when, in his brother's words, "He wished to concentrate all his powers upon a longer work which would either be better poetry than he had ever written, or a failure." Choosing as his theme the Civil War, Benét wrote **John Brown's Body,** which sold in the hundreds of thousands and received a Pulitzer Prize. His best-known short story, "The Devil and Daniel Webster," which you may have read, is another reflection of his interest in the American past. This short story is often anthologized and has appeared in practically every other entertainment medium. It has been made into a radio play, a stage play, a motion picture, an operetta, and most recently, a television drama.

ROBERT E. LEE

1. The phrase "Virginia's bright star" suggests one quality of Lee's character—leadership. List three other phrases or sentences which indicate other qualities in this man's character. Name the qualities.

2. In lines 17 and 18 there is a metaphor (an implied comparison). Explain it. What does it tell of the story of the Civil War with Meade as commander of the Union forces at Gettysburg?

3. In lines 25 and 43 Lee is referred to as "Marse Robert." Who is calling him "Marse"? Why did some people use this word?

4. After the Civil War, Lee became President of Washington College at Lexington, Virginia. In what particular way is this distinction a tribute to the man?

5. In lines 43 and 44 the pronouns "it" and "we" have particular meaning. To what and to whom do they refer? How do they add to the picture of Lee?

6. This poem is really a short biography. Write a paragraph giving your impression of Robert E. Lee.

A WORD TO REMEMBER: chivalrous

Robert E. Lee is called *chivalrous*, a word appropriate to describing his character. This word has several meanings, including "courteous, gallant." Why does it apply particularly to this man? Look up the origin of *chivalry*, from which *chivalrous* comes. What connection do you find between its origin and the present use of *chivalrous?*

Sam Houston: Lone Star

DONALD CULROSS PEATTIE

"Remember the Alamo!" shouted Sam Houston as he led the charge against the Mexican army to win Texas independence. Why did his state turn against him later?

One fine morning in 1809, a white boy of sixteen came striding into a Cherokee village at the foot of the Great Smokies[1] and announced, to the amazement of the redskins, that he had come to live with them. They looked him over and admired his rugged frame and solid muscles. They looked in his eyes, and they must have liked what they saw there. You can see it today, in the portraits of Sam Houston grown great and old—that look that is fixed on

[1] **Great Smokies:** a mountain range in North Carolina and Tennessee.

something far and bright, like a star that shines alone even in daylight blue.

Sam was of Scotch-Irish stock, born in Virginia at Timber Ridge near Lexington, March 2, 1793. But this father of the Lone Star State had from the beginning what it takes to make a Texan— indeed, what it took to make Texas. It was the strength and freedom in him that sent the widow Houston's wayward boy—second of nine children—away from his job of clerking in a Maryville, Tennessee, drygoods store, and over the river into wilderness. The Indians welcomed their strange convert. He presently became the chief's adopted son and was given the name of *Colonneh*, the Raven. To the Indian, your name is a part of your soul, and the raven is a bird of kingly destiny, handsome, mysterious, moody, farsighted, high-soaring. The Cherokees chose well when they named Houston.

Sam the Raven now sojourned intermittently for three years with the Cherokees. From them he learned how to do without, to go hungry and sleep hard. His love of adornment has been traced to them, and his style of oratory to their powwows, but so did he learn from them to shut his lips on a secret and keep it for life. Almost certainly the Cherokees armed Houston with the cunning strategy that would one day save Texas when it was all but lost.

Yet the savages could not hold him either; on his twentieth birthday, Sam picked off a recruiting sergeant's drum the silver dollar that was token that he had joined the colors to fight in the War of 1812. His mother gave him the musket of his father—a Revolutionary hero—and slipped a ring on his finger. As his hands grew bigger, and more rings adorned them, the little gold band was moved along till it reached the least finger of his left hand. But it never left him till he died, for inside it was engraved one word—*Honor*.

Beside his old friends the Cherokees, Sam went to war against the fierce Creek [1] tribes allied with the British. At the battle of Horseshoe Bend, perhaps the greatest Indian fight in history, Ensign Houston distinguished himself almost as conspicuously as General Andrew Jackson. With an arrow in his thigh, young Sam was borne from the field; "Old Hickory" himself paused to commend the death-pale lad and order

---

[1] **Creek:** warlike Indian tribes who once lived in Alabama and Georgia.

him to the rear. But when the fighting grew most desperate, Houston disobeyed, led a second charge, and fell with two musket wounds. Death stooped for him, then let him go; but his right arm was lamed for life.

The strength in Andy Jackson's right arm was doubled, for he had found in Houston the perfect lieutenant. He recommended Sam for the post of Indian agent to the Cherokees, and it became their young friend's thankless task to induce a portion of the tribe to remove beyond the Mississippi, yielding their fine lands to the whites—a bloodless victory that perhaps no other white man could have won. But Sam looked higher than Indian politics; already he could faintly see his star shining in the blue. He went to "reading law" in Nashville, amazing even his admirers by passing his bar examinations after only six months.

Steadily the star brightened through the next ten years, as Houston became in succession an attorney-general, Congressman at Washington, and at last Governor of Tennessee. The voters swept him on to one office after another not only because he was Jackson's right arm but because he had so many of the very qualities that made "Old Hickory" so popular. This Young Hickory was a born fighter, as politician, soldier, or (reluctantly) a duelist; he stood six feet two, and on his dapple-gray horse looked every inch a hero.

Such dignity and courtliness in one so young singled Houston out in any gathering, and he never forgot a name or a face; hundreds thought him their best friend on earth. Children followed him everywhere, begging him to whittle them a trinket with his famous knife and block of wood which he carried even into the halls of Congress. No barbecue or barn-raising was complete without Sam's strong back and great laugh. Only thirty-five when Jackson was sent to the White House, Sam Houston was becoming to the frontiersmen an ideal of themselves—one who lacked nothing good fortune could bestow, except a wife.

· In 1829 he married Eliza Allen, nineteen, daughter of a distinguished Tennessee family. Three months later, while he was running for reelection, the Governor's lady left him. Seizing upon this personal disaster as a political weapon, his foes attacked him with every calumny. Houston's lips were tight as a red man's; not to save himself from ruin would he strike back at a woman. In silence he resigned his governor's chair and vanished from the state. The secret of his broken marriage was never exposed to the public; too late his young wife regretted her departure and attempted a reconciliation.

For Sam Houston had gone back to his old friends the Cherokees, now in the western exile. Among them he found his second mate, Tiana Rogers (great-grandaunt of the late beloved Will Rogers [1]). Cast out by the white man, his brilliant career shattered by scandal, Houston accepted adoption by the Cherokee Nation and became a power at its council fires, even preventing it from joining a full-scale war with other tribes. It was as a Cherokee, and dressed as such, that he rode to Washington to denounce to President Jackson the rascality of the Indian agents who cheated government and red man alike. Jackson listened; many agents were dismissed, many dishonest contracts canceled.

Each year the Raven came to Washington to stay at the White House as the President's guest, always in magnificent Indian regalia. The society he had quit became as fascinated as it had been scandalized. In vain the political enemies of Jackson and Houston reviled Sam as a squaw-man, a man without a country, and destined for a drunkard's grave. The lone star was rising again; it hung now, prophetic, over the Alamo, as Sam Houston journeyed to San Antonio.

It was as a peacemaker in Indian affairs that Houston first swam his horse across the Red River [2] and entered the vast dominion which was to become Texas. Then, in 1832, it was still only a part of the Mexican province of Coahuila, stretching how far into the Rockies and out on the buffalo plains, no man knew.

All but unexplored, this realm of "Tejas" [3] was larger than any European country except Russia. One flank of it was washed by the Gulf, where the commerce of the world would come, another by the coiling snake of the Rio Grande; with one outstretched arm it touched the sea-voiced resinous pine belt in the east, and with the other reached to the ultimate desert ranges. Carpeted with bluebonnets, arched over by a taut sky, this seems a land designed from Creation for hoofbeats and flying-fields, for longhorns and long trains calling a cry like homesickness for Texas, as they bear away the cotton and the corn, the lumber or the fruit, the cattle and the wheat, from the Blacklands and the Redlands, the Big Thicket or the Big Bend, the Panhandle or the Valley, the Grand Prairie or the Cross Timbers. Not yet did any man guess what Texas was to bring America, with the greatest oil fields in the world, superabundance of natural gas, and nearly half the

---

[1] **Will Rogers:** American humorist and actor (1879–1935). ·

[2] **Red River:** a river forming much of the boundary between Texas and Oklahoma.

[3] **Tejas:** the Spanish name for Texas.

world's output of helium, with untapped supplies of coal, deposits of sulfur, iron, asphalt, potash, copper, silver, lead, mercury, tungsten, uranium, and titanium. But to Texas came at last a man big enough for her.

Sam Houston did not guess at first that he was to become the George Washington of Texas. But the great open lands drew him. There were men there who needed him, and soon knew it. For the past decade and more, Americans had been settling in Texas, an increasing stream of farmers with their families, of trappers, traders, filibusters, missionaries. Long had "Tejas" lain, an almost uninhabited land, under the somnolent rule of Spain; but when in 1821 Mexico won her independence and, turning an uneasy gaze at her northeastern border, officially closed it to American immigration, many districts were far more American than Mexican in blood and thought. A new breed was rising, men who "could ride like Mexicans, shoot like Tennesseans, and fight like the very devil." These men, these Texans, could now feel an approaching "norther" in their bones, and their toast, in the wilderness taverns, was "Liberty and Texas!"

Sam Houston was settled there by 1836, in Nacogdoches, to practice law. But Texas was rearing and bucking like a wild horse, stung by the gadfly, Santa Anna, ruthless dictator of Mexico who once threatened to plant his flag on the White House. A year later Houston the soldier, the leader, found himself commander in chief of the armies of the independent Republic of Texas. The rearing horse had found its rider.

These armies were at first but various little bands of patriots and filibusters, quick to wrath and independent of judgment. Already there had been many an armed clash with the Mexicans, but now as the spring of 1836 softened the Texas skies, Santa Anna, launching three drilled and veteran armies for a full-scale invasion, was marching toward San Antonio. In vain did General Houston order a retreat from the deathtrap of the Alamo.[1] Heroic rebellion defied military wisdom, and the siege ended in a massacre of martyrs. Other such disasters, unsung, took place all over Texas. In a few days Houston's little band of 374 men was all the force Texas had left in the field.

Now wilderness cunning served the Raven well. Rallying recruits from the backwoods, keeping a discipline over their wildcat spirits, he dodged like a fox before Santa Anna's advancing armies. For thirty-seven days Houston conducted this masterly retreat. It appeared that Santa Anna was about to make good his threat to drive every American out of Texas.

On April 21 the haughty and confident Mexican dictator lay at rest with his legions on a bit of coastal prairie between the San Jacinto River and Buffalo Bayou, near the present city of Houston —in just such a corner as Houston had waited to get him. It was the hour sacred to the siesta, midafternoon. Sam Houston, having burned the only bridge over which either force could retreat, rode out, a conspicuous target, toward the mightier enemy. A passion of inspiration seized him; "Remember the Alamo!" he cried as he led the charge, and the Texans behind him took it up in a bloodcurdling yell. "Remember the Alamo!"

In fifteen minutes the battle was won. By next morning the entire Mexican force was dead or had surrendered, and Santa Anna's cruel sword was in Houston's grasp. A weakened grasp, for

[1] **Alamo:** a Franciscan Mission, built about 1722 in what is now San Antonio; later used as a fortress.

of the twenty-four Texans injured in the fighting, the greatest of them was the most gravely wounded.

Though after many weeks Houston conquered blood poisoning, he was lamed for life. Even so, he outran all his rivals in the election for first President of the Republic of Texas. Though its capital was merely a village and its fleet might be only three ships, still it did have a navy, an army of sorts, a postal system, courts, Congress, and a Constitution. It strained its exchequer to maintain ambassadors at London, Paris, Washington. It had its own monetary system and its own flag, the Lone Star emblem.

Upon a wild and formless frontier society Sam Houston had left the imprint of a firm executive hand. But the Constitution of the Republic forbade him to succeed himself. Retiring with dignity, Sam now found consolation for the death of Tiana in his marriage to Margaret Lea of Alabama, who brought him gifts of cultivation and piety, and through their happy married life bore him eight children.

Meanwhile, Texas was riding for trouble under President Mirabeau Bonaparte Lamar. This reckless son of Georgia had headed off all negotiations for annexation to the United States, flirting instead with Great Britain and Napoleon III. He had started a war against the Cherokees, sent the navy to meddle in a Yucatan revolution, and so freely printed up money to pay for his adventures that soon Texas currency fell to twenty cents on the dollar, and then to three cents. The country was millions in debt, credit gone, the postal service breaking down, the Indians scalping in the very capital, when Lamar launched a foolhardy expedition to capture Santa Fe, which was ignominiously defeated.

Now once more, as Texas called back Houston to the presidency, Santa Anna was on the march, in greater force than ever and in revenge for the Santa Fe fiasco. The treasury was empty, the army disorganized, the navy insubordinate. Sam Houston, using the peril of Texas as a diplomatic instrument, brilliantly maneuvered London and Washington into pressing Santa Anna to withdraw. Next he pacified the Cherokees, as only the Raven could do, cut expenses to the bone, and so restored order and credit that Texas became again a land of promise.

For years annexation to the mother country had been Sam Houston's dream. But Texas must be received into the United States at her true worth. "Texas," said Houston—and Texans are still saying it—"could exist without the United States, but the United States cannot, except at very great hazard, exist without Texas." Thus it was as a sovereign nation that the Republic, in 1845, entered the Union. As its flag was run down the last time, Houston caught it in his hands, that the folds might never touch the earth. The Lone Star had taken its place in the Star-Spangled Banner.

The great new state sent Sam to Washington to represent her as Senator. For nearly fourteen years he served thus. But hot winds of sectionalism were rising to claw at the flag of stars; the great rent of the Civil War was threatening.

Sam Houston, son of the South, faced into the gale. "I make no distinction between southern rights and northern rights," he said. "Our rights are rights common to the whole Union, and my motto is, it shall be preserved!" Enraged, the Southern Democrats turned against him. Senator Sam whittled endless shavings onto the Senate floor, voting over and over for union. He had put principles above politics, and he stood by them.

More, he ran by them; in 1859, stumping the state on his game leg, setting the Texan crowd roaring with his wit, he ran for governor without benefit of party behind him—and won. For the seventh and last time Houston gathered up the reins of Texas destiny, even as the state bucked, on the brink of secession. He was against that; yet if quit the mother country she must, let her go out alone and in peace, he urged—not as an enemy. But Texas turned rebel. When it called on Governor Houston to take the oath of allegiance to the Confederacy, he answered simply, "I love Texas too well to bring strife and bloodshed on her. I will not yield those principles which I have fought for."

The office of governor was officially declared vacant.

Old Sam retired to his home at Huntsville, where he sat smoking among his wife's flowerbeds, his San Jacinto leg propped up, whittling and waiting for news of his son who was off fighting in the gray-clad armies. Where Texas went, Houston's heart followed her. His hopes for her, his faith in her, his loyalty to her never wavered. His dying words, breathed three weeks after Gettysburg and Vicksburg doomed the Confederacy, were "Texas—Texas!" And deep in her heart he lives today, the noblest Texan of them all.

THE FACT IS—

1. Sam Houston was known as "the Raven." Why?

2. What did he learn from the Indians?

3. Name four offices to which Sam was elected.

4. Texas at this time had vast untapped resources. Name six.

5. How did Sam feel about Texas' joining the Union?

6. How did he feel about Texas' leaving the Union?

"Texas—Texas!"

1. Sam Houston is called "Lone Star." At the battle of Horseshoe Bend, he "distinguished himself almost as conspicuously as General Andrew Jackson." Describe two other occasions when Sam "starred."

2. How did Sam Houston come to be called the George Washington of Texas? What similarities are there between Houston and Washington?

3. When the Republic of Texas joined the Union in 1845, "the Lone Star had taken its place in the Star-Spangled Banner." To what does the word *star* in "Lone Star" refer, and what does it suggest? Explain what the sentence means.

4. The author says that in the Senate, Sam voted over and over for union. He put "principles above politics." In a careful paragraph, explain the differences between *principles* and *politics*, using references to Sam and other leaders in American history.

SAM HOUSTON: LONE STAR

Lucinda Matlock

EDGAR LEE MASTERS

I went to the dances at Chandlerville,
And played snap-out at Winchester.
One time we changed partners,
Driving home in the moonlight of middle June,
And then I found Davis.   5
We were married and lived together for seventy years,
Enjoying, working, raising the twelve children,
Eight of whom we lost
Ere I had reached the age of sixty.
I spun, I wove, I kept the house, I nursed the sick,   10
I made the garden, and for holiday
Rambled over the fields where sang the larks,
And by Spoon River gathering many a shell,
And many a flower and medicinal weed—
Shouting to the wooded hills, singing to the green valleys.   15
At ninety-six I had lived enough, that is all,
And passed to a sweet repose.
What is this I hear of sorrow and weariness,
Anger, discontent, and drooping hopes?
Degenerate sons and daughters,   20
Life is too strong for you—
It takes life to love Life.

EDGAR LEE MASTERS (1869–1950).

Why do you marvel that the dead
Do not tell you of death?
Their silence shall be interpreted
As we approach them.

These lines are from Edgar Lee Masters' poem "Silence." In his masterpiece, **Spoon River Anthology,** Masters does approach the dead and interpret their silence. Masters was raised in Illinois and became a well-known lawyer in Chicago. All his life he wrote poetry, but none of it was successful until he came upon the rich vein of Americana which became **Spoon River.** Although Masters wrote more than forty books, his fame rests on this one volume. Few Americans who read these poems ever forget the picture of a small town and its people which Masters recreates in the form of epitaphs in a country churchyard. In this one volume he sums up the dreams and the failures, the hope and the hopelessness, the glitter and the drabness of American life. After you have read about the people of Spoon River, you feel that you know them—perhaps better than you know your neighbors or your friends.

LIFE IS TOO STRONG FOR YOU

1. Why did Lucinda Matlock love life? Select at least three lines which give her reasons, stated or implied. What qualities of character are revealed?

2. What is her attitude toward young people? Do you think she is justified? Explain.

3. The last line of this poem offers a suggestion for living: "It takes life to love Life." In a short paragraph, express your opinion of its meaning.

Superman

JOHN UPDIKE

I drive my car to supermarket,
   The way I take is superhigh,
A superlot is where I park it,
   And Super Suds are what I buy.

Supersalesmen sell me tonic—   5
   Super-Tone-O, for Relief.
The planes I ride are supersonic.
   In trains, I like the Super Chief.

Supercilious men and women
   Call me superficial—*me,*   10
Who so superbly learned to swim in
   Supercolossality.

Superphosphate-fed foods feed me;
   Superservice keeps me new.
Who would dare to supersede me,   15
   Super-super-superwho?

JOHN UPDIKE (1932–   ).

"I moved upward from grade to grade and birthday to birthday on a notched stick that itself was held perfectly steady."

The remarkable evenness of John Updike's youth contributed to the remarkable evenness of his writing. The reader is always surprised when Updike's commonplace pictures yield, as they most often do, to surprising images and strange views of life. Updike's genius lies in the fact that he sees the unusual in the usual. It is the usual that interests him; he says, "I like the middles." He finds that most conflicts take place in the middle ground of human relationships. He himself is a most unusual usual young man. Following his tranquil boyhood in Shillington, Pennsylvania, Updike went to Harvard, where he served as editor of the humor magazine, **The Lampoon.** From the time Updike was eleven, his ambition was to make **The New Yorker** magazine. While he was on a scholarship at Oxford, **The New Yorker** accepted from him four stories and ten poems. Soon he became a regular staff member. Although he is now a free-lance writer, **The New Yorker** still has first look at all his work. Updike, that most unusual usual young man, has poured out stories, poems, novels, and plays; but he seems to have no outside interests beyond his family and his religion. Jane Howard, in **Life** magazine, speaks of Updike quoting the theologian Karl Barth: "A drowning man cannot pull himself up by his own hair." To Updike this means that "there is no help from within—without the supernatural the natural is a pit of horror. . . . Faith is a leap out of total despair." Certainly from within or without, John Updike has conquered despair with superb style, deep compassion, magnificent wit, and humor.

WHAT'S *SUPER* TO YOU?

1. What does the prefix *super–* mean? How does it apply to the title?

2. What does the repetition of *super–* do for the poem?

3. Note the rhyme scheme used in each verse. What does this regularity add to the effectiveness of the poem?

4. What television programs and cartoons use the prefix *super–*? Why?

5. Why can this poem be included among "Americans Worth Remembering"? Write a well-developed paragraph expressing your opinion.

A WORD TO REMEMBER: superb

You have probably heard the expression: "He's super!" The word *superbly* is closely associated with it, since both mean "grand, great, imposing," as in the phrase "a superb athlete."

Amazon of God

EDWIN R. EMBREE

Do you believe that faith and prayer—and sweat—result in success? Mary McLeod Bethune thought so and fought until her death in 1955 to realize a dream.

Mrs. Mary McLeod Bethune [1] would be called motherly were it not for her jutting jaw and mighty stride. Square white teeth gleam from her wide smile, and she falls easily into the homely speech of the rural South, but she doesn't fall into anybody's fond picture of an old southern mammy. She has a deep and reverent faith in God, yet she doesn't sit around waiting for God— or anyone else—to do her work for her. The college in Florida that bears her name, the training of hundreds of thousands of colored boys and girls under her division of the National Youth Administration, her work in leading the Negro women of America, the crusades for decent public schools and for Negro rights—these are all talked over with God and with her friends. But having sought guidance, she goes out and works.

[1] Mrs. Bethune died after this article was written.

"Nothing comes without faith and prayer," she said the other day. Then, flashing her teeth in a wide smile, "And nothing in my life has ever come without sweat too."

Certainly there was sweat from the beginning. Her parents and her older brothers and sisters were slaves on the McLeod and the McIntosh plantations in South Carolina. Mary Jane McLeod was born just after the War Between the States, the middle child in a family of seventeen, the first of the children to be born in freedom. Her early recollections are of backbreaking toil in the fields, as her parents, one grandparent, and her brothers and sisters first worked out the purchase of a five-acre farm from one of their former masters, and then tried to keep their bodies fed and clothed on the products of this tiny farm plus whatever odd jobs could be found around the countryside.

"Mother worked in the fields at Father's side," Mrs. Bethune says, "cutting rice and cotton and chopping fodder. All the children worked too. When I was only nine, I could pick 250 pounds of cotton a day."

But in the little two-room shack that housed twenty people, there was always prayer and praise and a deep and simple faith.

"I was first stirred to serious thinking," Mrs. Bethune says, "by the custom of holding family prayers every morning and evening. In the corner, by our huge clay fireplace, sat my old grandmother, Sophia. All day she talked to God as if He were a person actually present: 'Dear God, I am so happy to be living in this loving family, where I can get hot biscuits and butter, and coffee with cream, sitting at my own fireside.' Mother, more restrained, would thank God for giving her freedom, shelter, and the privilege of having her children

with her. . . . My great joy was in those moments of spontaneous prayer and song which relieved our days of ceaseless toil."

Yet the mind of this eager child was not entirely on heavenly things. On market days, when she went to town with her father, she saw the contrast between the lives of the masters and their servants: the glass windows in the white houses, the carriages, the silk dresses and soft shoes that the little white girls wore, and the books they read.

Once, tagging along with her mother when she went to work at the "big house" of one of her former owners, little Mary Jane wandered into the playhouse of the white children. They received her gaily enough and showed her all their toys. But, as she picked up a book, one of the white girls said scornfully, "Put that down. You can't read." Mrs. Bethune says, "When that nice little white girl said that, it just did something to me. I thought, 'Maybe the difference between white folks and colored is just this matter of reading and writing.' I made up my mind I would know my letters before I ever visited the big house again."

A few days later, when the family were in the field picking cotton, a friend came by with the glad tidings that a colored woman, paid by some Presbyterians up North, was starting a school for colored children. All the rest of the day Mary Jane picked her cotton and dragged her great cotton sack to the rhythm of "I'm a-goin' to read. I'm a-goin' to get educated."

Next morning she was up at dawn and started on the five-mile trudge to school. Every school day for the next six years she walked this five miles back and forth, back and forth, day after day, summer and winter, rain or shine, seeking the new learning, the magic learning that would make her really free.

The mission school was held in a small church that stood near Maysville in Sumter County, South Carolina. "There were some homemade benches," Mrs. Bethune remembers, "a little table and desks, a little pulpit, a blackboard on the wall, an old iron stove in the corner that smoked all over the room as it burned the wood the children cut and brought in. The teacher, Miss Emma Wilson, was the first Negro I ever heard called 'Miss.' The first morning she was standing at the door and greeted us so pleasantly that we all felt easy, all these crude and crudely dressed boys and girls from the South Carolina rurals. We opened school the first day—and every day—with singing, prayer, and a Bible lesson. Then she started to teach us letters and numbers. We were on our way to learning."

Little Mary Jane, glowing with her new knowledge, wanted to pass it right on to everybody around her. She tried to din some of it into her family. But none of them took to it much. Her wiry little mother was too busy running the huge household. Her great, hulking father was too tired after his long days in the fields. Her brothers and sisters were too busy raising families of their own on the old pattern of "a baby oncet a year, 'scusin' leap year." One of her sisters achieved a total of thirteen children, another twelve, and another ten.

Mary Jane stood out from the rural pattern of her family and surroundings. If any of them resented it, they didn't show it in any way that Mrs. Bethune remembers. She says, "My mother said when I was born I was different from the rest. For one thing, I was the most homely child. The ordinary things the children did, I wouldn't. My sisters wanted to get married early. I had no inclinations that way. The other chil-

dren drank the grape wine that mother used to make. I didn't care for it. My ideas were different. My mother was proud of it. She felt: here comes one of the children who is going to do something. My father felt the same way. The children themselves were proud of me. They weren't mean to me about it. They accepted my leadership because I was always striving to set up something that was going in the opposite direction from the mass of things. When I got so I could count, everybody—white folks and colored—brought their papers to me to figure out the weight of the cotton and the price and what was each one's share. From the first I made my learning, what little it was, useful every way I could."

With unabashed candor she adds: "Of course I became a very definite favorite in the family: people in the community all loved me."

At fifteen she had learned all the local school could teach and was eager to go away to bigger things. But a tragedy occurred: the family mule died. The heartbroken girl took the mule's place in the plowing and watched the little farm go into debt to a white man—from which farms seldom returned to Negroes. One day as she knelt in the cotton fields praying for a chance for more schooling, her prayer seemed to be directly answered. Miss Wilson, her teacher, strode into the field telling a miracle. A white woman, a teacher 'way off in the Rocky Mountains in a place called Denver, had heard of the work of the Maysville mission school and, with the extra money she was making as a dressmaker, she wanted to send some little girl from that school off for further education. Of course the school had chosen Mary, and wanted to send her to the very place where her teacher had studied, Scotia Seminary in Concord, North Carolina.

"I pulled the cotton sack off my shoulder," Mrs. Bethune says, "got down on my knees, rolled my eyes toward heaven, and thanked God."

Going away for school, or for anything, was an event in the rural South of those days. The whole countryside rocked with excitement. "Some neighbors knitted a pair of stockings, some gave me little linsey dresses and aprons," Mrs. Bethune recalls. "Finally on an October day I went down to Maysville to get on a train for the first time in my life. All the neighbors stopped work that afternoon, got out the wagons, mules, and oxcarts, some riding, some walking to Maysville to put me on the train to go to school. My little heart was going pit-a-pat. My mother clasped me in her arms crying, 'God bless my child.' Tears and handshakes. As the train moved on, I had so strange a feeling, tears and pride too, for I was going to get educated, sure enough. I was going to be an Instrument of the Lord, to help my people rise. . . . When the train got to Concord, a teacher met me and took me to the beautiful brick building of Scotia Seminary. I had never seen a brick building before. I was taken upstairs. I had never been upstairs before. A beautiful little room with two beds. Oh, it was so different, different. I got down on my knees and thanked God."

It was different and beautiful and grand. She had a good deal of trouble at first with the array of knives and forks on the white tablecloth in the big dining room. And she was a good deal shocked at some of the studies that seemed to have nothing to do with anything Mary Jane knew or wanted to know. Hour after hour she wrestled with Latin grammar and a kind of crossword puzzle of numbers and letters called algebra.

There were exciting things, too. She worked out part of her expenses, and the hours in the kitchen and the laundry were a joy. She won prizes for her bread and cakes. Strong as a colt, she led all her fellows in scrubbing floors and in heaving wood and coal for the fires. She sang in the school chorus and led the debating team. Her classmates dubbed her "Dick" McLeod and soon began to bring their troubles and trials to this sturdy, wholesome girl. She liked her teachers, loved especially Hattie Bower and Rebecca Cantcy, "who along with Miss Wilson showed me what cultivated Negroes can be and can do." She met here for the first time white teachers as well as colored.

"I can never doubt the sincerity and wholeheartedness of some white people," she says, "when I remember my experience with these beloved, consecrated teachers who took so much time and patience with me when patience and tolerance were needed."

When she finished the course at Scotia Seminary, she "felt a call to be a missionary to Africa." But there were no openings. Instead she was given a scholarship by the Presbyterian Board and bundled off to a place almost as foreign as Africa—Chicago—where she worked and studied for two years at the Moody Bible Institute. After the Bible course she tried again to get to Africa, but in vain.

Coming back to her southern homeland after these rebuffs from the foreign field, she started to teach at Haines Institute in Augusta, Georgia. Here she was associated with a pioneer Negro educator, Lucy Laney, whom she regards as one of the great influences in her life. "She helped me see," Mrs. Bethune says, "that Africans in America need Christ and the school just as much as Negroes in Africa." For seven years she taught wherever the field seemed needy and fertile: in Sumter, South Carolina, in Savannah, Georgia, and in Palatka, Florida.

During the year at Savannah, she met and married Alburtus Bethune, "a fellow schoolteacher with a fine tenor voice but not deeply interested in education." She dropped out of teaching for one year to bear and tend a son. But she says, "This married life was not intended to impede things I had in mind to do. The birth of my boy had no tendency whatever to dim my ardor and determination." One feels a certain pity for any romance or family ties that might get in the way of this Amazon's driving zeal. Her husband died in a few years. While she has done her duty by her son, her preoccupation has been not love of family but her work.

During these early years of teaching, she kept looking for a chance to build a school of her own. She felt that the schools she saw were not feeding the basic wants of the newly freed race. "My people needed literacy," she says, "but they needed even more to learn the simples of farming, of making decent homes, of health and plain cleanliness."

As a matter of fact, she just had to have a place of her own. So dynamic—so bossy—a woman has to run her own show. Her despotism is benign. Her tremendous energy all goes to "the Cause." But from earliest childhood she and her cause have been one.

As she was teaching in Palatka, she learned that hundreds of Negroes were flocking into eastern Florida to work on the new Flagler railroad and that many were living in squalor and crime—and ignorance. After traveling up and down the east coast of Florida, she decided that the growing resort of Daytona Beach was the strategic spot. She had exactly $1.65 when she chose her site and decided to start her school. She borrowed a shabby four-room cottage near the resort, promising to pay some rent if she could, and on October 3, 1904,

opened what was the beginning of Bethune-Cookman College. Her first class was five little girls and her own son.

This school grew—as all Mrs. Bethune's projects have—by faith and work. "We burned logs," she says, "and used the charred splinters as pencils, and mashed elderberries for ink. I begged strangers for a broom, a lamp, a bit of cretonne to put around the packing case which served as my desk. I haunted the city dump and the trash piles behind hotels, picking up cracked dishes, broken chairs, discarded linen, pieces of old lumber. Everything was scoured and mended. This was part of the training: to salvage, to reconstruct, to make bricks without straw. As parents began gradually to leave their children overnight, I had to provide beds. I took corn sacks for mattresses. Then I picked Spanish moss from trees, dried and cured it, and used it as a substitute for mattress hair."

She worked, she begged; she used everyone and everything she could put her hands on. Also she prayed. With

faith, over and over she undertook the impossible—and it was fulfilled. Over the entrance of the first building that went up, she carved: "Faith Hall."

The annals of her college are full of what she regards as direct answers to prayer. Often in the early days she found herself with absolutely nothing to carry on—not even food for the children. One Saturday, having tried in vain to get credit from the grocer for $4 worth of supplies for the weekend, she came home almost beaten. Praying earnestly as she walked along, she found waiting on her porch four rough-looking men who counted out into her hand a dollar each in grateful payment for some adult teaching they had had weeks before. Shouting thanks to God, she bundled the astonished men off to pay their money to the store and bring back her groceries.

Once as she was getting ready for a festive Christmas dinner for the pupils, all the dishes were suddenly called back by the lady who had lent them to the school. As the children began to cry, Mrs. Bethune said, "Be quiet, the Lord will provide"—and, she says, "that instant a colored butler from one of the resort homes staggered up with a great basket, saying, 'Mrs. Lawrence Thompson sent this basket of dishes; her son just gave her a beautiful new set as a Christmas present.'"

Another time when the cupboard was bare, Mrs. Bethune, aroused in the night, was frightened to see outside her window two men in prison garb. They hastened to explain that the prison was so thankful for the singing service the school had given them on Sundays that keepers and inmates together had collected vegetables, fruits, groceries, and a little cash and sent it over by these two trusties.

When classes began to overrun the four rooms of the borrowed cabin, Mrs.

Bethune decided that it was time to get property of her own. Nearby was a large lot with beautiful live oaks, but it was mostly swamp ground used as a city dump and popularly known as "Hell Hole." She caught the owner at a lucky time, offered to take the dump off his hands and someday pay him $200 in installments. In a daze he finally agreed to accept $5 down and $5 every month that she could find it. "He never knew it," Mrs. Bethune says, "but at the time I didn't even have the first $5. But I got it all right—by selling ice cream and sweet potato pies to workmen who were putting up some new buildings at the beach." From this hell hole of a city dump has grown the present stately campus of Bethune-Cookman College.

To build her college Mrs. Bethune shamelessly exploited the tourists at Daytona Beach. She took her pupils around to sing at the hotels. She made speeches to groups and begged from individuals. She openly thanked the guests for gifts, however small, and secretly prayed God that the gifts would grow larger—and they did. James N. Gamble, the Ivory Soap king, J. S. Peabody of Columbia City, Indiana, Thomas H. White, the sewing machine magnate, were among those she prayed up from pittances—in one case 25 cents —to later gifts of $1,000, $10,000, $67,000.

Slowly through these forty years the institution has grown from a struggling little primary school to one of the important colleges of the Deep South, from an opening class of six children to two hundred and fifty college students through the year and six hundred for the special courses of the summer sessions, from an initial capital of $1.65 to a plant valued above a million dollars. At first it was a school for girls, but in 1922 Cookman College, a Methodist school for boys in Jacksonville, was merged with it, and since that time regular support has come from the Methodist Church Board of Education.

Knowing that book learning was not enough for people in need of everything, Mrs. Bethune built no academic college. Booker T. Washington, rather than Aristotle, was her ideal. With a solid grounding in the three R's, she led her students on to preparation for living and making a living. Farming, cooking, and sewing, care for food and health, hand skills were at the center of her course. "English and arithmetic? Yes, for they are necessary tools for modern living. But algebra and Latin and other highfalutin' academic courses? No, not for children who are going to live in everyday America."

In 1934 President Roosevelt called Mrs. Bethune to direct the colored division of the National Youth Administration. Mrs. Roosevelt delights to tell of the first interview between the President and the prospective head of the Negro NYA. Mrs. Bethune was naturally a good deal awed as she was received in the White House by stiff and formal ushers and shown into the President's office. She listened very quietly as President Roosevelt outlined the plans for emergency education. But as he mentioned the proposed division of funds between white and colored children, Mrs. Bethune forgot her awe, rose, strode over so that she towered above the President's desk, shook her square finger in his face, and cried: "Mr. President, you've got to do better than that for me." The President roared, admiring her directness, and understanding that she was demanding not anything for herself but more for the children of her race.

For eight years she was the vigorous and colorful leader of this "school" that has given hundreds of thousands of colored youth the only education they could hope to get. In one year 600,000 Negroes were in NYA classes. In these emergency schools, most of which for colored children were in the rural regions, Mrs. Bethune crowded as much as she could of her old home remedy of the three R's, plus the practical needs of country living: farming, homemaking, hand skills.

In 1935 she organized the National Council of Negro Women and began devoting her abundant energy to the direction of its work. Uniting almost all the Negro women's clubs of the country, which have a membership of over 800,000, this organization is trying to improve the position of Negroes and to promote better race relations. Mrs. Bethune is thus the official leader of the women's organizations of her race; unofficially she has long been recognized as the leader of all colored women in America.

Her labors for her school, for the nation's youth, and for Negro women are but the official part of her work and influence. Wherever education is discussed, Mrs. Bethune's voice is heard. Wherever two or three are gathered together in behalf of better race relations, there she is likely to be also. Ida Tarbell [1] selected her as one of the fifty women who have contributed most to the enrichment of American life.

She is burdened by no false modesty or self-consciousness. Knowing her own worth and the righteousness of her cause, she moves with determination and assurance that brook no interference. Her friends relate with pride an episode at the Southern Conference on Human Welfare held in Birmingham in 1940, when Mrs. Bethune, as head of an important section, presented a set of resolutions for better schools. The

[1] **Ida Tarbell** (1857–1944): an American biographer.

white lady chairman, wanting to record her approval but following naturally the taboos against titles for Negroes, called for "the adoption by the conference of Mary's resolutions." The motion was put and carried. Whereupon Mrs. Bethune arose and said as humbly as she could, which is never very humble: "I do not care what anyone calls me as an individual. But as a delegate from Florida, I must insist on respect to that sovereign state, and since there are probably dozens of Marys at this conference, I ask that it be entered on the record that the resolutions were presented by Mrs. Mary Bethune." The house stormed its applause, and the question of titles versus first names for Negro delegates was not an issue again in that convention.

It is as a representative of the people that Mrs. Bethune thinks and acts. She knows she is a public institution, that her own life shows the growth of her people.

Her life covers the complete span of Negro freedom. Against it can be viewed the swift progress of her race.

THE FACT IS—

1. When was Mary Jane McLeod born?

2. What first aroused her to "serious thinking"?

3. What did she think her people needed most?

4. What was the NYA and how did it contribute to Mrs. Bethune's fame?

THE MAKINGS OF A "PUBLIC INSTITUTION"

1. Mary Jane was different from her sixteen brothers and sisters. What differences explain her future leadership?

2. She served "the Cause" (page 108). What "Cause"? In a careful paragraph, explain how one or two other pioneers have served their fellowmen with causes of their own.

3. "The annals of her college are full of what she regards as direct answers to prayer" (page 109). Would you consider these "miracles"? Explain why, or why not. What other answers to prayer do you know of?

4. According to Greek mythology, the Amazons were a race of women warriors. In one or two well-developed paragraphs, explain how the word *Amazon* applies to Mary McLeod Bethune.

A WORD TO REMEMBER: exploited

One meaning for the verb *to exploit* is "to extract value or use from; to utilize." "To build her college Mrs. Bethune shamelessly exploited the tourists at Daytona Beach" (page 109). What does the adverb *shamelessly* contribute to this use of *exploit*? Write an original sentence illustrating your understanding of this word.

Act One

MOSS HART

If Moss Hart's story were any more American, it would be unbelievable. Son of immigrants, raised in poverty, he became one of the richest and most respected men in the Broadway theater. His success story began one Sunday afternoon . . .

It was a Sunday afternoon and I remember it well. The moment was not accompanied by any such sensible thought as "Why, I could write a better play than any of these myself." I was simply bored to distraction by the trash I had been thumbing through all day, and without thinking too much about it, I simply sat down at a battered typewriter that I had rescued from the ash heap of a Brooklyn relative's largess and wrote on a piece of paper, "Act One. Scene One." By twelve o'clock that night Act One was completed, and the next morning I took it into the office with me. Some demon of mischief was already at work, however, for on the title page I did not put my own name, but instead strung together the first three names of some of the boys on the block, and listed as the author of the play "Robert Arnold Conrad." Candor compels me to reveal that the title was *The Beloved Bandit*, a secret I have arranged to keep rather well through the years. But I do not believe the demands of candor decree that I reveal any more of the play than that.

The next morning I handed the act to Mr. Pitou, and with a proper edge of the casual in my voice said, "I read an act of a play last night that I think is very good. You ought to read it."

"Who wrote it?" asked Mr. Pitou.

"A fellow named Robert Arnold Conrad," I replied. "He's a friend of mine."

"All right, I'll read it this evening. Put it in my briefcase," he said. And that was that.

I do not believe I gave it even a passing thought during the rest of that day or evening. I'm certain to this day that I meant it to be no more than a mild joke between us to enliven the drudgery we were going through in the search for the new vehicle. But I was utterly unprepared for what happened the following morning when Mr. Pitou entered the office. With his hat still on his head, he slapped the act down on the desk, turned to me triumphantly, and said, "We found it. Don't have to look any further. This is it. If the second and third acts hold up anything like as well, we're home. When can I get the second act?"

"Tomorrow morning," I replied, too stunned to know what I was saying.

"Great," said Mr. Pitou. "Take a letter to Mr. Conrad—will you be seeing him tonight?"

"I guess so," I replied, truthfully enough, I suppose.

"Well, if you don't," said Mr. Pitou, still under the spell of being out of the woods at last, "mail it special delivery so that he gets it first thing in the morning. I want to point out a few things he ought to do in the second act."

Still stunned, I sat down at the typewriter and solemnly took the long letter to Robert Arnold Conrad that Mr. Pitou poured forth. Why I did not tell Mr. Pitou the truth then and there escapes me even now. Perhaps I was too startled by his completely unexpected enthu-

siasm to puncture the bubble so quickly, or it may be I was suddenly titillated by the idea of carrying the joke through to the end; but whatever it was that possessed me to keep silent in those first few minutes set in motion a chain of events that I was powerless afterward to stop. By the time he signed the letter and handed it over to me, I knew I was doomed to go on.

That night I went home and wrote Act Two. It took me until almost five o'clock in the morning to do it, but unbelievable as it may sound, I finished it that night. Bleary-eyed, I handed it to Mr. Pitou the next morning. He promptly turned off the telephone and read it at once. This time his enthusiasm was even greater.

"Mouse," he said, "telephone your friend and ask him to come and see me this afternoon, or give me his number —I'd like to speak to him myself."

Panic-stricken, I managed to blurt out, "Oh, he's very seldom in his office, Mr. Pitou. He's in court most of the day. He's a lawyer." Quick thinking and an unholy gift of invention seem to spring to the aid of all liars at moments like these.

"Well, ask him to come in and see me tomorrow," said Mr. Pitou after a moment. "And when do you think he'll have the third act finished? Did he say anything to you about it?"

"No, he didn't," I replied a little haltingly, "but I guess he could have it for you by tomorrow."

"Fine, fine," said Mr. Pitou. "He writes fast, just what we need right now. Better take a letter and give it to him tonight in case you can't get him on the phone."

And there poured forth under my panic-frozen fingers another four-page, single-spaced letter from Mr. Pitou. Glassy-eyed, I watched him sign it, and in a moment of sweet clarity, the thought flashed through my mind: "You've got to tell him now." But before I could screw up sufficient courage to speak, Mr. Pitou spoke instead.

"You know, Mouse," he said, a satisfied smile on his lips, "I don't often go around giving myself pats on the back, but I think my letter helped Mr. Conrad. I wish I had kept a copy of it. As a matter of fact, I wish you'd make a copy of this one right now. I'd like to take it home and show it to Mrs. Pitou tonight. I've been telling the family how you discovered this young fellow just in the nick of time."

That did it, of course. To confess to Mr. Pitou that he had been writing these wonderful letters to his office boy was bad enough; but to make him out an utter fool in the eyes of his family was something I could not face. Any kind of delay would give me time to think—something was bound to happen to make that terrible moment of confession a little less awful than it seemed to me just then.

That night I went home and tackled the third act. Alas, third acts are notoriously tough even for hardened veterans, and Robert Arnold Conrad, a tired and sorry spectacle by this time, did not finish the act that night. The next day another and still longer letter was tolled off to Mr. Conrad—longer, I believe, because Mr. Pitou was daily growing more proud of his new-found prowess as a teacher of playwriting, the while I sat there miserably taking it all down. During the day there was again the same insistence on Mr. Pitou's part of wanting to see Mr. Conrad or at least talk to him on the telephone, and I fended this off as best I could by muttering, "He's on a case—in court—he'll be finished in a couple of days." I was almost too tired to care. All I wanted was to finish the third act, tell Mr. Pitou the truth, and have it over with. All I cared

about now was not losing my wonderful job as a consequence of this miserable joke. I silently prayed for a propitious moment for telling him. If only I could get that act finished quickly, so that there need be no more letters, each one of which, of course, could only make him feel more foolish as he remembered sitting there and dictating them to me, all might not be lost.

That night I went to sleep after dinner and slept until midnight. Then I got up, sat down at the typewriter, and did not get up until I had typed "The curtain falls." It was eight o'clock in the morning. Now that it was done and I could tell Mr. Pitou at last, I felt strangely awake and refreshed. I could hardly wait to get down to the office and face him with the truth at last. When I walked in at nine o'clock, Mr. Pitou was already there. I was surprised to see him there so early, for he usually arrived at the office between ten and ten-thirty, and he looked immensely pleased with himself into the bargain. Oh, no, not another letter! I thought. I must tell him immediately. He spoke while I was still in the doorway.

"Got that third act?" he said. I nodded and handed it to him.

"Mr. Pitou," I began—but I got no farther than that.

"Get your friend on the phone right away," he interrupted; "the darndest thing has happened. I showed these two acts to Mrs. Henry B. Harris last night, and you know what? She says this play is too good for the road—she wants to coproduce it with me and do it on Broadway. I'm going to bring the company back to New York, rehearse the play here, open in Rochester, play Chicago for four weeks, and then we'll bring it in. It will be my first New York production, so get your friend on the phone right away and tell him to come up here and sign the contract—

I'm going downstairs to the booking office to book the time."

I stared numbly after him as he passed me in the doorway. After a moment, I sat down in a chair and tried hard to think, but I could not think; I could only keep looking around the office as though I were seeing it for the last time. I was still sitting there transfixed in the chair when Mr. Pitou returned from the booking office.

"What time is Mr. Conrad coming in?" he asked. "The theaters are all set. What time is he coming in?"

"Two o'clock," I replied, promptly and automatically, as though somebody else were using my voice.

"Fine," said Mr. Pitou, "let's get going—we've got a lot to do before lunch, and I want to read that third act before he gets here."

The enormity of what I had done settled over me like a suit of mail. It is bad enough to make a man look foolish within the confines of his family, but quite another thing to make him a figure of ridicule outside, for I had no doubt that he had told Mrs. Harris the whole story and had showed her his letters to Robert Arnold Conrad as well. I stared so hard at Mr. Pitou that he finally became aware of it and said, "What is it? Were you going to say something?" I shook my head. There are certain moments when the process of thinking is frozen, when the ability to act, speak, or move is completely and totally paralyzed. I could no more have told Mr. Pitou the truth right then, or even have given him the correct time had he asked me to, if my life had depended on it. I took down the telegrams, went through the morning's mail, and did the various other office chores without speaking and actually without quite knowing what I was doing.

When Mr. Pitou went out for lunch, taking the third act with him, I again

sat down in the chair and stared unseeingly around the office. I was still sitting there when Mr. Pitou returned from lunch a little before two o'clock.

"It's just right," he said as he closed the door behind him. "He certainly read my letters carefully." He looked at his watch. "You said he was coming in at two o'clock, didn't you?" I nodded. "I'm kind of anxious to meet him now," he said, as he picked up the *Railway Guide* and settled back to wait.

I sat silently in the chair and watched the moments drag by. Finally he put the *Railway Guide* back on the desk and looked at his watch unbelievingly. "Why, it's three o'clock," he said. "Where is he?"

This time I had to speak—tell the last lie to fend off approaching doom, if only for a little while longer. "He must have been held up in court, Mr. Pitou. Sometimes they don't recess until four o'clock," I said, pulling out a legal term from God knows where.

For the first time Mr. Pitou looked hard at me. He had, of course, no suspicion of the truth, but he sensed something was wrong. He rose from the desk and reached for his hat and coat. "Get your coat, Mouse," he said. "We'll go down to his office and wait for him, if we have to wait there all day. I'm bringing a company back from Omaha and I've got Rochester and Chicago booked. I've got to have those contracts signed. What's the matter with him, anyway? Come on, let's go." This last was added rather sharply, for I still sat there immobilized.

Somehow I put on my hat and coat and followed him to the elevator. I knew that I must tell him before we reached the lobby; I realized the terrible moment had come at last—for if we got to the street and he asked me for the address of the office where Robert Arnold Conrad worked, what in the world would I say? The moment had arrived —there could be no more delay. I was trapped and I knew it. We got into the elevator and it started down. I made my revelation between the eighth and fifth floors as the elevator shot downward, and I remember every word I spoke, for the two short declarative sentences I managed to get out had an enviable economy and a dramatic brevity that I was not able to appreciate fully until long afterward.

"Mr. Pitou," I began, "I have a confession to make."

Mr. Pitou turned and looked at me a little wonderingly, as well he might have, for my voice had gone at least two octaves higher and seemed even to

my own ears to be coming through an echo chamber some great distance away. I swallowed and got the rest of it out.

"Mr. Pitou," I said, "*I* am Robert Arnold Conrad."

The elevator doors opened and we both stepped out into the lobby. In silence we walked the length of the lobby and out into Forty-second Street. Only then did Mr. Pitou give any indication that he had heard me.

"Mouse," he said at last, "I don't know whether you know it or not, but when an author writes his first play, he doesn't get the regular royalties."

I could hardly believe my ears. "You mean—it's all right, Mr. Pitou?" I faltered.

"Certainly it's all right," he replied, "as long as you understand that a new author doesn't get the regular royalties. We'll have to make out new contracts. I guess I'd better go over and see Mrs. Harris and tell her the good news."

He patted me on the shoulder paternally, smiled down at me, and started off briskly toward Forty-fourth Street. I stood stock-still for a moment, and my first emotion, if such it may be called, was one of hunger. Suddenly I seemed to be literally starving. I could not remember having eaten anything at all for the last three days. I walked to the Nedick's orange-juice stand on the corner and ate one frankfurter after another, until all my money except the subway fare I needed to get home ran out. I must have eaten at least ten frankfurters, for the counterman finally said, "You'll be sick, buddy—better knock off."

He was right. I just managed to get back to the office and into the bathroom in time. My debut as a playwright was a portent for the future: I have been sick in the men's room every opening night of a play of mine in theaters all over the country.

THE FACT IS—

1. What started Moss Hart on his career? In what sense did he get off to a bad start?

2. Did he have any idea that his play would be taken seriously and, in fact, produced?

3. What was Mr. Hart's opinion of the first play he wrote? How do you know?

4. Why did Moss finally admit that he was the author of the play? How did his boss react?

"AN UNHOLY GIFT OF INVENTION"

1. Moss Hart said that "quick thinking and an unholy gift of invention seem to spring to the aid of all liars at moments like these." What kind of moments was he talking about? Do you think Hart meant this as a serious statement? Write a paragraph telling whether or not you think a moral issue is involved here.

2. Every year, in competitions all over America, beginning playwrights are given a chance to submit an original play for consideration. Imagine you are a contestant in one of these competitions. Write a paragraph describing a plot that you would like to see made into a play. Describe the major characters and write one scene of the play.

3. To find out what happened when his play was produced, and how he wrote his way to success, read more of Moss Hart's autobiography, *Act One.*

A WORD TO REMEMBER: playwright

Some words can fool you—*playwright,* for instance. At first glance you would guess that *wright* is perhaps an old way of spelling *write.* It isn't. The Old English *wryhta* meant "worker." A wheelwright "works" with wheels, and a playwright "works" with plays. Since last names in English often indicate the occupation of the man who originally took the name, Wright is a fairly common surname. What can you guess about the ancestry of someone named Smith? Webster? Chapman? Fuller? Fletcher? Cartwright? Your dictionary will help you with those names you can't figure out.

THINKING ABOUT AMERICANS WORTH REMEMBERING

WHY ARE THEY MEMORABLE?

1. Memorable people show certain character traits. Which of the people you read about displayed *most noticeably* one of the qualities listed below? In one or two well-developed sentences, justify your choice.

    a. faith   **d.** loyalty

    b. patriotism   **e.** endurance

    c. conviction   **f.** resourcefulness

2. One selection in this unit is obviously humorous. Which one is it? Explain how the author makes it entertaining.

3. Two Americans in this unit have long been recognized by historians as great leaders. Who are they? What qualities did they have in common? How did they differ? Write a paragraph comparing them.

4. To which memorable American does each of the following quotations refer?

    a. "It takes life to love Life."

    b. "She knows she is a public institution."

5. Identify each speaker and selection.

    a. "Remember the Alamo!"

    b. "Not guilty."

    c. "Let me fight him again . . . and I'll make him a Lord!"

DO YOU REMEMBER THESE WORDS?

Give the meanings of the following italicized words; then give antonyms according to their use in these sentences:

1. Men in politics must expect the criticisms of their *adversaries.*

2. The reporter's *candid* remarks aroused both candidates to anger.

3. A *chivalrous* young man gave his seat in the streetcar to an elderly lady.

4. In spite of severe pain, she performed *superbly.*

5. A player's *belligerent* behavior may result in penalty for the team.

6. During a long life of service to his country, he grew in *stature.*

7. Can we *exploit* our waterpower without polluting our streams?

UNIT THREE

Moments
of
Decision

Only one man could decide. The largest invasion fleet in history had been caught by a surprise storm and had been called back. Without calm weather the troops could not land, the heavy naval ships could not protect a landing, the 11,000 supporting planes could not fly. Weather experts predicted that thirty-six hours of calm would follow the storm; then would come another spell of really bad weather, which might cut off the attacking force and make it easy prey for the enemy. The fate of nations truly hung on the decision of one man, General Dwight D. Eisenhower. "The consequences of the delay justified great risk," he wrote later, "and I quickly announced the decision to go ahead with the attack on June 6." The rest, as they say, is history: the D-Day invasion was successful; within a year the German army surrendered to the allies.

Moments of decision are turning points in life, as well as in history. "Making up your mind" is neither simple nor easy. Knowing that we have to live by the results of our decisions is enough to make any of us pause and ponder. Unfortunately, we don't always have time for reflection; sometimes we must act quickly, trusting that our past training and experience have given us the wisdom for the quick decision and the positive action.

Captain William Carpenter in Vietnam had to make such a decision. He called down artillery fire on himself and his company in order to destroy the heavy attacking force. Some of his men were killed and wounded, but most of them escaped and Captain Carpenter was recommended for the Congressional Medal of Honor. Major Gaylord, in "The

Strike," is also faced by the need to call down a barrage that will mean death to some of his own men. Sometimes decisions are more difficult when we have more time to think about them, when two of our most cherished beliefs come into conflict with each other.

Wartime decisions carry their own life-and-death drama, but peacetime decisions can be as crucial. The world watched with bated breath when John Glenn was sealed into his space capsule ready to orbit the Earth, and delay after delay held up the launching of *Friendship 7*. Everyone knew that the smallest mechanical failure or error in judgment could mean death for the first American astronaut. Sometimes decisions in everyday life can seem as important and call for similar dedication and skill and action. Team sports call for decision after decision; one wrong move can make the difference between a hero and a goat. Individual sports—like golf or hunting or fishing—are also loaded with moments of decision. In "You've Got to Learn," Andy Gates, lying in the woods with rifle cocked and on target, discovers such a moment.

Decisions that change people's lives and nations' destinies don't always occur in one flashing moment. Outwardly no change at all may take place. When the first forty scripts by Rod Serling, author of "The Strike," were rejected, he had to take a job to support his family. Serling, however, determined to write during every spare minute. Eventually, he became the most sought-after writer in television. James Madison's decision to defend the United States Constitution was arrived at gradually and not at all dramatically; yet this was

one of the most important "moments of decision" in our history.

Sometimes the most difficult decisions are moral ones. Often it may be easy to convince ourselves to do wrong, even when we know what is right. It is usually easy to "go along with the crowd."

All of us have moments of decision. Shall I save my money to buy a car? Shall I study for the test or go out on the date? Shall I stay in school? Shall I join the Peace Corps, or enlist in the Navy, or get a job, or go to college—or

what? Life, which seemed to stretch out endlessly before us when we were young, suddenly won't wait. We must decide; we must choose one of the doors before us and enter a future seen only dimly. And we know that when we open one door, the rest may slam shut against us forever. So we choose carefully; we try to make our decisions bravely and wisely. We learn from our experiences to admire the men and women of decision, and we can learn from *their* experiences to face our own moments of decision with courage and wisdom.

You've Got to Learn

ROBERT MURPHY

The desire for revenge is a natural reaction when something you love is suddenly taken from you. But Andy had to learn there were some feelings even more natural than revenge.

It was a little after dawn when the big dog otter's broad, whiskered muzzle broke the calm and flawless mirror of the lake. A widening circle of ripples slid away from him, and he reared half-length from the water to look about. The near shore was dim and quiet; on the far shore, the spruce and hemlock made a dark band against the paling sky. The otter whistled, cocked his head to the rolling echoes, and dropped back into the water again. He was an animal of great and happy vitality; he began diving and rolling, with movements as effortless and fluid as a dance, hardly disturbing the calmness of the water.

Presently he vanished as silently as he had appeared. A swift line of bubbles followed him toward the bank; he dived deeper for the submerged entrance of the burrow, followed it above water line, and in the dark den bounded by roots found his mate with the one pup beside her, and waked them both. There was a short, good-natured scuffle among the three, and then they pushed the pup before them down the tunnel.

When they all appeared on the lake's surface, the pup tried to climb upon his mother's back and ride. She took him off and ducked him when he whimpered, and they began to hunt the bank. They hunted with great thoroughness, from surface to bottom, exploring every hole and cranny, every root hollow and crack among the stones, finding a few crawfish and an occasional frog. These were some easy kills and they let the pup make the most of them. His little belly began to bulge, and his mother, growing hungry, left them to catch a pickerel in deeper water and bring it in. They climbed out on the bank and shared it; then, gleaming and sleek from the water, they rolled and galloped about, hissing at one another with mock ferocity.

Day stole in upon them. Out on the lake, the trailing mists of night thinned and vanished; the serrated line of spruces on the distant shore took on depth and shape in the strengthening light. As the long rays of the sun fell on the otters, they gave over their play, cleaned their fur, and went into the water again. They continued up the lake toward one of the streams which fed it. When they reached the stream mouth, the mother and the pup swung away along the shoreline. The otter remembered the great brown trout which lived above the bend of the stream, and left them. The trout was old and wise, and the otter had missed it so many times that the contest between them had become a fascinating game.

It was characteristic of the otter that he didn't go directly, his mind fixed on the trout. He zigzagged to and fro across the stream, playing as he went. When he came out of the water to cross the rocks at the first shallows, he heard the distant barking of a dog, up the lake in the direction his mate and the pup had gone. He hesitated for a moment and went on.

He rounded the bend carefully, and began his stalk of the trout. He knew it would be lying like a shadow a little above the sandy bottom in the rushing green gloom of the pocket under a great gray rock. It would be facing upstream, and he would gain an advantage by coming up from the rear. He stretched out full-length and, paddling gently and slowly with his forepaws, slid through the water like a stealthy shadow, close to the bank and halfway to the bottom. He came to the corner of the rock and paused, sank until his belly softly scraped the sand, and became one with the bottom's shadows; then, sinuous as a snake, he began to flow around the rock. He saw the trout several yards away, hanging motionless, and tensed for the spring.

The trout caught a slight movement of the otter's shadowy form in the tail of its eye. It drifted a little farther out and swung quartering to him; the otter arched his back swiftly, thrust against the water, and darted in. An explosive burst of power sent the trout to the surface; the otter's teeth scored a thin bloody line on its side and the power of its tail stroke rolled him over and over. The trout reached the surface and shattered it by a leap, and the otter righted himself and breached for air. Although a wild chase upstream and through the rapids was as much a part of the game as the stalk, this time the otter didn't follow. He lay for a moment resting, his sleek head dappled by the sunlight falling through the leaves, and then remembered the barking of the dog.

His game with the trout was over. He started swiftly downstream and came to its mouth. Good fishing water was there, but he didn't hesitate; he turned up the lake. As he rounded the bend, he saw, fifty yards away, the head of his mate break water a good distance from the shore. The pup was just sliding down the bank; and, as the otter watched, the brown-and-white shape of the dog ran out of the hemlocks toward the pup and snapped at it. The pup was startled and confused; it scrambled between the dog's legs, turned again, and leaped from the bank. The dog leaped after it with a great splash; and, because the pup had lost time and couldn't get out of the shallows, the dog's long jaw closed on it and it was tossed into the air.

The otter was moving before the dog left the bank, swimming with desperate speed. As the pup curved into the air, a boy ran out on the bank, yelling, and although the otter avoided man above any other creature, he paid no attention to the boy now. He reached the dog a little before his mate, as it leaped for the falling pup, and, rising beneath it, fastened upon its throat. The female swirled away from them, getting behind the pup and driving it before her out into the lake.

The dog reared to free its throat, but the otter overbalanced it, fighting with deadly coolness to get it into deeper water. He was all about it, attacking and slipping away with disconcerting swiftness, always maneuvering it a little

farther out. The boy on the bank realized this; he grabbed a branch to use as a club, and, jumping from the bank, began to splash toward them. The otter saw the boy coming and pulled the dog into deeper water. The dog tried wildly to free itself, but the otter fastened implacably on its haunches, pulled it down, and entangled it in a pile of brush on the bottom. The dog struggled desperately in a world alien to it, but in which the otter was at home. But it was trapped; the air in its lungs fled in silver bubbles to the surface, and the otter struck again.

Standing up to his chest in the water, Andy Gates stared in helpless anguish at the spot where the dog had gone down. He saw the bubbles burst to the surface, and, a short time later, a swirl far out where the otter breached for air as it followed its mate and the pup. At first he couldn't believe that the dog wouldn't come up again. But time drew out and realization finally came upon him; he dropped the branch he was holding, his fists clenched at his

sides, and his blue eyes filled with tears. The world about him was suddenly a new and terrible place. He forgot that the dog had been brash and foolishly quarrelsome, that no one had ever been able to teach it anything, and that it had usually been a nuisance. All that he remembered was his brother, standing by the gate before he left for the South Pacific, saying, "Take care of the pup, Andy. We'll make a bird dog of him when I get back."

He didn't realize that Joe, who knew the dog would never amount to anything, had said that to make them feel closer to each other for a moment and hold off the threatening tears, to make the parting easier for them both. The dog was a trust Joe had placed upon him, his most immediate link with his brother, and he had let it be killed. He turned and stumbled out of the water, tears blurring his sight. When his feet found the hard-packed surface of the path, he started along it toward home, stumbling a little now and then. There was an aching emptiness within him, an emptiness which seemed to have swallowed up all his strength; halfway up the long hill, he had to stop, and stood panting, unconscious of the dry fragrance of sun-warmed hemlock on the morning air.

He stopped crying after a while, and the world slowly came back to him. He grew aware of the birds that moved about him, the leaf shadows on the path, and the slow movement of clouds across the sky. But he didn't go on. He sat down beside the path, dry-eyed now, but the emptiness hadn't gone, and he saw his surroundings as though from a great distance. Time stopped as his mind tried to rationalize the dog's death and soften the shock of it. The afternoon was growing late when he crossed the top of the hill and saw the farm in the little valley below, the big barn and the sprawling house among the willows, the file of ducks moving up from the stream shining white in the lowering sun, the cows coming in, and his father walking slowly between the house and the barn.

His father saw him and waited with his hands tucked into the top of his levis. Gates was a kindly and unhurried man; he looked at the boy's face and didn't mention the chores that he'd done himself.

"Trouble, Andy?" he asked.

The boy's chin trembled. "Nicky," he said. "There was an otter—" He couldn't go on. He began to cry again, and suddenly went to his father as he hadn't done for years, and leaned against him, crying. "He went after the little one," he said, shaking with sobs, "and the big one drowned him. And Joe—" He couldn't talk about Joe.

"Joe would understand it, boy," his father said, sliding an arm around him. "Joe would know you couldn't help it."

"I was keeping him for Joe," Andy said. "Joe left him with me. He was Joe's and mine." He began to cry violently again. "Joe's and mine," he repeated, remembering Joe at the gate, going away. "I'll kill him!" he burst out, thumping his father's broad chest. "I'll find him and kill him!"

The man started to speak and checked himself, realizing the futility of words. The boy was extraordinarily moved; it was useless to talk against an emotion so deep that he could only guess at it. Time would have to smooth it out—time and what patient understanding he could give. The man was silent for a long time, holding the boy in the crook of his arm.

"Supper, Andy," he said finally. "Get ready for supper, boy."

"I don't want any supper, Dad," Andy said. "I—I couldn't eat any supper."

"All right," Gates said. "Go along up to your room, then. Go up the front stairs. I'll tell Mother you won't be down."

The boy went into the house; after waiting for a few minutes, Gates went around to the back door and into the warm kitchen. Mrs. Gates was taking a pie from the oven. She looked around, smiled, and straightened up to put the pie on top of the stove. She was small and very neat; her movements were deft and quick, and her eyes were blue like the boy's.

"Andy won't be down, Helen," Gates said. "We'd better eat without him."

"Why?" she asked. "What's the matter?"

"Well," Gates said. He took off his hat, hung it behind the door, and thought a moment. "That fool dog," he said finally, "got himself killed by an otter. There was a young one, I think, and he went for it. Andy is—I've never seen him so worked up. Joe must have said something about taking care of the dog, and Andy thinks he's let Joe down. He's going to kill the otter, he says."

"But it's not like him," she said. "He doesn't kill things, Harry."

"No," Gates said. "He's not a cruel boy."

"You'll have to talk to him," she said. "I don't want him to be that way. Vengefullike, I mean."

"It's not revenge," Gates said. "It's—he's—" He shook his head, irritated by his inarticulateness. "This is a deep thing, Helen. He'll have to work it out himself. Maybe he'll kill that otter, but I hope not. If he kills it, then I'll have to talk to him."

She looked at him, puzzled. "What do you mean, Harry?"

"That's the devil of it," he said, exasperated. "I don't know what I mean. I can't say it, I just feel it. Let's eat, shall we?"

"All right," she said, and began to fill their plates.

Upstairs, the boy lay on his bed. The picture of Joe in his uniform smiled at him from the bureau, but he had stopped looking at it. He felt that he couldn't look at it again until he'd found the otter. As his father had said, he wasn't a cruel boy, but all his emotions confirmed the decision, made so suddenly, that the otter must pay with its life for the life of the dog. The justice of the matter, the fact that the otter had been defending the pup, never occurred to him. Many plans went through his mind, but there was no pleasure, no anticipation of exciting sport connected with any of them.

He went about his hunting with a singleness of purpose unusual in a boy, with a definite and unvarying schedule. First he'd do the chores, carefully and thoroughly, then get his old single-shot .22 rifle and go out. At first, he spent a lot of time at the lake, hiding near the place where the dog had been drowned. He knew, from remembered bits of Gates's talk, that otters didn't stay in one place, but made a wide, periodic circle about the ponds and streams of the countryside. Sooner or later, he thought, they'd come past him again. He spent days hidden among the hemlocks, and, although he learned a great deal about other animals and birds, he never saw the otters.

The thought came to him finally that they might have passed near dawn, before he got there, or after dusk, when he couldn't see them or had left for home. For several days, disappointment took all the energy out of him; he stayed at home, and his mother thought, with relief, that he'd given up.

"I'm glad it's over, Harry," she said to Gates. "It wasn't like a boy to act like that, going wherever he went, so regular all the time. It was more like a funny little old man."

But Gates had been quietly watching the boy, and he shook his head. "No," he said. "He's not through yet. He's just trying to get away from the place."

Gates was right; the boy was deciding that he would have to move about, to find the otters' route and intercept them somewhere. The place where the dog had died had held him through a wistful, boyish hope that somehow it might come back again. But the bond weakened; reality came closer to him than it had ever come before, and, as hope died, some of his boyishness died with it. He finally broke away from the place and made his first circuit of the lake.

He went too fast at first and found nothing. The otters left very little indication of their passing along the shore line—a few fish scales and bones in widely separated places, a single rare pad mark in damp ground not covered by leaves or vines. On his first trip up the shore, he found nothing. Slowing down and going very carefully, he found faint sign at last, and knew how painstakingly he would have to search from then on. He found the place where they left the lake, the stream they used, and how far they followed before leaving it.

In time he knew, between the actual points where they touched and guesses at the routes which connected these points, the otters' entire twenty-five-mile circuit of the country. It was an achievement in woodcraft which few men could have accomplished, because few men would have had the patience or the time. He had covered a tremendous amount of country; he was well-scratched by briers, but he was brown and strong, and had filled out surprisingly.

He changed, little by little, during those weeks. The boyish heedlessness with which he had formerly moved through the woods was gone. He grew somewhat like an Indian, a part of the woods rather than an alien presence, drifting quietly about with a mind empty of thought, but blank and clean for the impressions which flowed into it. Time ceased to exist for him. He took no more account of hours than a squirrel, and learned the causes of sounds and the little chains of circumstance which stem from them—the techniques of the hunters and the defenses of the hunted. He saw young grouse freeze and blend with the leaves when the shadow of a hawk swung over them; he watched the steps by which a litter of young foxes learned to catch mice. The play of life about him increased with his skill in seeing it, but his understanding of it and his growing sympathy with it were both completely subconscious until his adventure with the lynx.

He had found its tracks several times. They seemed to be near the places where he had walked or hidden, and he grew curious. He gave over the otters for a time and hunted it, and found that it was stalking him. He spent a good deal of time in the thick hemlocks it liked best; finally, he went through this woods noisily, backtracked with great care, and hid in a very thick place.

A long time went by before he saw a movement, an indistinct blur as the pale-fawn-colored fur slipped across a patch of sunlight. It came closer, silently, never distinct in the thicket; and then it was standing in a little opening not thirty feet away, the yellow eyes staring at him, the big, soft paws tense, and the tufted ears cocked. There was a good deal of wild power in it, but he never thought of being afraid. It stood regarding him, poised, unblinking, and feral, framed against the wild tangle of the thicket, but without menace. He smiled, and there suddenly seemed to come upon it a look, an expression, of shame that it had been outmaneuvered and taken in. It made a little sound, turned, and, with great care for its dignity, moved off and vanished.

This dignity was such a human sort of thing that it brought to life in his mind all the animals he had watched as abstractions, rather mechanical figures clothed in fur which had moved about him. For the first time, he realized how much a part of his life they had become and how much he liked them. He realized, too, how clear and simple their reasons for action were, even when they killed.

His thought naturally came to the otters, and swung quickly away, but the fact that he had almost looked upon them sympathetically confused him. He got up, puzzled and a little ashamed, and went home. The disturbing questions which came to him refused to be dismissed. His father was alone in the kitchen; he looked up and saw that the boy was troubled.

"Yes, son?" he asked.

"Dad," he began, knowing that his father would help him, "the otters—"

Just then, his mother came in. "There's a letter from Joe for you, Andrew," she said. "I put it in your room."

His father watched the swift change of his expression, the closing of his mind against the question, with regret. "I wish you hadn't mentioned that letter, Mother," he said after the boy left. "I wish you'd hidden it. I think he's seen something he liked about those otters, and it was about to change his mind."

"Oh, I'm so sorry," she said. "I'm so sorry, Harry. Do you think—"

"I think it's too late," Gates said. "He's right back now where he was before."

The uneasiness which at first had been like a formless shadow in the old dog otter's brain was sharper now, for he encountered the man-smell which evoked it more frequently. To be followed was a new experience to him, and he didn't know what to make of it. It had not been difficult to avoid the infrequent and casual encounters all animals have with man sooner or later; his senses were superior to theirs, and vigilance and care were all that was necessary. He saw or heard or scented them and got out of the way; they passed and were gone, and places which held evidence of their presence were better left alone. But this was different; the smell waited in many places for him, clinging to the underbrush or the banks. His temper grew short with constant watchfulness, and he began to avoid the daylight hours.

The female didn't take well to the curtailed activity either. She was of a more casual temperament than her mate; she had never, as he had long ago, been caught in a trap and nearly drowned. She had not felt the blind terror of it nor lost two toes; her brain wasn't marked by an experience impossible to forget. She chafed at being quiet in the dank blackness of a bankside den when she knew that the world was filled with sunshine and freedom and sport a few feet away. She remembered so many happy places—gloomy thickets they went through between streams where a complexity of fine scents lingered and birds flashed in and out of shadow; deep pools below falls where trout hid among the sunken rocks; long, easy stretches of lazily sparkling water, and precipitous banks where the three of them made slides and plunged down them until they were too weary for anything but lying happily in the sun.

She grew morose, as they all did. Their rollicking vitality, with its urge toward ceaseless activity and play, was frustrated and turned against them. They bickered and snarled at one another.

But this retreat, which would eventually have discouraged the ordinary hunter, was doomed to failure with the boy. All his determination and effort were concentrated solely upon them, and because they could not exist by moving about altogether in the dark, it was inevitable that he find them. The impulse to change his range came to the old otter many times, but he resisted it. The old range was home, familiar and somehow comforting; the memories of his life along its banks and streams were deeply etched into his brain, and they held him there.

Clouds were beginning to cover the late-afternoon sun when the boy found the pad mark on the little sandy margin of the stream. It was very fresh; water was still oozing slowly into it, and he began to tremble. The fact that he had always got home before dark, to avoid worrying his mother, and that he wouldn't be able to do it this time if he didn't start at once were forgotten. A strange sort of surety came upon him, and, after a moment, the trembling stopped and he grew calm. He knew that the stream didn't go much farther; that within a quarter of a mile the otters would leave it and go across country, through a hemlock swamp and over a low ridge, to reach the stream on the other side which flowed finally into the lake.

He knew the thicket so well that he could predict where they would pass through it—a marshy little path which had once been a lumber road, cut through a high and tangled bank. He knew he could intercept them there by going through the woods; he knew he had them.

He had so often imagined the feeling of triumph that would be his when he found them that he was confused by the lack of it, by a sort of unwillingness that had suddenly come into his heart. This emotion was inexplicable to him, and seemed like a betrayal of his brother. He thought of his father, who did not approve of the thing he was doing, but who had been patient and kind and had said nothing against it, and suddenly he felt lost and alone. He stood indecisively for a moment in the darkening woods; the thoughts of his father changed to thoughts of Joe, and his back stiffened.

He started to walk. A deeper gloom fell upon him as he went into the hemlock, and a deeper silence; he moved like a ghost, for his feet made no sound in the fallen needles. When he came to the place, the bank above the lumber road, the setting sun came out more brightly and the thicket was filled with a banded, coppery light. The low branches were so thick that he had to crawl to the top on his hands and knees. He reached the top and lay down, stretching out with the rifle cocked in his hands. It was very quiet. The swampy little path lay before him for a few yards, meandering and crooked, masked here and there by low hemlock branches and brown old stumps rotting and green with moss.

The coppery light faded again, and after a long time the brooding silence was suddenly broken by a spitting snarl. The boy raised himself on his elbows quickly; there was a rapid, slurred pattering of feet, and the three otters were bunched below him. The old male's back was clawraked and bleeding; he snarled at his mate and moved toward her as though to drive her along the path, then turned and galloped the other way. A lynx materialized in front of him, crouched and spitting, its ears laid flat and its teeth gleaming. He went at it

hissing, and it gave ground; another bounded off the bank toward the pup, but he whirled and drove it off. Short-legged and awkward on land, he was at a great disadvantage before the pair of lynxes, but somehow he managed to be everywhere at once.

The snarling lynxes, trying to draw both otters away from the pup, were very quick, but the old otter moved like a dark flame. He closed with one of them, took his raking and punished it, and broke away in time to fasten on the throat of the other, which was batting with a hooked claw at his mate. He shook its big body, threw it aside, and whirled again toward the first. Quiet suddenly fell; the lynxes drew off a little, and they all stood panting, glaring at one another.

The path had been so quiet and empty one moment and so full of violent action the next that the boy was held immobile and staring. The sudden quiet freed him. He got up on his knees, his eyes on the otter; he was so filled with a sudden overwhelming admiration for its courage that he nearly shouted en-couragement as it stood, black and bloody, and so obviously ready to carry the fight on. One of the lynxes moved;

it drew off a little farther, as though deciding to abandon the fight. The boy didn't think; he raised the rifle and fired a quick shot at it. The shot missed, but the lynx turned tail with a snarl and bounded off through the hemlocks. The other went after it, and the old otter turned its head and looked at him for a moment with curiosity, but no fear. Then it shook itself and drove the fe-male and the pup before it down the path and out of sight.

It was well after dark when the boy heard his father shouting in the distance and answered him; presently he saw the lantern moving far off among the dark trees, and hurried toward it.

"Are you all right, Andy?" Gates called. "Are you all right, boy?"

"Yes, Dad," he said. He came to the circle of yellow light and stopped.

"Your ma was a little worried," Gates said gently.

"I'm sorry," he said; and then, "I found them, Dad."

Gates didn't say anything. He just stood there holding the lantern, and the boy could see a star or two among the scattering clouds and branches high above his head. "I found them," he said again. "There were two lynxes after them, and he—the old one, the otter— fought them off. He was wonderful, Dad; he licked them both."

"Rabbits must be scarce," Gates said, "to make them tackle him."

"It was the little one," Andy said. "They were after him. But the old one— I—I shot at the lynxes, Dad."

There was silence for a long moment, then Gates said, "You're not sorry?"

"No," the boy said. "No. He's not mean, Dad. It was the little one all the time. He was watching out for it—even the day he took Nicky; but I didn't know it then. Do you think Joe will understand that, Dad?"

"Sure," Gates said. "He'll understand it. He'll be glad you understand it too." His long arm went around the boy's shoulders. "Come on," he said. "Let's get on home."

THE FACT IS—

1. How does Andy's dog get killed?

2. When Andy vows to kill the otter, why doesn't his father try to reason with him?

3. As Andy makes his plans to kill the otter, he finds "no pleasure, no anticipation of exciting sport connected with any of them." Compare this attitude with the otter's in his "game" with the trout.

4. Reread the paragraph beginning "He changed, little by little, during those weeks." In what way does the boy change? Is it possible for someone living in a town or city to undergo a similar change?

5. When the boy finally has a chance to get his revenge, he is confused by "a sort of unwillingness that had suddenly come into his heart." Why does he feel differently than he thought he would?

PEOPLE AND ANIMALS

1. When the otters were unable to satisfy their need for constant activity, they began to bicker and snarl at one another. Can you think of a situation in which human beings might react the same way? Prepare to tell about it in class.

2. When the lynx discovered Andy was watching him, Andy was impressed with how human the lynx's reaction was. Describe a situation in which some animal's behavior reminded you of a human being's.

3. It was a coincidence that a letter from Joe arrived just as Andy was about to tell his father about his new feeling about the otters. It was also a coincidence that Andy should have found the otters just as they were being attacked by the lynxes. Tell an anecdote in which your own behavior has been changed by a coincidence.

Corporal
Hardy

RICHARD ELY DANIELSON

To be a hero, it is not necessary to lead armies or win battles.

In those days, during the haying season, it was my duty to keep the men in the fields supplied with sufficient cooling drink to enable them to support the heat and burden of the day. According to our established custom, this cooling drink consisted of cold water from the spring, flavored, for some obscure New England reason, with molasses, and it had to be freshly renewed every hour. We had plenty of ice in the icehouse, but there was a stubborn tradition that ice water was "bad" for men working in hayfields under the hot sun.

So every hour I carried down a brown jug containing the innocent mixture of "molasses 'n' water" to the hands, each one of whom would pause in his work, throw the jug over his upper arm, drink deeply thereof, wipe the sweat off his forehead, say "Thanks, Bub," and go on making hay. I was only ten years old, but it was no hardship to carry the jug, and it was fun to see their Adam's apples working as they drank.

This was routine practice on our Connecticut farm. Mostly the farm hands —"hired men," we called them— came back to the house at noon and ate in the kitchen, after washing up at the pump outside. But in haymaking season each man sought a patch of shade, and his meal was carried to him there, to be eaten in the fields. I suppose the men's overheated bodies cooled off in the wisps of breeze drifting across the scorching "mowings" more effectively and comfortably than would have been possible in a hot summer kitchen. I am sure that my father did everything he could to make their lot as comfortable and healthy as possible. He worked with them, under the same conditions, setting them an example of careful, efficient labor. He differed from his men only in the fact that he was always cleanly shaved, that he gave orders and directions, and that he wore a silk shirt even in the hayfields. Nobody objected in the least to this token, for he was "the owner," and he had been to college, and everyone admitted that he was fair and square.

On such occasions, when the men were given their "dinners" out of doors, I always carried his victuals to Mr. Hardy, because I liked to sit with him while he ate and listen to his stories. I think he enjoyed talking, in his racy Connecticut vernacular, to such a fascinated audience of one. He was a Civil War veteran, like my father, who, however, had been too young to enlist until the last year of the war and had seen almost no active service. But Mr. Hardy was a soldier. Congress had given him a Medal of Honor and all men regarded him with respect.

As I look back and remember his stories, I think he must have been the most modest man I have ever known. Certainly he never thought of himself as a hero. He would accept no pension.

"I'm able-bodied. I can work, can't I?" But alas, he was not really able-bodied. He had been grievously wounded several times, and in 1895, when I fetched and carried for him and sat at his feet, it was pitiful to see his valiant efforts to fork hay on the wagon or do the other farming tasks which require muscular strength. He was thin and bent, but his face was brown and clean and his blue eyes bright and indomitable.

My father employed Mr. Hardy whenever there was work to give him, and treated him—I did not, at that time, know why—differently from the other hired men. He was poor, he lived alone, he was unsuccessful, and in New England then we rated people by their comparative "success." But he worked stoutly and asked no favors of anyone. It was generally conceded that Mr. Hardy, if a failure, was nevertheless a good man.

I remember the last day I served him, I brought him his dinner in a basket—cold meat 'n' potatoes, 'n' bread 'n' butter, 'n' cold coffee, 'n' pie. He was seated in the shade of an oak tree, leaning against a stack of hay. I put the food down beside him and sat down, hugging my knees and rocking back and forth. It was pleasant there, with the smell of the hay and the drone of the bees, and the good, warm feeling of the earth.

Mr. Hardy lay back against the haymow. "Thanks, Jackie," he said. "I don't seem to be hungry today. It's hot and this tree don't give much shade. Why, it's like that mean little oak tree down to Chancellorsville."

I said, "Oh, Mr. Hardy, you've told me about Antietam and the Wilderness,[1] but you've never told me about Chancellorsville. What was it like?"

---

[1] **Antietam** (an·TEE·tum) **and the Wilderness:** two major battles of the War Between the States.

He said slowly, "I ain't never told nobody about Chancellorsville, and I don't aim to tell nobody—grown-up, that is. But I'd kind of like to tell somebody that don't know nothing—like you—about it, for the first and last time. You'll forget it, and it would kind of ease my mind."

Mr. Hardy hoisted himself a little higher on the haymow and made a pretense of eating some bread and meat. "Chancellorsville," he said, "was a bad battle, an awful bad battle. We didn't fight good and they was too many of them and I lost my captain."

"Who was he?" I asked.

"Why," he said, incredulously, "you oughta know that! He was Captain William Armstrong, commandin' Company B, 39th Connecticut. 'N' his twin brother, Ezra, was lootenant. He was younger by an hour or so, and they was identical twins. They never was two men as much alike—in looks, that is, for they was quite unlike inside. The lootenant was always stompin' around an' shoutin' an' wavin' his arms, an' the captain, he was always quiet an' soft-spoken an' brave• an' gentle. He was a good man—he was an awful good man. I guess he was the best man I ever knowed!"

He paused and took a sip of his cold coffee. Then he said, "Why, when we come to leave town to go in the cars to Hartford and then to Washington, their father—he was old Judge Armstrong, who lived in that big place up on Armstrong Hill—the Judge come up to me an' says, 'Nathan, you look after my boys,' he said. 'They're younger than you be. You kind of keep an eye on them, for my sake,' he says. 'They is good boys,' he says. 'I will, Judge,' I says. 'I'll do my best.' An' he says to me, 'I know you will, Nathan Hardy.'"

"But tell me, Mr. Hardy," I broke in, for I was not interested in the Arm-strong twins, "what happened at Chancellorsville?"

"It was a bad battle, as I said. Them Rebs come charging out of the woods, hollerin' and yellin' and helligolarrupin', and they was too many of them. The lootenant, he kept stomping up and down, shouting, 'Never give ground, boys! Stay where you are! Take careful aim! Never retreat!' Those were his words. I will never forget them, because he meant them. But my captain— I was next to him—says, 'They're too many; we can't stop 'em. Tell the men to retreat slowly, firing as often as they can reload.' Just then it hit him right in the chest. *Thunk!* was the noise it made; just like thet—*thunk!* I caught him as he fell, and the blood began to come out of his mouth. He tried to speak, but he was vomiting blood dreadful, so all he could do was to make faces, and his lips said, 'Tell Elizabeth . . .' and then he died. I put him down and noticed we was under a mean little oak tree on the edge of our trenches.

"Then they was around us, hairy men with bayonets, stabbin' and shootin' and yellin', and we soldiers had kind of drifted together in groups and the lootenant was shouting, 'Don't retreat, men!' and he got his right in the knee and fell down; and so I picked him up and put him across my shoulder and started for the rear. He kep' hittin' me in the face and swearing. 'You coward! You left my brother there and you're making me retreat!' I says to him, 'Ezra, be reasonable; I'm takin' you to an ambulance. You ain't fit to fight, and as soon as I can, I'm goin' back to bury William. They ain't goin' to shovel him into no trench,' I said. So he stopped hitting at me.

"I was strong then, and I must 'a' carried him what seemed a mile or a mile and a few rods when we come to some stretcher men near a house, and

I said, 'You take this officer to the nearest surgeon. They got to saw his leg off.' And they said, 'We ain't carryin' no wounded. We're a burial detail.' I said, pulling my pistol out, 'You will be if you don't carry this man. I'm kind of tuckered, but I ain't too tuckered to shoot.' So two of them carried him, and I went along with my pistol till we come to a place where surgeons was carving men up and I handed over the lootenant. He come to as I did so, and said, 'You scoundrel, you made me retreat. I'll never forgive you!' I said, 'Ezra, they're going to saw your leg off and you'll never fight again, but I'll bury William if it's the last thing I do!' He says, 'Is that a promise?' and I says, 'That's a promise. But it ain't a promise to you—it's one I made to your pa.'

"So I stayed with him and helped hold him while they sawed his leg off. They havin' run out of chloroform, it took four of us to hold him. And when it was over, he was unconscious, and they put him in a cart with some others and took him away. So I went back to the house where the burial men were loafing. It was pretty ruined, but I found a shingle that was almos' clean and I wrote on it, in the light of a fire, 'cause it was dark then:

CAPT. WILLIAM ARMSTRONG
commanding co. B, 39 Connecticut
He was an awful good man

"When it come gray, I started out with my shingle and my spade and I went along till I was challenged by the Rebel pickets and sentries. I answered, 'Union burial detail. I'm comin' for to bury my captain.' They begun shootin' at me and I don't know as I blame them. I was alone an' wasn't armed. So they shot real hard, and one bullet struck me in the left thigh and I fell down. Fortunately I had a belt, and I sat up and took it off and strapped it real tight over my wound, and my britches was tight at the waist so they didn't come down, and I got up and went on.

"They stopped shootin' and a man with a bayonet got up and said, 'Yank, you're my pris'ner.' And I said, 'I know I be, but I ain't your pris'ner till I bury my captain.' And I held up my shingle and spade. He said, 'Where's he lie?' And I said, 'About quarter mile from here and maybe a few rods, under a mean little oak tree; and,' I says, 'you take me there and I'll bury him and then I'm your pris'ner. They ain't goin' to stuff my captain into no ditch,' I says. He says, 'You may be crazy, Yank, or you may be a spy. You come with me an' I'll turn you over to the captain.'

"'Your captain alive?' I asks.

"'I reckon so,' he says.

"'Mine's dead,' I says, 'and I aim for to bury him.'

"So he tuk me away with his bayonet in my back and the blood was squilchin' in my boot, but I got along to where his captain was and the captain asked questions, and the Rebel soldier, he tol' all he knew, an' the captain says, 'Where's he lie?' An' I says, 'By a mean little oak, where our lines was yesterday mornin'.'

"An' the captain says, 'That ain't far away. I'll send a detail to bury him.' I says, 'Ain't nobody goin' to bury the captain but me,' I says. 'After that, I'll be your pris'ner.'

"They was a young man dressed up all pretty with gold braid on his uniform, and he laughed kind of loud and he says, 'Saves us the trouble of buryin' him!' an' the captain turns on him, real stern, and says, 'Lootenant, this is a brave soldier,' he says, 'who come back under fire and was wounded to bury his company commander and give himself up as pris'ner. I will not have him insulted or laughed at,' he says. Then he turns to me an' says, 'What is your name an' rank?'

"'Corporal Nathan Hardy, Company B, Thirty-ninth Connecticut,' I says.

"An' he says, 'Corporal, you and I an' these men,' turnin' around to the five or six Rebs who was listenin', 'will go together to find your captain.'

"So we went and I found him, underneath that mean little oak tree, and he looked dreadful. His eyes was open and they was an awful lot of blood on his shirt where his coat was torn open, and he was lyin' all sprangled out an' undignified. An' the first thing I done was to straighten him out. I spit on my sleeve and wiped the blood off his mouth the best I could. An' I closed his eyes an' buttoned his coat an' crossed his arms. They was kind of stiff, but I done it, an' I brushed him off and laid him out regular.

"Then I started diggin', an' it would have been easy if it hadn't been for my leg and all the blood was in my boot. Six-foot-four or thereabouts it was, and three-foot deep—not as deep as I wanted, but I couldn't dig no deeper, I was so tuckered. But it was an honest grave, for I was real handy with a spade in them days. Then I stood up and said, 'Will two o' you Rebs hand the captain to me?' Which they done, and I laid him in the grave. An' as I stood lookin' down at him lyin' there, I says to myself, 'Ain't nobody goin' to shovel no dirt on the captain's face—nobody, nobody, nobody at all, not even me!' So I took my coat off and laid it over him, coverin' up his face best I could. I didn't want to go to no Rebel prison in my shirt, but I wouldn't have no one shovel dirt on the captain.

"Then the two Rebs pulled me out of the grave, real gentle and considerate. An' then I noticed they was a Rebel general there settin' on a blood horse. How long he bin there I don't know. He looked at me and see I was wounded and peaked, and he says, stern an' hard,

'Captain, what's the meanin' of this? This man's wounded and weak,' he says. 'Do you force wounded men to bury the dead?'

"The captain went over to him and began talkin' to him low and earnest, seemed like, all the time I was fillin' in the grave. An' when I had patted the mound even, so it looked good, and had stuck the shingle in the new earth at the head of the grave, I come over to where the general was, limpin' and leanin' on my spade, an' I saluted—couldn't help it; I kind of forgot he was a Rebel—an' I says, 'General, I'm your pris'ner. I buried my captain. I ain't a great hand at askin' favors, an' your captain and these Rebs has been real good to me. But I wanta ask one more. I was raised Episcopal, which was unusual in our town, and so was the captain. I'd kind of like to say a prayer before I surrender . . .'"

Here Mr. Hardy seemed to doze a little. "Where was I?" he asked, rousing after a few minutes.

"You had just gone up to the general and asked if you could say a prayer before you surrendered."

"Yes, yes, so it was. The general said, 'Corporal Hardy, I am an Episcopalian too, and you shall say your prayer.'

"So he dismounted and took off his hat, and he and I kneeled down by the grave, and it was awful hard for me to kneel. And when we was there kneelin', I looked up for a minute and all them Rebs was standin' with their caps off and their heads bowed, nice and decent, just like Northern people. An' then I had a dreadful time, for to save my life I couldn't remember a prayer, not a line, not a word. I had heard the burial service often enough and too often, what with Pa and Ma an' all kinds of relations, but my brains was all watery an' thin, seemed like, an' I couldn't remember

nothin' at all. I don't know how long 't was till somethin' come driftin' into my mind. It wa'n't from the burial service; 't was somethin' we used to chant in Evenin' Prayer. So I says it, loud as I could, for I was gettin' awful feeble.

"'Lord,' I says, 'Now lettest Thou Thy servant depart in peace, according to Thy Word . . .' An' I couldn't remember or say any more. The general, he helped me to my feet, spade an' all, an' I looked him in the face and, by creepers, they was tears in his beard. Soon as I could speak, I says, 'General, you've been real good to me and I thank you. An' now I'm your pris'ner, wherever you want to send me.'

"An' he says, 'Corporal Hardy, you will never be a pris'ner of our people as long as I live and command this corps.'

"An' I broke in, awful scared he had misunderstood, and I says, 'General, you don't think I was prayin' for me to go in peace! I'm your pris'ner; I'm not askin' for no favors. I was thinkin' of the captain—and me too, perhaps, but not that way. I can go anywhere now. I—'

"He cut me short. 'Corporal Hardy,' he says, 'I know to Whom you was prayin' and why, an' I haven't misunderstood you at all. Captain,' he says, 'I want a detail of six men an' a stretcher and a flag of truce to take this brave soldier an'—an' Christian gentleman back to the Union lines; an' I want this message, which I have dictated and signed, delivered to the commanding officer to be forwarded through channels to the Secretary of War or the President. Those people can hardly decline this courtesy, under the circumstances. . . . Wait, Carter, I wish to add a few lines.' So he put the paper against his saddle and he wrote for some time.

"Then, kind of in a dream, I heard the Rebel captain say, 'Sir, if the General permits, I would like to lead this detail to the Union lines and ask to be blindfolded and deliver your message

to the Division Commander.'

"An' the General says, 'Captain, I am very glad you made that request, and I commend your behavior. It is only fittin' that the officer escortin' Corporal Hardy with my message should be of field rank, and I shall put in my order for your promotion. You are a pretty good soldier, yourself,' he says—only he didn't say it that way.

"All this time I was kind of waverin' around, but I heard most all they said; and because I was feeble from losing blood an' the battle an' burying the captain an' a kind of feverish feelin', things begun to spin around, and I started walkin' this way and that way with my spade, tryin' to stand up, knowin' I couldn't much longer. I heard someone yell, 'Catch him!' An' the next thing I knowed I was in a bed of straw and they was probin' for the bullet in my leg. Then I don't remember nothin' till I woke up in a bed, a clean bed, with a nice-lookin' woman leanin' over me, wipin' my head with a cold, wet towel. I says, 'Where am I?'

"An' she says, 'You're in the hospital of the Sanitary Commission in Washington. An' oh, Corporal Hardy,' she says, 'I'm so glad you're conscious, for today the President is comin' to give you the Medal of Honor.' An' I says, 'Listen, Sister, I gotta get out of here. I don't care for no President or no medal —I gotta bury the captain. He's lyin' down there under a mean little oak. Gimme my clothes,' I says; 'I want a spade and a shingle.' An' she says, 'Corporal, you buried your captain an' buried him fine. That's why the President is comin' to see you. Now, you just drink this and go to sleep for a while, and I'll wake you when the President comes.'

"So I drank it and kind of slept, and when I woke up, there was the ugliest man I ever see, leanin' over and pinnin' something to my nightshirt, an' he says, 'Corporal Hardy, even the enemy call you a brave soldier and a good man. Congress has voted you this medal. God bless you,' he says.''

Mr. Hardy yawned and closed his eyes, and leaned against the haymow. He had told the tale he had to tell— once, to one person.

"But, Mr. Hardy," I said, "what happened to the lieutenant, and who was Elizabeth?" I wanted the story all tied up in ribbons.

"Who?" he said. "The lootenant? Oh, Ezra come back and married Elizabeth and they went to live in Massachusetts. Seems he went aroun' sayin' he couldn't live in no town where people pointed at him and thought he had run away leavin' his dead brother. Naturally no one done so or thought so. But, for all his stompin' and shoutin', he was sensitive, an' he bore me a grudge for takin' him away. I don't see as how I could-a done different. I'd promised the old Judge I'd look after his boys an' I've allus aimed to keep my promises."

Just then my father came up to us. It was unlike Mr. Hardy to sit in the shade while other men had started to work again, and Father looked worried. "How are you feeling, Nathan?" he asked.

"Why, John, I'm plumb tuckered out, and that's a fact. I don' know as I can do much more work today. Seems like I never did fare good under these mean little oak trees," and he glanced sharply at me with an expression that was almost a wink. We shared a secret.

Father looked startled, as if he thought Mr. Hardy's wits were wandering.

"I tell you what, Nathan," he said, "you've had all the sun you need. I'll send the wagon and they'll take you up to the house, where you can be cool and rest for a while." And, for once in his life, Mr. Hardy made no protest over having "favors" done for him. Father

took me aside. "Jackie," he said, "you run up to the house and tell your mother to make the bed in the spare room ready, and then you go to the village and tell Dr. Fordyce he's wanted. I don't like Nathan's looks."

Before I started running, I glanced at Mr. Hardy, and I saw what Father meant. He was pale and flushed in the wrong places, though I hadn't noticed it at all when he was telling me about Chancellorsville.

So Mr. Hardy was put to bed in the spare room, and given such care and aid as we knew how to give. For several days he lay quietly enough, and, as I look back on it after all these years, I think that the weight and burden of his long, valiant struggle must suddenly have proved too great. He couldn't go on forever. Mr. Hardy was tuckered out.

Then for some time he alternated between unconsciousness and a mild delirium. He kept mumbling phrases: "Take that quid out o' your mouth. 'T ain't soldierly!" ... "Ain't nobody goin' to bury the captain but me." I knew what lots of his bewildered sayings meant, but there were many which were obscure. I sat with him every day for an hour or so when the rest of the household were busy, and I had instructions to call my elders if Mr. Hardy needed help or became conscious.

One day he opened his eyes and said, "Here I am and I'm real easy in my mind—but I can't just remember what I said." I went out and called my parents, who told me to stay outside. But I listened and I heard Mr. Hardy say, "Call the boy in. He knows what I want said and I can't remember. He's young and 't won't hurt him and he'll forget." So Mother beckoned me to come in and I said, "What can I do, Mr. Hardy?"

"You can say what I said for the captain when I knelt down with the general."

So I knelt down, and, having the parrotlike memory of childhood, I said, "You knelt down and so did the general, and then you couldn't remember any of the words of the burial service, but you did remember something that was sung in the evening, and you said, 'Lord, now lettest Thou Thy servant depart in peace, according to Thy Word . . .'" And I began to cry.

"That's right," he said very faintly,

"that's right; that's it. Yes, Captain. . . ."

My mother gathered me up and took me out and held me very close, rocking back and forth with me while I wept out how I loved Mr. Hardy and what a good man he was.

And that was why I was sent to my aunt and cousins at New London, where I could swim and fish and forget about battles and wounds and Mr. Hardy. But I didn't forget.

THE FACT IS—

1. What was Mr. Hardy's position on the farm?

2. Why did Mr. Hardy want to tell Jackie about Chancellorsville? Why at this particular time?

3. What happened to the two Armstrong boys in the battle?

4. How did Corporal Hardy win the respect of the Rebels?

5. How did this war experience end for the corporal?

6. How did the story end?

WAR TALK

1. What made Mr. Hardy's account of Chancellorsville different from his other war stories?

2. Why do many soldiers refuse to talk about their battle experiences?

A WORD TO REMEMBER: obscure

The cooling drink given the men in the fields was "flavored, for some obscure New England reason, with molasses." The little boy didn't understand some things Mr. Hardy said just before he died because their meaning was obscure. Anything *obscure* is covered from sight, or from understanding, or sometimes from touch. Some modern poetry is obscure because the poet covers his thoughts too deeply.

An *obscurer* is a workman who darkens glass by dipping it in acid or by some other method. Can you see the meaning of *obscure* in this name?

Federalist Paper Number 14

JAMES MADISON

The Federalist Papers became in time a sort of textbook of government theory and practice for the courts, the Congress, and even for Presidents. These essays, originally published as a series in New York newspapers and signed "Publius," were written by Alexander Hamilton, James Madison, and John Jay, members of the Constitutional Convention of 1787. *Number 14,* written by Madison, appeals to the "manly spirit" of the various state legislatures to accept the Constitution and thus "secure the union of the thirteen primitive States." Two elements make this essay difficult but rewarding reading: Madison's eighteenth-century diction and his closely reasoned argument that strong central government was practical even for such a large territory as the United States was then.

To the People of the State of New York:

1. We have seen the necessity of the Union, as our bulwark against foreign danger, as the conservator of peace among ourselves, as the guardian of our commerce and other common interests, as the only substitute for those military establishments which have subverted the liberties of the Old World, and as the proper antidote for the diseases of faction, which have proved fatal to other popular governments, and of which alarming symptoms have been betrayed by our own. All that remains, within this branch of our inquiries, is to take notice of an objection that may be drawn from the great extent of country which the Union embraces. A few observations on this subject will be the more proper, as it is perceived that the adversaries of the new Constitution are availing themselves of the prevailing prejudice with regard to the practicable sphere of republican administration, in order to supply, by imaginary difficulties, the want of those solid objections which they endeavor in vain to find.

2. The error which limits republican government to a narrow district has been unfolded and refuted in preceding papers. I remark here only that it seems to owe its rise and prevalence chiefly to the confounding of a republic with a democracy, applying to the former reasonings drawn

from the nature of the latter. The true distinction between these forms was also adverted to on a former occasion. It is that in a democracy the people meet and exercise the government in person; in a republic they assemble and administer it by their representatives and agents. A democracy, consequently, will be confined to a small spot. A republic may be extended over a large region.

3. To this accidental source of the error may be added the artifice of some celebrated authors, whose writings have had a great share in forming the modern standard of political opinions. Being subjects either of an absolute or limited monarchy, they have endeavored to heighten the advantages, or palliate the evils of those forms, by placing in comparison the vices and defects of the republican, and by citing as specimens of the latter the turbulent democracies of ancient Greece and modern Italy. Under the confusion of names, it has been an easy task to transfer to a republic observations applicable to a democracy only; and among others, the observation that it can never be established but among a small number of people, living within a small compass of territory.

4. Such a fallacy may have been the less perceived, as most of the popular governments of antiquity were of the democratic species; and even in modern Europe, to which we owe the great principle of representation, no example is seen of a government wholly popular, and founded, at the same time, wholly on that principle. If Europe has the merit of discovering this great mechanical power in government, by the simple agency of which the will of the largest political body may be concentered, and its force directed to any object which the public good requires, America can claim the merit of making the discovery the basis of unmixed and extensive republics. It is only to be lamented that any of her citizens should wish to deprive her of the additional merit of displaying its full efficacy in the establishment of the comprehensive system now under her consideration.

5. As the natural limit of a democracy is that distance from the central point which will just permit the most remote citizens to assemble as often as their public functions demand, and will include no greater number than can join in those functions; so the natural limit of a republic is that distance from the center which will barely allow the representatives to meet as often as may be necessary for the administration of public affairs. Can it be said that the limits of the United States exceed this distance? It will not be said by those who recollect that the Atlantic coast is the longest side of the Union, that during the term of thirteen years, the representatives of the States have been almost continually assembled, and that the members from the most distant States are not chargeable with greater intermissions of attendance than those from the States in the neighborhood of Congress.

6. That we may form a juster estimate with regard to this interesting subject, let us resort to the actual dimensions of the Union. The limits, as fixed by the treaty of peace, are: on the east the Atlantic, on the south the latitude of thirty-one degrees, on the west the Mississippi, and on the north an irregular line running in some instances beyond the forty-fifth degree, in others falling as low as the forty-second. The southern shore of Lake Erie lies below that latitude. Computing the distance between the thirty-first and forty-fifth degrees, it amounts to nine hundred and seventy-three common miles; computing it from thirty-one to forty-two degrees, to seven hundred and sixty-four miles and a half. Taking the mean for the distance, the amount will be eight hundred and sixty-eight miles and three fourths. The mean distance from the At-

lantic to the Mississippi does not probably exceed seven hundred and fifty miles. On a comparison of this extent with that of several countries in Europe, the practicability of rendering our system commensurate to it appears to be demonstrable. It is not a great deal larger than Germany, where a diet representing the whole empire is continually assembled; or than Poland before the late dismemberment, where another national diet was the depositary of the supreme power. Passing by France and Spain, we find that in Great Britain, inferior as it may be in size, the representatives of the northern extremity of the island have as far to travel to the national council as will be required of those of the most remote parts of the Union.

7. Favorable as this view of the subject may be, some observations remain which will place it in the light still more satisfactory.

8. In the first place it is to be remembered that the general government is not to be charged with the whole power of making and administering laws. Its jurisdiction is limited to certain enumerated objects, which concern all the members of the republic, but which are not to be attained by the separate provisions of any. The subordinate governments, which can extend their care to all those other objects which can be separately provided for, will retain their due authority and activity. Were it proposed by the plan of the convention to abolish the governments of the particular States, its adversaries would have some ground for their objection; though it would not be difficult to show that if they were abolished, the general government would be compelled, by the principle of self-preservation, to reinstate them in their proper jurisdiction.

9. A second observation to be made is that the immediate object of the Federal Constitution is to secure the union of the thirteen primitive States, which we know

to be practicable; and to add to them such other States as may arise in their own bosoms, or in their neighborhoods, which we cannot doubt to be equally practicable. The arrangements that may be necessary for those angles and fractions of our territory which lie on our northwestern frontier must be left to those whom further discoveries and experience will render more equal to the task.

10. Let it be remarked, in the third place, that the intercourse throughout the Union will be facilitated by new improvements. Roads will everywhere be shortened and kept in better order; accommodations for travelers will be multiplied and meliorated; an interior navigation on our eastern side will be opened throughout, or nearly throughout, the whole extent of the thirteen States. The communication between the Western and Atlantic districts, and between different parts of each, will be rendered more and more easy by those numerous canals with which the beneficence of nature has intersected our country, and which art finds it so little difficult to connect and complete.

11. A fourth and still more important consideration is that as almost every State will, on one side or other, be a frontier, and will thus find, in a regard to its safety, an inducement to make some sacrifices for the sake of the general protection; so the States which lie at the greatest distance from the heart of the Union, and which, of course, may partake least of the ordinary circulation of its benefits, will be at the same time immediately contiguous to foreign nations, and will consequently stand, on particular occasions, in greatest need of its strength and resources. It may be inconvenient for Georgia, or the States forming our western or northeastern borders, to send their representatives to the seat of government; but they would find it more so to struggle alone against an invading enemy, or even to support alone the whole expense of

those precautions which may be dictated by the neighborhood of continual danger. If they should derive less benefit, therefore, from the Union in some respects than the less distant States, they will derive greater benefit from it in other respects, and thus the proper equilibrium will be maintained throughout.

12. I submit to you, my fellow-citizens, these considerations, in full confidence that the good sense which has so often marked your decisions will allow them their due weight and effect; and that you will never suffer difficulties, however formidable in appearance, or however fashionable the error on which they may be founded, to drive you into the gloomy and perilous scene into which the advocates for disunion would conduct you. Hearken not to the unnatural voice which tells you that the people of America, knit together as they are by so many cords of affection, can no longer live together as members of the same family; can no longer continue the mutual guardians of their mutual happiness; can no longer be fellow-citizens of one great, respectable, and flourishing empire. Hearken not to the voice which petulantly tells you that the form of government recommended for your adoption is a novelty in the political world; that it has never yet had a place in the theories of the wildest projectors; that it rashly attempts what it is impossible to accomplish. No, my countrymen, shut your ears against this unhallowed language. Shut your hearts against the poison which it conveys; the kindred blood which flows in the veins of American citizens, the mingled blood which they have shed in defense of their sacred rights, consecrate their Union, and excite horror at the idea of their becoming aliens, rivals, enemies. And if novelties are to be shunned, believe me, the most alarming of all novelties, the most wild of all projects, the most rash of all attempts, is that of rending us in pieces in order to preserve our liberties and promote our happiness. But why is the experiment of an extended republic to be rejected, merely because it may comprise what is new? Is it not the glory of the people of America, that, whilst they have paid a decent regard to the opinions of former times and other nations, they have not suffered a blind veneration for antiquity, for custom, or for names, to overrule the suggestions of their own good sense, the knowledge of their own situation, and the lessons of their own experience? To this manly spirit, posterity will be indebted for the possession, and the world for the example, of the numerous innovations displayed on the American theater, in favor of private rights and public happiness. Had no important step been taken by the leaders of the Revolution for which a precedent could not be discovered, no government established of which an exact model did not present itself, the people of the United States might, at this moment, have been numbered among the melancholy victims of misguided councils, must at best have been laboring under the weight of some of those forms which have crushed the liberties of the rest of mankind. Happily for America, happily, we trust, for the whole human race, they pursued a new and more noble course. They accomplished a revolution which has no parallel in the annals of human society. They reared the fabrics of governments which have no model on the face of the globe. They formed the design of a great Confederacy, which it is incumbent on their successors to improve and perpetuate. If their works betray imperfections, we wonder at the fewness of them. If they erred most in the structure of the Union, this was the work most difficult to be executed; this is the work which has been new modeled by the act of your convention, and it is that act on which you are now to deliberate and to decide.

—PUBLIUS

James Madison is called "the father of the Constitution." Madison was largely responsible for calling a convention to create a constitution. One of the first to realize that the Articles of Confederation bound our Union too loosely to be effective, he became the greatest authority on constitutional law of his time. Together with Alexander Hamilton and John Jay, he wrote **The Federalist,** a brilliant series of papers defending the Constitution and the federal form of government. Madison was a member of the first Congress, Secretary of State under Thomas Jefferson, and Jefferson's choice to be President of the United States, an office which he filled with distinction.

"A NOVELTY IN THE POLITICAL WORLD"

The twelve questions below are keyed to the twelve paragraphs of "Federalist Paper Number 14." They will help you discover the line of Madison's argument.

1. In the first sentence Madison sums up previous Federalist papers by listing reasons for "the necessity of the Union." What five reasons does he give? What objection does this paper "take notice of"?

2. What is the true distinction between a democracy and a republic?

3. What main opinion "applicable to a democracy only" did some writers apply to a republic?

4. According to Madison, what has been America's special contribution to the development of the republican form of government?

5. What limits the size of a democracy? of a republic?

6. Madison compares the travel distance to the capital from "the most remote parts of the Union" with similar distances in European countries. In general, how did these distances compare? Would such a comparison be equally valid today?

7. Paragraph 7 is Madison's transition from a general discussion of the republican form of government to a specific argument for the United States Constitution. What does he mean by "this view of the subject"?

8. What did Madison mean by "subordinate governments"? Did he feel that these governments were necessary?

9. What did Madison say was the immediate objective of the Constitution?

10. What transportation improvements did Madison foresee?

11. What inconvenience would a central government cause for the frontier states? Why might these same states stand "in greatest need of [the government's] resources?

12. Madison's stirring conclusion appeals to the American's sense of glory. What does he claim as "the glory of the people of America"?

The Strike

The Major knew he could not withdraw his troops safely unless he called for an air strike on the enemy artillery position. He also knew that such a strike would kill twenty of his own men. The Korean War is the background of this play, which was written for production on television. As you read it, imagine the events as they would appear on a television screen.

Cast of Characters

MAJOR GAYLORD

CAPTAIN FRANKS

LIEUTENANT PETERS

CHICK, *an engineer*

CAPTAIN SLOANE, *a doctor*

LIEUTENANT JONES

LIEUTENANT CHAXFIELD

CHAPLAIN WALKER

RADIO OPERATORS

OTHER SOLDIERS

ACT I

We open on a cover shot of a Command Post of what is a partially destroyed Korean farmhouse. The room is the remains of a cellar. Superimposed over this general shot is the legend, "Korea, January 1951." The camera moves in for a shot of a radio operator at the far end of the room. Another soldier cranks a hand-operated generator. The room is perhaps forty feet long. In it are little groups of soldiers in winter dress. At the far end are a map board and a rickety table. There are two or three Coleman lanterns at various parts of the room. An open fire burns very close to some makeshift curtains which are drawn across the entrance. The RADIO MAN'S voice is a continuous, monotonous drone that is sustained slightly over the quiet voices of the various officers and men in the room. Most of the attention is directed toward the map board at the far end. Outside is the occasional rumble of artillery. Short bursts of automatic weapons. Every now and then a swish of a shell overhead like the sound of a whiskbroom over a wooden floor.

Radio Man. Razor Red, this is Razor Blue C.P.[1] Razor Red, this is Razor Blue C.P. How do you hear me? Over. (*A pause.*) Razor Red . . . Razor Red . . . This is Razor Blue C.P.—come in, please, Razor Red.

[1] **C.P.:** Command Post.

[*His voice continues under as we pan over* MAJOR GAYLORD. *He is a man in his late thirties to early forties. Medium-built, dressed like the others, he shares the one quality of appearance that marks them all. This is fatigue, a deadening, numbing tiredness that comes from living with danger and with odds.*]

Gaylord (*leaves the map board, crosses over to a table, and sits down*). What would you call it? How 'bout you, Franks?

[FRANKS *is a youngish-looking captain with a blond beard stubble. He perpetually smokes a cigar, a soggy mess that he keeps between his teeth. There is a kind of toughness to this man. He tips his helmet back.*]

Franks. Don't ask me, Major. One minute I got a company on attack. The next minute—the next minute I got thirteen men designated as the rear guard of a division. What happened?

Gaylord. What we call a fluid situation. (*Taps a mess cup with his finger . . . then grips it thoughtfully.*) A fluid situation. (*Looks up at them.*) That's any battle you're losing when you don't want to admit it.

Franks. What's the plan now, Major?

Gaylord. We're to hold this riverbank until we get the order to move back.

Peters. That's some plan.

Gaylord. You think of a better one, Lieutenant, and I'll pin eagles on you and massage your feet until spring. (*Rises.*) I want to know where every company is dug in. I want to know how many effectives we've got—and that includes *walking* wounded! I want somebody to handle S-4.

Peters. That'd be Cap'n Mitchell. He's supply.

[*The others look at him in silence.*]

Gaylord. Captain Mitchell's dead. You handle it, Peters. Franks, you check the perimeter. (*To the two other officers*) You two stay close to this house where I can get a hold of you.

[*The men start to leave.* GAYLORD *moves over toward the curtains stretched across the entrance. He has a nervous little habit of scratching with his finger tips at his beard stubble. His voice is thoughtful and somewhat musing.*]

Gaylord. That was a nice bridge you put up, Chick.

[*The camera pans over for a medium close shot of* CHICK. *This is a round, cherubic-faced, portly little man, who looks out of place and uncomfortable in his uniform.*]

Chick. We aim to please. (*Joins him at the window.*) It *was* a nice bridge.

Gaylord. So if they want to come across now—they'll have to wade.

Chick. Know somethin'? I don't think that bothers 'em. Yesterday afternoon when they hit K Company, our boys were aimin' pointblank with heavy thirties—and they kept comin' and comin' in a solid wave an'—

Gaylord. Knock it off. (*He lights a cigarette . . . moves over to the* RADIO OPERATOR, *who has stopped trying to make contact.*) What's with you? This a break?

Radio Man. Don't do no good, Major. I been tryin' to make contact for the past hour. (*Points to the radio.*) Nothin'.

Gaylord. Keep trying. (*Looks at the* GENERATOR MAN *blowing on his fingers.*) What's-a-matter? Your fingers cold?

Soldier. Yes, sir. Like ice.

Gaylord. It's a lot colder outside in the holes. You want to change places with any of those boys?

Radio Man. Razor Red . . . Razor Red . . . This is Razor Blue C.P.

Soldier. No, sir.

Gaylord. How's that?

Soldier (*louder*). No, sir. I wasn't complainin'. You asked me if my fingers were cold and I—

Gaylord (*tiredly*). Awright, awright. (*Moves back to the table.*)

Chick. Crazy war. It took us three days to span that river. Three days standin' up to our hips in ice. Three days makin'—three minutes to blow it up. (*Shakes his head.*) The Army! When I get home, I'm not payin' five cents in taxes.

Gaylord. Sure. We shoulda left it standing. With a big sign in Red Chinese—This way to the 29th Division—(*Spits it out.*) Artistic engineers.

Chick. All I'm sayin' is that we went to a lot of trouble to put up a bridge in freezing weather with—

Gaylord. And all I'm saying is for you to knock it off! (*Again he rises and crosses to the* RADIO MAN.) Still no answer?

Radio Man. No, sir. (*Mumbles.*) Seems kinda silly—

Gaylord. What's that?

Radio Man. Hannify and me been on this radio since yesterday morning, sir. We're kinda beat.

Gaylord. Why, you poor boys. My heart bleeds! You know who you're tryin' to make contact with?

Radio Man. Platoon of A Company.

Gaylord. A platoon of A Company—that's right. Twenty men on a patrol—and I can guarantee they haven't had any sponge-rubber mattresses to lie on since yesterday morning, either. And if you were out there across the river with 'em—you'd be doing a little fancy praying that somebody'd talk *you* back home. How right am I?

Radio Man (*looking straight ahead*). Yes, sir . . .

Gaylord (*seems to relax slightly*). Is there anybody who can replace you out there?

Radio Man (*to the other soldier*). Grace still around? (*The soldier nods.*) Corporal Grace, sir. Headquarters Company. He can run this thing.

Gaylord. Awright—the both of you go on out and get him—with somebody to run the generator. Hop to it.

[*The two men go out.* GAYLORD *stands by the radio, fiddling with it.*]

Chick. Gay—I didn't mean anything by the bridge business. I was just—

Gaylord. I know you didn't. Nobody means anything by anything. All *I* know is that in two weeks a stinking, lousy

Major is in command of a five-hundred-man, half-frozen rump outfit that's supposed to be a division. *(Goes to the window.)* And out there are probably ten square divisions of slant-eyed bugle blowers who could ram through us like iron through lace. *(Turns to him.)* Chick —I got five hundred men ridin' on my back. All looking straight at me to tell them what to do. And I got a patrol of twenty men out probably all feet up by now—because *I* sent 'em out. I'm a stinking, lousy Major and all of a sudden I'm running my own private section of the war. So don't chip 'em at me about your bridge. *(He flings down his cigarette . . . and furiously rubs his beard stubble . . . opens and shuts his eyes.)*

Chick. You could do with a little sleep yourself.

[*A soldier enters . . . looks from one to the other—salutes.*]

Gaylord. What'll you have?

Soldier. Captain Sloane wants to know about evacuating wounded. We got ninety-three men who oughta go back, sir.

Gaylord. Tell Captain Sloane I've just reserved fifteen Pullmans from the New York Central. What's he think I got—a travel bureau in here? If I had transportation, we wouldn't be sitting here. *(To* CHICK*)* I got a real fantastic staff here. I got a—*(He stops . . . subsides and quietly)* I'll go with you. Chick, stick here, will you?

Radio Operator. Razor Red, Razor Red, this is Razor Blue, C.P. Come in, please.

[GAYLORD *goes out with the soldier as we dissolve to the interior of a cave. On a ledge there is a soldier sitting upright, staring straight ahead at nothing, and repeating over and over again in a sort of half-sob.*]

Soldier. My name is Richard Golden. I

live at 116 Lathrop Street, Endicott, New York. My name is Richard Golden. I live at 116 Lathrop Street, Endicott, New York. My name is Richard . . .

[*We pull back for a cover shot of the cave. On the ground are two rows of wounded men lying on stretchers.* SLOANE *is the only officer. He is assisted by two medics and goes from man to man. There are several plasma bottles strung up. A Coleman lantern is on a crate in the center of the cave. The talk is in whispers. Intermittently, aidmen come in carrying other wounded.* SLOANE'S *motions are like those of an automaton. He goes from one boy to the other numbly and as if by rote.* GAYLORD *enters.*]

Gaylord. You Sloane?

Sloane. Yes, sir. I've got men here who need to get evacuated.

Gaylord. I've got what's left of a division that needs the same thing. You got any ideas? *(And suddenly the scene in front of him registers. We pan with his eyes up and down the stretchers . . . stopping briefly by the delirious boy. He turns back to* SLOANE.*)* I can't help you. My orders are to hold this perimeter and that's all. Nobody's said anything about reinforcements or transportation. Can you hold out?

Sloane. I need ten crates of bandages. I need another hundred pints of plasma, a couple of cases of sulfathiazol, and a whole quartermaster full of dry clothing. Not to mention morphine, ether, and distilled water.

Gaylord. Doc, I wish I could help. *(Shakes his head.)*

[*The doctor bends over the soldier he's been working on.* GAYLORD *kneels close by.*]

Gaylord. Bad? *(Points to the soldier.)*

Sloane. Arm's all smashed. What he

needs really is three hours on a table. Hole in the limb cleaned. Tendons and muscle tissue reduced to about two-thirds normal bulk. Bones set. Broken in three places. Then about three strips of skin off his belly to graft on the arm. Then put it in a cast. That's what he needs for that arm.

Gaylord. Can't do it? (SLOANE *shakes his head.*) What *can* you do?

Sloane (*after a pause . . . looks up*). The only thing I *can* do . . . here. *Cut his arm off.* Next question?

[GAYLORD *rises . . . looks down at the boy on the stretcher.*]

Gaylord. As soon as we can make contact with the Ninth Army . . . maybe we can get some helicopters and medical supplies. Hold on as long as you can, Doc.

Sloane. I'll be here if you want me. And if you find any doctors running around unassigned—assign 'em here, will you?

Gaylord (*on his way out*). Right. I'll see if I can get some dry clothes to send, too.

Sloane. Socks, mostly. I got half a tent of frozen-foot cases.

[GAYLORD *goes out. The doc turns, goes over to the boy whom we've seen in the beginning.*]

Soldier. My name is Richard Golden . . .

Sloane. Son? Son—you hear me?

Soldier. I live at 116 Lathrop Street . . .

Sloane. You're OK now, soldier. You're OK.

Soldier. Endicott, New York. My name is Richard Golden . . .

[SLOANE *pats the boy's face as we pull back gradually. The boy's voice continuing and fading off gradually as we fade to black. We fade on with a shot of the Command Post as in the*

beginning. CHICK *is ⋅staring at the map board. A lamp has been lit on the table. Two soldiers sit by the radio. The officers sit and stand around the room as* GAYLORD *enters.*]

Franks. No word, Major?

Gaylord (*takes off his helmet*). From who?

Franks (*shrugs*). Anybody?

[GAYLORD *looks toward the* RADIO MAN, *who shakes his head.*]

Gaylord. It's getting dark. Maybe by tomorrow—

Peters. Ammo's low. Twenty—thirty rounds a man—and that's it.

Gaylord. For the machine guns?

Peters. We got three.

Gaylord. Three? That's all?

Peters. Three. And nothing heavier.

Gaylord. That's dandy. Put 'em on either end and in the center.

Peters. They *are* that way.

Gaylord. Food? Anything in the dump?

Peters. Nothin' that I could find.

Franks. That perimeter's thin, Major. You could drive a train through the gaps. And there's plenty of gaps.

Gaylord (*sits down*). Anybody in the room got a pleasant word?

Chick. Cleveland. Cleveland, Ohio. That's a pleasant word.

Franks. Can you give us the odds, Major?

Gaylord. I can give you the situation. Then you figure the odds. We're all that's left of one division. We hold down what is probably the right anchor of a very unstable line. We've got no depth, no guns, no communication with any main body. We've got a tent full of wounded and frozen men who should be back in Japan—and we can't move them twenty yards. We've got no supplies, no ammo, and our chances of holding back any sustained attack you could stick in a shot glass and it wouldn't fill it. Awright, Captain Franks—you make book. Tell me the odds?

Radio Man. Major—I've got something. It's on a key.

[*They congregate around the* RADIO MAN, *who hurriedly writes on a pad as the sound of the code is faintly coming from his earphones.*]

Radio Man. It's for us, all right. Razor Blue Command. (*Finishes writing . . .* GAYLORD *grabs the paper and reads.*)

Gaylord. Commanding Officer, Razor Blue Force—hold present position until 0600 tomorrow. Then attempt move forces southward. Marine Unit to your left effect junction with you at Grid seven . . . coordinate nine.

[FRANKS *is at the map immediately, points out the designated spot.*]

Franks. That's six miles south.

Peters. That's good.

Chick. It means somebody knows where we are. I feel like an orphan who just got adopted.

Gaylord. Peters—you and Anderson go down the line and give 'em the word. Password from now till then is Lily-White. Got it?

Peters. Lily-White. Check. Let's go, Andy.

[*They exit.*]

Gaylord (*to the* RADIO MAN). Every fifteen minutes, try to get A Company.

Radio Man. Yes, sir. I been trying. Nothin' yet.

Franks. Still out there, huh?

Gaylord (*nods*). Still out there—someplace.

[*There is the off-stage sound of truck engines in the distance. One by one the men look up . . . aware . . . then apprehensive . . . then sort of collectively they look toward* GAYLORD *questioningly.*]

Gaylord. Trucks. Across the river.

Franks. A lot of them.

Chick. Sounds like it. What do you figure, Gay? Buildup?

Gaylord. Probably. I've been trying to figure why they waited this long.

[*The men gradually lose their stiffness. But the tension doesn't decrease. It just hits a constant level . . . and remains that way. Cigarettes are lit . . . low conversation at odd parts of the room. And though the talk isn't directed toward* GAYLORD, *he still seems a sort of focal point in the room. Eyes watch his movements. Talk ends when he gets near. He paces around the room . . . going from map to radio, back to table. The truck noises stop . . . and in that moment eyes go upward . . . listening as if silence were a noise in itself. Then shells start again. Distant machine-gun rattling . . . a dull explosion. There is static on the radio and* GAYLORD *whirls around toward it . . . expectant. The operator shakes his head.*]

Radio Man. Just static, Major Gaylord.

Gaylord. Try the patrol again.

Radio Man. Yes, sir. (*He nudges the sleeping* GENERATOR MAN, *who automatically starts to crank again.*) Razor Red, this is Razor Blue C.P. Razor Red, this is Razor Blue C.P. Come in, Razor Red. Come in.

[*The men in the room look toward the radio, and then toward the door as a lieutenant comes in. He has an arm in a sling. His face is that of a college sophomore saturated with fear, pain,*

and the persistent question as to just what is going on.]

Jones. Major Gaylord? (GAYLORD *nods.*) I'm Jones, sir. A Company.

Gaylord. So?

Jones. You sent a platoon of my company out yesterday afternoon. *(With a concealed anger)* On a patrol.

Gaylord. We're trying to make contact now.

Jones. You haven't heard from them, then?

Gaylord. Not yet. *(He lights a cigarette, turns his back.)*

Jones. May I ask the purpose of that patrol?

Gaylord *(quick and sudden anger held down).* You're out of line, Lieutenant. *(Turns to him.)* It should be quite obvious why a patrol is sent out in a situation like ours.

Jones *(wryly).* To ascertain the strength and location of the enemy? You mean you don't know . . . sir?

Gaylord. You concerned about 'em, are you, Jones?

Jones. They're twenty of my men.

Gaylord. I didn't know that. Your brand wasn't on them. Had I known, I'd have sent out three ROK's [1] and a platoon of army nurses.

Jones. Major Gaylord—those men don't stand a chance across that river—and I want to know whose decision it was to send 'em across.

Gaylord. My decision. Are you satisfied?

Jones. How about another patrol to hunt for 'em?

Gaylord. Negative.

Jones. Just a couple of men . . . and myself, then.

[1] **ROK's:** Soldiers in the South Korean army.

Gaylord. Negative. We can't spare a couple of men now.

Jones. You could spare twenty yesterday afternoon!

Gaylord. That was yesterday afternoon.

Jones. Begging your pardon, sir—

Gaylord. Don't beg my pardon. Speak your piece and get back to your company.

Jones. My company is five effectives, forty litter cases—and the rest of 'em are facedown for three miles up the road.

Gaylord. What do you want, Jones? Taps and an invocation? At 0600 we're moving back . . . straight back. There's three miles of open country. If artillery's been brought up across the river, we couldn't be a better target if we got painted with red, white, and blue lines with a dot in the forehead. That's why a patrol went across to find out.

Jones. It did a lot of good, didn't it?

Gaylord *(looks at him for a long time).* Jonesy—this whole stinking war doesn't seem to be doing much good. But if it makes you happy—I'm sweatin' those boys of yours out like each one was a kid brother.

Jones. But not enough to send somebody out to save their necks.

Gaylord. That'll do it.

Jones. And when we move out, do we leave 'em out there?

[*We cut to a very tight close-up of* GAYLORD'S *face as this question sinks in and pierces. When he answers, he shouts.*]

Gaylord. I said, That'll do it!

Jones *(A pause, and then very quietly).* Yes sir. *(He turns and goes out.)*

Gaylord *(still at the table, not turning).* Franks, tell the medics we're moving out at 0600. See what they need in the way of litter bearers. We'll try to supply.

Franks. Yes sir. (*He goes out.*)

[GAYLORD *waits a moment. Then he moves across the room and outside. We cut to the exterior by the door of the farmhouse.* GAYLORD *stands there, a light snow falling.* CHICK *comes out to join him.*]

Gaylord (*After a pause, still staring straight ahead toward the river*). There's only one thing worse than a bad command—that's admitting it.

Chick. You called the shot as you saw it. You don't have to justify it—to me, to yourself, to anybody. (*Looking out.*) I think they'll make it back.

Gaylord. And if they don't?

Chick (*looks at him*). Check off twenty.

Gaylord. That simple, huh? Like bookwork. Like balancing a budget.

Chick. Look, Gay. I'm just an engineer. I don't know the niceties of a commander's conscience. I'm up on bridges and that's it. But I think you're missing the forest for the trees. You've done a nice job corraling five hundred men across a river and letting them save their skins. I don't see the point in eating your insides out for a single patrol that had bad luck.

Gaylord. I sent 'em out.

Chick. And who sent you out? And who sent the guy out who sent you out? And go on up the echelons pointing your finger. And what'll it prove? Which came first—the chicken or the egg? Haven't you ever given an order before that cost a life? That's the difference between the Army and running a laundry.

[*We pull in for a tight close-up of* GAY-LORD.]

Gaylord. Once before, something like this. Leyte Island, Philippines. (CHICK *turns to him, interested.*)

Gaylord. I was a platoon sergeant. We left a guy as a rear guard for a column. He disappeared in the jungle.

Chick. Go on.

[*We are on a tight close-up of* GAY-LORD'S *face now in the dim light that comes with the snow. We are looking deeply into lines and crevices of fatigue, hollow eyes, a bearded, dirty face. A portrait of what a human being must pay to engage in combat.*]

Gaylord. That night we set up a perimeter close by. I even remember the password. Lovely Lady. The Japs couldn't pronounce *l*'s. Lovely Lady. That was the password. There was a big moon and you could see out for a hundred yards at least. And then—(*He falters.*)

Chick. Go on, Gay.

Gaylord. This guy—the one we'd left out there—he comes out of the jungle and he starts to walk straight toward us. We could see him. We could even see his face. Somebody yelled, "Password. Give us the password." (*A pause*) He just kept coming toward us. Then somebody else yelled, "Say the password or we'll have to shoot." And he didn't say a word—just came toward us. Pretty soon . . . every man in the holes was standing up . . . screaming for the guy to give the password . . . or something. (*Another pause*) There was a platoon lieutenant with me. I was on a B.A.R. The looie waited . . . and waited, and then when this guy was . . . oh . . . maybe ten yards from us, he tells me . . . "Spray him." (*A pause*) And I did. I sprayed him.

Chick. Go on.

Gaylord. That was it . . . until morning. When we went out to get him . . . his hands were tied behind his back. And there were three Jap bodies behind him. All dead. (*A pause*) He didn't give the password. He didn't want to. He wanted us to shoot. So the Japs couldn't come in with him.

Chick. There . . . there was a brave guy.

Gaylord. And I was the one who did it. (*A deep breath.*) And every time after that . . . when I remember this guy walking toward me in the moonlight . . . and I'd get this . . . this sick feeling—I'd think to myself, It was an order. I just followed an order. That was all there was to it. An order . . . and I followed it. (*He turns away, then looks toward the river.*) Now it isn't just one guy in the moonlight. It's twenty. Only this time I can't point any fingers. When I feel sick . . . I have to stay sick. (*A long pause*) Because it was my own order.

[CHICK *doesn't say anything. And then he grips* GAYLORD'S *arm very tightly, as* GAYLORD *turns and starts back to the door. The* RADIO MAN *appears at it.*]

Radio Man. Major Gaylord—I think we've got 'em! (*He races inside followed by* CHICK.)

Radio Man (*pointing to the radio*). Listen—

Voice (*amid static, and filtered*). Razor Blue C.P. . . . Razor Blue C.P. . . . This is Razor Red. This is Razor Red. Repeat. This is Razor Red. (*And we start to fade.*) This is Razor Red . . .

[*We take a slow fade to black.*]

ACT II

We fade on with a shot of the group standing in a semicircle around the radio . . . as the operator continues in what has obviously been a long attempt to establish contact. He looks up at GAYLORD.

Gaylord. What's the matter?

Radio Man. They can transmit, sir—but they don't receive. They're not hearing us. (*He flicks a switch.*)

Voice (*filter*). Razor Blue C.P., this is Razor Red. Do you hear us at all? Over. (*A pause*) Razor Blue C.P., this is Razor Red—over. (*Another pause*)

Radio Man. Razor Red, this is Razor Blue C.P.—over.

Voice. Razor Blue, C.P.—our equipment may be bad . . . so we'll continue to send just in case we're coming through. We're two miles north of the bridge. We're going to wait until dawn and try to head downstream and cross over to you. In case you *can* hear us—I'm stating position now . . . repeat . . . I'm stating our position. Grid nine . . . coordinate seven. Repeat. Grid nine. Coordinate seven. There's a million Chinese all around us so we won't try to make contact again until we make our move. Over and out.

Radio Man. Razor Red . . . Razor Red . . . do you hear us now? Over. (*A long pause*) (*Looks up.*) That's it, sir. No need tryin' any more.

Gaylord. OK. In about a half hour, try Army again. Rest of you guys better try to get some sleep. (*Looks at his watch.*) We've got about six hours. (*Sees* FRANKS *across the room.*) How about the wounded, Franks?

Franks. Captain Sloane says that thirty cases shouldn't be moved at all on foot. And that fifteen of those are suicides if we try.

Gaylord (*to the* RADIO MAN). Mention that if you make contact. Ask if we can get helicopters in here.

Radio Man. Yes, sir.

[*There is a sudden sound of scattered rifle fire. The men react. Pistols are drawn. A soldier appears at the door.*]

Soldier. Major—some people outside the perimeter on the left. Don't know the password. Claim they're English.

Gaylord. Let 'em through one by one—

Soldier. Yes, sir. *(He leaves.)*

[GAYLORD *walks over to the map, traces a line with a finger.*]

Gaylord. Grid nine . . . coordinate seven . . . that puts the patrol about here.

Chick *(coming up to him).* Right in the middle of 'em.

Gaylord *(nods).* At least they're alive.

[*The door opens.* PETERS *enters with an English lieutenant and an American chaplain.*]

Peters. Lieutenant Chaxfield—Major Gaylord.

Chaxfield. How do you do, Major. Thanks for letting our chaps in. We've been wandering about out there since morning.

Gaylord. How many men do you have, Lieutenant?

Chaxfield. Nine all told. Our unit's the Tenth Fusiliers . . . on detached duty with your 31st Division. *(Grins.)* Same old story. We're here . . . and God knows where the rest of them are. Oh, this is Chaplain Walker. We found him hitchhiking up the road a bit.

Gaylord *(nods).* You people have anything to eat?

Chaxfield. If this is an invitation, Major—

Gaylord. I can give you some used and reused coffee. We're pulling out of here at 0600. We're not being supplied up here at all.

Chaxfield. Well, we can pull up a bit tighter, I suppose. You mentioned coffee?

Chick *(pours two mess cups, hands them to* CHAXFIELD *and* WALKER*).* Better take it at a gulp.

Chaxfield. Thanks very much.

Walker. Thank you.

Chaxfield. Well . . . let's see, now. What sort of toast? How about to all the discretion that's been the better part of valor the past few weeks? *(He looks around.)* Bad joke, I'm afraid. Sorry.

Walker. How about . . . to the victory?

Chaxfield. How about that? To the victory . . . cheers. *(He drinks, makes a face.)* Chappie—I told you we should hunt for a Brazilian unit. I was sure we'd get good coffee there. *(There are scattered laughs.)* Funny, stinking war —that's for certain.

Gaylord *(acidly).* They didn't teach this brand at Sandhurst, did they?

Chaxfield. No, as a matter of fact, we learned that a good offense was the best defense. *(He smiles, but as he does he looks around the room at the faces, and finally at* GAYLORD'S *tired, bearded, dirty face.)* You chaps have had a rough go, haven't you?

Gaylord. We've been taking a licking.

Chaxfield. Well, Britain always loses every battle except the last one. *(Puts on his helmet.)* We could ride along on that, I suppose. Any particular place you want us, Major?

Gaylord. Peters, put 'em where they're needed.

Peters. Yes, sir. *(He opens the door.* CHAXFIELD *goes out . . . after a salute and a wave.)*

Chick *(grins).* Thank God for the British sense of humor. Ready, Franks?

Franks. Where we going?

Chick. To plug up a couple of gaps.

Franks *(grins, buttons up his coat).* Oh, baby, it's cold outside. Call us if we're needed, Major.

[*They go out, leaving the chaplain sitting huddled over, both hands around the cup. He looks up at* GAYLORD.]

Walker. Afraid I'm just some added dead weight here now, aren't I?

Gaylord. We're not planning any services, if that's what you mean.

Walker. How about your wounded? I could probably help there.

Gaylord. Big squad tent about a hundred yards to the rear. (*Looks at him more closely.*) But you better stay in here and warm up a little more.

Walker. Thanks. I'll try not to get in the way.

[*There is the sound of CW on the radio.* GAYLORD *looks toward it.*]

Radio Man (*shakes his head*). Not for us. (*Listens a little closer.*) Some engineer outfit across the river. (*Listens more closely.*) Under attack . . . asking for support. They're in bad shape. (*Listens some more . . . and* GAYLORD *and* WALKER *automatically go closer . . . listening. Suddenly the sound stops and they wait expectantly.*)

Walker. What's it mean? The sound stopping like that—

Gaylord. Equipment probably gone—

Radio Man. Not just the equipment, Major. (*Shakes his head.*)

Walker (*turns, goes back across the room*). Poor devils.

Gaylord. Been out here long, Chaplain?

Walker. One month. One month to the day. I was on my way to Inchon when the Chinese came down. Since then it's been . . . sort of . . . sort of a grandstand seat to the calamity. (*Points to the radio.*) Like that. Like what we just listened to. Sort of like . . . like eavesdropping on death throes. (*Makes a gesture . . . something showing his utter inability to do anything.*) A chaplain should be able to be with men who are dying. Comfort them. But it seems that they die too quickly . . . in too many numbers . . . in too many diverse places.

So all I've been doing mainly is . . . is wringing my hands.

Gaylord. I wouldn't fret. Nothing's according to plan any more. There aren't any rules. Majors command divisions. Cooks are riflemen. Medics spot for artillery. I'll bet your Good Book is being used principally for sandbagging gun emplacements.

[WALKER *looks at him sharply.*]

Walker. You have a faith, Major?

Gaylord (*after a pause*). It's around here someplace. Momentarily mislaid.

Walker. Why?

Gaylord. Why? I suppose it's because order is suddenly turned upside-down and we find ourselves without any base. Things we thought were true . . . aren't true any more. Things we believed in . . . (*He stops, turns away.*) Ourselves for example. Some of us wring our hands inside of ourselves.

Walker. Are you? Wringing your hands inside yourself? You afraid? (*There's a pause.* GAYLORD *sees the* RADIO MAN *looking at him. He turns to* WALKER.)

Gaylord. I haven't had time to be afraid.

Radio Man. Check over here, Chap. Ask me.

Gaylord. Come on . . . I'll show you our aid station. (*To the* RADIO MAN) Stay on and get a runner to me if anything comes up.

Radio Man. Yes, sir.

[*We cut to the exterior as* GAYLORD *and the chaplain walk out.*]

Walker. Sorry I posed the unforgivable question in there. You never mention fear to enlisted men, do you? I mean letting them know that an officer might be afraid. Precipitates panic or something, doesn't it?

Gaylord. Chaplains have carte blanche in that respect. You can ask anything you want. You're the Army's chosen people.

Walker. Then, as a point of interest, Major—are you afraid?

Gaylord. What are you hunting for, Chaplain? Reassurance? I'm fresh out of reassurance. *(Points.)* See out there? That's our escape route. The only one available. I've got to lead these men through it in less than six hours. And across the river the Chinese are setting up artillery . . . setting it up someplace to look right smack down our throats . . . just waiting for our withdrawal—and then they let us have it.

Walker. Maybe . . . *you* need some reassurance?

Gaylord. I'll tell you what I need. I need somebody with a minimum one star on his shoulder to tell me this is right or this is wrong; this order is good . . . this order is bad. *(They start walking.)* I could have used it yesterday particularly. *(Points.)* That's your tent over there. Tell Captain Sloane I sent you over. You're at his disposal. Everything from bandaging to last rites. *You* can stop wringing your hands now, Chappie. You've got it made.

Walker. Major, I'd like to be able to help you. Take some of the weight off.

Gaylord. The good Lord himself couldn't help me now—unless he'd been commissioned and put in command of the 29th Division.

Walker. If it's any consolation—I think he's definitely on our side.

[GAYLORD *looks at him . . . a crooked smile . . . a tired, frustrated, bitter smile.*]

Gaylord. God's on the side of the strongest battalion. Napoleon said that. While he was tearing the Austrians to bits.

Walker *(quietly).* How about at Waterloo? Was he still saying it there?

Gaylord. Ask God to deliver a patrol of twenty men I sent across that river, deliver them safe and sound. And if he can't do that . . . *(Something shows on his face now . . . something akin to the grief that comes with guilt.)* If he can't do that, get a set of rules from him on how I can live with myself from this point on . . . That's your aid station over there.

[*Fade to Command Post.* GAYLORD *enters.*]

Radio Man. This came in, sir. *(Rips off a page of a pad.)*

[GAYLORD *grabs it, reads, goes over to the map as* CHICK *and* FRANKS *enter.*]

Franks. We brought you the next best thing to an armistice! *(He puts a bottle on the table.)*

Chick. South Korean Joy Juice—guaranteed twenty days old. That'll warm the cockles of your heart.

Franks. It'll probably *eat away* your heart.

Gaylord *(unsmiling).* Ninth Army just contacted us.

Chick. No kidding. What's the picture?

Franks. Plans changed?

Gaylord. Air Force is sending planes over to observe across the river. They're going to try to spot their artillery. Then call for an air strike simultaneous with our withdrawal.

Chick. God bless the wonderful, sweet, charming, lovable Air Force. I love those guys, I really do.

Gaylord. They're also going to try to land some helicopters here for our wounded. *(Puts on his helmet.)* I think I'll tell Sloane that. I want one smiling face in this mob—*(He stops . . . looks skyward . . . as there is the distant drone of aircraft approaching.)*

Chick. Love those guys! Love 'em. Love 'em to death.

Franks. We might get outa here with our skins yet!

Gaylord. I'll be right back. (*He goes out.*)

[FRANKS *goes over and picks up the bottle.*]

Franks. Be my guest. (*Proffers the bottle. Notices that* CHICK *stands there staring at the door.*) Chick? Want a swallow?

Chick. Wha—? Oh. Oh, yeah. Thanks. After you.

Franks (*drinks . . . wipes his mouth*). Go ahead.

[CHICK *drinks . . . then takes the bottle over to the* RADIO MAN *and his assistant.*]

Radio Man. Thanks, Captain.

Soldier. Yeah, thanks.

Franks. He's still sweating out that patrol, isn't he?

Chick. Wouldn't you?

Franks. Would and have. But there's a difference with him. With him it's personal. Like he hand-picked those twenty men out of his immediate family. What's his problem, Chick? You know him pretty good.

Chick. That *is* his problem. His job has always been logistics. So many men form this line. So many men go in this column. So many men eat so much . . . and fire this much . . . and can go this far with this number of vehicles. All of a sudden he gets put into a situation where men aren't just numbers. They're flesh and blood. They've got identity. And when you cross 'em off—it isn't just arithmetic any more.

Franks (*sitting down*). This boy is not what you'd call officer material.

Chick. This boy could be chief of staff— except for a flaw.

Franks. That flaw's a big one.

Chick (*nods thoughtfully*). In times of sanity—it's called an attribute. Concern for fellowman. Now it's a flaw. (*Laughs shortly.*) Values. All kinds of values. (*To the* RADIO MAN) How about it, Marconi? (*Points to the bottle.*) You put your name on that?

Radio Man. Lot's left, sir. I'm the only unselfish radio operator in the United States Army. (*He gives him the bottle.*)

[*There is introductory tapping of a telegraph key . . . then a message tapped out. The* RADIO OPERATOR *writes furiously as the message is transmitted. Motions to the* GENERATOR MAN *to crank . . . and he taps out an answering message.*]

Chick. What is it?

Radio Man. They spotted the Chinese artillery. Grid nine . . . coordinate seven. We're supposed to shoot up a blue flare when we want the strike.

Franks. I better get the Major.

Radio Man (*taking off his earphones . . . looks puzzled as if trying to remember . . . looks through a notebook of papers*). Grid nine . . . coordinate seven. (*Looks up suddenly.*) Captain?

[FRANKS *stops at the door. Both he and* CHICK *look at the operator . . . taken by some quality of fear in his voice. The operator rises . . . crosses over to the map.*]

Radio Man. Grid nine . . . coordinate seven. (*Traces it with his finger . . . first horizontally . . . then vertically . . . then diagonally across the map to a spot.*) If the Major wants to call the strike there—it won't be only Chinese artillery he'll get hit. (*Turns . . . looks from one officer to the other.*) That's where our patrol is. Right there.

Chick (*in a flat voice*). Franks . . . get him, will you?

Franks. Right. (*He leaves.*)

[CHICK *takes a long drink from the bottle. Then sits down heavily at the table . . . stares straight ahead.*]

Radio Man. If you ask me—

Chick (*without turning to him*). If I asked you for anything besides the time of day, it'd mean you were the only man left alive between here and Honolulu. Now, be at ease. (*He swigs at the bottle again.*)

Radio Man. Cap'n?

Chick. Come in.

Radio Man. What do you think the Major'll call?

Chick. Ask the Major.

Radio Man. What if it was your decision?

Chick. I don't know. I don't know very much—except bridges. (*Rises . . . goes to the window.*) I used to think I was a very limited guy. Bridges. Only bridges. (*Turns . . . looks across at the map.*) Build 'em. Blow 'em up. Build 'em again. Thank God I'm not an infantry major.

[*At this moment* GAYLORD *comes in followed by* FRANKS.]

Gaylord (*to the* RADIO MAN). Where's that message?

Radio Man. On the table, sir.

[GAYLORD *picks up the paper . . . starts to read it.* CHICK *gives* FRANKS *a questioning look . . .* FRANKS *shakes his head.*]

Gaylord (*suddenly lowers the paper . . . looks at the map. He stares at the map for a long, long moment, tapping it with his finger. Then he taps it again. Short staccato taps with his finger tips, wetting his lips. Then he scratches at his beard stubble, whirls away from the map, stares from face to face, a frightened, hunted, almost supplicating look*).

Grid nine . . . coordinate seven. And they want a strike called there. (*He goes to the map . . . taps it.*) That's where the patrol is. (*Turns to them.*) That's where that A Company platoon is. (*Looks around at them . . . his voice is shaky.*) They want to pulverize the area. Bombs and napalm. *And that's where the patrol is!*

Chick (*quietly*). And there's no way in the world to let 'em know so they can get out of there. What a deal. What a miserable deal.

Gaylord. What do we do, Chick? Franks? Anybody got any ideas? (*Dead silence.*) Up to me, huh? My decision again!

Chick (*quietly*). You wear the gold leaf, Gay. That makes you number one.

[GAYLORD *moves away from the map . . . stands in the center of the room. His fists clench and unclench.*]

Gaylord. I can't ask for an air strike there. (*Looks up.*) I can't slaughter twenty men. I can't do that.

Franks. Major—the alternative is moving five hundred men through an artillery barrage that an ant couldn't live through. I don't think there's much choice.

Gaylord. You don't, huh? That's because it isn't your decision. That's because you guys don't have a thing to do but second-guess me!

Franks. Major, there's a chain of command. It may stick in your craw to give an order—but you're elected to do it. Either that or take off that insignia and go out and roll snowballs. Are you the C.O. here or aren't you? Now, call it.

Gaylord (*a pause*). I'm . . . I'm the C.O.

Franks. Then, how'll you have it? A strike on all that cannon stickin' down our throats—or stick your head in the ground and make believe this is just a maneuver in Louisiana?

[GAYLORD *doesn't answer. He lifts his head about to ... when across the room he sees* JONES *standing there ... and behind him the chaplain. He tilts his helmet back ... rubs his face in a sort of massive fatigue that creeps over him.*]

Jones. They ... they said you made contact with the patrol. *(A pause)* Well ... are they all right? Major? Are they all right? Is there anything we can do?

Gaylord. Sure. Sure, there's something we can do. The chaplain can prepare the service. And you can give me their names. And me—I'm just about to give the order ... *(Looks around him.)* The order to blow 'em up. *(Picks up the bottle.)* Cheers! *(He flings the bottle across the room and it breaks against the wall. Then he remains seated ... his head down ... the others watching him.)*

[*We take a slow fade to black.*]

ACT III

We fade on with a shot along a row of foxholes representing a section of the perimeter. A light snow continues to fall ... and occasionally a soldier passes behind the holes. We pull back for a shot of the front of the farmhouse ... then dolly in for a shot of the canvas covering of the cellar, dissolving through to the interior. GAYLORD *sits alone at the table; the room is empty. He hears the sound of footsteps crunching in the snow ...* GAYLORD *fidgets nervously ... angrily ... then rises and goes to the door.*

Gaylord. Let's stay put out there!
Voice *(muffled)*. Sorry, sir.

[GAYLORD *turns ... goes back to the table, drums on it nervously.* FRANKS *enters and looks intently at him.*]

Gaylord. What do you want, Franks?

Franks. How do you feel, sir?

Gaylord. All right.

Franks. I thought maybe—

Gaylord *(turns to him)*. You thought maybe what?

Franks. Nothing, sir. *(A pause)* Getting close to that time.

Gaylord. I've got a watch, Franks.

Franks. Mine says 0300.

Gaylord. We're synchronized. Anything else?

Franks. Jones is a young kid. I wouldn't let him bother you. Young officers always think they're the mother hens ... and their platoon is their brood. I wouldn't let him bother you.

Gaylord. You said that.

Franks. How about transmitting that strike signal?

Gaylord. When we're ready to move out, then we call for a strike and not before.

Franks. Look, you asked for somebody else to make a decision. I'm trying to put some muscle into yours—

Gaylord. I'll recommend you for a Silver Star. Now, get out of here. (FRANKS *turns.*) Franks—

Franks. Yes, sir?

Gaylord. I'm sorry. I'm a lousy commanding officer. I'm too much like Lieutenant Jones. I know that.

Franks. You're not green, Major. You've fought before. Why is this any different?

Gaylord. Before—I always aimed at an enemy. I never got much of a bang out of killing anybody. But at least it was a simple equation. Them ... or me. Now ...

Franks. Now it's a different equation, huh? Lemme tell you my philosophy about a war. It doesn't make any difference what level you fight it on. It stinks on any level. Only when you give commands—it stinks worse.

[*The chaplain enters.*]

Walker. The wounded are ready to get evacuated. Any idea when the helicopters are due?

Gaylord. Any time before 0600. That's all I know.

Walker (*starts to go*). Thanks, Major. I'll tell Captain Sloane—

Gaylord. Want some coffee? You look dead on your feet.

Walker. Thanks. I could do with some coffee. (GAYLORD *motions to the pot on the squad cooker.* WALKER *goes over to it . . . pours a cup of coffee. Sits down on the crate near the door.*) Quiet out there. Hardly a sound. Anything new on that patrol? (GAYLORD *shakes his head.*)

Franks. We're going to have to cross 'em off, Chappie. (*With a look toward* GAYLORD.) Twenty for five hundred. That's not a bad price.

Gaylord (*almost a shout*). Cheap. Only twenty lives. This is bargain day in North Korea.

Franks. I'll see you later, Major. So long, Chaplain. (*He exits.*)

Walker. Those are the twenty men you sent out? (GAYLORD *nods.*) You feel responsible, don't you?

Gaylord. Very.

Walker. And I suppose you don't want any moralizing from an old minister.

Gaylord. I'll buy anything that helps. But that won't help. Something like this happened before. Just once. I moralized that one, too. I said it wasn't my command. I just followed orders.

Walker. But it still hurts, doesn't it?

Gaylord. It never stopped hurting.

Walker. I like you, Major. I like any professional soldier who's a human being. A human being with sensitivity. I like your heart—but your logic isn't commendable. (GAYLORD *looks up at him, about to speak.*) You tell me it was you who had to follow an order like the one you're going to give tonight . . . and it hurt. Then, tonight it isn't you who should suffer any pangs—it's those flyers who drop the bombs—

Gaylord. They don't know what's down there by the objective. They think it's Chinese artillery. They don't know there's a patrol of G.I.'s there, too.

Walker. And if they knew—would they refuse to handle the mission? Major Gaylord, I'm a man of God. My whole life is preaching compassion—love of fellowmen—and I'm telling you now to your face—there are some things we must do that are ugly and rotten. But we *must* do them.

Gaylord. You're not moralizing. You're rationalizing. I don't think you know what you're doing! I swear I don't.

Walker (*very gently*). What is it you want, Major? Someone to agree with you? That you're a butcher? That you're a stupid butcher who sent twenty men to their deaths? Is that what you want me to tell you?

Gaylord. I want somebody to bring back a patrol of twenty men—alive. And if they can't do that . . . if they can't do that—give me a reason why those men have to die. A reason I'll believe. In short . . . all I want is a miracle. And if I can't get that—I'd like to strip off this conscience of mine. Strip it off like an overcoat. Inject something into my immortal soul to make me numb—*so I'll quit feeling! So I'll be a commanding officer instead of my brother's keeper!*

[*The door is kicked open.*]

Peters *(with an urgency)*. Major—you better get out here!

[GAYLORD *rushes outside . . . The men are standing up in their holes looking toward the river.* GAYLORD *looks . . . almost recoils.*]

Gaylord. Who is it? Who's out there?

Peters. Lieutenant Jones.

Soldier. He said he was gonna get across and get the patrol out of there.

Gaylord. Maybe I can get him before—

[CHICK *steps up from behind, grabbing him.*]

Chick. Won't do any good. He's already started across.

Gaylord. All right, then . . . I want covering fire for him. *(Shouts down the line.)* Machine gunners . . . Aim over his head. Aim over the head of the man swimming there in the—

[*There is the off-stage sound of rifle shots . . . then a distant machine gun . . . and we can see the reaction on the faces of* GAYLORD *and the men around him.*]

Chick. He hardly made it off the shore. Poor little kid. Poor, crazy kid.

[*We are on a tight close-up of* GAY-LORD'S *face. His features work. His lips move soundlessly. Something is happening to him deep inside. He has stood everything else, but this he can't take.*]

Gaylord *(after a long pause)*. Maybe not so crazy. Maybe he's the only sane one we had. *(He looks at* WALKER, *whose eyes are closed and whose lips form the words of a soundless prayer . . . and suddenly he breaks. He breaks violently.)* Chappie! Do anything you like—understand? Sing a nice, melodic hymn! Prostrate yourself in the rich Korean dirt. But don't pray! Hear me? I don't want any prayers. Understand?

(His voice is a sob.) No prayers! *(He turns and goes back toward the farm-house . . . he stops by the front door . . . his back to everyone.)* Franks.

Franks. Yes, sir?

Gaylord. You're in command. When we get back—if we get back . . . you can write the whole thing up. Starting with my sending out the patrol. I'll witness it, myself. *(He goes into the farmhouse and sits by the table. After a moment* FRANKS *and* CHICK *enter silently. We hear* FRANKS *give an order by the door as he enters. In a moment the* RADIO MAN *and his assistant appear . . . and enter. Not a word is spoken. Finally* GAYLORD *lifts his head . . . slowly sticks out his wrist, and looks at his watch.* CAPTAIN FRANKS *steps in front of him.)* Captain Franks—it's a blue flare. That's the signal. The planes'll approach from the southwest. They'll watch this area for your signal. They'll start their run from directly above us . . . and they'll come in at treetop level. And when they've finished . . . bombs . . . napalm . . . when they're finished . . . you can move out and not worry about artillery. There shouldn't be any.

Chick. You've gone this far—

Gaylord *(shouts)*. And not one stinking, half-butted inch further. This is where I get off. *(Looks at* FRANKS.*)* This is where the boys separate from the men. *(He sees* WALKER *by the door.)* It isn't morality, it isn't conscience altogether. It's just . . . just that I can't give a command that'll kill twenty men. Something inside me won't let me. I don't know what that something is. Maybe it's a mixture. Cowardice . . . conscience . . . morality . . . stupidity—but inside me is this little nugget of a something that . . . that commands me. I can't cross it. I can't deny it. I've . . . I've got to let it take over.

Chick. Look—one of us can give that command. What is it beside a motion of the arm? Arm down . . . flare up . . . and it's over with. One of us can—

Franks (*his voice cutting in with a sharp, cutting clarity*). He can do it himself. (*To* GAYLORD) You can do it yourself. You don't need any crutches. This is your job, Major Gaylord, commanding. And by heaven, Major, you're going to command.

Gaylord. Why? Why am I?

Franks. Because nobody dies for nothing. And if you pull out now, it's admitting that twenty men across the river *are* dying for nothing. And I don't think they are. You talk about principles, Major—well, the other animals have principles, too. Your giving a command for an air strike is a principle with me now. If you give it—it *is* a command. If one of us has to give it—it's just an order for an execution. And if this doesn't make any sense to you . . . and any of you others—I'm sorry. But it makes sense to me.

Chick (*looking straight at* GAYLORD). It makes sense to me, Gay.

[*There is the sound of planes coming on in the distance. Several of the men look at their watches.*]

Walker. Maybe it's them. The helicopters.

[*From outside is the sound of voices . . . as the planes get nearer.* PETERS *sticks his head in.*]

Peters. Helicopters—five of 'em! They're coming down behind us.

[*The sound of planes throttling down and then descending.*]

Peters. Major? The helicopters . . . they're . . . they're here.

[GAYLORD *doesn't answer.*]

Franks. Peters—see that Captain Sloane gets a detail to help load the stretcher cases.

Peters (*a look at* GAYLORD). Yes, sir. (*He goes out with* WALKER *following him.*)

[*We cut to a shot of the aid station tent as the stretchers are borne out.* SLOANE *stands to one side directing . . . checking. One of the stretchers stops by him. The soldier on it pulls himself up and rests on his elbows.*]

Soldier. Captain?

Sloane. Come on . . . Let's look alive. These planes can't wait forever.

Soldier. I just wanted to tell yuh— thanks.

Sloane (*slaps the boy's leg . . . grins*). Forget it. Have a nice trip.

Soldier. How about you . . . and the rest?

[*There is the sound of plane engines throttling up.*]

Sloane. We'll meet you back there. (*Slaps the leg again . . . motions him on . . . and the stretcher following him. He moves off a few feet . . . looks toward the planes as we hear them ascend one by one . . . and he watches them rise into the air.*)

Peters. That's all of 'em, Doc.

Sloane. Good job. (*He turns and looks toward the tent.*) That makes the licking a whole lot easier to take. Now I'm going to go over and shake that Major's hand for keeping us alive . . . then I'm going to mix me up a highball of medicinal alcohol—and if it kills me—I'll die a very happy man. (*He stomps off in the snow.*)

[*We cut to the exterior of the farmhouse. The soldiers in the nearby holes are putting on shoulder packs and making preparations for a move out. Two of them have set up a mortar to fire the flare. The door to the farmhouse opens.* FRANKS *steps out. Over his shoulder we see the radio man,* CHICK

... and finally GAYLORD. *The doctor comes on from the left. Goes past* FRANKS *and into the room.*]

Sloane. Wounded are evacuated, Major. Anytime you want to start hiking—the doctor's ready.

Franks. There'll be an air strike across the river just as we start pulling back. That's to make sure a shell doesn't take away your practice.

Sloane. Good enough. *(Looks across at* GAYLORD.*)* Major . . . (GAYLORD *waits a moment . . . then he turns to him.)* A lot of the boys being evacuated . . . they were full of thanks. I took most of 'em by proxy. I think you rated most of them. For getting us back here in one piece. Pretty green boys—even I could tell that. You kept your nerve and—*(He stops . . . stares at* GAYLORD's *face . . . then looks around questioningly.)*

Gaylord. You . . . you congratulating me, Captain Sloane?

Sloane. I can't operate on dead men. And you kept plenty of them alive by taking over when you did . . . as you did.

Gaylord *(with the same crooked smile).* See, Captain Franks? Aren't I a brave man?

Franks *(listening).* I think I hear 'em. *(Turns to* GAYLORD.*)* We're all set, Major. Corporal here'll shoot up that flare whenever you say.

Gaylord. Whenever . . . whenever *I* say? *(They stand around watching* GAYLORD *—to a man. He rises . . . walks to the door . . . stands there.)* The privilege of rank, bless it!

Franks. Not just the privilege—the responsibility.

Gaylord. All right. The responsibility. I'm not shirking it, I'm analyzing it. And I've got to say this . . . these gold leaves give me the power of God—to give, take, and trade lives. And tonight

I'm trading lives, twenty boys across the river—for all of ours. That's a pretty fair numerical exchange. That's militarily sound. That's good, tactical procedure. Twenty for five hundred.

[We hear the planes approaching . . . the men stir uneasily . . . and look skyward.]

Gaylord. But deep inside my gut I'm going to ache from this second on. And this is an ache no medic's going to cure. These are the responsibilities of command you don't read in a West Point manual—these have first and last names —twenty of each.

Chick. You had a job, and they had a job. Yours was to make a decision. Theirs was to spot artillery and report back.

Gaylord. Is there actually any honest-to-God justification for the death of twenty human beings?

Sloane. When it saves five hundred. One of the pilots of those helicopters —he said it was a ground-to-air message from a patrol down there that told 'em where the artillery was. If it hadn't been for that message, they might not have spotted it. (GAYLORD *reacts to this . . . as do the others.)* That's another one we owe you for—sending out that patrol. Like the man says—I might have lost my practice.

[The planes get louder.]

Gaylord. All right—everybody . . . Let's start moving out . . . *(Raises his voice.)* You people on the left . . . follow this end out. Intervals of twenty yards between companies. Come on. Let's move out. *(He looks slowly at* FRANKS, *who grins at him.)* You too, Franks. Everybody out. *(The men shuffle forward and off . . . until only the sound of their clanking equipment and footsteps in the snow are heard . . . along with the* *planes circling overhead.)* You ready, Corporal?

Corporal. Yes, sir.

Gaylord *(A pause . . . his voice is tight).* On my signal . . . *(He sees WALKER step into the light.)* How goes the war, Chappie? Have you got a nice, apt, forceful quotation from the Good Book that covers a situation like this?

Walker *(nods slowly).* He giveth . . . and He taketh away.

Gaylord. And does He give us that power?

Walker. I think He does, Major. Sometimes I think He does.

Gaylord. All right, Corporal . . . let her go.

[*There is the off-stage sound of the shell hitting the detonator . . . and the swoosh sound of it heading out and up. As it explodes in the air,* there is a flickering bright light that plays on both men's faces . . . then we hear the planes heading into their dives . . . and the whistling, shrieking sound of their bombs as they head downward . . . and detonate with roars and then the sound of planes disappearing.*]

Gaylord *(his eyes are wet . . . his voice is tight).* God rest their souls . . . and God forgive me.

Walker. He'll do both, Major. I know He'll do both.

[*All three men start to move out. And only once does Gaylord stop and look toward the river . . . and we get a tight close-up of his face . . . and the tears rolling down his cheek . . . Then he turns abruptly and continues on. We take a long shot of them disappearing into the night . . . then a slow fade-out to black.*]

ROD SERLING (1924–   ).

"It's a crime, but scripts with social significance simply can't be done on TV."

Although Rod Serling finally gave up the censorship struggle and switched to the fantasy of **Twilight Zone,** he fought so well for more significance in TV drama that one critic called him "television's only angry young man." He had particular censorship trouble with two of his scripts, one about a lynch mob and the other about corruption in labor unions. Five times Serling has won the Emmy Award, television's equivalent of the movies' Oscar. For **Requiem for a Heavyweight,** he won the Peabody Award, television's highest honor. Serling's first big success was **Patterns,** a "man-eat-man" story of big business executives. Serling, who began his career in radio and television, those two "new" means of communication, could be termed one of the "new men." He has also written for the theater and motion pictures. Born and raised in upstate New York, he served as a paratrooper in the Pacific. After the war he went to Antioch College, where he wrote a script that won a prize and led directly to his present success. He now lives with his wife and two daughters in California and writes for motion pictures.

Act I

1. How does the author immediately establish the atmosphere of tension?

2. What happened to the bridge Chick's engineers put up?

3. Was Lieutenant Jones justified in blaming Gaylord for sending out the patrol?

Act II

1. Explain Gaylord's "acid" comment, "they didn't teach this brand at Sandhurst, did they?"

2. What is the problem facing Gaylord at the end of Act II?

Act III

1. Early in Act III, Walker tries to help Gaylord in his dilemma. Why is he unable to do so?

2. What finally reconciles Gaylord to the decision he has to make?

COMMAND DECISION

1. Explain Franks's statement, "If you give it—it *is* a command. If one of us has to give it—it's just an order for an execution."

2. When the chaplain assures Gaylord he believes God to be "on our side," Gaylord reminds him of Napoleon's comment that God is on the side of the strongest battalion. What two meanings of the phrase "God is on our side" are implied here?

3. Although Gaylord is concerned about the twenty Americans whose lives will be lost if he commands an air strike, he does not appear to be concerned about the enemies' lives lost at his command. Does he say anything anywhere in the play to justify this attitude?

The Big Day

PHILIP N. PIERCE
KARL SCHUON

The United States entered the Space Age on February 20, 1962, when Lt. Col. John H. Glenn, Jr., orbited the earth three times in the Project Mercury capsule, *Friendship 7*. This is a record of that day.

Tuesday, the twentieth of February [1962], began early for John Glenn. It was 2:20 A.M. when Lt. Col. Bill Douglas, the astronauts' physician, stepped into the bedroom of the quarters in Hangar S and snapped on the lights. "OK, Marine, rise and shine!" he called. "Today's the day."

John came awake and stretched. "Good morning, Bill. How's the weather look?"

"Socked in right now, John. But aerology says there's a good chance it'll clear up before launch time."

John grinned, heading for the shower. "Better keep your fingers crossed, Bill."

After a shower and a shave, Glenn joined the doctor and Astronaut Deke Slayton for breakfast. If everything went according to plan, it was going to be a long time between breakfast and lunch. Accordingly, John took on a pretty good load of personal fuel: a big glass of orange juice, two scrambled eggs, a small steak, several slices of toast and jelly, and a cup of Postum. The inner man taken care of, he declared that he was ready to go to work.

Bill Douglas went to work first, however, giving Glenn a complete physical check, then attaching to his body the biosensors which during the flight would record his physical reactions for radio transmission back to earth.

Joking with Deke Slayton, John donned his long underwear and, with the help of technician Joe Schmidt, climbed into his twenty-pound silver space suit. After a pressure check to be sure there were no leaks in the suit, the astronaut was ready for the ride in the special van out to Launching Pad 14.

Emerging from the big door of Hangar S, he flashed a big grin at the small crowd of workers and newsmen gathered around the entrance. One meticulous reporter carefully recorded that John gave three quick waves of his right hand to the crowd, and took exactly fourteen steps between the hangar door and the van. In his left hand he carried a portable air conditioner to keep his close-fitting space suit cool.

The four-mile trip to the launching pad took seventeen minutes—a slow journey indeed for a man who in a few hours would be covering almost five thousand miles in the same amount of time.

The weather still hadn't cleared by 5:59. But Glenn had already left the van and entered the gantry elevator which carried him his first 120 feet into space—up to the eleventh deck "white room" surrounding the space capsule atop the great Atlas missile. Stepping off the elevator, he exchanged pleasantries with the technicians and shook hands with Guenther Wendt, boss of the "white room." Like the astronaut, Wendt had flown his share of World War II missions. But he had logged his combat time a long way from the Pacific, and in a different uniform. During the war he had been a German Luftwaffe pilot.

Kicking off the outer boots which protected his space shoes from dirt and grime, Glenn eased himself into the capsule with the help of a couple of technicians. He was very careful not to snag his silver suit. It took considerable squirming to get himself onto the contoured couch of the six-foot, ten-inch spacecraft. "You don't just get into one of these things," he once explained. "You put it on!"

The word was passed down to Mercury Control that John had entered the capsule. The official time clock showed 6:03 A.M., seven minutes after sunrise. The hands on the counting clocks had been motionless since 5:30—stopped at T minus 120 minutes and holding. One of the thousands of checks made during the countdown had turned up a faulty transponder, a small part in the Atlas's radar tracking equipment. The new transponder was no sooner installed than it was discovered that the respiration measuring device in John's helmet wasn't working properly. There was another ten minutes' delay while that was replaced.

The countdown resumed at 6:25. By now many anxious eyes were watching the clock. John's takeoff was scheduled for 7:30. In order to make the planned three orbits, he had to launch by 9:30 at the very latest. This would allow three hours of daylight for the sea recovery forces in the impact area to make their search for the capsule after

Glenn had landed. A later launch would mean that the flight would have to be limited to two or even a single orbit.

In the east the sky began to lighten, showing a faint promise of clearing. Overhead the clouds still hung dark and heavy. From the north a cool breeze began to stir across the launching site. In the "white room" the technicians carefully fitted the side hatch onto the *Friendship 7.* It was 6:59. Astronaut Glenn was alone in his space capsule.

Swept by a brisk wind, now blowing from the west, the clouds began to break away. A few minutes after 7:00 the sun broke through, and conditions began to look more promising. Twenty minutes went by. Another "hold." One of the hatch-cover bolts was broken. It would have to be replaced.

Remove the hatch cover. . . .
Replace the broken bolt. . . .
Reinstall the hatch. . . .

It was 8:05 by the time the count down was resumed—T minus 60 minutes and counting.

At 8:30 there was another "hold" in order to add ten gallons of Rp-1 kerosene fuel to the rocket. The operation required fifteen minutes of precious time. While they were adding the fuel, the great orange gantry rolled back. Now the shining, silver missile towered alone above the launching pad, its slim nose reaching toward a bright, clear sky.

The critical task of pumping the liquid oxygen into the Atlas began at 8:44—T minus 35 minutes. As the "lox" flowed into the tanks at 200 degrees below zero, sparkling crystals of frost began to form on the rocket's outer skin. From a vent high on the side, near the base of the capsule, a feathery plume of white vapor curled upward. The missile was primed. All systems reported "Go." Weather in the launch area and downrange favorable. T minus 22. . . .

"Hold!"

Trouble with a valve in the liquid oxygen equipment. Ten to fifteen minutes to fix the valve. Resume the countdown.

9:35—T minus 10 minutes and counting.

All systems "Go."

"Hold!"

Trouble at the Bermuda tracking station. . . .

"Hello, Cape, this is Bermuda."

"Go ahead."

"We just lost power on our computer. Stand by for an estimate."

"Roger . . . standing by, Bermuda."

"Estimate 5 minutes, Cape . . . 5 minutes."

"Do you want us to continue to count?"

"Take it down to T minus 7. We may have it by then."

"Roger."

The speeding hands of the counting clock erased the seconds, the minutes . . .

"Do you want us to hold, Bermuda?"

"Uh . . . yes, we would like to hold at 7. We lost the main power on the computer and we just want to check that nothing else has gone wrong."

"What do you estimate?"

"Somewhere between 5 and 10 minutes."

"Can't you expedite?"

"Make it 5."

"All stations are holding at 6 minutes and 30 seconds. Estimate 5 minutes."

At 9:42, Bermuda came back on the air.

"Hello, Cape. We just got a 'Go.'"

"Are you ready? . . . Are you ready to continue?"

"OK, go ahead, Cape. . . ."

"All stations, your attention, please. On my mark we will pick up the count at T minus 6 minutes and 30 seconds. . . . Mark!"

Alone in his tiny, cramped world above the sands at Cape Canaveral, John Glenn waited.

"Four minutes. . ."

In the eighteen tracking stations around the world, tension began to mount. Everything was ready. Now the eleventh attempt to put *Friendship 7* into orbit rushed toward the climax they had waited for through two months of disappointments. On a ship in mid-Atlantic, in Africa, the Indian Ocean, Australia, across the Pacific, in California, Mexico, the stations watched the relentless sweep of the speeding second hands.

And they waited.

"Three minutes. . ."

"Two. . ."

"One minute. . ."

Now in the electrified atmosphere of the Control Center, the brittle click of switches, the tense, urgent voices swell in the rising crescendo of the last fleeting seconds.

"Five, four, three. . ."

Backup pilot Scott Carpenter sends his parting message to his fellow astronaut: "May the good Lord ride all the way!"

"Two, one, ZERO!"

"Ignition!"

The engines fire. A loud hiss, an earth-filling roar. With a blinding torrent of flame, the Atlas surges gently, breaking its last link with earth. The great silver rocket slowly begins its climb toward the limitless reaches of space.

In the Mercury Control Center, John's voice pours from the loudspeakers. *"Liftoff! The clock is operating. We're underway!"*

Astronaut Alan Shepard, the capsule communicator, flicks on his microphone. "Roger, reading you loud and clear. We're programing your roll OK."

To establish the right heading, the Atlas rocket has been programed to make a one-quarter turn during the first four feet after liftoff. "Roll OK." Glenn is safely over the first hurdle.

The second hurdle lies at an altitude of approximately 35,000 feet—the area of maximum vibration. Some of the earlier test rockets have shaken themselves to pieces at this critical point. John hits the maximum dynamic pressure area thirteen seconds after takeoff. His report sounds very matter-of-fact to the waiting listeners in the control room.

"Little bumpy along about here."

There is a hint of a smile on Al Shepard's face as he acknowledges John's report. "Roger . . . Stand by for twenty seconds."

"Roger."

"Three, two, one, mark!"

"Roger. Backup clock is started." After a slight pause, Glenn makes a brief report on the status of the capsule. *"Fuel one oh two, one oh one; oxygen, seven eight, one hundred . . . amps two seven."*

"Roger, loud and clear. Flight path is good [at] sixty-nine [seconds]."

"Roger, checks OK. Mine was seven zero on your mark. . . . Some vibration area coming up here now."

"Roger, reading you loud and clear, John."

"Coming into high gear a little bit. . . . A little contrail went by the window, or something, there. . . . Still OK. We're smoothing out some now, getting out of the vibration area."

"Roger. Flight path is very good."

"Smoothing out real fine. . . . Cabin pressure is coming down OK. Flight very smooth now. G's are building to six."

"Reading you loud and clear. Flight path looks good. . . . Stand by for staging."

John has been in flight for two minutes and twelve seconds, time for the three main Atlas engines to cut off. Already the giant motors have burned more fuel than two jet airliners would require to cross the continent.

"*BECO!* . . . *BECO!* [booster engine cutoff] *I saw the smoke go by the window.*"

"Roger, we confirm staging on TM [telemetry]."

Twenty-two seconds later, the escape tower rockets fire, jerking the tower away from the capsule.

"*The tower went right then. . . . I have the tower in sight, way out,*"

"Roger. We confirm on TM . . . jettison tower is green. . . . Flight path looks good."

"*G's starting to build again a little bit.*"

"Roger, Seven, reading you loud and clear. Cape is 'Go'. . . . We are standing by for you."

"*Roger, Cape is 'Go' and I am 'Go'. . . . Capsule is in good shape. . . . Cabin pressure holding steady. . . . All systems are 'Go'!*"

The clock is coming up on four minutes and forty-nine seconds, time for the small posigrade rockets that will separate the *Friendship 7* from the Atlas missile to fire.

"*Posigrades fired OK . . . Zero G and I feel fine. Capsule is turning around. . . . Oh, the view is tremendous!*"

"Roger, turnaround has started. . . ."

"*Capsule turning around and I can see the booster doing turnarounds just a couple of hundred yards behind me. It is beautiful.*"

"Roger, Seven. You have a 'Go' of at least seven orbits."

"*Understand 'Go' for at least seven orbits. . . . I can see clear back, a big cloud pattern way back across the Cape. Beautiful sight!*"

"Roger, Seven, still reading you loud and clear. Next transmission Bermuda."

From the Bermuda tracking station, Astronaut Gus Grissom,[1] the capsule

communicator, contacts *Friendship 7* and asks John to give him a rundown on his orbit check list. After completing his technical report, the high-flying Marine adds a few words on how it feels to be weightless: "*This is very comfortable at zero G. I have nothing but a very fine feeling. It feels very normal and very good.*"

The voice of Al Shepard cuts in from Cape Canaveral. "How does he look, Bermuda?"

"Looks real good, Cape. Surgeon reports everything OK. All systems OK. Good voice contact both ways."

Another minute and Glenn's voice begins to fade. Grissom loses radio contact. Hurtling across the Atlantic at almost 300 miles a minute, the capsule is over the Canary Islands eighteen minutes after takeoff.

"*Friendship 7 . . . Friendship 7,* this is Canary cap com [capsule communicator]. What is your spacecraft status?"

John gives the first of his regular half-hourly reports—switch positions, instrument readings, capsule's attitude, roll, yaw, pitch, oxygen supply, cabin and space suit temperatures. . . .

"*The horizon is a brilliant blue. . . . There, I have the mainland in sight at the present time, coming up on the scope. Have the Canaries in sight out through the window. . . . Have beautiful view of the African coast, both in the scope and out of the window. . . . Part of the Canaries hidden by clouds. . . . I can see a dust storm down there, blowing across the desert, a lot of dust. It is difficult to see the ground in some areas. . . .*"

Then the tracking station at Kano, Nigeria: "*Friendship 7,* this is Kano cap com reading you loud and clear. What is your status? Over."

"*This is* Friendship 7. *My status is excellent. I feel fine. Over.*"

"Roger . . . I monitored part of your transmission over Canary and heard

[1] Gus Grissom and two other astronauts— Edward White, first man to walk in space, and Roger Chaffee—were killed in an accident during a test for the Apollo moon mission, Jan. 27, 1967.

your comments on the weather over Africa. We've had dusty weather here, and as far as we can see, this part of Africa is covered with dust."

"That's exactly the way it looks from up here, too. . . ."

Now the space capsule has been airborne for thirty-one minutes. On Zanzibar, off the east coast of Africa, the Mercury tracking station begins to pick up the radio signals from the biosensors which are measuring Glenn's blood pressure. The aeromedics are interested in knowing how exercise affects the human body under conditions of weightlessness.

In the capsule Glenn has an "exercise machine"—a handle attached to an elastic cable. Using both hands, he is to pull the handle up to his chin, then let it spring back between his knees. He is to repeat this action thirty times— once a second for thirty seconds.

John reports in to Zanzibar on voice radio. The automatic signals reporting his normal blood pressure produce a good reading on the recording graph.

"Friendship 7 . . . Friendship 7, this is Sir John, Zanzibar. You've got a good blood-pressure trace." "Sir John" is the nickname of the flight surgeon at Zanzibar.

High over the African coast, the astronaut does his pullup exercises.

"Friendship 7, this is Sir John . . . Blood pressure one two nine systolic after exercise. . . . Recording well. . . . Diastolic coming down now to seven four. Everything on the dials indicates excellent aeromedical status."

America's first man in orbit has just passed his inflight physical exam.

Next Glenn has to prepare for his flight through the darkness that lies only ten minutes ahead. Night now covers most of the Indian Ocean and almost three quarters of the Pacific. For John Glenn it will be a short night, only a few seconds more than thirty minutes

from sunset to sunrise. During the period of darkness, he will fly from Tuesday to Wednesday, and back to Tuesday again.

Before dark, John must check the controls of the spacecraft. Once in darkness, he must make the same control check to see if the change in temperature has any effect on the jet devices which control the attitude of the capsule. While the *Friendship 7* remains in "daylight," the surface exposed to the sun registers a temperature of 250 degrees. The side away from the sun is approximately one hundred degrees cooler. In total darkness, the temperature on all surfaces will drop to zero.

The Indian Ocean tracking ship receives a report from the capsule, speeding through the star-studded night high overhead. The astronaut is in excellent voice, flight proceeding normally, all systems "Go."

In the Mercury station at Muchea, on the southwest coast of Australia, Astronaut Gordon Cooper checks the clock. Elapsed time since takeoff: forty-nine minutes and fifty seconds. He switches on his microphone. *"Friendship 7,* this is Muchea cap com. How do you read me? Over."

"Loud and clear. How are you doing, Gordo? We're doing real fine up here. Everything is going very well. Over."

"Very good, John. You sound good."

"Roger. That sure was a short day!"

"Time passes rapidly, eh?"

"Yes, sir!"

"John, shortly you may observe some lights down here. You want to take a check on them? Out to your right."

"Roger, I'm all set to see if I can't get them in sight."

"Any symptoms of vertigo or nausea at all? Over."

"Negative, no symptoms whatsoever. I feel fine."

"Good show."

"I do have lights in sight . . . on the ground. Over."

"Roger. Understand they are just off to your right there."

"That's affirmative, just to my right . . . I can see a big pattern of light, apparently right on the coast. I can see the outline of a town and a very bright light just to the south of it."

"Roger. That's Perth and Rockingham you're seeing there."

"Roger. The lights show up very well. Thank everybody for turning them on, will you?"

"Sure will, John."

On across the Pacific, into the rising sun speeds the capsule. Now the Canton Island communicator hears John's voice.

"This is Friendship 7. I have eaten one tube of food . . . shutting the visor . . . I had no problem eating. . . . The sun is coming up behind me in the periscope, a brilliant, brilliant red!"

"You are lucky."

"You're right. . . . Man, this is beautiful!"

As the sun begins to climb over the horizon, John can see thousands of tiny, luminous particles swirling across the window of the capsule. They look like glowing snowflakes. He reports the phenomenon to Canton.

"Friendship 7, this is Canton cap com. Can you hear any impact on the capsule from the particles?"

"Negative, Canton . . . negative."

Eight minutes later, Glenn is in contact with the tracking station at Guaymas, Mexico. Three more minutes and he will be over the North American continent.

"Hello, Guaymas. Are we still 'Go' from Control Center? Over."

"Roger, Seven. We're still 'Go.'"

"Roger. I still have some of the particles that I cannot identify coming around the capsule occasionally. Over."

"How big are the particles?"

"Very small; I would indicate that they are of the order of a sixteenth of an inch, or smaller. They drift by the window and I can see them against the dark sky. Just at sunrise there were literally thousands of them. It looked just like a myriad of stars. . . ."

Coming across the southern United States, the automatic control device which maintains the capsule in proper flight attitude develops trouble. Glenn's spacecraft begins to drift. John switches to "fly-by-wire," a system by which he can control the capsule's attitude himself. In a few minutes he will be over Cape Canaveral, completing his first orbit.

Glenn checks in with the Cape.

From Mercury Control, Al Shepard greets the returning spacecraft. "This is Cape cap com. Would you give us the difficulty you've been having on yaw?"

"Roger. I am on fly-by-wire so I can control more accurately. It just started as I got to Guaymas. It appears to drift off in yaw to the right, at about one degree per second."

Glenn continues with a technical explanation of the trouble.

"Roger. Friendship 7. We concur here. Recommend you remain fly-by-wire."

"Roger, Cape. Having no trouble controlling, very smooth and easy. It controls very nicely."

Friendship 7 streaks across the Cape and begins its second orbit at 11:21.

In the Mercury Control building at the Cape, technician Bill Saunders carefully checks the bank of ninety small meters mounted on the panel in front of him. Each of the dials registers one of the vital pieces of information being transmitted from the speeding capsule. One after another, Bill scans the meters. Suddenly the adrenalin shoots through his body. His gaze locks on meter number 51. Something's gone wrong in the capsule!

"I've got a valid signal on segment 51!" he barks into the phone which links him with both Christopher Kraft, the Mercury Flight director, and Al Shepard.

Astronaut Shepard's heart skips a beat. Segment 51! The heat shield! If the signal on the meter is accurate, it means that the heat shield on *Friendship 7* has come loose! Without the glass-fiber heat insulator to protect it, the capsule will burn to a cinder when it reenters the earth's atmosphere.

Shepard and Chris Kraft go into a quick huddle.

The heat shield actually has two functions. In addition to being the capsule's heat protection device during reentry, it acts as a landing shock absorber. After the capsule is safely back in the earth's atmosphere, the heat shield drops down to form the bottom of an air filled bag. Extending several feet below the base of the capsule, the bag provides a cushion of air which absorbs much of the landing shock.

After talking it over for a few minutes, the meter signal didn't make much sense to either Kraft or Shepard. How could the heat shield be loose if the retrorocket pack was still attached to the capsule? The round metal container which holds the rockets is positioned on the outside of the heat shield. Fastened in place by three extremely strong metal straps made of titanium, the retropack is firmly attached to the capsule itself—not the heat shield. There was no indication on any of the instruments in Mercury Control that there was anything wrong with the retropack. Maybe meter 51 was giving a faulty reading.

Maybe not.

Kraft spoke into the mouthpiece of his headset. "Bill, what's the signal strength on 51?"

"Eighty percent, Mr. Kraft."

Eighty percent! That really meant trouble. A reading of a hundred percent would mean a grounded circuit. Thirty-five or forty percent could mean a poor switch connection. Zero could mean a bad meter. But eighty percent could mean only one thing—somehow the heat shield had come loose.

There was a way to check the accuracy of Saunders' meter. Get a reading from the other tracking stations. See if their instruments were picking up the same signal. The order went flashing around the world. "Urgent! Request report on segment 51."

A few minutes later the answers started coming in. Bad, all bad. The reports confirmed Saunders' reading. The heat shield on *Friendship 7* was definitely loose.

Flight Director Kraft called a hurried meeting of the technical experts. Each fleeting minute was bringing John Glenn three hundred miles closer to the point of reentry. Something had to be done—and fast!

Unaware of the drama being enacted in Mercury Control, Glenn continues with his regular reports to the ground tracking stations along the way as he whizzes around the globe on his second orbit.

Passing over the Indian Ocean ship at 2:20 P.M., Eastern Standard Time, he has the first hint that something might be amiss.

"*Friendship 7*, we have a message from Mercury Control Center for you to keep your landing bag switch in the off position. Do you read? Over."

"*This is Seven. Roger. Understand . . .*"

Six or seven minutes later, Gordon

Cooper was in contact with the capsule from Muchea.

"Hello, *Friendship 7,* this is Muchea cap com. Will you confirm that your landing bag switch is in the off position? Over."

"*Affirmative, Gordo, landing bag switch is in the center off position.*"

"Roger, John. You haven't had any banging noises, or anything of this type, have you? Over."

"*Negative. . . .*"

"Roger, Seven; Control Center wanted this answer."

On across the Pacific, and Glenn sees the beauty of his second sunrise the same day. Again, he sees the mysterious luminous particles swarming across the window of the capsule. He checks in with the station on Canton Island.

"*Friendship 7,* this is Canton cap com. We have no indication that your landing bag might be deployed."

"*Roger, Canton. Did someone report that the landing bag could be down?*"

"Negative, Seven. We had a request to monitor this, and to ask if you heard any flapping when you had high-rate changes in capsule attitude."

"*That is negative. I think they probably thought these particles I saw might have come from that.*"

Then the station on the island of Kauai, Hawaii raises the capsule on voice radio. "This is Hawaii cap com. Do you still consider yourself 'Go' for the next orbit?"

"*That is affirmative. I am 'Go' for the next orbit.*"

As the spacecraft speeds across the coast of California, Astronaut Wally Schirra at Point Arguello acknowledges *Friendship 7*'s communication check. "Roger, read you loud and clear, John. The aeromedics are very happy with you, boy. You look real good up there."

"*All right, fine. . . . glad everything is working out. I feel real good, Wally. No problems at all.*"

"Good show. We're very pleased to let you go by this time. I'll see you next time around."

"*Roger, Wally. . . .*"

It had taken Glenn almost three and a half hours to cross the United States in his F8U Crusader during Operation Bullet. Today he makes the trip from California to Florida in just eight minutes.

From Cape Canaveral, Al Shepard greets the returning capsule. "Good afternoon, Seven . . ." The two astronauts discuss some minor difficulty Glenn has been having with the capsule's gyroscopes. Then Al gives John a time check on when the retrograde rockets should fire. "Also, Seven, we recommend that you allow the capsule to drift on manual, in order to conserve fuel."

"*Roger, Cape. . . .*"

Now Glenn is talking to Gus Grissom at Bermuda again. "*I have the Cape in sight. I can see the whole State of Florida just laid out like a map. Beautiful! I can see clear back to the Mississippi delta.*"

John's checkoff list calls for him to take a look at "Area Hotel"—the recovery area where the capsule is scheduled to land at the end of this orbit.

"*This is Seven, checking the weather down in Area Hotel. It looks very good down that way. Looks like we'll have no problem on recovery.*"

"Very good," Grissom replies. "We'll see you on Grand Turk."

"*No problem on recovery.*" So far no one has told Glenn that there is every indication that the capsule's heat shield is loose. But in a small cubicle off the main control room at Cape Canaveral, a handful of engineers and scientists are going through some agonizing minutes. John Glenn's life depends on their decision. Flight Director Kraft needs a recommendation, and he needs it soon.

Kraft calls from Main Control. "Either you guys are going to give me a decision within the next five minutes, or I'm going to make one myself. I have no choice."

Back and forth the discussion goes. It would be a foolish risk to assume that the signal on meter 51 was false. Besides, it has been confirmed by valid readings from other tracking stations.

OK, the meter is telling the truth.

If the heat shield drops off before reentry, John Glenn will burn to death.

No argument about that.

The question, then, is whether to make the reentry normally, with the retropack off, or to make it with the pack still left on. If the retropack is jettisoned before reentry, there will be nothing to hold the heat shield in place. It may drop away prematurely. On the other hand, if the pack is left on, it should hold the shield in place.

Yes—but the heat shield wasn't designed to do its job with the retropack strapped outside of it. No reentry tests have ever been made with the pack on. The heat shield works on the principle of melting itself away, thus dissipating the terrific heat that would otherwise be absorbed by the capsule. What's going to happen to the smooth, glass-fiber surface of the shield with a metal object the size of a peach basket in the middle of it? Will it work as it is supposed to, or won't it?

There is one person who might be able to supply the answer—Maxime Faget, the man who conceived the capsule's shape.

A hurried phone call is made to Houston, Texas. Faget makes it clear that his studies were purely theoretical; however, he is convinced that the heat shield will still function properly with the retropack attached.

Without the heat shield in place, the capsule is certain to be destroyed. But with the retropack to hold it, at least John has a fighting chance. That is the recommendation, then—leave the pack in place.

They quickly make their decision known to Kraft.

By this time, Glenn is passing over Australia for the third time. He calls Gordon Cooper: *"Hey, Gordo, I want you to send a message to the Commandant of the U.S. Marine Corps in Washington. Tell him I have my four hours required flight time for this month, and request a flight chit be made out for me."*

"Roger, John, will do. Think they will pay it?"

"Don't know. Going to find out."

"Is this flying time or rocket time?"

"Lighter-than-air, buddy!"

Minutes later, Wally Schirra hears John calling Point Arguello. He acknowledges it.

"This is Friendship 7. *My capsule elapsed time is zero four, plus three one, plus three five on my mark . . . two, three, four, mark. Will you relay that immediately to Cape? I think we're several seconds off. Over."*

"Roger. Will give you the countdown for retrosequence time, John. You're looking good."

"We have only five zero seconds to retrograde."

"That is affirm. I will give you a forty-five mark. . . . Mark!"

"Roger."

"Thirty seconds, John."

"Retro warning light is on."

"Good. John, leave your retropack on until you've passed over Texas. Do you read?"

"Roger."

"One five seconds to sequence . . . five, four, three, two, one, FIRE!"

"Roger. Retros are firing."

"Yeah, they be."

"Are they ever! It feels like I'm going back toward Hawaii!"

"Don't do that. You want to go to the east coast."

"Roger. Fire retro light is green."

"Roger, retros have stopped . . . Do you understand to keep your retropack on until you pass over Texas?"

"That's affirmative."

"It's a real good-looking sight from what we can see."

"Yes, sir, it looks good, Wally. We'll see you back East . . . Jettison retro is red. I'm holding on to it."

"Good head."

"I'll tell you, there's no doubt about it when the retros fire!"

"I gathered that from your comments."

"Do you have a time for going to jettison retro?"

"Texas will give you that message."

Another four minutes and Glenn checks in with the tracking station at Corpus Christi, Texas.

"This is Texas cap com. We are recommending that you leave the retropackage on through the entire reentry. This means you will have to override the zero five G switch, which is expected to occur at oh four, four three, five three. That is approximately four and one-half minutes from now. This also means that you will have to manually retract the scope. Over."

Now there is a note of apprehension in the astronaut's voice. "This is Friendship 7. What is the reason for this? Do you have any reason? Over."

"Not at this time. This is the judgment of Cape Flight."

"Roger, understand I will have to make a manual oh five G when it occurs and bring the scope in manually. Is that affirm?"

"That is affirmative, Friendship 7."

"Roger. This is Seven. Going to reentry attitude in that case."

Now they can hear John's voice coming from the loud-speakers in Mercury Control.

"Friendship 7, this is Cape. Recommend you go to reentry attitude and retract your scope manually at this time."

"Roger, retracting scope manually."

"While you're doing that, we're not sure whether or not your landing bag is deployed. We feel it's safer to reenter with the retropackage on. We see no difficulty at this time in that type of reentry. Over."

"Roger, understand. . . . Going to fly-by-wire."

"Roger. You're going to use fly-by-wire for reentry. We recommend that you do the best you can to keep a zero angle."

"Roger. Understand."

"Friendship 7, this is Cape."

"Go ahead, Cape. You're fading out . . ."

"We recommend that you jettison your retropack upon reaching one to one and a half G's. Do you understand? Over."

There is no answer.

"Seven, this is Cape transmitting blind. Recommend you jettison retropack at one to one and a half G's. Over."

The earphones and the loud-speakers on the ground are silent.

Friendship 7 is reentering the earth's atmosphere. The terrific heat, generated by the capsule plunging into the atmosphere, has formed an envelope of electrified air around the spacecraft which radio waves cannot penetrate. John Glenn is locked in lonely silence.

Once again all eyes in Mercury Control stare at the hands of the clock. One minute. Two minutes. Three. Four . . . four minutes and ten seconds, fifteen, twenty.

"*This is* Friendship 7. *A real fireball outside!*"

"Roger, Seven, Roger. How are you doing?"

"*Oh, pretty good.*"

"Seven, this is Cape. What is your general condition? Are you feeling pretty well?"

"*My condition is good, but that was a real fireball, boy! I had great chunks of that retropack breaking off all the way through!*"

"It did break off, is that correct?"

"*Roger . . . altimeter indicating one eight thousand.*"

"Roger, reading you loud and clear."

"*Rocking quite a bit. I may still have some of that pack on. I can't drop it, either.*"

For a few seconds there is no sound from the capsule.

"*The drogue is out . . . drogue is out. Came out in about a ninety-degree yaw.*"

"Is the drogue holding all right?"

"*Roger, drogue looks good . . . Standing by for main chute at ten thousand.*"

Another long pause.

"*Main chute is on green. . . . Chute is out. In reef condition at ten thousand eight hundred feet. BEAUTIFUL chute! Chute looks good, chute looks VERY good! Rate of descent has gone to about four two feet per second. The chute looks very good!*"

"Hello, Seven. Your IP [impact point] is within one mile of the uprange destroyer. Voice call is 'Steelhead.'"

ment, then hurried back down the glistening steel ladders to his duty. Man after man followed him, among them Thomas Andrews, one of the ship's designers, and Archie Frost, the builder's chief engineer, with his twenty assistants—men who had no posts of duty in the engine room but whose traditions called them there.

On deck, in corridor and stateroom, life flowed again. Men, women, and children awoke and asked questions; orders were given to uncover the lifeboats; water rose into the firemen's quarters; half-dressed stokers streamed up on deck. But the passengers—most of them—did not know that the *Titanic* was sinking. The shock of the collision had been so slight that some were not awakened by it; the *Titanic* was so huge that she could not be damaged by floating ice; the night was too calm, too beautiful, to think of death at sea.

Captain Smith half-ran to the door of the radio shack. Bride, partly dressed, eyes dulled with sleep, was standing behind Phillips, waiting.

"Send the call for assistance."

The blue spark danced: "C Q D— C Q D—C Q D—C Q—" Miles away Marconi men heard. Cape Race heard it, and the steamships *La Provence* and *Mt. Temple*.

The sea was surging into the *Titanic*'s hold. At 12:20 the water burst into the seamen's quarters through a collapsed fore-and-aft wooden bulkhead. Pumps strained in the engine rooms, men and machinery making a futile fight against the sea. Steadily the water rose.

The boats were swung out—slowly; for the deck hands were late in reaching their stations, there had been no boat drill, and many of the crew did not know to what boats they were assigned. Orders were shouted; the safety valves

had lifted, and steam was blowing off in a great rushing roar. In the charthouse Fourth Officer Boxhall bent above a chart, working rapidly with pencil and dividers.

12:20 A.M. Boxhall's position goes out to a fleet of vessels: "Come at once; we have struck a berg."

To the Cunarder *Carpathia* (Arthur Henry Rostron, Master, New York to Liverpool, fifty-eight miles away):

"It's a C Q D, old man. Position 41— 46 N.; 50—14 W."

The blue spark dancing: "Sinking; cannot hear for noise of steam."

12:30 A.M. The word is passed: "Women and children in the boats." Stewards finish waking their passengers below; life preservers are tied on; some men smile at the precaution. "The *Titanic* is unsinkable." The *Mt. Temple* starts for the *Titanic*; the *Carpathia*, with a double watch in her stokeholds, radios, "Coming hard." The C Q D changes the course of many ships—but not of one: the operator of the *Californian*, nearby, has just put down his earphones and turned in.

The C Q D flashes over land and sea from Cape Race to New York; newspaper city rooms leap to life and presses whir.

On the *Titanic*, water creeps over the bulkhead between No. 5 and No. 6 firerooms. She is going down by the head; the engineers—fighting a losing battle— are forced back foot by foot by the rising water. Down the promenade deck Happy Jock Hume, the bandsman, runs with his instrument.

12:45 A.M. Murdoch, in charge on the starboard side, eyes tragic, but calm and cool, orders boat No. 7 lowered. The women hang back; they want no boat ride on an ice-strewn sea; surely the *Titanic* will not sink! The men encourage them, explain that this is just a precautionary measure: "We'll see you again at breakfast." There is little confusion; passengers stream slowly to the boat deck. In the steerage the immigrants chatter excitedly.

A sudden sharp hiss—a streaked flare against the night: Boxhall sends a rocket toward the sky. It explodes, and a parachute of white stars lights up the icy sea. "God! Rockets!" The band plays ragtime.

No. 8 is lowered, and No. 5. Ismay, still in dressing gown, calls for women and children, handles lines, stumbles in the way of an officer, is told, "Get out of here." Third Officer Pitman takes charge of No. 5; as he swings into the boat, Murdoch grasps his hand. "Good-by and good luck, old man."

No. 6 goes over the side. There are only twenty-eight people in a lifeboat with a capacity of sixty-five.

A light stabs from the bridge; Boxhall is calling in Morse flashes, again and again, to a strange ship stopped in the ice jam five to ten miles away. Another rocket drops its shower of sparks above the ice-strewn sea and the dying ship.

1 A.M. Slowly the water creeps higher; the fore ports of the *Titanic* are dipping into the sea. Rope squeaks through blocks; lifeboats drop jerkily seaward. Through the shouting on the decks comes the sound of the band.

The "Millionaires' Special" leaves the ship—boat No. 1. With a capacity of forty people, it carries only Sir Cosmo and Lady Duff Gordon and ten others. Aft, the frightened immigrants mill and jostle and rush for a boat. An officer's fist flies out; three shots are fired in the air, and the panic is quelled. . . . Four Chinese sneak unseen into a boat and hide in its bottom.

1:20 A.M. Water is coming into No. 4 boiler room. Stokers slice and shovel as it laps about their ankles—steam for the dynamos, steam for the wireless

spark! As the water rises, great ash hoes rake the flaming coals from the furnaces. Safety valves pop; the stokers retreat aft, and the watertight doors clang shut behind them.

The rockets fling their splendor toward the stars. The boats are more heavily loaded now, for the passengers know the *Titanic* is sinking. Women cling to each other and sob. The great screws aft are rising clear of the sea. Half-filled boats are ordered to come alongside the cargo ports and take on more passengers; but the ports are never opened, and the boats are never filled. Others pull for the lights of a steamer, clear but miles away. They never reach it; the lights disappear, the unknown ship steams off.

The water rises and the band plays ragtime.

1:30 A.M. Lightoller is getting the port boats off; Murdoch, the starboard. As one boat is lowered into the sea, a boat officer fires his gun along the ship's side to stop a rush from the lower decks. A woman tries to take her Great Dane into the boat with her; she is refused and steps out of the boat to die with her dog. Millet's "little smile, which had played on his lips all through the voyage" plays no more; his lips are grim, but he waves good-by and brings wraps for the women.

Benjamin Guggenheim, in evening clothes, smiles and says, "We've dressed up in our best and are prepared to go down like gentlemen."

1:40 A.M. Boat No. 14 is clear, then 13, 16, 15, and C. The lights still shine, but the *Baltic* hears the blue spark say, "Engine room getting flooded."

The *Olympic* signals, "Am lighting up all possible boilers as fast as can."

Major Butts helps women into the last boats and waves good-by to them. Mrs. Straus puts her foot on the gunwale of a lifeboat, then she draws back and

goes to her husband: "We have been together many years; where you go I will go." Colonel John Jacob Astor puts his young wife in a lifeboat, steps back, taps cigarette on fingernail: "Good-by, dearie; I'll join you later."

1:45 A.M. The foredeck is under water, the fo'c'sle head almost awash; the great stern is lifted high toward the bright stars; and still the band plays. Mr. and Mrs. Harris approach a lifeboat arm in arm.

Officer: "Ladies first, please."

Harris bows, smiles, steps back: "Of course, certainly; ladies first."

Boxhall fires the last rocket, then leaves in charge of boat No. 2.

2 A.M. She is dying now; her bow goes deeper, her stern higher. But there must be steam. Below in the stokeholds, the sweaty firemen keep steam up for the flaring lights and the dancing spark. The glowing coals slide and tumble over the slanted grate bars; the sea pounds behind that yielding bulkhead. But the spark dances on.

The *Asian* hears Phillips try the new signal: S O S.

Boat No. 4 has left now; boat D leaves ten minutes later. Jacques Futrelle clasps his wife: "For God's sake, go! It's your last chance; go!" Mme. Futrelle is half-forced into the boat. It clears the side.

There are about 660 people in the boats—and 1,500 still on the sinking *Titanic*.

On top of the officers' quarters, men work frantically to get the two collapsible boats stored there over the side. Water is over the forward part of A deck now; it surges up the companionways toward the boat deck. In the radio shack Bride has slipped a coat and life jacket about Phillips as the first operator sits hunched over his key, sending, still sending—"41—46 N., 50—14 W. C Q D —C Q D—S O S—S O S—"

The captain's tired white face appears at the radio-room door: "Men, you have done your full duty. You can do no more. Now, it's every man for himself." The captain disappears—back to his sinking bridge, where Painter, his personal steward, stands quietly waiting for orders. The spark dances on. Bride turns his back and goes into the inner cabin. As he does so, a stoker, grimed with coal, mad with fear, steals into the shack and reaches for the life jacket on Phillips' back. Bride wheels about and brains him with a wrench.

2:10 A.M. Below decks the steam is still holding, though the pressure is falling—rapidly. In the gymnasium on the boat deck, the athletic instructor watches quietly as two gentlemen ride the bicycles and another swings casually at the punching bag. Mail clerks stagger up the boat-deck stairways, dragging soaked mail sacks. The spark still crackles. The band still plays, but not ragtime:

Nearer my God to Thee,
Nearer to Thee . . .

A few men take up the refrain; others kneel on the slanting decks to pray. Many run and scramble aft, where hundreds are clinging above the silent screws on the great uptilted stern. The spark still signals and the lights still flare; the engineers are on the job. The hymn comes to its close. Bandmaster Hartley, Yorkshireman violinist, taps his bow against a bulkhead, calls for "Autumn" as the water curls about his feet, and the eight musicians brace themselves against the ship's slant. People are leaping from the decks into the nearby water—the icy water. A woman cries, "Oh, save me, save me!" A man answers, "Good lady, save yourself. Only God can save you now." The band plays "Autumn":

God of Mercy and Compassion!
Look with pity on my pain. . .

The water creeps over the bridge where the *Titanic*'s master stands; heavily he steps out to meet it.

2:17 A.M. "C Q—" The *Virginian* hears a ragged, blurred C Q, then an abrupt stop. The blue spark dances no more. The lights flicker out; the engineers have lost their battle.

2:18 A.M. Men run about blackened decks, leap into the night, are swept into the sea by the curling wave which licks up the *Titanic*'s length. Lightoller does not leave the ship—the ship leaves him; there are hundreds like him, but only a few who live to tell of it. The funnels still swim above the water, but the ship is climbing to the perpendicular; the bridge is under, and most of the foremast; the great stern rises like a squat leviathan. Men swim away from the sinking ship; others drop from the stern.

The band plays in the darkness, the water lapping upward:

Hold me up in mighty waters,
Keep my eyes on things above,
Righteousness, divine atonement
Peace and everlas . . .

The forward funnel snaps and crashes into the sea; its steel tons hammer out of existence swimmers struggling in the freezing water. Streams of sparks, of smoke and steam, burst from the after funnels. The ship upends to fifty, to sixty degrees.

Down in the black abyss of the stokeholds, in the engine room where the dynamos have whirred at last to a stop, the stokers and the engineers are reeling against hot metal, the rising water clutching at their knees. The boilers and the engine cylinders rip from the bed plates and crash through the bulkheads —steel against steel.

The *Titanic* stands on end, poised briefly for the plunge. Slowly she slides to her grave . . . slowly at first, and then more quickly—quickly—quickly.

2:20 A.M. The greatest ship in the world has sunk. From the calm dark waters where the floating lifeboats move, there goes up, in the white wake of her passing, "one long continuous moan."

The boats that the *Titanic* had launched pulled safely away from the slight suction of the sinking ship, pulled away from the screams that came from the lips of the freezing men and women in the water. The boats were poorly manned and badly equipped, and they had been unevenly loaded. Some carried so few seamen that women bent to the oars. Mrs. Astor tugged at an oar handle; the Countess of Rothes took a tiller. Shivering stokers in sweaty coal-blackened singlets and light trousers steered in some boats; stewards in white coats rowed in others. Ismay was in the last boat that left the ship from the starboard side; with Mr. Carter of Philadelphia and two seamen, he tugged at the oars. In one of the lifeboats, an Italian with a broken wrist—disguised in a woman's shawl and hat—huddled on the floorboards, ashamed now that fear had left him. In another rode the only baggage saved from the *Titanic*: the carryall of Samuel L. Goldenberg, one of the rescued passengers.

There were only a few boats that were heavily loaded; most of those that were half-empty made but perfunctory efforts to pick up the moaning swimmers, their officers and crew fearing they would endanger the living if they pulled back into the midst of the dying. Some boats beat off the freezing victims; fear-crazed men and women struck with oars at the heads of swimmers. One woman drove her fist into the face of a half-dead man as he tried feebly to climb over the gunwale. Two other women helped him in and stanched the flow of blood from the ring cuts on his face.

One of the collapsible boats, which had floated off the top of the officers' quarters when the *Titanic* sank, was an icy haven for thirty or forty men. The boat had capsized as the ship sank; men swam to it, clung to it, climbed upon its slippery bottom, stood knee-deep in water in the freezing air. Chunks of ice swirled about their legs; their soaked clothing clutched their bodies in icy folds. Colonel Archibald Gracie was cast up there, Gracie who had leaped from the stern as the *Titanic* sank; young Thayer who had seen his father die; Lightoller who had twice been sucked down with the ship and twice blown to the surface by a belch of air; Bride, the second wireless operator, and Phillips, the first. There were many stokers, half-naked; it was a shivering company. They stood there in the icy sea, under the far stars, and sang and prayed—the Lord's Prayer. After a while a lifeboat came and picked them off, but Phillips was dead then or died soon afterward in the boat.

Only a few of the boats had lights; only one, No. 2, had a light that was of any use to the *Carpathia*, twisting through the ice field to the rescue. Other ships were coming hard too; but one, the *Californian*, was still dead to opportunity.

The blue sparks still danced, but not the *Titanic*'s; *La Provence* to the *Celtic*: "Nobody has heard the *Titanic* for about two hours."

It was 2:40 when the *Carpathia* first sighted the green light from No. 2 boat; it was 4:10 when she picked up the first boat and learned that the *Titanic* had foundered. The last of the moaning cries had just died away then.

Captain Rostron took the survivors aboard, boatload by boatload. He was ready for them, though only a small minority of them required much medical attention. Bride's feet were twisted and frozen; others were suffering from exposure; one died; seven were dead when taken from the boats, and were buried at sea.

It was then that the fleet of racing ships learned they were too late; the *Parisian* heard the weak signals of MPA, the *Carpathia*, report the death of the *Titanic*. It was then—or soon afterward, when her radio operator put on his earphones—that the *Californian*, the ship that had been within sight as the *Titanic* was sinking, first learned of the disaster.

And it was then, in all its white-green majesty, that the *Titanic*'s survivors saw the iceberg, tinted with the sunrise, floating idly, pack ice jammed about its base, other bergs heaving slowly nearby on the blue breast of the sea.

It was not until later that the world knew, for wireless then was not what wireless is today, and garbled messages had nourished a hope that all of the *Titanic*'s company were safe. Not until Monday evening—when P. A. S. Franklin, vice-president of the International Mercantile Marine Company, received relayed messages in New York that left little hope—did the full extent of the disaster begin to be known. Partial and garbled lists of the survivors, rumors of heroism and cowardice, stories spun out of newspaper imagination, based on a few bare facts and many false reports, misled the world, terrified and frightened it. It was not until Thursday night, when the *Carpathia* steamed into the North River, that the full truth was pieced together.

Flashlights flared on the black river when she stood up to her dock. Tugs nosed about her, shunted her toward Pier 54. Thirty thousand people jammed the streets; ambulances and stretchers stood on the pier; coroners and physicians waited.

In midstream the Cunarder dropped over the *Titanic*'s lifeboats; then she headed toward the dock. Beneath the customs letters on the pier stood relatives of the 711 survivors, and relatives of the missing—hoping against hope. The *Carpathia* cast her lines ashore; stevedores looped them over bollards.

The dense throngs stood quiet as the first survivor stepped down the gangway. It was a woman; she was half-staggering, led by customs guards, and stopped beneath her letter. A moan came from the crowd; fell, grew in volume, and dropped again.

Thus ended the maiden voyage of the *Titanic*, the greatest ship in the world.

THE FACT IS—

1. How did the *Titanic* compare in size with other ships of that time? What had the builders done to make her safe?

2. What warnings came to the *Titanic*'s officers before the collision? What was their reaction to these warnings?

3. What convinced the officers that the *Titanic*'s wound was mortal?

4. Why were so few passengers saved?

5. There were many deeds of courage that night. Which surprised you most? What evidence was there of discipline among the crew?

6. Do you think the same kind of disaster at sea could happen today? Why?

7. People react differently in times of crisis. What different reactions did you notice?

FOR THOUGHT AND ACTION

1. What scientific improvements have been made over the years to assure ship passengers greater safety?

2. Had you been the captain of the *Titanic*, how differently would you have conducted her maiden voyage?

3. Was the sinking of the *Titanic* an unavoidable accident or was it the result of human error?

4. You are on a Congressional Committee probing the reasons for this tragedy. What questions might you ask of the survivors?

Two Boys on a Mountain

WILLIAM O. DOUGLAS

When two boys avoid the easy way and search for the risky route to the top of a mountain, they are in search of an experience which will help them grow up. One false step, however, and the boys will not live to grow up. . . .

Kloochman Rock stands on the southern side of the Tieton Basin in the Cascade Mountains of the state of Washington. It is an oval-shaped lava rock, running lengthwise northwest by southeast a half-mile or more. It rises 3,000 feet above the basin. A third or more of its elevation is gained through gentle slopes of pine and fir. Next are a few hundred yards of tumbled rock. Then there is the cliff rising to the sky, 1,500 feet or more—straight as the Washington Monument and over twice as high.

It was in 1913, when my friend Douglas Corpron was nineteen and I was not quite fifteen, that the two of us climbed Kloochman. Walter Kohagen, Doug, and I were camped in the Tieton Basin at a soda spring. The basin was then in large part a vast rich bottomland. We were traveling light, one blanket each. The night, I recall, was so bitter cold that we took turns refueling the campfire so that we could keep our backs warm enough to sleep. We rose at the first show of dawn, and cooked frying pan bread and trout for breakfast. We had not planned to climb Kloochman, but somehow the challenge came to us as the sun touched her crest.

After breakfast we started circling the rock. There are fairly easy routes up Kloochman, but we shunned them. When we came to the southeast face (the one that never has been conquered, I believe), we chose it. Walter decided not to make the climb, but to wait at the base of the cliff for Doug and me. We started in midmorning. By then the July day was warm and cloudless. Doug led. The beginning was easy. For one hundred feet or so we found ledges six to twelve inches wide we could follow to the left or right. Some ledges ran up the rock ten feet or more at a gentle grade. Others were merely steps to another ledge higher up. Thus by hugging the wall, we could either ease ourselves upward or hoist ourselves from one ledge to another.

When we were about one hundred feet up the wall, the ledges became narrower and the footwork more precarious. Doug suggested we take off our shoes. This we did, tying them behind us on our belts. In stocking feet we wormed up the wall, clinging like flies to the dark rock. The pace was slow. We gingerly tested each toehold and fingerhold for loose rock before putting our weight on it. At times we had to inch along sidewise, our stomachs pressed tightly against the rock, in order to gain a point where we could reach the ledge above us. If we got on a ledge that turned out to be a cul-de-sac,[1] the much more dangerous task of going down the rock wall would confront us. So we

picked our route with care and weighed the advantages of several choices which frequently were given us. At times we could not climb easily from one ledge to another. The one above might be a foot or so high. Then we would have to reach it with one knee, slowly bring the other knee up, and then, delicately balancing on both knees on the upper ledge, come slowly to our feet by pressing close to the wall and getting such purchase with our fingers as the lava rock permitted.

In that tortuous way we made perhaps eight hundred feet in two hours. It was late forenoon when we stopped to appraise our situation. We were in serious trouble. We had reached the feared cul-de-sac. The two- or three-inch ledge on which we stood ended. There seemed none above us within Doug's reach. I was longer-legged than Doug; so perhaps I could have reached some ledge with my fingers if I were ahead. But it was impossible to change positions on the wall. Doug was ahead, and there he must stay. The problem was to find a way to get him up.

Feeling along the wall, Doug discovered a tiny groove into which he could press the tips of the fingers of his left hand. It might help him maintain balance as his weight began to shift from the lower ledge to the upper one. But there was within reach not even a lip of rock for his right hand. Just out of reach, however, was a substantial crevasse, one that would hold several men. How could Doug reach it? I could not boost him, for my own balance was insecure. Clearly, Doug would have to jump to reach it—and he would have but one jump. Since he was standing on a ledge only a few inches wide, he could not expect to jump for his handhold, miss it, and land safely. A slip meant he would go hurtling down some eight hundred feet onto the rocks. After much

[1] **cul-de-sac** (KOOL·de·SAK): a blind alley.

discussion and indecision, Doug decided to take the chance and go up.

He asked me to do him a favor. If he failed and fell, I might still make it, since I was longer-legged; would I give certain messages to his family in that event? I nodded.

"Then, listen carefully. Try to remember my exact words," he told me. "Tell Mother that I love her dearly. Tell her I think she is the most wonderful person in the world. Tell her not to worry—that I did not suffer, that God willed it so. Tell Sister that I have been a mean little devil but I had no malice toward her. Tell Dad I was brave and died unafraid. Tell him I have always been very proud of him, that someday I had planned to be a doctor, too. Tell Mother, Sister, and Dad I prayed for them."

Every word burned into me. My heart was sick, my lips quivered. I pressed my face against the rock so that Doug could not see.

All was silent. A pebble fell from the ledge on which I was squeezed. I counted seconds before it hit below with a faint, faraway tinkling sound. Would Doug drop through the same space? Would I follow? When you fall eight hundred feet, do you die before you hit the bottom? Closing my eyes, I asked God to help Doug up the wall.

In a second Doug said in a cheery voice, "Well, here goes."

A false bravado took hold of us. I said he could do it. He said he would. He wiped first one hand then the other on his trousers. He placed both palms against the wall, bent his knees slowly, paused a split second, and jumped straight up. It was not much of a jump—only six inches or so. But that jump by one pressed against a cliff eight hundred feet in the air had daredevil proportions. I held my breath; my heart pounded. The suspense was over at once. Doug made the jump, and in a second was hanging by two hands from a strong, wide ledge. There was no toehold; he would have to hoist himself by his arms alone. He did just that. His body went slowly up as if pulled by some unseen winch. Soon he had the weight of his body above the ledge and was resting on the palms of his hands. He then put his left knee on the ledge, rolled over on his side, and chuckled as he said: "Nothing to it."

A greater disappointment followed. Doug's exploration of the ledge showed he was in a final cul-de-sac. There was no way up. There was not even a higher ledge he could reach by jumping. We were now faced with the nightmare of going down the sheer rock wall. We could not go down frontward because the ledges were too narrow and the wall too steep. We needed our toes, not our heels, on the rock; and we needed to have our stomachs pressed tightly against it. Then we could perhaps feel our way. But as every rock expert knows, descent of a cliff without ropes is often much more difficult than ascent.

That difficulty was impressed on us by the first move. Doug had to leave the ledge he had reached by jumping. He dared not slide blindly to the skimpy ledge he had just left. I must help him. I must move up the wall and stand closer to him. Though I could not possibly hold his weight, I must exert sufficient pressure to slow up his descent and to direct his toe onto the narrow ledge from which he had just jumped.

I was hanging to the rock like a fly, twelve feet or more to Doug's left. So I inched my way toward him, first dropping to a lower ledge, and then climbing to a higher one, using such toeholds as the rock afforded and edging my way crabwise.

When I reached him, I said, "I'll help."

Doug lowered himself and hung by his fingers full length. His feet were about six inches above the ledge from which he had jumped. He was now my responsibility. If he dropped without aid or direction, he was gone. He could not catch and hold to the scanty ledge. I had little space for maneuvering. The surface on which I stood was not more than three inches wide. My left hand fortunately found an overhead crevasse that gave a solid anchor in case my feet slipped.

I placed my right hand in the small of Doug's back and pressed upward with all my might. "Now you can come," I said.

He let go gently, and the full weight of his body came against my arm. My arm trembled under the tension. My left hand hung onto the crack in the rock like a grappling hook. My stomach pressed against the wall as if to find mucilage in its pores. My toes dug in as I threw in every ounce of strength.

Down Doug came—a full inch. I couldn't help glancing down and seeing the rocks far below.

Down Doug moved another inch, then a third. My left hand seemed paralyzed. The muscles of my toes were aching. My right arm shook. I could not hold much longer.

Down came Doug a fourth inch. I thought he was headed for destruction. His feet would miss the only toehold within reach. I could not possibly hold him. He would plunge to his death because my arm was not strong enough to hold him. The messages he had given me for his family raced through my mind. And I saw myself, sick and ashamed, standing before them, testifying to my own inadequacy, repeating his last words.

I wanted to pray again but there was no time for it.

"Steady, Doug. The ledge is a foot to your right." He pawed the wall with the toes of his foot, searching.

"I can't find it. Don't let go. The only hold I have is with my left hand and it's not much."

The crisis was on us. Even if I had been safely anchored, my cramped position would have kept me from helping him much more. I felt helpless. In a few seconds I would reach the physical breaking point and Doug would go hurtling off the cliff. I did not see how I could keep him from slipping through and yet maintain my own balance.

I will never know how I did it. But I tapped some reserve and directed his right foot onto the ledge from which he had earlier jumped. I did it by standing for a moment on my left foot alone and then using my right leg as a rod to guide his right foot to the ledge his swinging feet had missed.

His toes grabbed the ledge as if they were the talons of a bird. My right leg swung back to my perch.

"Are you OK?" I asked.

"Yes," said Doug. "Good work."

My right arm fell from him, numb and paralyzed. I shook from exhaustion and for the first time noticed that my face was wet with perspiration. We stood against the rock in silence for several minutes, relaxing and regaining our composure.

Doug said, "Let's throw our shoes down. It will be easier going." So we untied them from our belts and dropped them to Walter Kohagen, who was waiting at the rock field below us.

Our descent was painfully slow but uneventful. We went down backward, weaving a strange pattern across the face of the cliff as we moved from one side to the other. It was perhaps mid-afternoon when we reached the bottom, retrieved our shoes, and started around the other side of the rock. We left the southeast wall unconquered.

But, being young, we were determined to climb the rock. So once more we started to circle. When we came to the northwest wall, we selected it as our route.

Here, too, is a cliff rising 1,500 feet like some unfinished pyramid. But close examination shows numerous toe- and fingerholds that make the start at least fairly easy. So we set out with our shoes on.

When we were part way up the rock, for a while Doug and I were separated. I worked laterally along a ledge to the south, found easier going, and in a short time was two hundred feet or more up the rock wall. I was above Doug, twenty-five feet or more, and fifty feet to his right. We had been extremely careful to test each toe- and fingerhold before putting our trust in it. Kloochman is full of treacherous rock. We often discovered thin ledges that crumbled under pressure and showered handfuls of rock and dust down below. Perhaps I was careless; but whatever the cause, the thin ledge on which I was standing gave way.

As I felt it slip, I grabbed for a hold above me. The crevasse I seized was solid. But there I was, hanging by my hands two hundred feet in the air, my feet pawing the rock. To make matters worse, my camera had swung between me and the cliff when I slipped. It was a crude and clumsy instrument, a box type that I carried on a leather strap across my shoulders. Its hulk was actually pushing me from the cliff. I twisted in an endeavor to get rid of it, but it was firmly lodged between me and the wall.

I yelled to Doug for help. He at once started edging toward me. It seemed hours, though it was probably not over a few minutes. He shouted: "Hang on. I'll be there."

Hang on I did. My fingers ached beyond description. They were frozen to the rock. My exertion in pawing with my feet had added to the fatigue. The ache of my fingers extended to my wrists and then along my arms. I stopped thrashing and hung like a sack, motionless. Every second seemed a minute, every minute an hour. I did not see how I could possibly hold.

I would slip, I thought, slip to sure death. I could not look down because of my position. But in my mind's eye I saw in sharp outline the jagged rocks that seemed to pull me toward them. The camera kept pushing my fingers from the ledge. I felt them move. They began to give way before the pull of a force too great for flesh to resist.

Fright grew in me. The idea of hanging helpless two hundred feet above the abyss brought panic. I cried out to Doug but the words caught in my dry throat. I was like one in a nightmare who struggles to shout—who is then seized with a fear that promises to destroy him.

Then there flashed through my mind a family scene. Mother was sitting in the living room talking to me, telling me what a wonderful man Father was. She told me of his last illness and his death. She told me of his departure from Cleveland, Washington, to Portland, Oregon, for what proved to be a fatal operation. His last words to her were: "If I die, it will be glory. If I live, it will be grace."

The panic passed. The memory of those words restored reason. Glory to die? I could not understand why it would be glory to die. It would be glory to live. But as Father said, it might take grace to live, grace from One more powerful than either Doug or I.

And so again that day I prayed. I asked God to give me guts, to give me power to do the impossible.

My fingers were as numb as flesh

that is full of Novocain. They seemed detached from me, as if they belonged to someone else. My wrists, my shoulders, cried out for respite from the pain. It would be such welcome relief if they could be released from the weight that was on them.

Hang on? You can't hang on. You are a weakling—puny. The weaklings die in the woods.

Puny, eh? I'll show you. Weakling? I'll show you. How long must I hang on? All day? OK, it's all day, then. I'll hang on, I'll hang on. By God, I'll hang on. O God, dear God, help me hang on!

I felt someone pushing my left foot upward. It was Doug. As if through a dream, his voice was saying, "Your feet are eighteen inches below your toehold." Doug found those toeholds for my feet.

I felt my shoes resting in solid cracks. I pulled myself up and rested on my elbows on the ledge to which my hands had been glued. I flexed my fingers and bent my wrists to bring life back.

Doug came up abreast of me and said, "We're even Stephen now."

"Even Stephen?"

"Today each of us has saved the other's life."

It was shortly above the point where Doug saved my life that we discovered a classic path up Kloochman. It is a three-sided chimney chute, a few feet wide, that leads almost to the top. There are several small chutes on Kloochman. In later years Cragg Gilbert and Louis Ulrich went up Devil's Chimney on the northeast face in a seven-hour, nerve-racking climb with ropes. Clarence Truitt and many others have gone up the chimney chute that Doug and I discovered. Then as now this chute was filled with loose rock that had to be cleared away. To negotiate the chute we took off our shoes and tied them to our belts. We climbed the chute in stocking feet,

pressing our hands and feet against the opposing walls as we kept our backs to the abyss below us. This day we went up the chute with ease, stopping every eight feet or so to measure our progress.

The sun was setting when we reached the top. We were gay and buoyant. We talked about the glories of the scene in front of us. We bragged a bit about our skill in rock work—how we must be part mountain goat to have reached the top. We shouted and hallooed to the empty meadows far below us.

On Kloochman Rock that July afternoon both Doug and I valued life more because death had passed so close. It was wonderful to be alive, breathing, using our muscles, shouting, seeing.

We stayed briefly at the top. We went down as we came up, in stocking feet. We raced against darkness, propelled by the thought of spending the night on Kloochman's treacherous wall.

It was deep dusk when we rejoined Walter on the rock fields at the base.

I climbed Kloochman again in the summer of 1948. This time my steps were more cautious and measured than they had been in 1913. There was less dash, less abandon in this adult ascent. I took my ease, feeling my way with care. But the memories of the earlier trip were still fresh in my mind as if it had happened only the previous week instead of thirty-five years ago.

As I climbed, I realized how conservative man becomes in his physical endeavors as he passes his thirties. I was not thinking of wind or stamina, for mine were both good. I was thinking of the subtle forces that control reflexes. It struck home why only young men make good fighter pilots—how it is that age fast takes the daredevil out of man. There was a thrill in this adult climb, but the reckless, carefree attitude of the earlier day had gone.

Yet I relived the experience of 1913. All the sensations of the earlier trip returned to me. There was the trembling excitement of the start. Doug's messages to his family raced once more through my mind, as if he had just uttered them. I saw Doug make his jump up the side of the cliff while he was eight hundred feet in the air. I saw him hanging on the ledge, doomed to die. I felt the weight of his body against my arm. I felt myself slipping slowly from the rock to destruction. It seemed once more that demons were pulling at my feet with a power too great for flesh and blood to resist. Once again little vestiges of the old fear passed through me.

Those, however, were fleeting sensations. When I came to the top, a sense of calm came over me, a deep peace. I knew now what a boy could not know, that fear of death was the compound of all other fears. I knew that long years ago I had begun to shed on Kloochman's walls the great, overpowering fear. Kloochman became for me that day a symbol of adversity and challenge—of the forces that have drawn from man his greatest spiritual and physical achievements.

THE FACT IS—

1. Why was it a "challenge" to climb Kloochman?

2. What difficulties did these boys face in climbing?

3. What tests of endurance did each have to undergo?

4. How did each save the other's life?

5. Why were the two boys so joyful when they reached the top?

6. What difference did Douglas observe in himself in 1948?

7. Which incident in this story called for the greatest courage?

8. What similarities can you see between a spaceman who seeks to land on the moon and a climber who seeks the top of a mountain?

9. Suppose you were face-to-face with imminent death—what would the message to your family or best friend say?

10. A visit to the library will reveal many accounts of many men who have climbed many mountains. Report on one such account.

A WORD TO REMEMBER: adversities

Change is the one thing constant in life. Some changes are improvements; others are *adversities* (ad·VER·sih·teez). Loss of job, loss of health, loss of family or friends are all adversities. Can you think of others? Some people are overwhelmed by their adversities; others rise above them. Franklin D. Roosevelt overcame an *adverse* fate (paralysis) to become a great world leader.

Justice Douglas said that Kloochman became for him a symbol of adversity and challenge. What adversities did he experience? How did they challenge him?

Eleven Blue Men

BERTON ROUECHÉ

What could turn eleven men so blue—a gas, a germ, a food, some unsuspected poison? It took a special team of medical sleuths to solve the mystery.

At about eight o'clock on Monday morning, September 25, 1944, a ragged, aimless old man of eighty-two collapsed on the sidewalk on Dey Street, near the Hudson Terminal. Innumerable people must have noticed him, but he lay there alone for several minutes, dazed, doubled up with abdominal cramps, and in an agony of retching. Then a policeman came along. Until the policeman bent over the old man, he may have supposed that he had just a sick drunk on his hands; wanderers dropped by drink are common in that part of town in the early morning. It was not an opinion that he could have held for long. The old man's nose, lips, ears, and fingers were sky-blue. The policeman went to a telephone and put in an ambulance call to Beekman-Downtown Hospital, half a dozen blocks away. The old man was carried into the emergency room there at eight-thirty. By that time, he was unconscious and the blueness had spread over a large part of his body. The examining physician attributed the old man's morbid color to cyanosis, a condition that usually results from an insufficient supply of oxygen in the blood, and also noted that he was diarrheic and in a severe state of shock. The course of treatment prescribed by the doctor was conventional. It included an instant gastric lavage,[1] heart stimulants, bed rest, and oxygen therapy. Presently, the old man recovered an encouraging, if painful, consciousness and demanded, irascibly and in the name of God, to know what had happened to him. It was a question that, at the moment, nobody could answer with much confidence.

For the immediate record, the doctor made a free-hand diagnosis of carbon-monoxide poisoning—from what source, whether an automobile or a gas pipe, it was, of course, pointless even to guess. Then, because an isolated instance of gas poisoning is something of a rarity in a section of the city as crammed with human beings as downtown Manhattan, he and his colleagues in the emergency room braced themselves for at least a couple more victims. Their foresight was promptly and generously rewarded. A second man was rolled in at ten-twenty-five. Forty minutes later, an ambulance drove up with three more men. At eleven-twenty, two others were brought in. An additional two arrived during the next fifteen minutes. Around noon, still another was admitted. All of these nine men were also elderly and dilapidated, all had been in misery for at least an hour, and all were rigid, cyanotic, and in a state of shock. The entire body of one, a bony, seventy-three-year-old consumptive named John Mitchell, was blue. Five of the nine, including Mitchell, had been stricken in the Globe Hotel, a sunless, upstairs flophouse at 190 Park Row, and two in a similar place, called the Star Hotel, at 3 James Street. Another had been found slumped in the doorway of a condemned building on Park Row, not far from City Hall Park, by a policeman. The ninth had keeled over in front of the Eclipse Cafeteria, at 6 Chatham Square. At a quarter to seven that evening, one more aged blue man was brought in. He had been lying, too sick to ask for help, on his cot in a cubicle in the Lion Hotel, another flophouse, at 26 Bowery, since ten o'clock that morning. A clerk had finally looked in and seen him.

By the time this last blue man arrived at the hospital, an investigation of the case by the Department of Health, to which all outbreaks of an epidemiological nature must be reported, had been under way for five hours. Its findings thus far had not been illuminating. The investigation was conducted by two men. One was the Health Department's chief epidemiologist, Dr. Morris Greenberg, a small, fragile, reflective man of fifty-seven . . . ; the other was Dr. Ottavio Pellitteri, a field epidemiologist, who since 1946 has been administrative medical inspector for the Bureau. He is thirty-six years old, pale, and stocky, and has a bristling black mustache. One day, when I was in Dr. Greenberg's office, he and Dr. Pellitteri told me about the case. Their recollection of it is, understandably, vivid. The derelicts were the victims of a type of poisoning so rare that only ten previous outbreaks of it had been recorded in medical literature. Of these, two were in the United States and two in Germany; the others had been reported in France, England, Switzerland, Algeria, Australia, and India. Up to September 25, 1944, the largest number of people stricken in a single outbreak was four. That was in Algeria in 1926.

The Beekman-Downtown Hospital telephoned a report of the occurrence

[1] **gastric lavage** (LAV·ihj): a washing out of the stomach.

to the Health Department just before noon. As is customary, copies of the report were sent to all the department's administrative officers. "Mine was on my desk when I got back from lunch," Dr. Greenberg said to me. "It didn't sound like much. Nine persons believed to be suffering from carbon-monoxide poisoning had been admitted during the morning, and all of them said that they had eaten breakfast at the Eclipse Cafeteria, at 6 Chatham Square. Still, it was a job for us. I checked with the clerk who handles assignments and found that Pellitteri had gone out on it. That was all I wanted to know. If it amounted to anything, I knew he'd phone me before making a written report. That's an arrangement we have here. Well, a couple of hours later I got a call from him. My interest perked right up."

"I was at the hospital," Dr. Pellitteri told me, "and I'd talked to the staff and most of the men. There were ten of them by then, of course. They were sick as dogs, but only one was in really bad shape."

"That was John Mitchell," Dr. Greenberg put in. "He died the next night. I understand his condition was hopeless from the start. The others, including the old boy who came in last, pulled through all right. Excuse me, Ottavio, but I just thought I'd get that out of the way. Go on."

Dr. Pellitteri nodded. "I wasn't at all convinced that it was gas poisoning," he continued. "The staff was beginning to doubt it, too. The symptoms weren't quite right. There didn't seem to be any of the headache and general dopiness that you get with gas. What really made me suspicious was this: Only two or three of the men had eaten breakfast in the cafeteria at the same time. They had straggled in all the way from seven o'clock to ten. That meant that the place would have had to be full of gas for at

least three hours, which is preposterous. It also indicated that we ought to have had a lot more sick people than we did. Those Chatham Square eating places have a big turnover. Well, to make sure, I checked with Bellevue, Gouverneur, St. Vincent's, and the other downtown hospitals. None of them had seen a trace of cyanosis. Then I talked to the sick men some more. I learned two interesting things. One was that they had all got sick right after eating. Within thirty minutes. The other was that all but one had eaten oatmeal, rolls, and coffee. He ate just oatmeal. When ten men eat the same thing in the same place on the same day and then all come down with the same illness . . . I told Greenberg that my hunch was food poisoning."

"I was willing to rule out gas," Dr. Greenberg said. A folder containing data on the case lay on the desk before him. He lifted the cover thoughtfully, then let it drop. "And I agreed that the oatmeal sounded pretty suspicious. That was as far as I was willing to go. Common, ordinary, everyday food poisoning—I gathered that was what Pellitteri had in mind—wasn't a very satisfying answer. For one thing, cyanosis is hardly symptomatic of that. On the other hand, diarrhea and severe vomiting are, almost invariably. But they weren't in the clinical picture, I found, except in two or three of the cases. Moreover, the incubation periods —the time lapse between eating and illness—were extremely short. As you probably know, most food poisoning is caused by eating something that has been contaminated by bacteria. The usual offenders are the staphylococci [1]— they're mostly responsible for boils and skin infections and so on—and the salmonella. The latter are related to

[1] **staphylococci** (staf·ih·lo·KOK·sy): a kind of bacteria.

some bakery rolls, a five-pound carton of dry oatmeal, and some salt. The salt had been used in preparing the oatmeal. That morning, like every morning, the cook told me, he had prepared six gallons of oatmeal, enough to serve around a hundred and twenty-five people. To make it, he used five pounds of dry cereal, four gallons of water—regular city water—and a handful of salt. That was his term—a handful. There was an open gallon can of salt standing on the stove. He said the handful he'd put in that morning's oatmeal had come from that. He refilled the can on the stove every morning from a big supply can. He pointed out the big can—it was up on a shelf—and as I was getting it down to take with me, I saw another can just like it nearby. I took that one down, too. It was also full of salt, or, rather, something that looked like salt. The proprietor said it wasn't salt. He said it was saltpeter—sodium nitrate—that he used in corning beef and in making pastrami. Well, there isn't any harm in saltpeter . . . but I wrapped it up with the other loot and took it along, just for fun. The fact is, I guess, everything in that place looked like poison."

After Dr. Pellitteri had deposited his loot with a Health Department chemist, Andrew J. Pensa, who promised to have a report ready by the following afternoon, he dined hurriedly at a restaurant in which he had confidence and returned to Chatham Square. There he spent the evening making the rounds of the lodging houses in the neighborhood. He had heard at Mr. Pensa's office that an eleventh blue man had been admitted to the hospital, and before going home, he wanted to make sure that no other victims had been overlooked. By midnight, having covered all the likely places and having rechecked the downtown hospitals, he was satisfied. He repaired to his office

and composed a formal progress report for Dr. Greenberg. Then he went home and to bed.

The next morning, Tuesday, Dr. Pellitteri dropped by the Eclipse, which was still closed but whose proprietor and staff he had told to return for questioning. Dr. Pellitteri had another talk with the proprietor and the cook. He also had a few inconclusive words with the rest of the cafeteria's employees— two dishwashers, a bus boy, and a counterman. As he was leaving, the cook, who had apparently passed an uneasy night with his conscience, remarked that it was possible that he had absent-mindedly refilled the salt can on the stove from the one that contained saltpeter. "That was interesting," Dr. Pellitteri told me, "even though such a possibility had already occurred to me, and even though I didn't know whether it was important or not. I assured him that he had nothing to worry about. We had been certain all along that nobody had deliberately poisoned the old men." From the Eclipse, Dr. Pellitteri went on to Dr. Greenberg's office, where Dr. Gettler's report was waiting.

"Gettler's test for methemoglobin was positive," Dr. Greenberg said. "It had to be a drug now. Well, so far so good. Then we heard from Pensa."

"Greenberg almost fell out of his chair when he read Pensa's report," Dr. Pellitteri observed cheerfully.

"That's an exaggeration," Dr. Greenberg said. "I'm not easily dumfounded. We're inured to the incredible around here. Why, a few years ago we had a case involving some numskull who stuck a fistful of potassium-thiocyanate crystals, a very nasty poison, in the coils of an office water cooler, just for a practical joke. However, I can't deny that Pensa rather taxed our credulity. What he had found was that the small salt can and the one that was supposed to be full of sodium nitrate both contained sodium nitrite. The other food samples, incidentally, were OK."

"That also taxed my credulity," Dr. Pellitteri said.

Dr. Greenberg smiled. "There's a great deal of difference between nitrate and nitrite," he continued. "Their only similarity, which is an unfortunate one, is that they both look and taste more or less like ordinary table salt. Sodium nitrite isn't the most powerful poison in the world, but a little of it will do a lot of harm. If you remember, I said before that this case was almost without precedent—only ten outbreaks like it on record. Ten is practically none. In fact, sodium-nitrite poisoning is so unusual that some of the standard texts on toxicology don't even mention it. So Pensa's report was pretty startling. But we accepted it, of course, without question or hesitation. Facts are facts. And we were glad to. It seemed to explain everything very nicely. What I've been saying about sodium-nitrite poisoning doesn't mean that sodium nitrite itself is rare. Actually, it's fairly common. It's used in the manufacture of dyes and as a medical drug. We use it in treating certain heart conditions and for high blood pressure. But it also has another important use, one that made its presence at the Eclipse sound plausible. In recent years, and particularly during the war, sodium nitrite has been used as a substitute for sodium nitrate in preserving meat. The government permits it but stipulates that the finished meat must not contain more than one part of sodium nitrite per five thousand parts of meat. Cooking will safely destroy enough of that small quantity of the drug." Dr. Greenberg shrugged. "Well, Pellitteri had had the cook pick up a handful of salt—the same amount, as nearly as possible, as went into the oatmeal—and then had taken this to his office and found that

it weighed approximately a hundred grams. So we didn't have to think twice to realize that the proportion of nitrite in that batch of cereal was considerably higher than one to five thousand. Roughly, it must have been around one to about eighty before cooking destroyed part of the nitrite. It certainly looked as though Gettler, Pensa, and the cafeteria cook between them had given us our answer. I called up Gettler and told him what Pensa had discovered and asked him to run a specific test for nitrites on his blood samples. He had, as a matter of course, held some blood back for later examination. His confirmation came through in a couple of hours. I went home that night feeling pretty good."

Dr. Greenberg's serenity was a fugitive one. He awoke on Wednesday morning troubled in mind. A question had occurred to him that he was unable to ignore. "Something like a hundred and twenty-five people ate oatmeal at the Eclipse that morning," he said to me, "but only eleven of them got sick. Why? The undeniable fact that those eleven old men were made sick by the ingestion of a toxic dose of sodium nitrite wasn't enough to rest on. I wanted to know exactly how much sodium nitrite each portion of that cooked oatmeal had contained. With Pensa's help again, I found out. We prepared a batch just like the one the cook had made on Monday. Then Pensa measured out six ounces, the size of the average portion served at the Eclipse, and analyzed it. It contained two and a half grains of sodium nitrite. That explained why the hundred and fourteen other people did not become ill. The toxic dose of sodium nitrite is three grains. But it didn't explain how each of our eleven old men had received an additional half grain. It seemed extremely unlikely that the extra touch of nitrite had been in the oatmeal when it was served. It had to come in later. Then I began to get a glimmer. Some people sprinkle a little salt, instead of sugar, on hot cereal. Suppose, I thought, that the bus boy, or whoever had the job of keeping the table salt shakers filled, had made the same mistake that the cook had. It seemed plausible. Pellitteri was out of the office—I've forgotten where—so I got Food and Drugs to step over to the Eclipse, which was still under embargo, and bring back the shakers for Pensa to work on. There were seventeen of them, all good-sized, one for each table. Sixteen contained either pure sodium chloride or just a few inconsequential traces of sodium nitrite mixed in with the real salt, but the other was point thirty-seven percent nitrite. That one was enough. A spoonful of that salt contained a bit more than half a grain."

"I went over to the hospital Thursday morning," Dr. Pellitteri said. "Greenberg wanted me to check the table-salt angle with the men. They could tie the case up neatly for us. I drew a blank. They'd been discharged the night before, and God only knew where they were."

"Naturally," Dr. Greenberg said, "it would have been nice to know for a fact that the old boys all sat at a certain table and that all of them put about a spoonful of salt from that particular shaker on their oatmeal, but it wasn't essential. I was morally certain that they had. There just wasn't any other explanation. There was one other question, however. Why did they use so much salt? For my own peace of mind, I wanted to know. All of a sudden, I remembered Pellitteri had said they were all heavy drinkers. Well, several recent clinical studies have demonstrated that there is usually a subnormal concentration of sodium chloride in the blood of alcoholics. Either they don't eat enough to get sufficient salt or they lose it more rapidly than other people do, or both. Whatever the reasons are, the conclusion was all I needed. Any animal, you know, whether a mouse or a man, tends to try to obtain a necessary substance that his body lacks. The final question had been answered."

THE FACT IS—

1. What made the eleven men turn blue? Were there any fatalities?

2. Who was at fault in this accident? What can be done to prevent such occurrences?

3. Although 125 people ate oatmeal containing sodium nitrate, only eleven came down with sodium nitrate poisoning. Why?

A WORD TO REMEMBER: plausible

Plausible is a word whose meaning has changed radically from its Latin root *plaud* or *plod*, meaning "to clap hands." *Applaud* and *applause* belong to the same word family as *plausible;* so do *explode* and *explosive.* Can you see the connection in root and in meaning between *applaud* and *explode?*

"Moran," the doctor told the young sergeant, "this is the greatest day of my life, and I owe it to you."

Yellow Terror

JOHN J. FLOHERTY

Here and there throughout the world in the drug-laden atmosphere of laboratories, men and women work unceasingly to safeguard mankind against its greatest enemy, disease.

Surrounded by the complex apparatus of science, they delve without fanfare into the unknown; a culture in a test tube, a brew in a Florence flask, a distillate from a bubbling retort may be an answer to the prayer of millions. Or it may be that a human, a faithful helper, offers his body, the only receptacle in which the genesis of a malady may be observed and studied.

This labor of science is often attended by danger more deadly than the conflict of war. The roster of those who have given their lives in the service of humanity includes names of scientists that will live for centuries. Yet few ever hear of the humble volunteers who have faced death without reward or glory. One was Johnny Moran, whose story is unequaled as a document of bravery and unselfishness, an epic of a man without fear.

Within the memory of our fathers, the scourge of yellow fever gripped the United States periodically. To the south of us in the West Indies and in Central America, the dreaded "yellow jack," as it was called, levied a toll in human life that was appalling. At intervals it broke bounds and invaded our southern states.

Even New York and other ports in the North suffered from its onslaught.

No one knew what caused the dread disease, nor how it was transmitted. Physicians were as baffled as their patients. Medication was worthless. Preventive measures failed; all except fleeing the infected spot. The saffron eyeballs and black vomit were usually the signal for desertion by all but the faithful few who invariably come forth in a crisis.

Yellow jack was a worldwide topic of that day. The heart-rending scenes in stricken communities were discussed in all countries. Epidemics broke out far from the Caribbean hotbed of the disease. West Africa and South America were in its grip. Sporadic cases were found in many European ports.

Even in Galway, Ireland, little Johnny Moran, who was then nine, often heard neighbors tell of the plague that was ravaging America.

Johnny was one of a large family that lived on a small farm. His oldest brother had emigrated to the United States and was doing well. As times were hard and there were many mouths to feed, it was decided that Johnny should join his brother in the land of plenty.

The Irish boy thrived on American soil and in a few years had grown into a strapping young fellow anxious to make his own way in the world. He sold papers and magazines and did all kinds of odd jobs. Among those for whom he worked was a woman physician. Pleased with his cheery spirit and quick wit, she gave him a steady job as handyman and bodyguard. At that time it was not considered entirely safe for a woman to go alone into some parts of the city in which she labored.

In his new job, Johnny had access to several medical books and soon became thoroughly engrossed in them. Before long his newly acquired interest in medicine had become so strong he determined to become a doctor. He saved his scant wages and took up a course in a commercial school, hoping it would lead to a larger salary. It did. He secured a job as hotel clerk.

In the meantime the Spanish-American War had begun, and Johnny became fired with a patriotic fervor. He decided to abandon the hotel desk for the cavalry. He felt he could save more money in the army than in civilian life, and if the war brought with it a bit of adventure—well and good.

He enlisted at Fort Meyer, Virginia, in the hope that he would be assigned to a mounted regiment. While undergoing the usual medical examination, Fate, in the person of an army surgeon, began to mold a career for the ambitious lad that was to deprive the world of a physician and give it a hero.

The army surgeon was quick to see that Johnny had an unusually keen mind and that he had at least a speaking acquaintance with medicine. He advised the lad to forget the glamor of the cavalry and join the hospital corps instead. This appealed to Johnny, and he gave up all idea of dashing horses and flashing sabers.

Johnny's progress in the medical corps was rapid. In a few months he was made acting hospital steward with the rank of sergeant. He was attached to Guarajay barracks near Havana, where he saw disease levy frightful toll on the American troops. Malaria, dysentery, typhoid, and the ghastly yellow fever were killing a score to every one that died from wounds.

For several months following the end of the war, the fever-ridden troops were held in Cuba. To bring them home might unleash an epidemic that would make the number of war casualties look insignificant.

During this postwar period, Johnny

was stricken with tropical malaria, which, while not so deadly as yellow jack, racks its victims with devastating chills and fevers. Aching bones, prostrating lassitude, and loss of strength bring the victim to a state of semicollapse. Although suffering all these torments, Johnny carried on, ministering to his patients, many of whom were not so sick as he.

Conditions in Havana and vicinity became so deplorable that the United States government sent a four-man commission to Cuba. It was headed by Major Walter Reed and was instructed to use every means possible to rid the army of disease, but more particularly to find the source of yellow-fever infection and to stamp it out. Quinine was a well-known specific for malaria; furthermore it was conceded that the disease was transmitted by the anopheles, or tiger-wing mosquito. Typhoid and dysentery were caused by pollution and were controllable through intensive sanitation. Yellow fever was the unknown quantity. It struck from nowhere, reaped its grim harvest, and left for no apparent reason. Some maintained it was infectious, others that it was contagious. Victims were often stricken, however, under conditions that would seem to disprove both.

There were high hopes that the cleanup of Havana as conducted by Major Gorgas would end the plague, but in spite of the improved sanitary conditions yellow fever claimed more and more victims.

While the fight against the disease was in progress, a Havana physician, Dr. Charles Finlay, drew upon himself the ridicule of the medical profession and of the entire population. He proclaimed that yellow fever, like malaria, was transmitted only by the mosquito. He went so far as to give the formidable name of the insect, Stegomyia calopus,

sometimes called by scientists Stegomyia fasciata, the Greek for fly with striped legs.

When Major Reed and his companions arrived in Cuba, they knew no more about the origin of yellow fever than did the rest of the world.

The practice hitherto had been to isolate yellow-fever patients. In spite of the isolation, however, the disease spread.

Meanwhile, Dr. Finlay loudly insisted that the Stegomyia was the sole carrying agent.

Major Reed was impressed by the doctor's sincerity. Although contrary to medical opinion, the mosquito theory was at least worth scientific attention.

A quarantine camp had been erected on the outskirts of Havana: a cheerless building surrounded by barbed wire and patrolled by armed sentries. It soon became a proving ground to determine whether yellow fever was caused by contagion or mosquito bite.

At that time science did not know of any animal susceptible to the germ. Humans must volunteer as guinea pigs. For weeks the Major was stalemated. The deadliness of the disease had so terrified the population that no one would volunteer.

In the meantime, Johnny Moran's enlistment had expired. Still intent on laying aside money for his medical education, he accepted a civilian job in Havana.

One day while Major Reed was telling an army contract surgeon of his difficulty in securing volunteers, his luck turned. The surgeon said, "I know the very man to start the ball rolling." He saw Johnny that very day. The ravages of tropical malaria had left their mark on the tough young Irishman. The racking chills and delirium of fever were still fresh in his memory.

Johnny listened attentively to the

Major as he told of the vital need of volunteers, and of the offer of five hundred dollars bonus from the government.

When the surgeon had finished, Johnny was deep in thought. Then with his usual grin he replied, "Much obliged, Doc. I'll let you know in the morning."

That evening Johnny waited for his roommate, Jack Kissinger, who also had been in the hospital corps, to come home. When he arrived, Johnny told him of the surgeon's proposal. Kissinger, who also had seen yellow fever at its worst, was horrified. "Are you crazy?" he shouted.

"No, only thinking," Johnny replied with a quiet deliberation.

Kissinger paced the room while Johnny sat on the bed. "You," he said, anger in his voice, "you of all guys in the world to let yourself in for a dose of yellow jack! Haven't you seen enough of the old crowd go out feet first? Have you forgotten what they went through before they left?"

"That's what I'm thinking of." Johnny's voice was low, but there was a determined note in it.

The hall clock struck hour after hour while the friends argued. At five o'clock, as dawn came through the windows, Kissinger quietly said, "OK! Let's go to bed."

Later that morning the two buddies swaggered into the administration building at the quarantine camp. They found Major Reed in his office, busy with a sheaf of reports that lay on his desk. He looked up wearily.

"Well?" he said.

Johnny, in whom army discipline was still strong, stepped forward a pace and came to attention.

"Sir, we have come to report for volunteer duty."

The Major could not believe his ears. He stood up and approached the men.

"Do you boys know what you are doing?" he asked. There was anxiety in his voice.

"Yes, sir."

"Sorry the reward is not greater for the risk you are taking." Both men stiffened. Johnny growled, "We do not want any reward. I said we're volunteers."

For a moment the three men stood silent. The hard-boiled Major recognized heroism when he saw it. He raised his hand in salute, and in a voice not entirely steady said:

"Gentlemen, I salute you."

An orderly escorted the men to their quarters.

The news spread through Havana that Reed had succeeded in getting two volunteers at last. When it was learned that they were none other than Moran and Kissinger, two medical corps men who really knew what they were doing, more volunteers appeared. Several of them were Spaniards to whom the mosquito theory was a joke, as indeed it was to the doctors. Five hundred dollars was a fortune to these men. If the Americans were crazy enough to hand it to them, they would be crazy not to accept it.

Two rooms had been specially built for the tests. One was virtually without ventilation and thoroughly screened against mosquitoes. The bedding on the cots had been taken from the beds on which yellow fever victims had died. The clothing worn by the volunteers had also been taken from the dead victims of the disease and left in an undisinfected state. If ever there were perfect conditions for contagion, they were in this room, yet at the end of the test period, not a man had contracted the disease.

After many similar tests it became evident that the centuries-old belief that yellow fever was contagious was unfounded.

While the tests proved that contagion was a myth, they did not demonstrate, however, how the disease was transmitted, or that the Stegomyia was the carrying agent. This was done in the other room. The second room, in violent contrast with the first, was a model of hygienic system; a masterpiece of sanitary construction and equipment. It, too, was perfectly screened, but to keep mosquitoes in rather than to keep them out.

It was in one of the screened cubicles in this room that Johnny was placed naked on a cot. As he lay waiting for the doctors to arrive, he knew the zero hour had come; the battle was on. A hand mirror lay beside him on a small table. Outside his cage an orderly busied himself with preparation for the coming test. A cool breeze wafted through the room. It felt good to Johnny, for the weather outside was sultry.

Major Reed and two assistants entered and went directly to Johnny's enclosure.

"Hello, Moran, how do you feel?" The Major's voice had a touch of banter in it.

"OK, Doc. Have you the little bloodhounds with you?" A grin as broad as the map of Ireland spread over Johnny's face.

"Eleven little beauties all ready to go to work." The Major held up a wide-mouthed jar. "They've just had a good meal over in the fever ward. They may not be very hungry, but we'll see."

One of the assistants placed the mouth of the jar against an opening in the screen, and in a few moments the mosquitoes had left the jar for the inside of the screened cubicle.

Johnny watched them as they flew, reconnoitering in their new surroundings. One by one they landed on the screen without showing interest in his soft white skin. A flick of a towel on the screen started them in flight again. They circled for several minutes before one of them swooped toward the pillow on which the victim lay. He could hear the buzzing whine of the little devil's wings. Then another and another hovered over his head. Soon the pack was in full cry. Johnny waved them away from his head. He wanted them to land on his chest where he could see them at work. One landed and bored in without delay. Johnny slowly reached for the mirror so he could see the bloodthirsty insect gorge itself. His interest in medicine was still strong. The scientific as well as the humanitarian aspect of the test gripped him. Another and still another of the Stegomyia joined the blood feast. Unlike other mosquitoes, their bites did not sting, neither did they itch. In fact, if he had not seen them bore in and suck until their slender little bodies had become swollen, he would not have known he had been bitten.

Outside the cage the Major and his assistants stood marveling at Moran's nerve as he encouraged the gluttonous insects to drink their fill. As they became gorged, they lazily flew away, and alighted on the screen to await digestion.

Then began the anxious period of waiting—the period of incubation. For ten dreary days Moran watched for symptoms, taking his own temperature every hour, and an accurate record of how he felt and functioned. He ate and slept normally and in fact enjoyed the best of health. It was with keen disappointment he said to Major Reed one morning, "I'm afraid there's nothin' doin', Doc. Guess we'd better try again."

The Major's face lit with admiration. Here was a man!

By all the rules of the game, Johnny was entitled to quit. He had willingly faced disease and probable death. It was not his fault that he was not now in the delirium of fever.

Once again they imprisoned Sgt. Moran in his sanitary cell, and again they unleashed a pack of the little winged wolves. This time he knew their behavior. Gently waving his arms, he herded them onto his naked chest where he could watch them and count their bites.

While awaiting the results of the inoculation, Johnny was given a job in the Major's office. His clerical duties kept his mind occupied and made the waiting less tedious. He kept a chart on his desk on which he entered temperatures and other data on his condition. As the days went by without a symptom, he felt depressed. He dreaded disappointing the Major again.

The other volunteers looked on Johnny as a mild lunatic. With the possible exception of Kissinger, every one of them was firm in his belief that he would escape infection; besides, the bonus of five hundred cash was not to be taken lightly.

"Think of a guy," they would say, "going for a second shot and praying it will take!"

While the tests were progressing, Major Reed and his assistants worked endless hours in the laboratory. They delved into the habits and biology of the Stegomyia and acquired a collection of the ravenous pests that, unless carefully guarded, might well become an army of destruction. They learned from Dr. Finlay that a period of ten days must elapse after a mosquito had bitten a yellow-fever patient if it were to transmit the disease. When at the end of two weeks Johnny showed no symptoms, the doctors were inclined to declare him immune. The Major, however, had other plans. Calling Johnny to his office, he told him bluntly that the tests had failed because the mosquitoes used had not been "ripe." He told of their newly acquired knowledge of the ten-day period that must elapse between the bite of the yellow-fever patient and the inoculating bite. Moran's face brightened as the Major told of the ripeness and prime condition of the insects he

had on hand. They were as sure-fire as a rifle cartridge.

"How about a shot from a batch of those new little devils, Doc? I'm sure it will take this time." There was pleading in his voice.

The Major hesitated. He was torn between concern and admiration for the young Irishman.

"Moran," he said gravely, "I think you should know the chances you are taking. There will be no misfire this time; you will get yellow fever, and you know as much about the outcome as I do. Don't you think you'd better think it over?"

Moran did not hesitate. "When do we start, Doc?" he said quietly.

That afternoon Johnny was back in his screened cubicle. Fifteen fever-infected Stegomyia were swirling around him. Johnny waved them away from his head and kicked at them viciously when they tried to alight on his legs. He coaxed and urged them to land on his chest where he could watch them in the mirror as they drilled through his skin.

The new batch of insects was ravenous. Without food for ten days, they lost no time getting to work. In a few minutes a dozen of them had pierced the skin of Johnny's chest and were busily making up for lost time.

Outside the enclosure Major Reed and his assistants made notes of each bite as Johnny reported. "There's that little devil again. She's got her drill in me up to the hilt, here on my chest. There's another a little higher up. She's just starting to dig in. My, oh, my, what a starved lot!" Johnny babbled along as each Stegomyia left its load of poison.

Twice the next day Moran entered the cage. Each time a flock of poison-bloated mosquitoes went to the attack. His chest was polka-dotted with tiny red spots.

The inoculation over, there was little for Johnny to do but wait for the first symptoms of yellow fever that he felt sure would appear in a few days.

The insufferable heat of the midday sun parched the plain on which the isolation camp was built. Vultures wheeled lazily overhead. The sentries did their rounds with monotonous regularity. The deadly stillness was broken only by the occasional buzzing of a winged insect. Johnny came to hate the white-faced office clock because it ticked off the seconds so slowly.

Days passed. Johnny's temperature did not vary a fraction of a degree. His general health was excellent. Frequent examinations showed him to be normal. He began to feel that maybe after all he was immune. What a disappointment that would be to Major Reed! He hated to think of it. He felt that somehow he had let the Major down, and it depressed him. He played cards occasionally but his heart was not in it. A feeling of complete frustration had taken hold of him. He envied Kissinger, who was then fighting it out with yellow jack as the result of a single shot of ripe Stegomyia. "Why couldn't it be me?" he muttered over and over. "I got him into this; it should have been my turn first."

His turn came. Shortly after breakfast the next morning he felt a little giddy. His eyes hurt when he moved them. The thermometer showed a slight increase in his temperature. His spirits rose. Maybe after all he could serve the Major in his fight against the disease that was still killing off the troops in great numbers.

By noon he had a severe headache. A lassitude that made it difficult to move took hold of him. The warm breeze that came through the windows chilled him. His temperature had risen two degrees. This looked like it, yet he was not sure. He would wait before reporting it to the Major.

As the afternoon wore on, he grew steadily worse. With each new symptom his spirits rose higher. He confided to a buddy that he believed he had it at last. Then he was sorry he had spoken; the friend ridiculed him.

"Say, Johnny, you ain't got no more yellow jack 'n I have. You've got the old malaria coming back on you."

Johnny remained silent. Could it be that his friend was right? The sickness that was on him was as nothing to the disappointment that gripped him.

He tottered back to his quarters and went at once to the mirror that hung near the window. Already his face was drawn and his skin had lost its ruddy color. Then his spirits rose again. In the corners of his eyes were patches of saffron yellow. This was no malaria. This was the real thing!

Although Johnny went to the mess hall that evening, he did not eat. Food and yellow fever do not go well together. He tried to appear in his usual good humor, but his messmates saw at once something was wrong. "Malaria," they said, for it was believed among them that Johnny was immune. But Johnny knew better.

Leaving the mess hall, he stumbled to the Major's quarters. Pushing the orderly aside, he staggered into the room in which the Major was settling down to read the day's reports.

"It worked, Major, I've got it!" he shouted, his eyes burning with fever and excitement.

The Major rose and slowly approached the sick man, for he was now sick indeed. He looked at Johnny searchingly. "Yes, Moran, you've got it this time sure." His voice was low and had a note of pity in it.

A grin spread over Johnny's drawn face. "I knew we'd lick it, Doc," he said weakly.

The Major placed a hand on Johnny's swaying shoulder and looked into his yellowing eyes.

"Moran, this is the greatest day of

my life, and I owe it to you. You may name your own doctor, whoever he is. You shall have the best hospital care that can be provided."

"That's all right, Doc. You're good enough for me."

The fight was won. Yellow fever had been tracked down. Its final defeat was but a matter of weeks. Science with the aid of Johnny Moran had won one of its greatest victories.

They took Johnny to the hospital that evening, where for two terrible weeks he wavered between life and death. His strong constitution and the heroic effort of Major Reed pulled him through.

When Johnny left the hospital and again picked up the threads of his life, he did not, as he had expected, enter the study of medicine. After what he had been through, it seemed like an anticlimax. He had contributed more to medical science and to humanity in a few short weeks than most doctors do in a lifetime.

It was for this contribution that a grateful Congress awarded him its most cherished gift, the Congressional Medal, on which was inscribed:

AWARDED TO
JOHN J. MORAN
IN RECOGNITION OF THE
HIGH PUBLIC SERVICE
OF MAJOR REED U.S.A.
AND ASSOCIATES WHO GAVE TO
MAN CONTROL OF
YELLOW FEVER

THE FACT IS—

1. What did John Moran do to earn a Congressional Medal?

2. How did John become interested in medicine?

3. Why was yellow fever regarded by the United States as a serious problem?

4. What was known about the origin of yellow fever before Major Reed began his work? What was Dr. Finlay's idea about its origin?

5. What did Major Reed and Johnny prove to be the actual cause of yellow fever? How could the disease be controlled?

"HERE WAS A MAN!"

1. Which of these drives—desire for money, love of adventure, patriotism, humanitarianism—led Johnny Moran to risk his life in a scientific experiment? Do you agree with Johnny's friends that he was a "mild lunatic"?

2. Describe orally or in writing an "unsung hero" you have known.

3. Find out what happened to Johnny Moran after this great moment in his life.

4. Where does the term *yellow jack*, meaning "yellow fever," come from? An unabridged dictionary will tell you.

Trapped in the Desert

GARY BEEMAN

Their car trapped in desert sand, two young men struggle for a way to survive and escape. Scientific knowledge, common sense, and a little bit of luck play a part in what finally happens.

It began innocently enough, that hot June night in 1959, when I turned off U.S. 91 in the middle of California's Mojave Desert and headed the old black coupé down a gravel road. I was only eighteen, and I didn't understand how a moment of thoughtlessness in the midsummer desert can lead you, step by irrevocable step, to disaster.

An aged prospector had told us—my sixteen-year-old school friend Jim Twomey and me—that the road led to derelict Rasor Ranch, on the edge of an area called the Devil's Playground. Desert "ghost settlements" fascinated me, and so did the prospector's report of rattlesnakes there. As a budding zoology major, I collected animal specimens to help pay for such wandering vacations as this.

We had a couple of days' food in the car, and there was supposed to be a good well at Rasor. Still, I'd never have turned off the highway with only two pints of water in our canteens if I hadn't been so tired. It was almost midnight. We'd driven more than four hundred miles from San Francisco; then we'd bird-watched most of a sun-scorched afternoon.

Turning off the highway at a half-buried tire the prospector had told us about, I drove down the moonlit gravel road. After a long way—I didn't notice just *how* long—we hit a little finger of sand that had drifted across the road. I gunned the car, and we plowed over it, then over three more drifts. After the fourth, our headlights showed no firm gravel road, only pale, undulating sand. For a few feet the car gained momentum. Then its spinning wheels began to dig down. We shuddered to a halt.

Obviously I'd taken a wrong turn. We got out and paced the distance back to the road: two hundred feet. Jim wanted to sleep and dig out next morning. "No," I said. "Let's get out now. It'll only take a few minutes."

An hour later, we hadn't moved an inch. The rear wheels had dug deeper, that was all. Then, searching for rocks in the moonlight, we stumbled onto the remains of an old railroad track. The steel had been salvaged, but a few ties remained. We found nine in various degrees of preservation.

Using one as a firm base, we jacked up the car and laid a double strip of ties, starting at the front wheels and extending out behind. Then I eased the car backward. It moved slowly but steadily: two feet—six feet—ten feet. Then one wheel slipped off a tie and the car stopped.

All through that long, frustrating night we jacked up the car, rearranged the ties, reversed a few feet until the inevitable slip. I figured we'd come at least twelve miles from the highway, perhaps twenty. But what really mattered was that two hundred feet of sand between the car and the gravel road. By five o'clock in the morning we'd covered perhaps fifty feet—still one hundred fifty to go. Exhausted, we drank all but two cupfuls of our water, then slept on the bare sand.

Almost at once, it seemed, the sun was beating fiercely down. Now, in stark daylight, things looked more serious. We could see why this sandbowl was called the Devil's Playground. Only scraggly bushes broke the barren, stony slopes. Ahead, a dry soda lake glared blindingly white.

Stripped to the waist, we went to work on the car. Within half an hour the sun was burning our skin. The sand soon grew too hot to touch. "Let's rest till evening," I suggested. "We'll get her out once it cools down." Jim didn't need much persuading. We decided we'd shelter in one of the rock faces of a hill that thrust up a quarter mile across the sand. I still wasn't really worried. In fact, before we left the car, I shot a few feet of movie film.

We found two shady hideaways, thirty feet apart. Sprawled under a shallow overhang, I dozed fitfully. The sunlight moved steadily closer, beating savagely up from pale sand. Soon a bare foot of shade remained. My lips began to crack.

About noon we shared the last two cupfuls of water. Afterward, I lay and watched the line of sunlight, waiting for it to retreat. I kept wondering how hot it really was. (Official June temperatures near the Devil's Playground have touched 121 degrees.)

At last, a wedge of shade moved up

unexpectedly from one side. The sun set; a wonderful coolness fell. Somewhere out in the desert, a whippoorwill began its plaintive song. Jim and I went down to the car and ate our first food in twenty-four hours—the first we'd wanted. We each finished a can of chicken noodle soup—preheated by the inferno inside the black coupé—then shared the juice from a small can of pineapple.

The food revived us, and we discussed whether to try walking out. Jim felt too weak for such a long trek, and I rated my own chances a bare 50–50. We decided to keep working on the car. I didn't really grasp, even then, that we were in desperate danger. I knew that unwary motorists had died of thirst in the desert; not long before, in Death Valley, just thirty miles to the north, the dried-out corpses of two young men had been found close beside their stalled car. But somehow I felt it couldn't happen to us.

My memories of that second night are blurred. It was all we could do to jack up the car and run it back a few feet until it slipped off the disintegrating ties. We kept resting, I remember, and half-dozing. About four o'clock we fell asleep.

When I awoke, the half-risen sun was already burning my skin like an infrared lamp. Every movement demanded effort. And now for the first time I understood our peril: during the night we had moved the car barely fifteen feet; more than one hundred thirty feet remained! Jim, weak and listless, seemed to have lost hope. With rocks and twigs I laid out a four-foot SOS; then we started toward our rock shelters.

Right from the start, that second day was terrible. Even in my shady overhang, I could feel the heat sucking moisture out of my body. And it wasn't only the heat. The silence was almost as bad. I found myself straining for sounds, but all I could hear was my heartbeat. The drumbeat inside me swamped everything.

Occasionally I'd hear Jim's heavy breathing. Then he began to babble, in dream or delirium. "What about my grape drink?" he kept saying. "I've paid for it, and I want my grape drink." At last he fell silent.

Soon, the noonday sun was pressing my strip of shade tight against the overhang. Once I heard the lisp of sifting sand. Four feet away, a rattlesnake was moving past, from shade to shade.

I lay in a daze now, never quite dozing, never fully awake. I had given up hope that the day would ever pass its peak. Once, when I squinted out at the car, shimmering in the heat haze a quarter mile away, there was another car parked beside our coupé—and a stream of vehicles rushing up and down the black highway on which they stood. Had I, after all, walked out to the highway? I twisted my head; then squinted out again: the old black coupé stood on pale sand, alone.

Panic swept me. I knew dehydration eventually unbalanced your mind. If I could already see a nonexistent highway, had I been *acting* irrationally?

At last, in midafternoon, I could stand the terrible dryness no longer. Struggling to my feet, I went out into the sun. When I looked down toward the car, I saw for the first time that the flat sand near it had once been a lake. "If I dig," I thought, "perhaps I'll find water." I staggered down the hill.

There were green-leaved creosote bushes growing on a small sand dune, and I remembered that when digging for lizards in such places I had found moisture. I began digging into the side of the dune, in among the bushes' roots. There was no water; but suddenly I realized that my hands felt almost cool. Perhaps I could dig a cave and crawl into that wonderful coolness!

I don't know how long it took me to scoop out a hole. But at last it was big enough. I stripped off all my sweat-grimed clothes and crawled in. The cool sand soothed me like a balm. I fell asleep.

I woke to see the sun sinking below a line of hills. The plaintive whistle of my whippoorwill came at last. I felt cool and rested. Then, without warning, Jim staggered past. His head lolled; his arms hung loose at his sides. Suddenly he sank to one knee, then pitched forward and lay still. I shook him. He moaned faintly.

Alarmed, I hurried to the car and searched feverishly through the inferno inside it. Under the seat I found a bottle of aftershave lotion. I wrenched off the top and put it to my lips. The shock of what tasted like hot rubbing alcohol brought me up short. Again I had that horrible, fleeting comprehension of my unhinged state of mind.

I began rubbing lotion on my face and neck. It felt good. So I went back to Jim, rubbed lotion on his face and poured it over his T-shirt. He was deathly pale, his mouth hung open, and dried mucus flecked his scaly white lips. "We need a drink," I kept thinking. "We both need a drink."

Desperately, I ran my eyes over the car. And suddenly I was thinking, *"The radiator!"* I'd always known that in the desert your radiator water could save you; yet for two days I'd ignored it! I grabbed a saucepan, squirmed under the front bumper, and unscrewed the radiator drainage tap. A stream of rust-brown water poured down over the greasy sway bar and splashed into my saucepan. It was the most wonderful sight I had ever seen.

Still lying under the car, I took several huge gulps. The water was thick with oil and rust. Almost at once, though, I began to feel better. When I had drained the radiator and filled a canteen, I went back to Jim and poured water into his open mouth. He stirred.

Then I returned to the car, got a can of chow mein, and ate half of it. Soon Jim was sitting up and eating his half of the chow mein.

My mind felt clearer, and I realized that if we were to get out I'd have to try something new. After a while I saw what would have been obvious if I had been thinking clearly: that I would have to run the car back off the ties at high speed and just hope I could keep it going.

We were still pitifully weak. When Jim tried to help, he collapsed over the jack, and the rest of that third night he lay prostrate. I must have spent five or six hours over a job that would normally take twenty minutes: aligning the car perfectly on the ties for our final attempt. I knew that if we failed the first time I wouldn't have the strength to try again. At last, utterly exhausted, I fell asleep.

I awoke in hot sunlight. Hurriedly we drank the last of the water. I helped Jim into the car, started the motor, and let it idle for a few moments. Then I looked at Jim, sprawled across the seat. "This is it," I said. He didn't seem to hear.

I revved the motor, slammed the automatic transmission into reverse, and stamped on the accelerator. The car leaped backward. It gained speed, slipped off the ties . . . kept going. All at once, a tie banged hard, somewhere up front. The car faltered, almost stopped. Then the tie snapped, and we were moving again.

But soon we were slowing down. The rear wheels started to dig in with a horribly familiar sinking motion.

They would spin, grip for a moment, then spin again. And, all the time, the motor was slowing down, the car sinking into the sand. We'd almost stopped when I felt the tires grab something solid. They spun again . . . grabbed and spun . . . grabbed. For interminable moments we hung poised between life and death. Then the tires took firm grip and we were moving smoothly. At last we were out on the gravel road, and I was whooping like an idiot. Beside me, Jim was smiling weakly.

Four hours later, after many sweltering halts for the now-dry motor to cool, we turned onto the highway: we'd been stuck only six miles off U.S. 91. And within another mile—less than seven miles from the desolate sand-bowl where we'd faced a terrible death—we came to a modern roadside café.

We parked the old coupé and went inside.

"Kinda warm today, boys," the man behind the counter said. Then he took another look at us and saw that we were drained dry, caked with grime, and dead-tired.

He put two glasses of water on the counter.

"Just sip it a little, boys," he said, "until you get used to it."

We sat on the clean stools, sipping the cool water slowly and gratefully, each sip confirming what we were beginning to dare to believe: we were going to be permitted to stay in the land of the living.

THE FACT IS—

1. For what two reasons did the author want to visit a derelict ranch?

2. The author told of "a moment" of thoughtlessness that nearly cost him his life. Can you think of more than one such moment? Explain.

3. Why didn't the boys abandon the car and walk back to civilization?

4. How did the boys finally manage to escape their trap?

TWO HUNDRED FEET OF SAND

1. If you had to go through a similar experience and had to choose either boy as your partner, whom would you choose? Why? What suggestions for survival, rescue, or escape would you have offered? What precautions would you have taken? Explain and defend your ideas.

2. Scientific intelligence, common sense, and luck played a part in this story. Give one example of each, and describe one scientific principle that was put to use here.

3. With the modern stress on auto safety, assume that the automobile industry and the National Safety Council are offering a prize for the best essay (or blueprint, or proposal) on how automobiles can be better equipped for just such a jaunt into the desert. Write the essay or prepare the blueprint or make the proposal.

Margaret Mead

WILL LANG

Scientists study everything from atoms to rocks to zoology.

This woman was among the first to study people

—in civilizations thousands of years old and

in communities thousands of miles from her native land.

Margaret Mead is an alert, brown-haired woman who has found time in her busy life to be wife, mother, teacher, author, museum curator, consultant to governments and international organizations, and one of the best-known anthropologists on earth.

The last of these is the most unusual. Very few women are outstanding anthropologists. Anthropologists study primitive people or dig up the relics of past civilizations. They often have to live for long periods in jungles or wilderness, among savage tribes, far from civilized comforts. It doesn't sound like women's work. But don't tell that to Margaret Mead!

How did she decide to become an anthropologist?

She was born into a family where research was a tradition. Her father was a professor of economics at the University of Pennsylvania. But in the Mead family, the women could be scholars too. Margaret's grandmother had been for many years a teacher and a principal. It was she who took over much of the job of educating Margaret. She did it in a most remarkable way—"fifty years ahead of her time," Margaret said many years later. She taught Margaret algebra before arithmetic, botany before spelling. Most important, she taught the girl to observe closely things around her, the flowers, trees, grasses, what her little sister did and said, and so forth. She taught Margaret to keep a notebook, and to set down observations in it. From the time she was a small child, Margaret Mead practiced this basic habit of science—close, accurate observation.

Her mother was a sociologist who studied immigrants. Many an afternoon or evening the house was full of people who had just come from a foreign country and could speak very little English. As Margaret grew up, "foreigners" didn't seem strange to her. In fact, she became very interested in their manners and customs and tried to learn a few words of their languages.

When she went to college, therefore, she had respect for research, and she saw no reason why women could not be as good research scholars as men could. And she had an interest in people from other countries. These interests came into focus when she had to choose a career.

She went to DePauw University for one year, and then transferred to Barnard College. Here she is remembered as a bright student with many talents and interests who had difficulty deciding which career she was going to follow. For a while it looked as though she might go into literature or writing. When she was a little girl, she would write seemingly endless plays which even her family tried to avoid having to read. Her most spectacular achievement in drama is still remembered by the actors. When she was in high school, she had directed a student pageant which was given at the end of summer vacation in a beautiful meadow with the actors in cheesecloth costumes. Unfortunately, the meadow was full of poison ivy. The opening of school was postponed a week until the senior class stopped itching.

But despite these setbacks in her dramatic career, it was clear to her college teachers and friends that Margaret Mead could write. And she was interested in the theater and in books. As college students do everywhere, she was willing to sit up half the night arguing about a play or a novel.

Toward the end of her college years, she had two teachers who were distinguished anthropologists. These were Professor Franz Boas and Professor Ruth Benedict. From them she learned to be a cultural anthropologist. That is not the kind of anthropologist who digs up the ruins of ancient cities, but rather the kind who studies primitive tribes and what people in different societies believe and do. Ruth Benedict was one of the few women who, like Margaret Mead, became well-known as an anthropologist. And as Margaret listened to these stimulating teachers, she began to see more clearly what she wanted to do.

More and more, the problem which most interested her was human nature: in what respects is it the same everywhere, and in what respects is it different? For instance, is it human nature for little boys to be aggressive and fight, and for men to be aggressive and fight wars? Is it human nature for children (and adults too) to want what their friends have and try to snatch it from them? Is it human nature for men to be head of the household, and for women to be dependent on them? Are all these things born into man because human nature is what it is, or are they things that man has learned through living for generations under man-made rules? And if they *are* man-made, can man change some of his undesirable customs—such as war?

Anthropologists have a way to study questions like those. They can go to primitive tribes which have not grown up under the rules of modern civilization. If these tribes differ from each other and from modern societies, then it is possible to tell which modern behaviors are "human nature," and which are man-made. And it should be possible to find out how these different customs are learned, and therefore how they can be changed when change is desirable.

To Margaret Mead, this began to seem like the problem she wanted to study. But was she up to it?

In the 1920's, when she was in college, there were still a number of tribes which had not yet come into contact with civilization. Many of them lived on lonely and distant islands in the Pacific Ocean. To study them, one would have to learn languages completely different from any languages ever read or spoken here. There are no grammars or dictionaries of most of these languages; the only way to learn them is to go to the islands. Furthermore, these people do not live as civilized people do. They do not sleep in beds. They do not have doctors; instead of antibiotics, they have magic. They eat things that were never served in the Mead home or at Barnard College—dragonflies, octopus, grubs.

It didn't sound like women's work, but neither the hard work with the languages nor the hardships of living in the Stone Age discouraged Margaret Mead. Rather, they challenged her. But she asked, what is a woman's part in studying this kind of problem? What can a woman anthropologist do that a male anthropologist can't do as well or better?

When she saw the answer to this question, she decided on a career. A woman anthropologist could study and understand women, girls, and family life in these primitive tribes with an insight that no man could possibly bring to the problem. These tribes would never be fully understood until their women and girls were understood. Margaret Mead decided to become an anthropologist.

It was necessary to hurry. Each year there were fewer primitive tribes to study. Each year, more of them came into contact with missionaries or traders and learned the ways of civilization. In a few years, or at most a few decades, there would be no really primitive cultures for anthropologists to look at.

So Margaret Mead hurried through a Ph.D. at Columbia. Then, as later, she worked fifteen hours a day. She supported herself by grading undergraduate papers and by acting as editorial assistant on a scholarly journal. She studied primitive languages, not the languages she was going to have to speak—no one in America could teach her those—but languages with strange and difficult sounds. She studied under Columbia's distinguished anthropologists. She worked always with a sense of urgency, worried lest the primitive civilizations be contaminated before she got to them. She says, "I used to wake in the morning with the sense of a need for haste, with the dreadful thought that the last man on Raratonga might be dying this very morning." (Raratonga is an island in the South Pacific.) She worked and studied in such a hurry that when she was only twenty-three she had finished her courses at Columbia, had won a fellowship to study among some of the natives of Samoa, and was on her way to a task which no American woman had ever undertaken before.

What does a girl from a well-to-do Philadelphia family do when she is transported suddenly from civilization to the Stone Age? Margaret Mead herself tells us something about this. "When an anthropologist arrives among the primitive people he wants to study, he must find someone who can interpret at least a little, so that he can ask what people call things and how they ask questions and ask other people to do things. Probably no one there will have any idea what a word or a sentence is; nor will anyone know that their language has a grammar. They know how

to speak it and how to correct children when they make mistakes. So the anthropologist must behave partly like a child who is being taught to speak and partly like the first person who made a grammar; and he must patiently collect a great many sentences: 'I see a man, I see a woman, I see a dog; I see it (a woman), I see it (a man), I see it (a dog),' on and on, until he can both speak the language and write down its grammar.

"While he is doing this, he must also learn people's names and where they live, and how they spend their time, and what the rules are which he must be careful not to break. Then he must find two or three people who enjoy talking—people who do not mind answering thousands of questions about things that seem perfectly natural to them, such as why animals from the sea and animals from the land may not be eaten on the same day, or why it is a bad thing to walk on the roads at high noon, or why children may not shout and play in a tent where a sacred pipe is kept. . . .

"As he works, the anthropologist writes down hundreds of pages of notes and makes little sketches showing how a bird is snared, or how a fish trap is made and used, or where the different Indian bands set up their tents when a whole tribe meets for a summer buffalo hunt, or how people play string games on their fingers. When someone takes sick, the anthropologist must find out why people think the sick person got that way. Was it because he was hurt by black magic, or because he broke a rule; or was a ghost trying to kill him, or is the sickness a sign that he will become a holy man?

"As far as possible, the anthropologist tries to get close to the people. A man anthropologist goes hunting and fishing with the men; a woman anthropologist holds the babies on her lap and strings beads or flowers or makes baskets. The anthropologist . . . learns to sit in new positions which he may find very uncomfortable—cross-legged or squatting on one heel. All these things make it possible to understand the people better." [1]

So what Margaret Mead did in Samoa was to share the life of the people, their hardships and their customs, their pleasures and their sorrows. Because she is such a tiny woman (actually smaller than some of the girls she studied), she found it easy to be received into the chief's family and to live as his daughters did. She slept on the floor of a thatched hut. She ate breadfruit, bananas, taro, fish, wild pigeon, coconut milk pudding, and land crabs. She took part in the rituals that are part of the training of a Samoan girl. She had to be careful not to transgress any of the rules the Samoans live by. In other words, she put completely behind her the life of an American college girl and became a Samoan girl—with two exceptions: her college-trained mind, and the notebooks which she filled with observations. It was a hard but thrilling experience. Her father had once told her that adding to the sum of exact knowledge in the world was the one thing worth doing. When her notebooks were crammed with exact knowledge, when she thought she understood, so far as this tribe was concerned, the problem she had come to study, she returned to the United States and wrote a book called *Coming of Age in Samoa.*

Unlike most scientific books, hers became a best seller. She had made good use of her early experience with writing. But before Margaret Mead (now *Dr.* Mead) knew that it was going to be a best seller, she was on her way back to the Pacific to study another island, an-

[1] From *People and Places,* World Publishing Co., Cleveland, 1959. Used by permission.

other tribe, trying to find out what elements of human behavior are inborn and which are learned from society. Again she went through the same process—learning the language, getting the people to trust her, living as they did, asking thousands of questions, trying to understand why they did what they did.

This was the general pattern of her life in the years before the world war began in 1939. She learned seven primitive languages. She studied primitive people of many different kinds. And she came up with an answer to the great problem that had, from the first, challenged her.

She found that human nature is to a lesser degree "inborn" than most people had believed. Adolescent children are not necessarily aggressive and do not necessarily quarrel with their parents; she could point to primitive tribes where the opposite was true, and therefore this behavior had been *learned*, not *inborn*. Children are not necessarily creative and imaginative and needing only freedom to do what they wish in order to live rich and charming lives. In answer to this, she could point to the children of the Manus tribe, who are given almost complete freedom to do what they wish, and are "intelligent children . . . but their play is like that of young puppies or kittens. . . . They have a dull, uninteresting child life, romping good-humoredly until they are tired, then lying inert and breathless until rested sufficiently to romp again." Husbands are not necessarily dominant and wives dependent. She could point to primitive tribes where the woman is dominant and the husband dependent, and to others in which the woman is not allowed to cook because cooking is thought to be too sacred for a woman to do. She could find no evidence that competition, aggressiveness, fighting are necessarily parts of human nature.

Rather, she could point to primitive people where cooperation, rather than competition, is the rule. Among the Arapesh, the ideal is to have mild, responsive adults; among the Mundugumors, the ideal is to have violent and aggressive people.

In other words, all these behaviors had been *learned*. Thought by most people to be "natural" and "inborn," they were rather the results of living in a certain kind of society.

Now, the important thing about this is that what has been learned can be relearned in a different way, or a new generation can be taught something else. This is the great message that Margaret brought back from her studies of primitive people: that man is a great deal more changeable than he thinks; and that there is nothing in human nature to make it necessary to live always and forever with some of the customs and behaviors we don't approve.

Think what this means:

1. War has been invented and learned; as a matter of fact, among some peoples it has never existed. Therefore, it can be *un*learned, and human beings intelligent enough to invent it are also intelligent enough to do away with it and invent better ways to solve their problems.

2. The industrialized countries have learned how to live in a way that provides enough education, food, shelter, and medical care for everybody. The "underdeveloped" countries can also learn this. And by studying how societies learn, we can speed up the process of giving underprivileged peoples the privileges they want.

3. But we can go beyond this. The world can be made a healthier, more comfortable, more productive place than it has ever been before. We can turn our energies into this activity rather than into war. Rather than inventing new

ways to fight or compete, we can invent new ways to cooperate to our mutual benefit.

4. If learning is going to be so important in the future of the human race, no one's education is ever going to be complete when he leaves school. Learning will have to go on throughout life.

This is the message that Margaret Mead brought back from her studies in the South Pacific. Most of these studies were done before 1939, but she has made two return trips since World War II. She has also been an associate curator of the American Museum of Natural History and a teacher of anthropology at Columbia, where she once studied. She is in demand everywhere for lectures. She has written a number of exciting, challenging books. She has been married and now has a grown daughter.

Her understanding of primitive cultures has been useful in many important ways. When the war spread to the Pacific, the United States government called on her for help in understanding Pacific problems. For example, our fliers had to be taught what to expect and do if they were forced down on one of the Pacific islands. Dr. Mead says the fliers were taught first "to respect the people they might meet. Of course, they would not be able to talk with them, but as all human beings get hungry and need food, get thirsty and need water, get tired and need rest, these are needs that all human beings can understand; and the idea of what is wanted can easily be put into understandable sign language. Then, as all human beings have some idea about strangers, the fliers were taught that they would have to convince the natives that they were friendly and needed help, but that they were not so weak and helpless that they could easily be killed, and that, as they were human beings like their hosts, they really could understand each other. . . . The fliers

were warned how differently people communicate with each other. A nod of the head might mean "no" instead of "yes"; a shake of the head might mean "yes"; raised eyebrows might mean only a simple question. Being patted all over by the men of the tribe might be a gesture of great friendliness and not, as one might suspect, an attempt to find out if a person was fat enough to be eaten. They had to learn that, lost in a remote mountain valley, the only thing they could really count on was that their respect for other human beings and their trust in them would somehow show in their faces and be heard in their voices, despite all the differences between their hosts and themselves."

If the things American fliers were taught about how to get along with strangers in the South Pacific resemble in any way the things that modern nations must learn in order to get along with each other—respect, friendliness, will to cooperate, neither weakness nor bullying, and belief that people can understand each other without having the same language or the same religion—that is no accident. For Margaret Mead has more and more turned her anthropologist's skill to modern problems. She was called in to help explain and solve some of the difficulties between American servicemen and English civilians; and she found out that many of these troubles arose because they misunderstood each other's customs. She has written a book to explain to us some Soviet behavior in terms of Russian customs and beliefs. For UNESCO she has edited a book about the problems of new and developing nations. This book is intended to put the skills, methods, and knowledge of anthropology at the service of these countries who want to develop an advanced civilization without going through the thousands of years it usually requires.

All this is part of Margaret Mead's busy life. She still hurries, because there is so much to do. She still often works a fifteen-hour day, because there is so much to learn. And in that respect, her life has not changed much from the days when she was in her early twenties, learning the sounds of primitive languages as fast as possible, in order to be able to study primitive tribes before they were contaminated by civilization. She has little sympathy with people who say, "We've got to go slowly, as we always did before." She says we don't have time to wait. She regards the present edge-of-space, brink-of-nuclear-war period as man's most crucial era since the invention of fire. To some of the people who disagree with her that man has so much control over his behavior and his destiny, her answer is simply that the best evidence we have supports her viewpoint, and in the absence of any better ideas, we had better try it. *Now,* she says; not when it's too late!

THE FACT IS—

1. Describe the kind of work that an anthropologist does.

2. What were some of the influences in her childhood and youth that led Margaret Mead to become a social scientist?

3. Where did she do her first important research? What did she learn?

MAN'S MOST CRUCIAL ERA

1. What lessons for our life today can we learn from Dr. Mead's work? What does she suggest we try *now;* not when it is too late? Find some quotations in the article that give her opinion. Do you agree or disagree that we don't have time to wait for our customs to change slowly?

2. In what ways are social science and natural science alike?

3. Visit your library to do the following work.

> **a.** Report on the findings of another prominent anthropologist.
>
> **b.** Learn of the more recent work Margaret Mead has done.
>
> **c.** Examine some of the other fresh new careers in the world of science which women have begun to explore.

A WORD TO REMEMBER: museum

The word *museum* (myoo·ZEE·um) had a noble origin. It was supposed to be the home of the Muses, the Greek goddesses who presided over the arts and sciences. The first building to be given the name was the university built at Alexandria by Ptolemy at about 300 B.C. Does the word mean the same now as it did to Ptolemy?

THINKING ABOUT SEARCHINGS

DIFFERENT KINDS OF SEARCHES

1. All of the selections in this unit concern search but not all concern scientific search. Which two essays are the most scientific? Which two are the least? The noted British scientist Thomas Henry Huxley once wrote: "All men are scientists." Do you agree or disagree? Explain.

2. Although the scientist or inventor is commonly pictured working alone in his laboratory, teamwork is the usual mark of the successful human endeavor. Can you find any essay in this unit in which teamwork *does not* play an important part?

3. An American woman who lived through the *Titanic* disaster gained fame as "the unsinkable Molly Brown." Considering the difficulties they overcame, difficulties that might have "sunk" other people, which characters in this unit might be called "unsinkable"?

4. Margaret Mead is an outstanding example of a woman succeeding in what is generally considered a man's field. What other examples can you find of American women who have competed successfully against men in science? in medicine or law? in politics? Do you think that in other countries—Russia or India, for example—it is easier for women to achieve that kind of success?

5. Every selection in this unit tells a true story; every selection in Unit One, is fiction. By using incidents described in these two units, defend or dispute the statement "Truth is stranger than fiction."

6. You are a newspaper reporter interviewing a character whose story is told in "Searchings." Answering the newspaperman's four questions (who, what, where, and when), write your lead paragraph.

DO YOU REMEMBER THESE WORDS?

Some words reveal their origins in the most obvious manner—like *museum* from *muse* and *adversities* and *adverse*. With other words, the origins are most difficult to discover. Can you match each numbered word to the word at the right which suggests its origin?

1. *abominable*

2. *applaud*　　　　　　*moon*

3. *explode*　　　　　　*omen*

4. *lunatic*　　　　　　*plausible*

5. *ominous*

The World of Sports

"I never feel more at home in America than at a baseball game," wrote Robert Frost, America's favorite modern poet. We have always been a nation that feels at home with sports. Probably the United States is the only modern nation to invent two games played before enthusiastic audiences all over the world. Civil War General Abner Doubleday is "the father of baseball"; a Springfield College teacher, Dr. James Naismith, invented basketball. Athletic ability has always been admired, but excellence is not essential to enjoyment. Most American men remember some athletic achievement of their own or others: the four-run homer in the sandlot game, the victory in a race across the schoolyard, the ninety-yard punt return, the highest jump over a clothesline, the last-minute basket in a neighborhood game, the surprise punch that floored the bully. George Washington carried the memory of throwing a silver dollar across the Rappahannock River, Abraham Lincoln of outwrestling the village champion, Jack London of rough-and-tumble waterfront fights, Robert Frost of having "pitched baseball with distinction."

From the Olympic Games of ancient Athens and arena combats of Rome to the cricket fields of England and the soccer stadiums of Russia, skill at sports has been admired and rewarded. One former gladiator became a Roman emperor; and David, partly as a result of his victory over Goliath, became King of Israel. These, of course, are exceptional cases. Most athletes settle for lesser rewards, like the laurel wreath or the high school letter.

All of sports, however, is not the moment of glory—the home run, the touchdown, the knockout. Athletics is a mirror of life. It is the crippled arm that ended the career of Sandy Koufax; the prejudice that kept Satchel Paige out of major league baseball until he was past his prime; the pain, obscurity, and humiliation of an old and mediocre prize fighter like Tom King in Jack London's story "A Piece of Steak"; the moral conflict of a high school hero like Bill Czerny in "Football Punk—That's Me"; the physical agony of never-say-die athletes like the golfer Ben Hogan and the batting champion Roberto Clemente.

You may be surprised that two of the most revealing views of sports in this unit are provided by two modern poets, James Emanuel and John Updike. Updike portrays "The Ex-Basketball Player," while Emanuel warns, "Remember men when records fall." These two unusual poems may change your attitude toward athletics and athletes.

A Piece of Steak

JACK LONDON

In this corner sits Age in the person of Tom King, a clever fighter the boxing fans have long admired. In the opposite corner sits Youth in the person of Sandel, a powerful newcomer. It is, to Tom King, "a plain business proposition."

With the last morsel of bread, Tom King wiped his plate clean of the last particle of flour gravy and chewed the resulting mouthful in a slow and meditative way. When he arose from the table, he was oppressed by the feeling that he was distinctly hungry. Yet he alone had eaten. The two children in the other room had been sent early to bed in order that in sleep they might forget they had gone supperless. His wife had touched nothing, and had sat silently and watched him with solicitous eyes. She was a thin, worn woman of the working class, though signs of an earlier prettiness were not wanting in her face. The flour for the gravy she had borrowed from the neighbor across the hall. The last two ha'pennies had gone to buy the bread.

He sat down by the window on a rickety chair that protested under his weight, and quite mechanically he put his pipe in his mouth and dipped into the side pocket of his coat. The absence of any tobacco made him aware of his action, and, with a scowl for his forgetfulness, he put the pipe away. His movements were slow, almost hulking, as though he were burdened by the heavy weight of his muscles. He was a solid-bodied, stolid-looking man, and his appearance did not suffer from being overprepossessing. His rough clothes were old and slouchy. The uppers of his shoes were too weak to carry the heavy resoling that was itself of no recent date. And his cotton shirt, a cheap, two-shilling affair, showed a frayed collar and ineradicable paint stains.

But it was Tom King's face that advertised him unmistakably for what he was. It was the face of a typical prize fighter; of one who had put in long years of service in the squared ring and, by that means, developed and emphasized all the marks of the fighting beast. It was distinctly a lowering countenance, and, that no feature of it might escape notice, it was clean-shaven. The lips were shapeless, and constituted a mouth harsh to excess that was like a gash in his face. The jaw was aggressive, brutal, heavy. The eyes, slow of movement and heavy-lidded, were almost expressionless under the shaggy, indrawn brows. Sheer animal that he was, the eyes were the most animallike feature about him. They were sleepy, lionlike—the eyes of a fighting animal. The forehead slanted quickly back to the hair, which, clipped close, showed every bump of a villainous-looking head. A nose, twice broken and molded variously by countless blows, and a cauliflower ear, permanently swollen and distorted to twice its size, completed his adornment, while the beard, fresh-shaven as it was, sprouted in the skin and gave the face a blue-black stain.

All together, it was the face of a man to be afraid of in a dark alley or lonely place. And yet Tom King was not a criminal, nor had he ever done anything criminal. Outside of brawls, common to his walk in life, he had harmed no one. Nor had he ever been known to pick a quarrel. He was a professional, and all the fighting brutishness of him was reserved for his professional appearances. Outside the ring he was slow-going, easy-natured, and, in his younger days, when money was flush, too openhanded for his own good. He bore no grudges and had few enemies. Fighting was a business with him. In the ring he struck to hurt, struck to maim, struck to destroy; but there was no animus in it. It was a plain business proposition. Audiences assembled and paid for the spectacle of men knocking each other out. The winner took the big end of the purse. When Tom King faced the Woolloomoolloo Gouger, twenty years before, he knew that the Gouger's jaw was only four months healed after having been broken in a Newcastle bout. And he had played for that jaw and broken it again in the ninth round, not because he bore the Gouger any ill will, but because that was the surest way to put the Gouger out and win the big end of the purse. Nor had the Gouger borne him any ill will for it. It was the game, and both knew the game and played it.

Tom King had never been a talker, and he sat by the window, morosely silent, staring at his hands. The veins stood out on the backs of the hands, large and swollen; and the knuckles, smashed and battered and malformed, testified to the use to which they had been put. He had never heard that a man's life was the life of his arteries, but well he knew the meaning of those big, upstanding veins. His heart had pumped too much blood through them at top pressure. They no longer did the work. He had stretched the elasticity out of them, and with their distention had passed his endurance. He tired easily now. No longer could he do a fast twenty rounds, hammer and tongs, fight, fight, fight, from gong to gong, with fierce rally on top of fierce rally, beaten to the ropes and in turn beating his opponent to the ropes, and rallying fiercest and fastest of all in that last, twentieth round, with the house on its feet and yelling, himself rushing, striking, ducking, raining showers of blows upon showers of blows, and receiving showers of blows in return, and all the time the heart faithfully pumping the surging blood through the adequate veins. The veins, swollen at the time, had always shrunk down again, though not quite—each time, imperceptibly at first, remaining just a trifle larger than before. He stared at them and at his battered knuckles, and, for the moment, caught a vision of the youthful excellence of those hands before the first knuckle had been smashed on the head of Benny Jones, otherwise known as the Welsh Terror.

The impression of his hunger came back on him.

"Blimey, but couldn't I go a piece of steak!" he muttered aloud, clenching his huge fists and spitting out a smothered oath.

"I tried both Burke's an' Sawley's," his wife said half apologetically.

"An' they wouldn't?" he demanded.

"Not a ha'penny. Burke said—" She faltered.

"G'wan! Wot'd he say?"

"As how 'e was thinkin' Sandel ud do ye tonight, an' as how yer score was comfortable big as it was."

Tom King grunted, but did not reply. He was busy thinking of the bull terrier he had kept in his younger days to which he had fed steaks without end. Burke would have given him credit for a thousand steaks—then. But times had changed. Tom King was getting old; and

old men, fighting before second-rate clubs, couldn't expect to run bills of any size with the tradesmen.

He had got up in the morning with a longing for a piece of steak, and the longing had not abated. He had not had a fair training for this fight. It was a drought year in Australia, times were hard, and even the most irregular work was difficult to find. He had had no sparring partner, and his food had not been of the best nor always sufficient. He had done a few days' navvy work when he could get it, and he had run around the Domain in the early mornings to get his legs in shape. But it was hard, training without a partner and with a wife and two kiddies that must be fed. Credit with the tradesmen had undergone very slight expansion when he was matched with Sandel. The secretary of the Gayety Club had advanced him three pounds—the loser's end of the purse—and beyond that had refused to go. Now and again he had managed to borrow a few shillings from old pals, who would have lent more only that it was a drought year and they were hard put themselves. No—and there was no use in disguising the fact—his training had not been satisfactory. He should have had better food and no worries. Besides, when a man is forty, it is harder to get into condition than when he is twenty.

"What time is it, Lizzie?" he asked.

His wife went across the hall to inquire, and came back.

"Quarter before eight."

"They'll be startin' the first bout in a few minutes," he said. "Only a tryout. Then there's a four-round spar 'tween Dealer Wells an' Gridley, an' a ten-round go 'tween Starlight an' some sailor bloke. I don't come on for over an hour."

At the end of another silent ten minutes, he rose to his feet.

"Truth is, Lizzie, I ain't had proper trainin'."

He reached for his hat and started for the door. He did not offer to kiss her —he never did on going out—but on this night she dared to kiss him, throwing her arms around him and compelling him to bend down to her face. She looked quite small against the massive bulk of the man.

"Good luck, Tom," she said. "You gotter do 'im."

"Ay, I gotter do 'im," he repeated. "That's all there is to it. I jus' gotter do 'im."

He laughed with an attempt at heartiness, while she pressed more closely against him. Across her shoulders he looked around the bare room. It was all he had in the world, with the rent overdue, and her and the kiddies. And he was leaving it to go out into the night to get meat for his mate and cubs—not like a modern workingman going to his machine grind, but in the old, primitive, royal, animal way, by fighting for it.

"I gotter do 'im," he repeated, this time a hint of desperation in his voice. "If it's a win, it's thirty quid—an' I can pay all that's owin', with a lump o' money left over. If it's a lose, I get naught—not even a penny for me to ride home on the tram. The secretary's give all that's comin' from a loser's end. Good-by, old woman. I'll come straight home if it's a win."

"An' I'll be waitin' up," she called to him along the hall.

It was full two miles to the Gayety, and as he walked along, he remembered how in his palmy days—he had once been the heavyweight champion of New South Wales—he would have ridden in a cab to the fight, and how, most likely, some heavy backer would have paid for the cab and ridden with him. There were Tommy Burns and Jack Johnson—they rode about in motor cars. And he walked! And, as any man knew, a hard two miles was not the best preliminary to a fight. He was an old un, and the world did not wag well with old uns. He was good for nothing now except navvy work, and his broken nose and swollen ear were against him even in that. He found himself wishing that he had learned a trade. It would have been better in the long run. But no one had told him, and he knew, deep down in his heart, that he would not have listened if they had. It had been so easy. Big money—sharp, glorious fights— periods of rest and loafing in between— a following of eager flatterers, the slaps on the back, the shakes of the hand, the toffs glad to buy him a drink for the privilege of five minutes' talk—and the glory of it, the yelling houses, the whirlwind finish, the referee's "King wins!" and his name in the sporting columns next day.

Those had been times! But he realized now, in his slow, ruminating way, that it was the old uns he had been putting away. He was Youth, rising; and they were Age, sinking. No wonder it had been easy—they with their swollen veins and battered knuckles and weary in the bones of them from the long battles they had already fought. He remembered the time he put out old Stowsher Bill, at Rush-Cutters Bay, in the eighteenth round, and how old Bill had cried afterward in the dressing room like a baby. Perhaps old Bill's rent had been overdue. Perhaps he'd had at home a missus an' a couple of kiddies. And perhaps Bill, that very day of the fight, had had a hungering for a piece of steak. Bill had fought game and taken incredible punishment. He could see now, after he had gone through the mill himself, that Stowsher Bill had fought for a bigger stake that night twenty years ago than had young Tom King, who had fought for glory and easy money. No wonder Stowsher Bill had cried afterward in the dressing room.

Well, a man had only so many fights in him, to begin with. It was the iron law of the game. One man might have a hundred hard fights in him, another man only twenty; each, according to the make of him and the quality of his fiber, had a definite number, and, when he had fought them, he was done. Yes, he had had more fights in him than most of them, and he had had far more than his share of the hard, grueling fights—the kind that worked the heart and lungs to bursting, that took the elastic out of the arteries and made hard knots of muscle out of Youth's sleek suppleness, that wore out nerve and stamina and made brain and bones weary from excess of effort and endurance overwrought. Yes, he had done better than all of them. There was none of his old fighting partners left. He was the last of the old guard. He had seen them all finished, and he had had a hand in finishing some of them.

They had tried him out against the old uns, and one after another he had put them away—laughing when, like old Stowsher Bill, they cried in the dressing room. And now he was an old un, and they tried out the youngsters on him. There was that bloke Sandel. He had come over from New Zealand with a record behind him. But nobody in Australia knew anything about him, so they put him up against old Tom King. If Sandel made a showing, he would be given better men to fight, with bigger purses to win; so it was to be depended upon that he would put up a fierce battle. He had everything to win by it— money and glory and career; and Tom King was the grizzled old chopping block that guarded the highway to fame and fortune. And he had nothing to win except thirty quid, to pay the landlord and the tradesmen. And, as Tom King thus ruminated, there came to his stolid vision the form of Youth, glorious Youth, rising exultant and invincible, supple of muscle and silken of skin, with heart and lungs that had never been tired and torn and that laughed at limitation of effort. Yes, Youth was the Nemesis. It destroyed the old uns and recked not that, in so doing, it destroyed itself. It enlarged its arteries and smashed its knuckles, and was in turn destroyed by Youth. For Youth was ever youthful. It was only Age that grew old.

At Castlereagh Street he turned to the left, and three blocks along came to the Gayety. A crowd of young larrikins hanging outside the door made respectful way for him, and he heard one say to another: "That's 'im! That's Tom King!"

Inside, on the way to his dressing room, he encountered the secretary, a keen-eyed, shrewd-faced young man, who shook his hand.

"How are you feelin', Tom?" he asked.

"Fit as a fiddle," King, answered, though he knew that he lied, and that if he had a quid, he would give it right there for a good piece of steak.

When he emerged from the dressing room, his seconds behind him, and came down the aisle to the squared ring in the center of the hall, a burst of greeting and applause went up from the waiting crowd. He acknowledged salutations right and left, though few of the faces did he know. Most of them were the faces of kiddies unborn when he was winning his first laurels in the squared ring. He leaped lightly to the raised platform and ducked through the ropes to his corner, where he sat down on a folding stool. Jack Ball, the referee, came over and shook his hand. Ball was a broken-down pugilist who for over ten years had not entered the ring as a principal. King was glad that he had him for referee. They were both old uns. If he should rough it with Sandel a bit beyond the rules, he knew Ball could be depended upon to pass it by.

Aspiring young heavyweights, one after another, were climbing into the ring and being presented to the audience by the referee. Also, he issued their challenges for them.

"Young Pronto," Ball announced, "from North Sydney, challenges the winner for fifty pounds side bet."

The audience applauded, and applauded again as Sandel himself sprang through the ropes and sat down in his corner. Tom King looked across the ring at him curiously, for in a few minutes they would be locked together in merciless combat, each trying with all the force of him to knock the other into unconsciousness. But little could he see, for Sandel, like himself, had trousers and sweater on over his ring costume. His face was strongly handsome, crowned with a curly mop of yellow hair, while his thick, muscular neck hinted at bodily magnificence.

Young Pronto went to one corner and then the other, shaking hands with the principals and dropping down out of the ring. The challenges went on. Ever Youth climbed through the ropes—Youth unknown, but insatiable—crying out to mankind that with strength and skill it would match issues with the winner. A few years before, in his own heyday of invincibleness, Tom King would have been amused and bored by these preliminaries. But now he sat fascinated, unable to shake the vision of Youth from his eyes. Always were these youngsters rising up in the boxing game, springing through the ropes and shouting their defiance; and always were the old uns going down before them. They climbed to success over the bodies of the old uns. And ever they came, more and more youngsters—Youth unquench-

able and irresistible—and ever they put the old uns away, themselves becoming old uns and traveling the same downward path, while behind them, ever pressing on them, was Youth eternal—the new babies, grown lusty and dragging their elders down, with behind them more babies to the end of time—Youth that must have its will and that will never die.

King glanced over to the press box and nodded to Morgan, of the *Sportsman,* and Corbett of the *Referee.* Then he held out his hands, while Sid Sullivan and Charley Bates, his seconds, slipped on his gloves and laced them tight, closely watched by one of Sandel's seconds, who first examined critically the tapes on King's knuckles. A second of his own was in Sandel's corner, performing a like office. Sandel's trousers were pulled off, and, as he stood up, his sweater was skinned off over his head. And Tom King, looking, saw Youth incarnate, deep-chested, heavy-thewed, with muscles that slipped and slid like live things under the white satin skin. The whole body was acrawl with life, and Tom King knew that it was a life that had never oozed its freshness out through the aching pores during the long fights wherein Youth paid its toll and departed not quite so young as when it entered.

The two men advanced to meet each other, and, as the gong sounded and the seconds clattered out of the ring with the folding stools, they shook hands and instantly took their fighting attitudes. And instantly, like a mechanism of steel and springs balanced on a hair trigger, Sandel was in and out and in again, landing a left to the eyes, a right to the ribs, ducking a counter, dancing lightly away and dancing menacingly back again. He was swift and clever. It was a dazzling exhibition. The house yelled its approbation. But King was not dazzled. He had fought too many fights and too many youngsters. He knew the blows for what they were—too quick and too deft to be dangerous. Evidently Sandel was going to rush things from the start. It was to be expected. It was the way of Youth, expending its splendor and excellence in wild insurgence and furious onslaught, overwhelming opposition with its own unlimited glory of strength and desire.

Sandel was in and out, here, there, and everywhere, lightfooted and eager-hearted, a living wonder of white flesh and stinging muscle that wove itself into a dazzling fabric of attack, slipping and leaping like a flying shuttle from action to action through a thousand actions, all of them centered upon the destruction of Tom King, who stood between him and fortune. And Tom King patiently endured. He knew his business, and he knew Youth now that Youth was no longer his. There was nothing to do till the other lost some of his steam, was his thought, and he grinned to himself as he deliberately ducked so as to receive a heavy blow on the top of his head. It was a wicked thing to do, yet eminently fair according to the rules of the boxing game. A man was supposed to take care of his own knuckles, and, if he insisted on hitting an opponent on the top of the head, he did so at his own peril. King could have ducked lower and let the blow whiz harmlessly past, but he remembered his own early fights and how he smashed his first knuckle on the head of the Welsh Terror. He was but playing the game. That duck had accounted for one of Sandel's knuckles. Not that Sandel would mind it now. He would go on, superbly regardless, hitting as hard as ever throughout the fight. But later on, when the long ring battles had begun to tell, he would regret that knuckle and look back and remember how he smashed it on Tom King's head.

The first round was all Sandel's, and he had the house yelling with the rapidity of his whirlwind rushes. He overwhelmed King with avalanches of punches, and King did nothing. He never struck once, contenting himself with covering up, blocking and ducking and clinching to avoid punishment. He occasionally feinted, shook his head when the weight of a punch landed, and moved stolidly about, never leaping or springing or wasting an ounce of strength. Sandel must foam the froth of Youth away before discreet Age could dare to retaliate. All King's movements were slow and methodical, and his heavy-lidded, slow-moving eyes gave him the appearance of being half-asleep or dazed. Yet they were eyes that saw everything, that had been trained to see everything through all his twenty years and odd in the ring. They were eyes that did not blink or waver before an impending blow, but that coolly saw and measured distance.

Seated in his corner for the minute's rest at the end of the round, he lay back with outstretched legs, his arms resting on the right angle of the ropes, his chest and abdomen heaving frankly and deeply as he gulped down the air driven by the towels of his seconds. He listened with closed eyes to the voices of the house, "Why don't yeh fight, Tom?" Many were crying, "Yeh ain't afraid of 'im, are yeh?"

"Muscle-bound," he heard a man on a front seat comment. "He can't move quicker. Two to one on Sandel, in quids."

The gong struck and the two men advanced from their corners. Sandel came forward fully three quarters of the distance, eager to begin again; but King was content to advance the shorter distance. It was in line with his policy of economy. He had not been well trained, and he had not had enough to eat, and every step counted. Besides, he had already walked two miles to the ringside. It was a repetition of the first round, with Sandel attacking like a whirlwind and with the audience indignantly demanding why King did not fight. Beyond feinting and several slowly delivered and ineffectual blows, he did nothing save block and stall and clinch. Sandel wanted to make the pace fast, while King, out of his wisdom, refused to accommodate him. He grinned with a certain wistful pathos in his ring-battered countenance, and went on cherishing his strength with the jealousy of which only Age is capable. Sandel was Youth, and he threw his strength away with the munificent abandon of Youth. To King belonged the ring generalship, the wisdom bred of long, aching fights. He watched with cool eyes and head, moving slowly and waiting for Sandel's froth to foam away. To the majority of the onlookers, it seemed as though King was hopelessly outclassed, and they voiced their opinion in offers of three to one on Sandel. But there were wise ones, a few, who knew King of old time, and who covered what they considered money.

The third round began as usual, one-sided, with Sandel doing all the leading and delivering all the punishment. A half-minute had passed when Sandel, overconfident, left an opening. King's eyes and right arm flashed in the same instant. It was his first real blow—a hook, with the twisted arch of the arm to make it rigid, and with all the weight of the half-pivoted body behind it. It was like a sleepy-seeming lion suddenly thrusting out a lightning paw. Sandel, caught on the side of the jaw, was felled like a bullock. The audience gasped and murmured awe-stricken applause. The man was not muscle-bound, after all, and he could drive a blow like a trip hammer.

Sandel was shaken. He rolled over and attempted to rise, but the sharp yells from his seconds to take the count restrained him. He knelt on one knee, ready to rise, and waited, while the referee stood over him, counting the seconds loudly in his ear. At the ninth he rose in fighting attitude, and Tom King, facing him, knew regret that the blow had not been an inch nearer the point of the jaw. That would have been a knock-out, and he could have carried the thirty quid home to the missus and the kiddies.

The round continued to the end of its three minutes, Sandel for the first time respectful of his opponent and King slow of movement and sleepy-eyed as ever. As the round neared its close, King, warned of the fact by sight of the seconds crouching outside ready for the spring in through the ropes, worked the fight around to his own corner. And when the gong struck, he sat down immediately on the waiting stool, while Sandel had to walk all the way across the diagonal of the square to his own corner. It was a little thing, but it was the sum of little things that counted. Sandel was compelled to walk that many more steps, to give up that much energy, and to lose a part of the precious minute of rest. At the beginning of every round, King loafed slowly out from his corner, forcing his opponent to advance the greater distance. The end of every round found the fight maneuvered by King into his own corner so that he could immediately sit down.

Two more rounds went by, in which King was parsimonious of effort and Sandel prodigal. The latter's attempt to force a fast pace made King uncomfortable, for a fair percentage of the multitudinous blows showered upon him went home. Yet King persisted in his dogged slowness, despite the crying of the young hotheads for him to go in and fight. Again, in the sixth round, Sandel

was careless, again Tom King's fearful right flashed out to the jaw, and again Sandel took the nine-seconds count.

By the seventh round Sandel's pink of condition was gone, and he settled down to what he knew was to be the hardest fight in his experience. Tom King was an old un, but a better old un than he had ever encountered—an old un who never lost his head, who was remarkably able at defense, whose blows had the impact of a knotted club, and who had a knockout in either hand. Nevertheless, Tom King dared not hit often. He never forgot his battered knuckles, and knew that every hit must count if the knuckles were to last out the fight. As he sat in his corner, glancing across at his opponent, the thought came to him that the sum of his wisdom and Sandel's youth would constitute a world's champion heavyweight. But that was the trouble. Sandel would never become a world champion. He lacked the wisdom, and the only way for him to get it was to buy it with Youth; and when wisdom was his, Youth would have been spent in buying it.

King took every advantage he knew. He never missed an opportunity to clinch, and in effecting most of the clinches, his shoulder drove stiffly into the other's ribs. In the philosophy of the ring, a shoulder was as good as a punch so far as damage was concerned, and a great deal better so far as concerned expenditure of effort. Also, in the clinches King rested his weight on his opponent, and was loath to let go. This compelled the interference of the referee, who tore them apart, always assisted by Sandel, who had not yet learned to rest. He could not refrain from using those glorious flying arms and writhing muscles of his, and when the other rushed into a clinch, striking shoulder against ribs, and with head resting under Sandel's left arm, Sandel almost invariably swung his right behind his own back and into the projecting face. It was a clever stroke, much admired by the audience, but it was not dangerous, and was, therefore, just that much wasted strength. But Sandel was tireless and unaware of limitations, and King grinned and doggedly endured.

Sandel developed a fierce right to the body, which made it appear that King was taking an enormous amount of punishment, and it was only the old ringsters who appreciated the deft touch of King's left glove to the other's biceps just before the impact of the blow. It was true, the blow landed each time; but each time it was robbed of its power by that touch on the biceps. In the ninth round, three times inside a minute, King's right hooked its twisted arch to the jaw; and three times Sandel's body, heavy as it was, was leveled to the mat. Each time he took the nine seconds allowed him and rose to his feet, shaken and jarred, but still strong. He had lost much of his speed, and he wasted less effort. He was fighting grimly; but he continued to draw upon his chief asset, which was Youth. King's chief asset was experience. As his vitality had dimmed and his vigor abated, he had replaced them with cunning, with wisdom born of the long fights and with a careful shepherding of strength. Not alone had he learned never to make a superfluous movement, but he had learned how to seduce an opponent into throwing his strength away. Again and again, by feint of foot and hand and body, he continued to inveigle Sandel into leaping back, ducking, or countering. King rested, but he never permitted Sandel to rest. It was the strategy of Age.

Early in the tenth round King began stopping the other's rushes with straight lefts to the face, and Sandel, grown wary, responded by drawing the left, then by ducking it and delivering his right in a swinging hook to the side of the head. It was too high up to be vitally effective; but when first it landed, King knew the old, familiar descent of the black veil of unconsciousness across his mind. For the instant, or for the slightest fraction of an instant, rather, he ceased. In the one moment he saw his opponent ducking out of his field of vision and the background of white, watching faces; in the next moment he again saw his opponent and the background of faces. It was as if he had slept for a time and just opened his eyes again, and yet the interval of unconsciousness was so microscopically short that there had been no time for him to fall. The audience saw him totter and his knees give, and then saw him recover and tuck his chin deeper into the shelter of his left shoulder.

Several times Sandel repeated the blow, keeping King partially dazed, and then the latter worked out his defense, which was also a counter. Feinting with his left, he took a half-step backward, at the same time uppercutting with the whole strength of his right. So accurately was it timed that it landed squarely on Sandel's face in the full, downward sweep of the duck, and Sandel lifted in the air and curled backward, striking the mat on his head and shoulders. Twice King achieved this, then turned loose and hammered his opponent to the ropes. He gave Sandel no chance to rest or to set himself, but smashed blow in upon blow till the house rose to its feet and the air was filled with an unbroken roar of applause. But Sandel's strength and endurance were superb, and he continued to stay on his feet. A knockout seemed certain, and a captain of police, appalled at the dreadful punishment, arose by the ringside to stop the fight. The gong struck for the end of the round and Sandel staggered to his corner, pro-

testing to the captain that he was sound and strong. To prove it, he threw two back airsprings, and the police captain gave in.

Tom King, leaning back in his corner and breathing hard, was disappointed. If the fight had been stopped, the referee, perforce, would have rendered him the decision and the purse would have been his. Unlike Sandel, he was not fighting for glory or career, but for thirty quid. And now Sandel would recuperate in the minute of rest.

Youth will be served—this saying flashed into King's mind, and he remembered the first time he had heard it, the night when he had put away Stowsher Bill. The toff who had bought him a drink after the fight and patted him on the shoulder had used those words. Youth will be served! The toff was right. And on that night in the long ago, he had been Youth. Tonight Youth sat in the opposite corner. As for himself, he had been fighting for half an hour now, and he was an old man. Had he fought like Sandel, he would not have lasted fifteen minutes. But the point was that he did not recuperate. Those upstanding arteries and that sorely tried heart would not enable him to gather strength in the intervals between the rounds. And he had not had sufficient strength in him to begin with. His legs were heavy under him and beginning to cramp. He should not have walked those two miles to the fight. And there was the steak which he had got up longing for that morning. A great and terrible hatred rose up in him for the butchers who had refused him credit. It was hard for an old man to go into a fight without enough to eat. And a piece of steak was such a little thing, a few pennies at best; yet it meant thirty quid to him.

With the gong that opened the eleventh round, Sandel rushed, making a show of freshness which he did not really possess. King knew it for what it was—a bluff as old as the game itself. He clinched to save himself, then, going free, allowed Sandel to get set. This was what King desired. He feinted with his left, drew the answering duck and swinging upward hook, then made the half-step backward, delivered the uppercut full to the face, and crumpled Sandel over to the mat. After that he never let him rest, receiving punishment himself, but inflicting far more, smashing Sandel to the ropes, hooking and driving all manner of blows into him, tearing away from his clinches or punching him out of attempted clinches, and even when Sandel would have fallen, catching him with one uplifting hand and with the other immediately smashing him into the ropes where he could not fall.

The house by this time had gone mad, and it was his house, nearly every voice yelling: "Go it, Tom!" "Get 'im! Get 'im!" "You've got 'im, Tom! You've got 'im!" It was to be a whirlwind finish, and that was what a ringside audience paid to see.

And Tom King, who for half an hour had conserved his strength, now expended it prodigally in the one great effort he knew he had in him. It was his one chance—now or not at all. His strength was waning fast, and his hope was that before the last of it ebbed out of him, he would have beaten his opponent down for the count. And as he continued to strike and force, coolly estimating the weight of his blows and the quality of the damage wrought, he realized how hard a man Sandel was to knock out. Stamina and endurance were his to an extreme degree, and they were the virgin stamina and endurance of Youth. Sandel was certainly a coming man. He had it in him. Only out of such rugged fiber were successful fighters fashioned.

Sandel was reeling and staggering, but Tom King's legs were cramping and his knuckles going back on him. Yet he steeled himself to strike the fierce blows, every one of which brought anguish to his tortured hands. Though now he was receiving practically no punishment, he was weakening as rapidly as the other. His blows went home, but there was no longer the weight behind them, and each blow was the result of a severe effort of will. His legs were like lead, and they dragged visibly under him; while Sandel's backers, cheered by this symptom, began calling encouragement to their man.

King was spurred to a burst of effort. He delivered two blows in succession— a left, a trifle too high, to the solar plexus, and a right cross to the jaw. They were not heavy blows, yet so weak and dazed was Sandel that he went down and lay quivering. The referee stood over him, shouting the count of the fatal seconds in his ear. If before the tenth second was called, he did not rise, the fight was lost. The house stood in hushed silence. King rested on trembling legs. A mortal dizziness was upon him, and before his eyes the sea of faces sagged and swayed, while to his ears, as from a remote distance, came the count of the referee. Yet he looked upon the fight as his. It was impossible that a man so punished could rise.

Only Youth could rise, and Sandel rose. At the fourth second he rolled over on his face and groped blindly for the ropes. By the seventh second he had dragged himself to his knee, where he rested, his head rolling groggily on his shoulders. As the referee cried "Nine!" Sandel stood upright, in proper stalling position, his left arm wrapped about his face, his right wrapped about his stomach. Thus were his vital points guarded, while he lurched forward toward King in the hope of effecting a clinch and gaining more time.

At the instant Sandel arose, King was at him, but the two blows he delivered were muffled on the stalled arms. The next moment Sandel was in the clinch and holding on desperately while the referee strove to drag the two men apart. King helped to force himself free. He knew the rapidity with which Youth recovered, and he knew that Sandel was his if he could prevent that recovery. One stiff punch would do it. Sandel was his, indubitably his. He had outgeneraled him, outfought him, outpointed him. Sandel reeled out of the clinch, balanced on the hairline between defeat or survival. One good blow would topple him over and down and out. And Tom King, in a flash of bitterness, remembered the piece of steak and wished that he had it then behind that necessary punch he must deliver. He nerved himself for the blow, but it was not heavy enough nor swift enough. Sandel swayed, but did not fall, staggering back to the ropes and holding on. King staggered after him, and, with a pang like that of dissolution, delivered another blow. But his body had deserted him. All that was left of him was a fighting intelligence that was dimmed and clouded from exhaustion. The blow that was aimed for the jaw struck no higher than the shoulder. He had willed the blow higher, but the tired muscles had not been able to obey. And, from the impact of the blow, Tom King himself reeled back and nearly fell. Once again he strove. This time his punch missed altogether, and, from absolute weakness, he fell against Sandel and clinched, holding on to him to save himself from sinking to the floor.

King did not attempt to free himself. He had shot his bolt. He was gone. And Youth had been served. Even in the clinch he could feel Sandel growing stronger against him. When the referee thrust them apart, there, before his eyes, he saw Youth recuperate. From instant to instant, Sandel grew stronger. His punches, weak and futile at first, became stiff and accurate. Tom King's bleared eyes saw the gloved fist driving at his jaw, and he willed to guard it by interposing his arm. He saw the danger, willed the act; but the arm was too heavy. It seemed burdened with a hundredweight of lead. It would not lift itself, and he strove to lift it with his soul. Then the gloved fist landed home. He experienced a sharp snap that was like an electric spark, and, simultaneously, the veil of blackness enveloped him.

When he opened his eyes again, he was in his corner, and he heard the yelling of the audience like the roar of the surf at Bondi Beach. A wet sponge was being pressed against the base of his brain, and Sid Sullivan was blowing cold water in a refreshing spray over his face and chest. His gloves had already been removed, and Sandel, bending over him, was shaking his hand. He bore no ill will toward the man who had put him out, and he returned the grip with a heartiness that made his battered knuckles protest. Then Sandel stepped to the center of the ring and the audience hushed its pandemonium to hear him accept young Pronto's challenge and offer to increase the side bet to one hundred pounds. King looked on apathetically while his seconds mopped the streaming water from him, dried his face, and prepared him to leave the ring. He felt hungry. It was not the ordinary gnawing kind, but a great faintness, a palpitation at the pit of the stomach that communicated itself to all his body. He remembered back into the fight to the moment when he had Sandel swaying and tottering on the hairline balance of defeat. Ah, that piece of steak would have done it! He had lacked just that for the decisive blow, and he had lost. It was all because of the piece of steak.

His seconds were half-supporting him as they helped him through the ropes. He tore free from them, ducked through the ropes unaided, and leaped heavily to the floor, following on their heels as they forced a passage for him down the crowded center aisle. Leaving the dressing room for the street, in the entrance to the hall, some young fellow spoke to him.

"W'y didn't yuh go in an' get 'im when yuh 'ad 'im?" the young fellow asked.

"Aw, go to the devil!" said Tom King, and passed down the steps to the sidewalk.

The doors of the public house at the corner were swinging wide, and he saw the lights and the smiling barmaids, heard the many voices discussing the fight and the prosperous chink of money on the bar. Somebody called to him to have a drink. He hesitated perceptibly, then refused, and went on his way.

He had not a copper in his pocket, and the two-mile walk home seemed very long. He was certainly getting old. Crossing the Domain, he sat down suddenly on a bench, unnerved by the thought of the missus sitting up for him, waiting to learn the outcome of the fight. That was harder than any knockout, and it seemed almost impossible to face.

He felt weak and sore, and the pain of his smashed knuckles warned him that, even if he could find a job at navvy work, it would be a week before he could grip a pick handle or a shovel. The hunger palpitation at the pit of the stomach was sickening. His wretchedness overwhelmed him, and into his eyes came an unwonted moisture. He covered his face with his hands, and, as he cried, he remembered Stowsher Bill and how he had served him that night in the long ago. Poor old Stowsher Bill! He could understand now why Bill had cried in the dressing room.

JACK LONDON (1876–1916).

Black eye, broken nose, punch in the jaw, savage click of a wolf's fangs—all of these things Jack London knew from his own experience. Born in San Francisco, the son of a wandering astrologer, he had no real home and almost no formal schooling. London said he had no childhood. So chronic and intense was his family's poverty that Jack went to work before he was ten—selling papers, peddling ice, working in canneries and mills—sometimes for ten hours a day. At fifteen he went on the road as a tramp; at sixteen he was a longshoreman and oyster pirate; at eighteen he rode the freights east and was even jailed as a vagrant. But with all the roughness of his life, he read everything he could lay his hands on and managed to work in a semester at the University of California. In 1897, he joined the gold rush to the Yukon and on his return began to write novels which reflected his experience. Even in the most brutal and violent circumstances, London was studying animals and nature. Indeed, for his observation of animals in such famous novels as **The Call of the Wild** and **White Fang**, London drew praise from great naturalists as well as from a worldwide public which has bought his books by the millions.

THE FACT IS—

1. Boxing is a sport for the young. Why, then, was Tom King still fighting at the age of forty?

2. What did Sandel stand to gain?

3. How did Tom King feel as he began the fight? What was he thinking about?

4. What finally defeated King?

5. Why did Jack London call this story "A Piece of Steak"?

THE IRON LAW OF THE GAME

1. Does it seem strange that a defeated boxer cried? Exactly why did he cry?

2. How might this story have ended if Tom King had succeeded in getting a piece of steak? Write the new ending.

3. Imagine Sandel and Tom King during the few days following the fight. Compare:

> **a.** The way people talked to them on the street, and in the shops.

> **b.** The plans for the future both are now making.

4. Jack London's writings frequently tell of battle and conflict. What stories can you find to support this statement? What experiences in life did London himself have that helped him write so knowingly of violence?

A WORD TO REMEMBER: Nemesis

To understand what Tom King means when he thinks "Youth was the Nemesis," you must know that the Greeks not only "had a word for it" but, very often, had a god. Nemesis (NEM·eh·sis) was the goddess of vengeance, of "paying back" one injury by inflicting another. In this story, how was Youth the Nemesis for Tom King? Did Tom deserve what he got?

Football Punk—
That's Me

BOOTON HERNDON

Bill Czerny went from star
fullback to second-string
center to bench-bound
"stupid punk." He thought,
"Brother, if there's anybody
on this field who's got
nothing to lose, I'm it. Man,
let's have some fun!"

Somewhere in this country, according to the sports magazines, the sun is bright and the air is clear on Monday afternoons in October, and happy American boys shout gaily in the locker rooms as they suit up for the great game of football. That is a pretty picture, all right, but, brother, that is not the way it is in Mohican, my home town. On Monday afternoons in October, in Mohican, the sun is just the way it always is—a dirty yellow blob—the air is nine-tenths coal smoke, and the happy American boys are punks like me, stiff and sore and bruised, sitting on a bench in the locker room, staring at the floor.

We won the game on Saturday, but it had been a bruiser. Metzger, the sub-offensive center, had busted six ribs and was out for the year. He was lucky. Maybe some people thought I was lucky. I was first-string fullback. I scored one touchdown and piled up a mess of yardage, and the word was out that the big teams were scouting me.

Oh, boy! Cash on the line, money under the table every week. Four more years of football, four more years of knees in the kidneys, and fists in the face.

But still, if I wanted to go to college, that was the only way I could do it. You split the dough my old man makes in the mill with six kids and a brewery, and you haven't got much left for higher education.

Somebody yelled, "Hey, Bill!" and grabbed my head and knuckled it, and I drew back and was going to let the jerk have it, only it was Chuck Lathrop. Chuck was offensive center and co-captain and president of the senior class. He was a good guy, too, but he could afford to be. On the day he was born, his old man, who taught English and helped coach the team, started a savings account to send him to Hardy University. Hardy, I said, not Southwest F. and M. In case you haven't heard, Hardy is a school where they permit athletes to attend classes. The kind of school I was going to didn't like their hired men to have their minds cluttered up.

"How you feel, boy?" Chuck asked. "Say, Grizer wants to see you before you suit up."

He went off to slap somebody else's sore back, and I went into the coach's office right away. The Great Grizer liked his boys to jump when he cracked the whip.

He and Mr. Lathrop were in the little cinder-blockwalled office, and Mr. Lathrop smiled and said hello. Grizer pointed his beak at me and said in his harsh voice, "Oh, Kuhserny."

My name is Czerny, and it's Czech, and it's pronounced Cherney, but Grizer pronounced everybody's name wrong.

"Look," he said. "The doc says Metzger's out for the season. I got to have me another center."

"Yeah," I said. What did he want me to do about it? Go hire him one?

"An' you're it," he said. "You're my new center."

And all I could say was, "Me? Why me? I can't even throw a ball back."

"We use the T," Grizer said; "all you have to do is hand it to the quarterback."

"I never played in the line," I said. "I'm not that heavy."

"You're plenty heavy and you're fast," Grizer said. "A natural athlete is good anywhere."

"I don't know the signals," I said.

"Lathrop says you're smart," Grizer said. "He says you can learn 'em. That's another reason I picked you."

"But I'll never play," I said. "I'd be behind Chuck all the time."

Mr. Lathrop cleared his throat. "We talked about that, too, Bill," he said. "Chuck doesn't have your natural ability. He might be your substitute."

Boy, that took the cake. This guy was selling his own son to the scrubs. And the captain of the offense, too. They'd do anything to put a winning team on the field.

"But I won't get a scholarship," I said, and my voice broke. "I won't get to go to college."

Grizer slammed his pencil down on his desk. "OK, Kuhserny," he said. "That's enough. I don't have to explain what I do to every high school punk. I can tell you one thing: when a school gives one of my men a scholarship, they know they're getting a man who does what he's told and earns his pay. Now, get in your suit or turn it in. I don't care which."

He turned his back on me. Mr. Lathrop smiled sorrowfully and shrugged. They had me, and they knew it. The civic league was slipping me ten bucks a week, and if I quit football, my old man would make me go to work. And that's how, grandchildren, I became second-string offensive center for Mohican.

Grizer was right. I was a natural athlete, and, with the Lathrops helping me, the fundamentals came easy. Funny about those Lathrops. Chuck not only helped me on the field, he wanted me to come over to his house at night. I'd always wanted to go there, but now, somehow, I couldn't.

At scrimmage on Wednesday, I found out what I didn't know about playing center. Say the play diagram calls for you to brush-block the guard and then get the left halfback. Well, you bend over and hand the ball back and go for the guard, only he isn't there. He moved when you had your head down. So you run after the left halfback, only he isn't there either. He moved when you were looking for the guard. So you don't get either one. Grizer chewed me out good, and Mr. Lathrop shook his head, which was worse, and Chuck Lathrop asked me to come over to his house for the third night in a row, and I went.

The Lathrops were once People in Mohican and they lived in a nice old house on River Avenue. Chuck took me back to his father's den, pulled out his diagrams, and we began talking, not about what the diagrams say to do but what to do when you can't do what the diagrams say do. They were all things I could have learned myself, the hard way, but Chuck made them easier. One thing he couldn't get me to do, though. He always came running out of the huddle as if he were personally going to take the ball down the field, and he wanted me to do the same thing. I admit it looks good in the newsreels, but what Chuck didn't know was that the rest of the team laughed at him behind his back, especially the paid guys. We called him the school-spirit kid.

After a while, Mr. Lathrop came in, and Mrs. Lathrop brought in some swell hot chocolate, and Mr. Lathrop started talking about a famous novelist he'd known back in college, and it was the most stimulating evening I ever had in my whole life. Once I almost said out loud that I wished I could go to a school like that instead of Southwest F. and M., but I remembered that I wasn't even going there now, so I kept my mouth shut.

Chuck started the game on Saturday, but he knew and I knew and Grizer knew and the whole town knew that I was going to get to play. About the middle of the first quarter, no score, we got the ball on our twenty and Grizer put me in.

The Bessemer guard spit in his fist and said, "Well, look who's here," when I came up to the line.

We bent over and I felt Novotny behind me and I slipped him the ball. I'm not quite sure what happened next, but I think it went like this: The Bessemer guard hit me in the nose, and then the linebacker—he must have got a running start—piled into me with both knees going. They started me going back and my own men piled into me from behind.

I lay there wondering what happened until finally they all piled off. I went back in the huddle, and the fullback, my old substitute Hruska, that punk, said, "What'sa matter, Czern'? You expect fullbacks to drill their own holes, huh?"

"Look, you punk!" I said. "You'd be back warmin' that bench and I'd still be runnin' if—"

"Shut up," Novotny said. Novotny had a chance at Carolina Central, all expenses paid and a job guarantee after graduation, and he was all business. He called O'Rourke around end.

I went up to the line, and the Bessemer guard said, "Hey, baby, your nose is running."

I swiped at it, and sure enough, I'd started bleeding already. I bent over and dug in. I was supposed to get the defensive halfback. I handed back the ball and took off. The guard stuck his foot out and I hit the ground like two tons of bricks. I got up and started after the halfback again, but he'd disappeared. The whistle blew and I found him. He was on top of O'Rourke.

The officials called the play back. We were offside.

"Who was offside?" Novotny said.

"The center," the head linesman said. "But don't ask me how."

So it was second down, seventeen yards to go. "Quick kick," Novotny said.

"You crazy?" Jablonski said. He was the kicker. He already had a couple of offers, and he didn't want to take a chance with his punting average. "Czerny can't get that ball back right for a quick kick. Get Chuck back in here."

"You got mothballs in your head," Novotny said. "Then they know we gonna kick."

"So don't kick," Jablonski said. "Or kick it yourself."

Novotny growled, but he knew better than to fool around with a man's future just for the sake of a football game, so he called a play in the line to waste a down. Then Chuck came out.

Football teams are like chickens. When they find the weakest chicken, they peck him to death. Chuck Lathrop was our weakest chicken, so Bessemer worked on him. They kneed him, they slugged him, they elbowed him. The jerk never hit back either. He took it like a little man.

Mr. Lathrop talked to him during the half, and I saw them both look at me, and then Mr. Lathrop went over to Grizer, and they both looked at me, and then it was my turn. "Chuck's taking a beating," Mr. Lathrop told me. "Do you think you could try it again this half?"

And all at once, then, it was plain to me just what the score was. They didn't want a new center to win games for them, oh, no. They wanted a tough punk from the other side of the tracks to take the rough stuff. And all along I thought they liked me. Boy, that kind of people can sure fool you.

"What'sa matter?" I said. "Afraid little precious is going to get hurt? Want to keep his pretty little nose in shape for Hardy, huh?"

I was spitting it out a mile a minute when Mr. Lathrop grabbed me by the shoulders. His eyes were looking straight into mine. "Bill," he said, "Bill," and for a minute there I thought maybe I was wrong, but then Grizer called him and he had to go.

They got to Chuck again in the third quarter. His face looked like a glob of hamburger. They were walking right through him, and Grizer sent me in. Chuck tried to grin at me, But I gave him the brushoff. If the game was too rough for him, why didn't he turn in his suit and get it over with?

"Look who's here," said the Bessemer guard. "Did you count your teeth before you came in?"

I didn't say anything. I handed the ball back to Novotny, then, still bent over so the referee couldn't see, I swung, both fists, all the way from my knees. The Bessemer guard said "Glug" and that was that. They carried that boy off the field.

But it didn't make much difference, because the next one was just as bad. I finished up the game, except when Chuck came in on punts, and I didn't make any bad mistakes, but I didn't knock myself out either. I just didn't have much to do with the game. Nobody said a thing to me after it was all over, not even Chuck Lathrop.

Usually, I went down to the candy store on Saturday nights after a game, but that night I stayed at home. I kept thinking of Chuck Lathrop and his old man, and I decided I'd return the autographed copies of books that Mr. Lathrop had lent me. I didn't want to do it at dinnertime, though, so I started reading one of them for something to do, and the first thing I knew it had me. I read the whole thing.

The next day I still didn't want to see anybody, so I read another one. There was a copy of some poems by Rupert Brooke, and the leather cover looked good and smelled good, so, even when I didn't understand everything I was reading, it was nice to hold it. I read all day Sunday; there wasn't anything else to do.

I kind of settled into a rut. Afternoons I spent on the football field. Nights I spent reading and studying. I didn't have anything else to do.

All this time we weren't speaking. I wasn't speaking to any Lathrop. I wasn't speaking to anybody much. I stayed at home and read and studied. I played football, but I didn't knock myself out. The other guys did that. I played good enough so they couldn't get me to turn in my suit, but I didn't play good enough for them to play me instead of Chuck Lathrop. And it went on like that up until our last game, the big one with New Cardiff.

I guess that's what woke me up, the last game. I realized I was in the wrong league. I was Bill Czerny, Mohican football bum. I had no more business reading Rupert Brooke than Rupert Brooke had putting the slug on a New Cardiff tackle. I was no Lathrop. I hated to think it, but I was a Grizer. And so I stopped in his office and asked him what I should do.

"Are you kiddin'?" he asked. "Do you wanta be cannon fodder?" I shook my head. "Muddle steel?" I shook my head. "Then, play football. What else is there for guys like you and me?"

Grizer pulled a five-dollar bill out of his pocket and snapped it.

"Look," he said. "Forget this school-spirit business. This is what you get for playing football. This is dough, see?"

"Where can I get it now?" I said. "What school wants me now?"

"Nobody wants you now," Grizer said. "You fixed that. But I tell you what I'll do. I need one more winning team, one more after this. Then some big football school will come after me, the same way Ohio State went after Paul Brown. I got to have me a center next year. What do you say?"

"Huh?" I asked. This was coming too fast for me.

"Here's what I mean," he said: "You flunk a subject or two, see, so you can't graduate, and then come back here next year. I'll get you a job this summer. I'll tip off the scouts and back you a hundred percent. You put in a good year here next year and I'll promise you a new car, a cash-down payment, and fifty bucks a week from any one of a dozen schools." He turned his back on me. "Think it over," he said.

I walked home. All the way I was thinking. I was thinking that this was too much for me. I was thinking that even if I was old enough to join the army, or even if I was old enough to bargain with football scouts, I still was only eighteen years old, a high school boy. I choked up a little, and I thought that I was even young enough to bawl or want to sit on my mother's lap.

And what it all boiled down to, I guess, was that I didn't want to flunk any subjects and mess up my scholastic rating and hire out in a dishonest, crooked, thieving way to play football. I wanted to play it clean, and have people say that Bill Czerny was a good football player, and a good sport. I wanted to love honor more and be Sir Galahad. What I wanted was what Grizer said didn't exist. I wanted to play football as if it were a game.

I still didn't know what to say next day when I was suiting up. Grizer called me in, told me to close the door, and said, "Well?" I looked at him and saw the muscles in his face twitching, and I saw the bottle of ulcer pills on his desk, and his greedy eyes, and then I knew what to say.

"To heck with you," I told Leo Grizer. "Do you want my suit?"

"You stupid punk!" he said. "Get out of here!" But he didn't tell me not to suit up, and I got ready for the game. My last game, the one I wouldn't play in.

The stands were full. You could see the sun glinting off a dozen of those expensive hand movie cameras—the stadium was full of talent scouts. The cream of the state's high school football was represented in this game. Each team played the platoon system, so there were forty-four first-stringers to watch. Add a dozen-odd top substitutes, kickers, and passers, and you'd get around sixty potential college-football players. Average them out at $7,500 for four years, and you had nearly a half-million bucks' worth of beef on that field.

It was a pretty good game, but it wasn't very exciting. Every man, and the coaches, too, had too much at stake to take any chances. About the middle of the first quarter, New Cardiff went down the field in a nice series of plays and made a touchdown. Then Novotny hit our end with a pass, and he went over. In the second quarter, New Cardiff worked a smooth reverse on a punt return, got it down to our ten, and took it over.

Both teams had point-after-touchdown kickers who never missed and the score was 14–7, favor New Cardiff. Then we got a break on a short-pass interception, and were on their thirty. Novotny called O'Rourke on a hand-off, but New Cardiff threw him for a loss. Novotny sent Hruska off-tackle to get it back, but they stopped him for no gain. Novotny called for a pass, but they hurried him and he had to throw it away.

All he could do then was punt, but Chuck's pass was weak and Jablonski missed the corner. There went that chance.

The offensive team came off the field, and everybody looked at Chuck. There were tears in his eyes and his lip was quivering. Blood was trickling out of his nose. That boy was just plain in the wrong league. New Cardiff had worked him over, softened him up, and from now on in, they had a direct channel to our backfield, right over center.

During the half Grizer tried to make a pep talk, but he was so used to snarling that he didn't get over. Mr. Lathrop tried to give us the old college spirit, but I guess the team figured they'd had enough Lathrop for the day. Chuck just sat there. Once he caught my eye and just looked at me sadly, until I looked away. It wasn't my fault. Grizer could put me in if he wanted to, but I knew he wouldn't.

They got to Chuck quickly in the third quarter. Their right guard let him have it every chance he got, and he knew enough to do it smoothly and get away with it. Twice in a row we had to kick on third down, and the second time their offense brought the ball right on down the field and over. The score was 21–7. Third quarter, and we were whipped.

Then all of a sudden Chuck came running up out of the huddle the way he used to, yelling at the team to c'mon. The New Cardiff guard looked at him, rubbed his knuckles, and grinned. Chuck bent over the ball, handed it back, and then stood up straight. He balled up his fist, wound up, and hung one on that New Cardiff guard that knocked him cold. Man, what a punch that was!

Everybody saw it, of course, and the officials had no choice but to penalize us a mile and throw Chuck out of the game. Grizer looked down the bench at the third-string kid, a sophomore already turning green at the thought of playing, but Chuck ran off the field straight up to Grizer and stuck his face right up to his.

"Put Czerny in there!" he shouted. "Go on, put him in!"

Grizer waved at me, and I was in the ball game. Novotny called a running play and O'Rourke got a few yards. I had a new guard opposite me, and we were both feeling each other out. I didn't know what I was doing in there. I couldn't figure it out.

We kicked and came off the field, and Chuck yelled at me to come and sit by him on the bench. What else could I do? He grabbed me by the arm. "Look," he said. "I got you on the field and now I'm going to tell you what to do and you're gonna do it. Their left guard, now—"

"Wait a minute, now," I said. "What do you mean, you got me on that field?"

"Why, gosh," Chuck said. That's just what he said. He lays a man out cold and then he says "gosh." "I wasn't doing the team any good, and—"

"But you don't like to slug people," I said.

He looked at me for a minute. "This is probably the last real game of football I'll ever play," he said slowly. "I didn't want to wind up this way. But I had to get you in there."

"Yeah," I said. I remembered how I'd thought he was yellow and couldn't take a beating. Why that guy had more guts than any other man on that field. I just sat there, listening to Chuck, until the defense started coming off the field.

I got the signal and walked up to the line with the rest of the team. The play went off all right, but something was missing. We needed somebody like Chuck, running up to the scrimmage line, yelling, "C'mon, guys!" playing his heart out, not afraid to make a mis-take that might get the scouts down on him.

And then it hit. *Brother*, I thought, *if there's anybody on this field who's got nothing to lose, I'm it. Man*, I thought, *let's have some fun.*

I was in the huddle then, and while Novotny was waiting for the last men to come in, I said, "C'mon, guys; let's get this gang."

Nobody even looked up. We ran another play and we made another yard. And again I got it. Those guys had resented Chuck Lathrop too. They resented that nice clean guy from the right side of the tracks sounding off. And now they were taking it out on me.

Third down, six yards to go. "We better kick," Novotny said.

"Wait a minute," I said. "Wait a minute. Look here, gang; we can make that six yards. C'mon, let's try it."

"What's got into you?" Novotny asked, but he didn't sound tough. He wanted to win that game, too, I thought. All of us. We might act pretty cynical, but we were really all just a bunch of kids playing a game. And we wanted to win, too.

"I want to win this game," I said. "That's what got into me. I want to win this game for Mohican and for Chuck Lathrop and for you and me and— C'mon, let's take this gang!"

Novotny squinted at me and made up his mind. "OK," he said. "Open up that hole. We'll be right over you."

"Lookin' for somebody?" the New Cardiff guard asked. I handed Novotny the ball, and the guard took a cut at me, but I got my shoulder in his gut and you could hear him grunt in the press box. I heard Hruska's footsteps come through, and the thud when he hit the line-backer. Jablonski came through with the ball and nobody was near him. He made ten yards.

Hruska came up as I went back to the

huddle. "Man, that was it!" he said. "Y'know, Czern'?"

I knew, all right. The fullback used to have to help Chuck with the guard. No more, because I wasn't Chuck. And then I realized I'd made that ten yards just as much as Jablonski—me, the center.

I smacked him on the back. "I'll get my man," I told him. "You get yours."

And I did, and he did, and the team did. We were clicking, smooth and sure, like the professionals we were, but somehow we had the spirit of a bunch of amateurs too. It was fun. After I got my man, I listened to the ballcarrier go by, and it was almost as good as lugging it myself. I led that team right on down the field and over the goal line, and then we started all over again. The ends wanted to get in the act, so we gave Novotny plenty of time to pass, scoring again through the air.

New Cardiff was fighting back, but now our defense had our spirit, and they held. On in the last quarter New Cardiff started trying to break the tie with passes, and Mariani, our linebacker, intercepted one for a touchdown. I was sitting on the bench with the rest of the offensive team when he caught it, but I was on my feet yelling at him when he went over the goal line. Chuck Lathrop grinned.

"I bet that's the first touchdown you ever made on the bench," he said.

"That's the first touchdown you ever made slugging," I said. "Ain't you 'shamed?"

We won 28–21, and everybody was happy, and it wasn't until after I'd showered and started to dress that I realized this was the last time. It hit me a little hard, and I was glad when Chuck put his arm around my shoulder and walked me out the door. Mr. Lathrop was waiting to take Chuck home and offered to drop me off. We drove along a-while, and Mr. Lathrop kept starting to say something and changing his mind, but finally it looked as if he'd got his courage up and he started out all in a rush.

"Uh—Bill," he said, "you know down at Hardy, they've asked me to keep my eyes open for boys, but it looks as though I never can find any. They've got to be good athletes and good sports and smart enough to pass those rugged entrance examinations and take a full academic course and play football and work, too, because they don't pay any money under the table there. I suppose it's silly for a boy like you even to think about it, when you could get good money at some big state school, but—"

"I don't know what you're getting at, Mr. Lathrop," I said, "but I can't get good money at some big state school. Grizer said I was through."

"My goodness!" Mr. Lathrop said. "I'd say you were just beginning. You can buy athletes a dime a dozen, but not spirit and sportsmanship. That's what I'd like to send my school. And how many other fullbacks know what it's like to be up in the line? All this is dependent on a lot of things, of course, but maybe we could swing a four-hundred-dollar scholarship, and you could get a job in the library, say, and run that up to enough to get by on, but you really would have to work and study and—"

He kept on apologizing, and I guess it was rude of me, but I stopped listening to him, as I thought of playing Ivy League football, for the fun of it, and reading all those books, and coming home to Mom on vacations and telling her what I'd learned, and seeing her eyes shine. And she could come to the graduation exercises too.

"Excuse me, Mr. Lathrop," I said, "but you don't have to argue. I mean—"

"Dad," Chuck said, "I think you just got yourself a fullback."

1. Coach Grizer had his own reason for wanting Bill to fail a few subjects. What was it?

2. Bill might have profited financially if he had followed the coach's advice. How? Why did he reject the coach's offer?

3. At the beginning of the story, how did Bill feel toward Chuck Lathrop and his father? What made him suspect their friendship later?

4. What did Bill really want to do after he finished high school? What stood in his way?

5. How did Chuck and Mr. Lathrop show that they were really Bill's friends?

TEAMWORK

1. Should outstanding high school or college athletes ever be given special privileges or jobs to encourage their remaining at a school? Defend your position.

2. Suggest a plan that could keep high school and college athletic programs strictly amateur, essentially an aspect of school spirit, and clear of outside commercial, business influences.

3. Who in this story learned the most important lesson for later living? What was the lesson?

4. How was the importance of team play rather than personal glory, demonstrated here?

A WORD TO REMEMBER: cynical

"We might act pretty cynical," Bill says on page 258, "but we were really all just a bunch of kids playing a game." A person who acts cynical is a cynic, someone who believes that all men are motivated by selfishness. The name *cynic* comes from an ancient Greek word meaning "doglike" and was given to a group of philosophers noted for their surly bad manners. The Cynics believed that ordinary pleasures are harmful, as they interfere with man's reason and turn him from natural to artificial things. Over the centuries the meaning of *cynic* has, as you can see, changed considerably. Our modern word *stoic* comes from the name of a group of philosophers who followed the Cynics. Find out what the Stoics believed and what *stoic* means today. Has the meaning of this word changed as much as that of *cynic*?

The Fabulous Satchel Paige

RICHARD DONOVAN

No wonder the baseball fans called Satchel Paige "fabulous." No pitcher had played on more teams, pitched more innings, or won more games. His ads read: "World's Greatest Pitcher, Guaranteed to Strike Out the First Nine Men."

Any sight of Mr. Paige is arresting.[1] Rising six-feet-three-and-a-quarter inches above size twelves, on semi-invisible legs, with scarcely 180 pounds strung between foot and crown, he sometimes seems more shadow than substance. His face mystifies many fans who peer at it to discover the secrets of time. Head on, it seems to belong to a cheerful man about thirty. From another angle, it looks melancholy and old, as though Paige had walked too long in a world made up exclusively of pickpockets. From a third angle, it seems a frontispiece for the great book of experience, with expressions of wisdom, restrained violence, cunning, and easy humor crossing it in slow succession.

[1] In 1953, when this article was written, Satchel Paige was pitching for the St. Louis Browns. In 1968, after a break in his career, the Atlanta Braves signed Paige to a major league contract.

"We seen some sights, it and I," says Paige of his face.

Inside Paige, conditions are even more confusing. He faces batters, crowds, TV cameras, or whatever, with the regal calm of a Watusi [1] chieftain; yet his nervous stomach shows signs of long and severe emotional tension. He is a congenital AWOL, missing appointments, practice, and, on a couple of occasions, games without much excuse. ("My feet told me it was gonna rain," he explained after failing to show for a Red Sox game.) He is one of the last surviving totally unregimented souls. Contracts box him in; off-field demands on his time make him jumpy; long stays in one place give him nervous stomach. With ballplayers, he is the soul of ease and friendliness; with reporters, people after him for public appearances, promoters of one kind and another, he is wary, abrupt, or sullen.

When it is recalled that he had to pitch out most of his best years on cow pastures because of big-league baseball's color line, and that every time he pitched he was expected to win or else, Paige's more antic attitudes are easy to understand. It is also understandable that he should feel opposed to being called a legend. Legends are tricky. On this point, however, Paige should feel entirely at ease. For underneath all the mythology lies a fact. Paige threw, and occasionally he still throws, probably the fastest ball ever to leave the hand of man. This is the main and enduring reason for his having been raised to the supernatural.

There are other good reasons, of course. Although records of his career are lost, forgotten, or twisted by generations of sports writers, it is reasonably certain that he pitched twenty-two years

of organized sand-lot, semipro, or Negro league ball (about one and a half lifetimes for the average pitcher), before he ever ascended to the majors, and he has been in that high company almost five years. Although he may be the oldest man on record to perform regularly in the big leagues, in 1952 he was invited to play in the All-Star game. Year upon year, he has pitched summer (over most of the United States and Canada) and winter (in California and Central and South America), and has pulled in more customers than Babe Ruth.

When historians meet, the matter of Paige's performance over the years is often the subject of mettlesome debate. It seems certain that Paige has worked a record total of at least 2,500 ball games in his life, often pitching 125 games a year, frequently working five to seven days a week without rest. He has won around two thousand of those games, it is estimated, including some 250 shutouts and 45 no-hitters. In one month in 1935, he pitched twenty-nine days in a row against smart hitters with but one loss; in four winter seasons (1932 to 1936), often playing against the best of the Negro leaguers and various off-season combinations of major league all-stars, he lost but four games.

For some twenty years Paige was booked as a solo star, wearing a uniform with "Satchel" across the shirt, and playing with any team that could dig up five hundred to two thousand dollars for three innings of his work. His travel average was thirty thousand miles per year, and his earnings, in some years, thirty-five thousand dollars. He was advertised as "Satchel Paige, World's Greatest Pitcher, Guaranteed to Strike Out the First Nine Men." Either he performed as advertised or he took side streets back to his hotel.

The Browns, who have the legend as

[1] **Watusi** (wah·TOO·see): a tribe in Africa.

well as the man under contract, sometimes aren't sure whether it is a disadvantage or a benefit. On the disadvantage side, Paige's presence often tends to make opposing teams gun for early scores. Whenever the Yankees start to take the Browns too lightly, for example, Yankee manager Casey Stengel begins to pace up and down in front of the bench, pointing toward Paige warming up, and intoning: "Get the runs now! Father Time is coming!"

On the benefit side, rookie hitters, their little heads stuffed with stories of Paige's fast ball, are often retired flailing when they get nothing but floaters, slow curves, and bloopers from the old gentleman. Many seasoned hitters are even more delightful to Paige because they are convinced he has lost his blinding speed and are laying for the soft one. These fellows seem perpetually outraged when the ball, delivered with the same motion Paige uses for his cute stuff, blazes across the sound barrier.

Once Walt Dropo, Detroit's giant first baseman, swung embarrassingly wide of two Paige pitches, lost his head, and loudly accused him of showboating. For reply, Paige threw a vicious fast ball.

Dropo swung so hard that he whirled around, ending in an odd, stooped position with the seat of his pants pointing toward the stands.

"My, my," clucked Paige, reproachfully, "talk about showboatin'."

The anxious desire of most hitters, old and new, to drive him from the mound is regarded by Paige with fatherly amusement. Hitters have been trying it for approximately thirty years. As his legend grew, he became an individual target, like an old Western gun fighter whose reputation had gone out before him. Every hot-eyed bush kid,

burning for immortality around the feed store, was fired up to knock him off as he rode through.

"Bangin' around the way I was, playing for guarantees on one team after another that I never heard of, in towns I never seen before, with players I didn't know and never saw again, I got lonesome," says Paige. "People didn't come to see the ball game. They came to see me strike out everybody, all the time. Occasionally I didn't."

One such breakdown took place in Union Springs, Alabama, one steaming Sunday in 1939. Paige had ridden all night in a bus, and had holed up at a hotel for a few hours' sleep before game time. He overslept, but it made little difference since the game was a social occasion and it was considered gross to arrive much before the third inning.

When Paige appeared, red-eyed and dragged out, in the middle of the fourth, the folks were just settling themselves, waving to friends, talking, sweating, looking everywhere but at the field.

"Then," says Paige, "I went in and it got quiet."

He went to work as usual and retired the first five men in order. Then, with the nonchalance of a seasoned barnstormer, he turned and waved the outfielders off the field. The crowd rose with a roar.

"I laughed to see it," Paige says. "I was still laughing when a little, no-account-looking fella come up, took that big, greasy swing, and put my fast ball where my left fielder formerly was."

Paige sighed heavily at the memory. "The police escorted me from the place as the little man crossed home," he said. "Without my guarantee."

As the terror of the northern Midwest, the 1935 Bismarck team was invited to play in the national semipro tournament at Wichita, Kansas. En route, in McPherson, Kansas, they encountered a problem. Local citizens, apparently rendered unsteady by a winning team of their own, openly referred to the Bismarcks as hayshakers.

A six-inning challenge game was promptly arranged and the Bismarcks took an early two-run lead. In the final inning, the disgruntled McPherson fans began to hoot at Paige.

That was a mistake. Paige fanned the first man. Then he called in his outfield and struck out the next man. Then he called in his infield. With nobody representing Bismarck but Paige and catcher Quincy Troupe, he struck out the third man. He used nine fast balls in all.

Country boys were not the only ones seized with intimations of immortality after hitting Paige. In 1935, Joe DiMaggio, who was to go up to the Yankees the next year, got a single off Satchel and immediately lost all

doubts about how he would fare in the majors.

Paige has forgotten this game, along with a couple of thousand others, but Oakland, California, sports writers have not. At the time, DiMaggio was playing around the Bay Area with an off-season team of major-league all-stars. Yankee scouts, who wished to see how their new find reacted to serious fire, finally got hold of Paige, who was taking the sun in Los Angeles. Paige was willing, after hearing about the guarantee, and started north with his team, composed entirely of Ebel Brooks, catcher for the New York Black Yankees of the Negro National League.

In Oakland, Paige found three local semipro players, filled out the roster with high school boys, and gazed solemnly at the terrifying lineup of major-league talent. Then he proceeded with the business of the day, which was to fan fifteen, allow three hits in ten in-

nings, and lose the game, two to one, when his youths, possibly rendered hysterical by the reputation of the opposition, threw to the winds the three balls that came their way. With a man on third in the tenth inning, DiMaggio, who had struck out twice and fouled out once in his previous official times at bat, finally hit a hopper which Paige lost in the shadows of dusk. One ex-Yankee scout remembers sending a telegram east: DIMAGGIO ALL WE HOPED HE'D BE. HIT SATCH ONE FOR FOUR.

Leroy Robert Paige started down the road during the Teddy Roosevelt administration from a small frame house in the Negro section of Mobile, Alabama. His father was a gardener. His mother, Tula Paige, who is now eighty-three and for whom Satchel bought a house in Mobile recently, said he was the sixth of eight children, when questioned a while ago. She also put his birth year at 1903.

"What mama knows when her little child was born?" Paige said patiently when he got this news. "My draft card says 1906. I say 1908. Take your pick."

Food and living room were permanent problems for the family, but for Leroy, who was almost six feet tall at age twelve, the big problems apparently lay on the outside. One problem—where to find money to buy baseball equipment—he solved by becoming a redcap at a Mobile railroad station. After a couple of days' labor, the headwork for which he is now revered manifested itself and he rigged a "totin' device" of sticks and ropes on which he could hang as many as ten bags for one trip. Staggering along one day, looking like a tree of satchels, he caught the eye of someone who gave him the name he has carried down the road.

The predatory warfare between Mo-

bile's boy gangs was a much bigger problem for Paige. Several times he was beaten; just as often, he participated in the gang-beating of others. He rarely went to school. Reasoning that continuous battle against odds was the staff of life, he turned sniper, breaking windows and lumping heads with deadly, accurate rocks from his hand. The truant officer became a weekly caller; the police called, too, with complaints from parents of winged children. Finally, a juvenile judge sentenced him to the Alabama Reform School for Boys, at Mount Meigs. He was approximately twelve when he went in, sixteen when he got out.

"One thing they told me in the refawm school," Paige says, "they told me that all that wild-a'-loose feelin' I put in rock throwin', I ought to put in throwin' baseballs. Well, I listened to that. Many men have watched my fast ball all these years without thinkin' what put that mean little hop on it. That's the wild-a'-loose."

Paige was six-feet-three inches tall and weighed 140 pounds when he rejoined society; he was reedy, solemn, and taciturn in conversation but highly expressive on the mound. His mother kept him home nights but most afternoons he spent in sand-lot games, one of which happened to be witnessed by a pullman porter in from Chattanooga. This man spoke to Alex Herman, owner of the Chattanooga Black Lookouts, and forthwith Mr. Herman appeared at the Paige house with offers. Mrs. Paige, who smelled sin in the footloose baseball life, refused to let Satchel go until Herman promised to watch him like a father and send his fifty-dollar-a-month salary home. Full of reform-school warnings and memories at seventeen years of age, Satchel took the next train into the outer world.

When he appeared on the Lookouts'

field for the first time, the legend-to-be was an arresting sight. His uniform flapped about him, his neck, arms, and legs indicated severe emaciation, spikes had to be nailed to his street shoes until some size twelve, triple-A baseball shoes could be found, his walk was labored, he cranked up like the Tin Woodman of Oz, and he appeared to be speechless. Looking at him, veteran players expressed the gravest fears for owner Herman's judgment. The first man to face him in a practice session held his bat in one hand, for charity's sake.

Then Satchel threw his fast ball.

That evening, as the newly established most valuable player on the Lookouts, he was invited to dinner by several veterans. But he informed them that he had to eat at Mr. Herman's house and go to bed at nine-thirty.

When the team went on the road, Herman's watchfulness trebled. Crowds were wild about Satchel, female eyes followed him relentlessly, and scented notes, addressed to Mr. Paige, appeared at every hotel desk. This was heady stuff to Mrs. Paige's child; sometimes, after Herman had locked him in his hotel room, Paige felt the strain was too much for flesh to bear. In the warm Southern dusk, Satchel, gazing down from high hotel windows, could see the older players talking to the girls down below. When he chanced to hear soft voices inquiring as to the whereabouts of the tall pitcher, there were times he felt he'd have to jump.

Although Alex Herman delivered Satchel to his mother, as was, at the end of his first season, it was obvious that this arrangement could not go on. By the time he was twenty-one, Satchel Paige was a seasoned traveler and an apprentice philosopher, to say the least. He had run through two roadsters. He had sat in with Louis Armstrong and his band ("I played my own chords on the Spanish guitar"); he had had ham with ol' Jelly Roll Morton at a wake in Memphis ("I didn't know the dead man but Jelly thought he'd want me to be there"); he had gone across the river from New Orleans to have his palm read by the seers of Algiers, who found a short lifeline; he had been a running story in the Negro press, and from Savannah to Abilene and Mobile to St. Joe; he had heard of dozens of young ladies he had never seen who were letting it be known that they might shortly become Mrs. Paige.

"It was an education," Paige recalls now. "I was tired all the time."

As he put on a little more meat, Paige's fast ball got faster. This phenomenon has been explained by Biz Mackey, a memorable catcher for the Baltimore Elite Giants, of the late Negro National League.

"A lot of pitchers have a fast ball," says Mackey, "but a very, very few—Feller, Grove, Johnson, a couple of others besides Satchel—have had that little extra juice that makes the difference between the good and the great man. When it's that fast, it will hop a little at the end of the line. Beyond that, it tends to disappear.

"Yes, disappear. I've heard about Satchel throwing pitches that weren't hit but that never showed up in the catcher's mitt, nevertheless. They say the catcher, the umpire, and the bat boys looked all over for that ball, but it was gone. Now, how do you account for that?"

Word of such disappearances got around the Negro leagues quickly, it seems, for competition for Satchel's services was intense. Since clubs issued loosely worded agreements in lieu of contracts, players could switch to the highest bidder.

When Paige joined the Pittsburgh

Crawfords in 1931, his receiver was Josh Gibson, a better-than-average catcher, and one of the great right-hand hitters. With the Paige-Gibson battery in action, the Crawfords could afford to be big.

At one time, for example, they were playing an exhibition game against a champion team from the U.S. Marine Corps. In the last of the ninth with the Marines up, two out, and the score 12–0 in favor of the Crawfords, Satchel and Gibson had a worried consultation.

"The United States Marines have got to have at least one run," said Paige.

Back behind the plate, Gibson asked who was the captain of the Marine team. It was the man at bat. "You're gonna be the hero," Gibson said.

Thereupon, Satchel pitched one so fat the surprised Marine chopped it into the ground a few feet in front of home. Gibson grabbed it and threw it thirty feet over the first baseman's head. While the Marine rounded the bases and dug for the plate, the astonished right fielder retrieved the ball and threw it home for the putout. The ball hit Gibson's chest protector and bounded high in the air. "I had a feeling you were gonna be the hero," Gibson informed the Marine captain later.

In the autumn of 1934, Paige and his wife headed for Denver, where he had been invited to pitch for the House of David in the *Denver Post* semipro tournament. The House had a talented organization, but what impressed Paige most was the amazing growth of whiskers on all the players. Paige had never been able to grow any whiskers himself, and he felt naked and alone. Although he won his first three tournament games for the House without facial hair, he complained bitterly. Finally, his teammates presented him with a lengthy false beard of reddish hue.

Thoroughly pleased, Paige wore the red whiskers in his final appearance. While he was winding up to deliver a hesitation pitch in the fourth inning, however, the beard became entwined with his pitching arm and was torn from his jaws with the delivery.

Finding himself denuded again, Paige became so unsettled that he very nearly lost the game. He squeaked through, however, and the House went on to win the tournament.

"It was the tamperin' with nature that rattled me," Satchel says.

In California that winter, Paige commanded the Satchel Paige All-Stars, an impressive pickup team of Negro-league players. This team included catcher Josh Gibson, third baseman Judy (Sweet Juice) Johnson, the catlike Harry Williams at second base, and Cool Papa Bell, whose speed and daring in the outfield and on the bases may have surpassed that of Willie Mays. In three previous years wintering on the West Coast, the Paige Stars, with or without the members named, had won some 128 games—at least forty of them against teams of major-league all-stars—while losing twenty-three.

The games against big leaguers were of tremendous importance to Paige and the others. They knew, the sports writers knew, and many of the fans knew that many of the Negro stars were better ballplayers than some of the high-salaried, internationally famous men they faced. Yet they were denied a shot at the big fame, big money, big records, and big company.

The bigger the major-league stars, the more Paige bore down. According to accounts passed down by witnesses, he struck out Rogers Hornsby five times in one game, Charley Gehringer three times in another, Jimmy Foxx three times in a third. In 1934 in Hollywood, Paige pitched what Bill Veeck says is the greatest game he ever saw. In that ʰhich lasted thirteen innings, as opposed by Dizzy Dean, a ᵐe winner for the Cardinals. ᵃs superlative, holding the Paige ᵒ one run and fanning fifteen. But Paige shut out the Dean Stars and fanned seventeen. After the game, Dean informed the press that Paige was the best pitcher in the business.

An air of uneasiness hung over the home stadium of the last-place St. Louis Browns one day in August of 1952. Local fans, accustomed to great suffering, had the feeling that their team was about to throw away another ball game. Over six innings, the Browns had compiled a 2–0 edge over the league-leading Yankees. But now, with two out in the last of the seventh, pitcher Gene Bearden was beginning to wobble. One Yankee run scored. Then, while St. Louis supporters cringed, Bearden loaded the bases.

Among those shrinking into themselves at this critical moment was the Brown's shortstop-manager, Marty Marion. He glanced guiltily at his relief pitchers warming up in the bullpen. Then, stifling an impulse to call for volunteers, he made what seemed to be the only possible decision. He nominated Leroy Satchel Paige to douse the fire.

Languorous and serene, Mr. Paige, the eminent traveler, linguist, sage, and relief-pitching mainstay of the Browns, rose and began his usual interminable stroll toward the mound.

In his thirty-or-so years in professional baseball, he had been in worse spots. If he failed here, at least he would not have to sprint from the field before enraged masses of machete-wielding fans, as he had so often had to do in the twenty years he played winter ball in Latin America. Nor would his outfielders stroll off the diamond without his knowing it, as had happened in North Dakota in 1934.

Humming a little tune, Paige took his regular half-dozen warm-up pitches on the mound, sighted on pinch hitter Irv Noren, and fed him a fast curve. He smiled pleasantly as Marion gathered in a short pop-up, retiring the side.

Later, still humming contentedly, Mr. Paige did away with Phil Rizzuto, Joe Collins, and Hank Bauer in the eighth, and Yogi Berra, Gil McDougald, and Gene Woodling in the ninth, to save the game.

Afterward, despite the satisfactory outcome, there was some discussion among local fans over the soundness of manager Marion's strategy in selecting the aging Paige at a time of such crisis.

When these comments reached the sensitive ears of Browns owner Bill Veeck, he seemed astonished. "Well, what else was there to do?" he inquired of one doubter. "Marion needed the greatest baseball brains, experience, speed, control, and coolness he could find in one man. So he put in the world's greatest relief pitcher. No particular strategy about that!"

Veeck's was a generous but not a wildly extravagant statement. By any yardstick, the venerable Paige is one of the two or three best relief men in baseball. In the first eleven games the Browns played in 1953, he was called upon four times. He helped save three of the games, and was compelled to retire from the fourth when a line drive struck his foot. In 1952 he pitched in almost one third of the St. Louis Browns' contests, struck out ninety-one batters, won twelve games, lost ten, saved ten, and ended up by making the American League All-Star team and becoming— in the opinion of most experts—the most valuable relief hurler in that circuit.

In his approximately thirty years of baseball, two lifetimes for the average pitcher, Paige has broken all records for number of games pitched and won (some 2,000 out of 2,500). Working winter and summer in many lands, often as an itinerant solo star, for some 250 different sand-lot, semipro, and Negro-league teams—not to mention the Cleveland Indians and St. Louis Browns —he has also very probably broken all records for travel and number of customers drawn by any individual ballplayer.

"They was tall times, tall times," Paige says of those years. "But let whosomever wishes sit around recollecting. I'm looking up the line."

The prospect does not dampen Paige's celebrated self-confidence.

Now, as always, Satchel is so certain of his powers, both physical and mental, that sometimes he makes himself uneasy.

In the Browns' shower room after a recent game, for example, several players were tossing a slippery cake of soap at a wall dish, trying without success to make it stick there. Paige entered, picked up the soap casually, and tossed it. It stuck. There was a general raising of eyebrows, none higher than Satchel's. He tossed another bar, even more slippery. It stuck, too. Paige looked thoughtfully at the sober faces around him.

"Boys," he said, "there is apparently things that even I don't know I can do."

THE FACT IS—

1. Baseball is often called a game of statistics. What are some of the remarkable statistics of Satchel Paige's career?

2. The author says Paige has probably broken all records for "number of customers drawn by any individual ballplayer." Why have people flocked to see Paige perform?

3. What does Paige himself say about his career?

4. How does Paige show his sense of humor?

A WORD TO REMEMBER: unregimented

On page 262, the author says of Satchel Paige: "He is one of the last surviving totally unregimented souls." You probably guessed from the description what this word means: that he does not permit outside systems or orders to control him; he retains his independence. A *regimen* (REJ·ih·men), from the Latin word for "rule" or "guide," is a system; one who is regimented is controlled by a system. The prefix *un–*, of course, means "not." Another related word in common use is *regime* (ray·-ZHEEM), meaning "rule" or "the prevailing governmental system."

What is your opinion of regimentation (rej·ih·men·TAY·shun) in the lives of young people? Can you think of examples of regimentation at home or at school? Are they necessary or unnecessary?

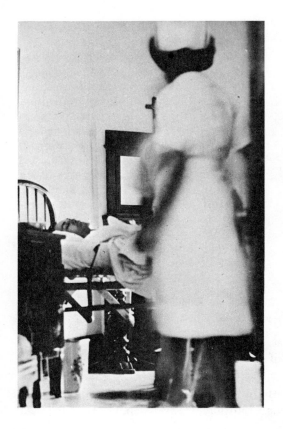

The Hawk
They Couldn't
Kill

with Frank Graham, Jr.

"Comeback" is a proud word

in sports, and there has

rarely been a comeback

braver than Ben Hogan's.

Near death, in deep pain,

and given up as a cripple,

this great golfer was fired

with the will to win again.

𝕴 won't know until I play whether I can get back the edge I had before. I don't know if I'll start favoring a shoulder or an ankle that's paining me and then throw my game off. But there's one thing I'm sure of. There's nothing about death that will ever frighten me now."

Pain had torn at the little man for months, and death had made a run at him, and the hard lines in his face had been etched there as if by acid. The Texas sun had tanned him, but his gaunt, still-handsome face reflected his ordeal just as surely as did the scars on his body. His jacket hung slackly on him, making him look like a small boy in a big brother's coat and underscoring his frailness. The laces of his GI boots were loosened at the tops to ease the pressure on his swollen ankles. Yet in his eyes there was neither despair nor desperation. There was the same icy stare which was the outward manifestation of the most indomitable spirit golf has known, the look which had chilled his competitors as he drove himself to the top of his profession and had helped to earn him that scarcely endearing nickname, "The Hawk."

It was the summer of 1949, and Ben Hogan sat in the living room of his home in Fort Worth. The friend who had come expecting to see a hopeless invalid —to view, as it were, the mortal remains of the greatest golfer of his time— abruptly lost the feeling that he was there to offer Ben or anyone else his condolences. As Hogan talked of his hopes and his plans for the future in the same intense way he approached a ball in a difficult lie, taking nothing for granted yet determined not to fail because of anything over which he had control, the visitor began to absorb his confidence. When the man left, he took with him, as did others who visited Hogan at that time, a conviction that he might yet live to see a miracle.

If only men of superior faith can believe in miracles, it must be said that, where Hogan was concerned, most of the country's sports fans were infidels. The terrible highway accident which shattered the little golf champion's body, and the even more ravaging complications which followed a month later must surely have put an end to his career. Most of his friends were grateful that he was still alive. They looked forward to the day when he could join them on the veranda of one of the country clubs he had once conquered and, perhaps, at some distant date, even hit a few balls in a friendly foursome. They remembered the reports from the scene of the accident, how a giant bus had roared down on the Hogan car, plowed into it head-on, and squashed it as a stampeding elephant would mangle a small animal that had wandered into its path.

Yet, even as they consigned him to the graveyard of champions and debated the identity of his successor as the country's finest golfer, Hogan was slowly conditioning himself for what was to be the most incredible comeback in the history of American sports. The doctors had mended his shattered bones and tied up his torn veins; now it was up to him to strengthen his muscles, regain his coordination, and bring under control the nerves which had carried him to the top of the most nerve-racking of all games. At the age of thirty-seven, he was faced with the task of rebuilding what had been a nearly flawless golfing machine. To understand the magnitude of that task, remember that Bobby Jones, the sport's most famous player before Hogan, had retired from competitive golf at twenty-eight.

But William Benjamin Hogan seemed to have been put on this earth for the purpose of hurdling obstacles. Looking back now on his career, it can be said that Hogan first overcame the greatest handicap any athlete can have —no talent. That deficiency alone was enough to endear him to millions of duffers. Though born in Dublin, Texas, a son of the village blacksmith, on August 13, 1912, Ben spent most of his boyhood in Fort Worth, where his mother had moved the family after his father's death. In common with so many other great athletes, he lived his early years in poverty. When he grew up, the memory of those lean days still haunted him and added its weight to the desperate hunger for victory which we associate with him. He sold papers for a time but, hearing that caddies were paid sixty-five cents an hour, plus tips, he applied for a job at one of the city's finest golf courses, the Glen Garden Country Club.

The skinny, underfed little Hogan, only twelve years old, had his first battle on his hands. He was a natural mark for the older, bigger boys. He had only been at work a day or two when his "colleagues" stuffed him into a frail barrel and rolled him down a hill. Having survived that ordeal with little damage except to his dignity, he was forced to fight one of the other caddies. Hogan, who even today looks as if he would have made a champion boxer, sailed into his unlucky opponent and proved himself with his fists.

There was another battle that was not to be won so easily. As they made their living from golf, all of the caddies wanted to be able to play the game, too, and they spent their spare hours practicing driving and putting. And, as all boys do, they made even their practice sessions a form of competition. The boy who hit the shortest drive was forced to retrieve the balls for the other caddies. Ben was small and skinny; he was left-handed and there were only right-handed clubs available for him at the club; and so he became the regular retriever for his colleagues.

It was here that Hogan formulated what has since become his motto, the true secret of his success: "If you can't outplay them, outwork them." Though worn out from hauling heavy bags of clubs over the rolling course all day, he stayed there after the others had gone home, and worked long hours at the practice tee. Slowly he began to feel that hitting a ball right-handed was the natural way. Slowly he began to get the distance on his drives that would end his days as a "retriever" for the other caddies. This was the origin of his powerful backswing, the mighty effort which was to propel the longest drives any little man has ever hit on a golf course.

"There is no such thing as a natural swing," Hogan has often said, and the young Ben Hogan was certainly the living proof of that conviction. Veteran golfers who watched the little fellow on the course were impressed by his determination but appalled by his form. One friend from those days still carries a vivid picture in his mind of the clumsy beginner. "He couldn't do one thing right. He sure couldn't putt. Everybody used to laugh at him because he practically ran at the ball to hit it."

But Hogan loved golf and he saw in it a way out of the poverty which had darkened all of his early life. He had neither the size nor the natural talent. Such considerations were as nothing to a man with Ben's fierce singleness of purpose. He worked and worked on his game, and soon he was beating most of the other young men around Fort Worth. He stopped growing when he reached five feet eight and a half inches and 140 pounds. Yet out of such refractory material was evolving a fine golfer—one good enough to leave Fort Worth and hit the tournament trail. Or so he thought.

The few dollars in his pockets couldn't carry him very far. There was little chance to win any real money against the tough veterans of the tournament circuit then, and Ben was usually forced to return to Fort Worth and earn his living with any one of a half-dozen jobs. And, in 1935, he married his childhood sweetheart, Valerie Fox. Knowing how much he loved the game, Valerie urged him to go back to the golf circuit, feeling that he was now ready to compete with the old pros. Ben thought so, too. "When I made the tour before," he told a friend some years later, "I'd have an occasional good round, but I couldn't keep it up. One good shot or one good round doesn't mean a thing in this game. You've got to keep it up for seventy-two holes."

Ben and Valerie set out together in

1937. He had never won a tournament, and there were times when it appeared that he never would. Everything seemed to go against him. In 1938 the Hogans drove their battered jalopy into Oakland for a tournament and, because they couldn't afford a parking lot, left the car in a vacant lot. He played badly in the tournament, winning but a few dollars, and when they got back to the lot, they found that the car had been jacked up by thieves and stripped of its tires.

"You might say that that was a break for me," Ben will tell you. "I knew then that things couldn't get much worse for us. And Valerie, who must have figured I was beginning to lose heart, pretended she was more optimistic than ever."

Things did take a turn for the better. There were no tournament victories, but he gave the winner a run for it almost every time. In fact, he was beginning to finish second with such regularity that he earned for himself the nickname "Runner-up Hogan." Anyone who has ever met him can tell you how much that name must have rankled him.

Through it all he worked harder than any other man in golf. "I never heard of a harder worker in golf or any other sport," Bobby Jones once said of him. He had mastered nearly every shot now except the putt, and that was costing him tournaments.

"I used to feel sorry for the little guy," Jimmy Demaret, the colorful pro, says. "Imagine anybody feeling sorry for Hogan now! I get tired of seeing his rear end and his elbows when he bends down to pick the ball out of the cup. But then it just seemed that he *never* was going to learn to putt."

Nineteen forty was his year. He finished second in his first six tournaments, meanwhile keeping Valerie awake at night as he practiced putting on the rug in their hotel rooms. It had been eight years since he first set out on the tour in 1932. When he finally broke through, winning the Pinehurst North and South Open, he was on his way to greatness. He just kept winning. By the end of the year, he was golf's biggest money winner. Again in 1941 and 1942 he was the leading money winner in the country, and he was acclaimed the finest golfer in the world.

And then, when he had perfected his marvelous style, the bottom dropped out of his world, just as it did for so many other people. World War II had reached America, and Ben was off to join the air corps. He returned after the war and regained his peak much more quickly than most of his colleagues did. He was working as hard as ever. At the top of his game in 1947, he was audacious enough to alter his golfing style, having learned to control his hook by fading the ball. And in 1948 he accomplished the unprecedented feat of sweeping the U.S. Open (his first), the Western Open, and the PGA tournament.

To win the U.S. Open, he had to top a magnificent performance by his old friend, Demaret. Jimmy had finished with a score of 278, an all-time low for the Open. "But I knew I didn't have this tournament won," Demaret recalls. "I knew that Hogan was going great, too, and so I sat on the clubhouse veranda to watch him come in. Then I saw him walking down the eighteenth fairway and I knew my goose was cooked. His head was so low he looked like a gopher climbing out of a hole. When Ben walks like that you know there's nothing going to stop him. I just began figuring out what I was going to do with my second-place money."

Demaret knew what he was talking about. Ben finished with a new record of 276 and captured the Open title.

He was now in a class by himself, but there was always his obsession to improve on perfection. "It takes him three hours to play nine holes in practice," one of his caddies said. "He'll make me drop a dozen or so balls in a sand trap and then he'll go down there and blast every darn one of them out. Then, like as not, he'll knock another dozen out of there."

A reporter once asked Hogan if he ever relaxed on the course. A look of genuine astonishment crossed his face. "Relax? How can anybody relax and play golf? You have to grip the club, don't you?"

Every other golfer in the business realized what Demaret meant when he said that he knew, after one look at Hogan, that he had no chance to win the 1948 Open. A group stood around the fifteenth green at a tournament one day and watched another famous golfer line up a putt. It was a tournament which Hogan had not entered. "Look at that fellow," one of the group said. "He's as calm as can be out there. I even saw him grinning a few minutes ago. But if Hogan was in this tournament, you'd see this guy shake when he lit his cigarette. He's got ulcers, and do you know who gave them to him? Ben Hogan."

There was something menacing about Hogan in his prime. He chose his club and strode toward the ball with all the grim purposefulness of an executioner approaching his grisly job. Standing over the ball, his knees loose, his toes pointing outward at a slight angle, he was an extraordinary symbol of the great athlete about to spring into action. That stance foretold the powerful, beautifully coordinated swing and the graceful follow-through. It sprang out inevitably, like the bright spectacular patterns from a Chinese firecracker.

Nineteen forty-nine promised to be another brilliant year for Ben. He began by winning the Bing Crosby Invitational and the Long Beach Open, then lost in a playoff to Demaret at Phoenix. Most of the golfers were pushing on to Tucson, but Ben decided to pass up the tournament there and go home for a brief rest before setting out again in quest of the season's more important prizes. Many of his friends urged him to reconsider and go to Tucson.

"No, I want the rest," he told them. "It isn't the golf that wears you out, it's the traveling. I want to die an old man, not a young one."

Less than twenty-four hours later he lay near death in an El Paso hospital.

It was early in the morning of February 2. Ben and Valerie were driving toward Fort Worth on Highway 80, a straight, flat road which stretched interminably across the desolate west Texas prairie. They drove through an early-morning brightness and frequent patches of thick fog which had descended on them. Then they drove for miles wrapped in the fog, the climbing sun only occasionally showing wanly through the murky wall. Ben switched on his headlights. Sometimes the ghost of a car would take form ahead, become palpable only as it reached them, and then fade again into the fog behind. Ben slowed his car to thirty miles an hour. Peering through the windshield, he detected two luminous circles coming toward him. He crept closer to the right side of the road. And then the two circles became four and were right on top of him. Out of the fog rushed a mountain of a bus, passing a six-wheeler truck, and Hogan, kept on the road by the culvert to his right, didn't have a chance in the world.

"I put my head down and dived across Valerie like I was diving into a pool of water."

That reflexive action saved both of their lives. The shuddering impact hurled part of the engine back into the driver's seat and demolished the car.

Valerie, suffering cuts and bruises, had been saved by her husband's protecting body. She pulled the crushed little champion from his car. Hogan lay there by the roadside for well over an hour as, in the confusion, each bystander thought the other had called an ambulance.

"I thought he was dying," one witness said later. "He just got grayer and grayer."

Finally an ambulance arrived from the nearby town of Van Horn and carried Hogan to a hospital in El Paso, 119 miles away. There the doctors recorded his more serious injuries: a fractured pelvis, a broken left collarbone, a broken left ankle, and a chipped rib. The extent of his internal injuries was not to be realized until a month later.

The blood clot that threatened to choke off his life suddenly developed early in March. It came just at a time when the doctors believed Ben was on the way back to health. Moving up his left leg, the clot appeared headed for his heart. The doctors in El Paso thinned Ben's blood and sent for Dr. Alton S. Ochsner, a famous New Orleans surgeon. Because there was difficulty in arranging the surgeon's air passage from New Orleans to El Paso, Hogan's friends finally had him picked up in an Air Force bomber.

When Ochsner arrived, he found the golfer in critical condition. Hogan's blood count was dangerously low, and the clot seemed deadly. He was immediately given a blood transfusion. In a two-hour abdominal operation, Ochsner tied off the *vena cava*, a large vein which feeds blood into the right auricle of the heart. There were serious doubts about Ben's survival, and one major news service sent out an up-to-date obituary of him, ready to be put into type when the reporters keeping the "death watch" at the hospital flashed the signal.

The obituary's only possible use came a little over a year later when it might have been valuable in throwing together a biography of Hogan in his hour of triumph. From the moment he began to shake off the dulling effects of the operation, Ben was on the road back to the top of the golf world. He seemed not to care, or even to be aware, that so many knowledgeable people were saying that he would never again play tournament golf.

Two weeks later he was being wheeled about the hospital's grounds to soak up the warm Texas sun. Soon he was out of the hospital and back in his own home in Fort Worth. There were long hours of massage and then the first halting steps as he learned to walk again. When this obstacle was past, he began taking short walks around his bedroom. Later he jogged up and down on the living-room rug, strengthening the muscles in his legs and at the same time squeezing in his hand a rubber ball in an effort to regain his powerful grip. Finally there were long walks around the block, walks that sometimes stretched out so that a worried Valerie drove through the neighborhood looking for him. And almost everywhere he went he carried with him a golf club, partly because he wanted to get the feel of it in his hands again and partly because he often needed it to rest on. Friends who feared that he was pushing himself too fast invariably got this answer:

"There's no point in just getting up and standing," Ben would tell them. "I've got to walk to get back in shape. I just walk as far as I can and then I lie down and rest."

Nemesis itself must grow weary of pursuing a man like that.

There came inevitably the day when Hogan took his clubs and went out to the golf course. He could play only a few holes, and he brought a chair with him so that he could occasionally stop to rest. The damage to his veins had affected the circulation of his blood, and his legs and feet were badly swollen after even the least exertion. And then a curious thing happened. As Ben's strength and stamina returned, so did his marvelous coordination. He was amazed to find that, after an eight-month break, his golf game was rapidly returning to what it had been before the accident.

When asked if he planned to go back to competitive golf, Hogan gave his interviewers an honest answer. "There's a good possibility," he said, "but right now I can't say for sure. I'll just have to wait and see how I'm feeling and how my game shapes up. But there's one thing I can say for sure: I'm not going out there and shoot in the eighties."

By then Hogan must have felt fairly certain that he could play golf as well as he ever had. What worried him was the condition of his legs. Would they stand up for a grueling eighteen holes? Or, even worse, the thirty-six holes that he would sometimes have to play in one day? He didn't wait very long to put himself to a test. In January, 1950, less than a year after his accident, Hogan entered the Los Angeles Open. Nobody, of course, expected him to make any kind of a showing. This was just a warm-up, a dress rehearsal for the big tournaments of the future. Many of the onlookers believed that Hogan wouldn't even be able to finish the seventy-two-hole tournament over the rugged Riviera Club course.

Then Hogan began to play, and it suddenly seemed that he had never been away at all. He almost dominated the field, and on the verge of winning off by himself, he was overhauled on the final day when Slammin' Sammy Snead turned in one of the most brilliant rounds of his career. The two old rivals had finished in a tie. Hogan (or, more accurately, Hogan's legs) weren't quite ready for the extra round of golf required for the playoff, and Snead walked off with the title. Yet this had been a minor miracle. Hogan was back on the tour and he was a threat to every golfer in the land.

"Losing that playoff was one of the best breaks I ever got," Ben said later. "My game had rounded into shape so easily that I was getting cocky about it. I might have begun taking my comeback less seriously. I might have let down."

No one who knows Hogan could take that last remark seriously. Whenever he picked up a golf club, the little champion became all business, an attitude which led him into many misunderstandings throughout the great days of his career. Reporters, fans, even his colleagues in professional golf, were frequently irritated by what they considered Hogan's rudeness, aloofness, or insatiable greed. In each case the "misunderstanding" could be traced directly to Ben's almost demonic craving for victory—a craving which made him so intent on the course that he often neglected the niceties which the public expects from its heroes.

As the 1950 U.S. Open, the year's biggest tournament, drew closer, Hogan was on better terms with the press than ever before. The writers, aware of the awesome demands he was making on himself, were openly rooting for him to make a successful comeback, and were more than willing to forget their past differences with him. Hogan, too, was ready to bury the hatchet. He had only one complaint. With the Open approaching, he wanted the newspapermen to treat him as a golfer, not as a cripple; he wanted them to write about the tournament, not his aching legs. In reply to one question, he snapped:

"It doesn't make any difference how my legs are doing. I'm hurting all over and these legs have got to take it just the same as I'm doing."

But whether Ben liked it or not, people were talking about his legs and his courageous attempt to win back the Open title. Adding spice to his quest was his impressive showing in the tournament at Los Angeles. Though it hardly seemed likely that he could make a serious run at the Open title, his earlier performance had created the notion in people's minds that he would cause some excitement at Ardmore, Pennsylvania, where the Open was to be played. It was a wonderful thought.

The greatest golfers in the country descended on the Merion Country Club at Ardmore on Thursday, June 8, for the start of the 1950 Open. The course was one of the toughest on the entire circuit, with treacherous stretches of rough bordering its narrow fairways. To these natural hazards was added the huge gallery which followed Hogan and clogged the fairways. The weather was unseasonably hot at Ardmore, and fans who trouped the entire eighteen holes were weary and soaked with perspiration when they finally made their way back to the clubhouse.

Most of the excitement that first day centered around Lee Mackey, Jr., an obscure young pro from Birmingham, Alabama, who fired an astounding 64. Hogan shot a 72, two over par and good enough to place him well up among the leaders. On Friday, Hogan came back with a brilliant 69 to move within two strokes of Dutch Harrison, who had taken over the lead from Mackey. That unfortunate young man, whose record-breaking performance had made him a hero only the day before, shot a dismal 81 and dropped completely out of the running.

Hogan could not be overlooked now,

but the odds were against him. The tournament was scheduled to end on Saturday with thirty-six holes of golf, eighteen in the morning and eighteen in the afternoon, to be played under the most excruciating pressure. The murderous par 70 course had already taken its toll of many of the finest golfers in the 165-man field, including Demaret, Snead, and Cary Middlecoff. "I'm putting like my doggone arm is broke," muttered Snead as he walked off the course after one particularly upsetting round.

Nothing seemed to be upsetting Hogan. He played his first eighteen holes that day in 72; another such round would undoubtedly win the title for him. But it had been two years since he had played thirty-six holes in one day, and the heat out there on the course was enough to melt legs that were younger and sounder than his. He started well enough but the thousands of fans who made up his gallery saw that he was wilting. Sixteen months was not time enough to repair the frightful damage. He went one over par on both the fifteenth and seventeenth holes. By then the word had reached him: Lloyd Mangrum and George Fazio had each finished with a final total of 287. Ben needed a par four on the last hole to tie the two leaders and join them in a play-off on Sunday.

Hogan bowed his neck for a tremendous effort. He drove down the middle of the fairway, a good drive which put him in a favorable position on this dangerous 458-yard hole. His next shot went on the green, and then he was in the cup in two putts for his par four. There would be a playoff on Sunday, and Ben Hogan would be in it.

He trudged painfully back to the clubhouse. Mangrum, winner of the 1946 Open, grinned at him. "See you tomorrow, Ben," he said.

Hogan let himself down into a chair.

Then he settled back and a faint smile crossed his sweat-streaked face. "Yep, see you tomorrow."

"Tomorrow" was another hot day. Hogan was convinced that he could win the playoff by carding a par. Fazio was not a first-rate golfer and did not figure to offer him the competition he could expect from Mangrum. Lloyd was a gambler, and when his shots were falling right, he was as good as anybody. Refreshed by a good night's sleep, the swelling in his legs down again, Hogan was bolstered by the confidence that is part of the make-up of every great champion. At the end of nine holes, Hogan and Mangrum were tied with 36 each, while Fazio clung doggedly on with 37.

Now they were on the last nine holes. Hogan took a stroke lead over Mangrum on the tenth, but Lloyd got it back on the eleventh. Then Ben moved ahead again. Fazio finally dropped out of serious contention on the fourteenth and, after fifteen holes, Ben still had his one-stroke lead. And then came an incredible break. On the sixteenth, Mangrum lifted his ball to blow an insect from it. This was a stupendous blunder, a clear violation of the professional golfing rules against picking up a ball. He was penalized two strokes.

When Hogan learned of the incident, his face, for the first time during the tournament, broke into a wide grin. Victory, he felt, was now assured, but victory in this tournament meant so much to him that he wanted it without the slightest taint. He wanted to win by more than the two penalty strokes. On the short seventeenth hole he drove his first shot to within fifty feet of the cup. He did not have a clear shot at it, though, for he had to putt over a rise. This was certainly a moment for caution. But Ben refused to "back in" to his title. The long putt, confidently stroked, rolled true to the cup and dropped in. As the spectators roared their approval, the usually stolid Hogan took off his cap, twirled it in his fingers, and bowed low to acknowledge their tribute.

That was it. Ben shot a par four on the last hole to finish with a spectacular final round score of 69, four strokes ahead of Mangrum. The little man had come all the way back. As columnist Red Smith wrote the next day: "This was a spiritual victory, an absolute triumph of will."

And who won the 1951 Open? Why, Ben Hogan won that one, too.

THE FACT IS—

1. List some of the handicaps Ben Hogan had to overcome in his golfing career.

2. After his tires were stolen, Ben said, "That was a break for me." Why was it a break?

3. Describe the accident that almost ended his career. How was he injured?

4. Why was it important to Hogan to beat Mangrum by at least four strokes?

COMEBACK

1. Using this essay as your evidence, write a short essay stating Hogan's philosophy of life.

2. Examine the sports pages of your favorite newspaper for the nicknames athletes are given. Then write a brief essay on nicknames. One approach might be "Where Do They Get Those Nicknames?"

3. Prepare to debate either side of any one of these propositions:

    a. It Takes More Than Talent

    b. Golf Is the Most Nerve-racking of All Games

    c. Athletes Are Made, Not Born

    d. Where There's a Will, There's a Way

A WORD TO REMEMBER: talent

Hogan's greatest handicap, the authors say, was "no talent." *Talent* comes from the Greek word *talanton*, which was used as the name of a weight or an amount of silver in that weight. The amount of "talents" a servant received was decided according to his ability or worth. What does *talent* mean now? Can you see how the present meaning developed from the original Greek?

After the Record Is Broken

JAMES A. EMANUEL

My mind slips back to lesser men,
Their how, their when.
Champions then:
Big Stilley, with his bandaged hands,
Broke through the Sidney line, the stands   5
Hysterical, profuse the rival bands.
Poor Ackerman, his spikes undone,
His strap awry, gave way to none,
Not even pride. The mile he won.

Now higher, faster, farther, Stars crossed   10
Recede, and legends twinkle out, far lost,
Far discus-spun and javelin-tossed,
Nor raise again that pull and sweat,
That dig and burn, that crouch-get-set
A glimmer in old trophies yet.   15
Now smoother, softer, trimmed for speed,
The champion seems a better breed,
His victory a showroom deed.

Oh, what have we to do with men
Like champions, but cry again   20
How high, how fast, how far? What then?
Remember men when records fall.
Unclap your hands, draw close your shawl:
The lesser men have done it all.

RECORDS ARE FOR BREAKING

In an interview with the poet, the editors learned that the poem is autobiographical. Dr. James A. Emanuel lived in Alliance, Nebraska, and he knew both Stilley and Ackerman. Sidney, Nebraska, was a neighboring town with a rival team. Though his poem refers to only two sports (football and track), his theme embraces the whole sports scene and, indeed, life itself. You, too, says Dr. Emanuel, are included as a record holder, so long as you have performed at your best.

Given this background—

1. How does the poet mean "lesser men . . . champions then" (stanza 1)? In what sense are they "lesser"?

2. If the modern champion is "softer," in what way does he seem a "better breed" (stanza 2)?

3. Which lines in stanza 3 tell you that any man who has broken the best record in his own lifetime is deemed worthy of honor and respect?

4. Poems are frequently read to set the tone for special occasions— holidays, festivals, award dinners, etc. On what occasion would this poem be suitable for reading? Why?

Ex-Basketball Player

JOHN UPDIKE

Pearl Avenue runs past the high-school lot,
Bends with the trolley tracks, and stops, cut off
Before it has a chance to go two blocks,
At Colonel McComsky Plaza. Berth's Garage
Is on the corner facing west, and there,   5
Most days, you'll find Flick Webb, who helps Berth out.

Flick stands tall among the idiot pumps—
Five on a side, the old bubble-head style,
Their rubber elbows hanging loose and low.
One's nostrils are two S's, and his eyes   10
An E and O. And one is squat, without
A head at all—more of a football type.

Once Flick played for the high-school team, the Wizards.
He was good: in fact, the best. In '46
He bucketed three hundred ninety points,   15
A county record still. The ball loved Flick.
I saw him rack up thirty-eight or forty
In one home game. His hands were like wild birds.

He never learned a trade, he just sells gas,
Checks oil, and changes flats. Once in a while,   20
As a gag, he dribbles an inner tube,
But most of us remember anyway.
His hands are fine and nervous on the lug wrench.
It makes no difference to the lug wrench, though.

Off work, he hangs around Mae's Luncheonette.   25
Grease-gray and kind of coiled, he plays pinball,
Sips lemon cokes, and smokes those thin cigars;
Flick seldom speaks to Mae, just sits and nods
Beyond her face toward bright applauding tiers
Of Necco Wafers, Nibs, and Juju Beads.   30

THE FACT IS—

In this poem about a basketball star turned garage helper:

1. What outstanding feats did Flick perform on the basketball court?

2. What special physical advantage did Flick have that helped him become a fine ballplayer?

3. Updike describes one of the gas pumps as "more of a football type." What type were the other pumps?

4. How does Flick now spend his leisure hours?

FOR THOUGHT AND ACTION

1. When was Flick a happier person, as a high school boy or at the time of the poem? Why?

2. What does the poet mean by "The ball loved Flick"? by "His hands were like wild birds"?

3. Do you think Flick is satisfied with the "bright applauding tiers of Necco Wafers, Nibs, and Juju Beads"?

4. Suppose you had been Flick's guidance counselor, personal friend, or basketball coach. What counsel might you have given him as he approached the end of his high school career?

5. Examine and report on the resources available in your community that try to help people.

        a. enjoy their leisure time.

        b. improve their vocational skills.

Aches and Pains and Three Batting Titles

MYRON COPE

From head to toe, he has enough ailments to put him into a hospital bed. And yet he continues to be the greatest baseball batter, fielder, and competitor Puerto Rico has sent to the big leagues. How does he do it?

The batting champion of the major leagues lowered himself to the pea-green carpet of his 48-foot living room and sprawled on his right side, flinging his left leg over his right leg. He wore gold Oriental pajama tops, tan slacks, battered bedroom slippers, and—for purposes of the demonstration he was conducting—a tortured grimace. "Like dis!" he cried, and then dug his fingers into his flesh, just above his upraised left hip. Roberto Clemente, the Pittsburgh Pirates' marvelous right fielder and their steadiest customer of the medical profession, was showing how he must greet each new day in his life. He has a disc in his back that insists on wandering, so when he awakens, he must cross those legs, dig at that flesh, and listen for the sound of the disc popping back where it belongs.

Around the room necks were craned and ears alerted for the successful conclusion of the demonstration. "No, you cannot hear the disc now," shouted Roberto. "It is in place now. But every morning you can hear it from here to there, in the whole room. *Boop!*"

Boop? Certainly, boop. Not only one boop but two, for there is another disc running around up in the vicinity of Roberto's neck. For that one he must have someone manipulate his neck muscles until the sound of the boop is heard.

All this herding of discs, mind you, is but a nub on the staggering list of medical attentions that Clemente has undergone during his eleven years as a Pirate. Relatively small at 5 feet 10 inches and 180 pounds when able to take nourishment, the chronic invalid has smooth skin, glistening muscles, and perfect facial contours that suggest the sturdy mahogany sculpture peddled in the souvenir shops of his native Puerto Rico. His countrymen regard him as the most superb all-round big-leaguer to emerge from their island, while many Pittsburghers have concluded that the only thing that can keep Clemente from making them forget Paul Waner is a sudden attack of good health.

Now thirty-one, Clemente over the past five pain-filled years has won three National League batting championships (to say nothing of leading *both* leagues for the past two years) and has averaged .330, a level of consistency that no other big-leaguer has equaled during this half decade. In strength and accuracy his throwing arm has surpassed that of the old Brooklyn cannon, Carl Furillo, and if Roberto's genes are any indication, his arm is not about to weaken. "My mother is seventy-five," he says. "Last year she threw out the first pitch of the season. She put something on it, too." Because Roberto smolders with an intense belief in himself, some ballplayers argue that his only real malady is a serious puffing of the head, but the clicking of X-ray machines, the scraping of scalpels, the trickle of intravenous feeding, and the scratching of pens upon prescription pads have mounted to such a fortissimo that Roberto would seem to be a fit subject for graduate research. The moment when Roberto first set eyes on his wife is the story of his life: he spied her in a drugstore, where he had gone to buy medication for an ailing leg.

Surely the Lord cannot be punishing Roberto. A generous man and the devoted father of an infant son, he has been the sole support—since age seventeen—of his parents, a niece, and nephew Pablo, to whom he recently gave an eighteen-foot cruiser. Before that he built a house for his parents. When Pitcher Diomedes Olivo joined the Pirates at age forty, too late to make a pile, Roberto gave him half of all his banquet fees.

"I always try to lead the clean life," says Roberto. He does not smoke and rarely drinks, indulging himself only in his original milkshake recipes. His fruit-cocktail milkshake consists of milk, fruit cocktail, the yolks of eggs, banana ice cream, sugar, orange juice, and crushed ice. "As much as you want of each," he says. "If I want a peach milkshake, I put a peach in it. If I want a pear milkshake, I put a pear in it."

Sighing and limping through his clean life, Roberto has acquired a reputation as baseball's champion hypochondriac, but his personal physician, Dr. Roberto Busó of San Juan, says, "I wouldn't call him a true hypochondriac, because he doesn't go to the extreme of just sitting down and brooding." Far from it. Roberto gallops across the outfield making acrobatic catches; with a bat in his hands, he is all over the batter's box, spinning like a top when he swings. "I'm convinced of his weakness," says Dodger Vice-President Fresco Thompson. "Throw the best ball you've got right down the middle. If you pitch him high and outside, he'll rap a shot into right field. If you throw one to him on one hop, he'll bounce it back through the mound and it'll probably take your pitcher and second baseman with it." In the past few years, alas, Roberto has become relatively orthodox. "If I have to jump three feet over my head to hit the ball now, I don't do it," he points out, deadly serious.

For all his exertions, Roberto *is* perpetually unfit, because, as Dr. Busó goes on to explain, he has a low threshold of pain, which causes him to take minor ailments for crippling debilitations. "If his back hurts, he worries," says Dr. Busó, "and then it becomes a vicious circle, leading to more things. If he has a little diarrhea, he worries that he has a serious stomach difficulty." Roberto is endowed with an exceptionally supple musculature that enables him to race full speed into a base and then stop cold on it—which he likes to do instead of rounding it. But even he pulls muscles, twists ligaments, and generally raises the devil with his supple musculature that way. "It's his natural style," sighs Dr. Busó.

Still, ballplayers wink and giggle whenever Roberto announces that something or other is killing him; his problem is that he is seldom able to come up with a good, visible injury— say, a nice compound fracture with the bone sticking through the flesh. He spent four of his first five big-league years complaining of an agonizing back ailment that a battery of Pirate specialists could not track down. When a chiro-practor, whom Roberto consulted in defiance of front-office warnings, told him he had a curved spine, a pair of legs that did not weigh the same, and a couple of wayward discs, Roberto immediately saw why the physicians had overlooked such a mess. "They always X-rayed me lying down," he says. "They never X-rayed me standing up."

Then, a little later, there were chips floating in his elbow. Nobody doubted they were there, because Dr. George Bennett of Johns Hopkins said so, and promised he'd remove them at the end of the season. But when the time came— great Scott!—the chips had floated off somewhere. Dr. Bennett could not find them.

For Roberto, life in the big leagues has been a series of outrages. He is by no means anti-gringo—in fact, his relationship with Pittsburgh fans is one of the unwavering love stories of the national pastime—but, as a Latin, he feels persecuted. He is vociferously resentful of the fact that he is the least-known, least-sung superstar in baseball. "With my eyes blind I can throw to the base," he snaps. "I *know* that. If Mantle have the arm I have, you will put it in headlines 'cause he is an American. You never give me credit. How many players in history win three batting titles?" Not including Roberto, only eleven since 1876. "The sportswriters don't mention that. They ask me, 'What you think about dis, what you think about dat?' "

Refusing to underestimate himself, Roberto repeatedly has declared, "For me, I am the best ballplayer in the world." His words provoke indignation on all sides, and his efforts to explain them merely stiffen the indignation. "I say, 'For *me*, for *myself!*' " he shouts. The stateside listener, taking him literally, can only conclude that in Roberto's own mind he does think he is better than Mays or Aaron or anyone else in the business, and the impression remains fixed until one happens across a man named Libertario Avilés, a worldly San Juan engineer who built Roberto's house and is one of his good friends. Says Avilés: "You have to understand that the Latin is touchy. If you say to me, 'Who is the best engineer in town?' I will say, 'For me, I am the best.' It is a Spanish saying, an expression of self-respect. You are not to underestimate yourself, but that does not mean you are to underestimate anyone else's ability."

Though Roberto's imperfect command of English has prevented him from explaining himself as clearly as Avilés does, he bristles that no amount of fluency would spare him from being portrayed in the American press as a stupid greenhorn. "I'm gonna tell you dis—it's one of the things that kill me most in the States," he says. "I know I don't speak as bad as they say I speak. I know that I don't have the good English pronunciation, because my tongue belong to Spanish, but I know where the verb, the article, the pronoun, whatever it is, go. I never in my life start a sentence with 'me,' but if I start it with 'I' the sportwriters say 'me.' 'Me Tarzan, you Jane.'" For a fact, Roberto is typed, even by ballplayers who dress alongside him daily. Says one Pirate, "Just before he goes out and wears the ball out, he'll say, 'Me no feel good today. Maybe me no play.'" During Roberto's one season of minor league ball, at Montreal in 1954, he understood practically no English. A player whom he had robbed of an extra-base hit called him a name, whereupon Roberto, assuming he was being complimented on the catch, replied, "Sank you." But he worked hard at his English. He still garbles an occasional phrase, says "dis" and "dat" somewhat more often than "this" and "that" and sometimes is

stumped for the word he seeks, yet his conversation is perfectly intelligible. He resents coming off in print like an M-G-M Sioux chief, almost as much as he resented the Pittsburgh women who once asked him if he wears a loincloth when home in Puerto Rico.

Clemente probably is wrong to think the stateside press has neglected his talent because he's a Latin, but his batting averages of the past six years—.314, .351, .312, .320, .339, and .329—make it seem incredible that his name has not entered the elite Mays-Mantle-Aaron circle.

In the outfield he has done it all. Although not exceptionally swift, he is the master of the shoestring catch. ("I can run very fast bending down," he explains.) Only last season Roberto fielded a bunt—that's right, a bunt—that had rolled to shortstop. Shortstop Gene Alley had gone to cover third base, but as if from nowhere, Roberto dived headlong at the ball, and with his face in the dirt, threw out Houston base runner Walter Bond at third.

Scarcely credible? Nevertheless, the description suits Clemente's throwing arm, too. From Forbes Field's right-center-field gate, a distance of about 420 feet, he once threw out Harvey Haddix at the plate, on one bounce. "I tear a ligament," he of course recalls.

Roberto's value, so far as Brave Manager Bobby Bragan is concerned, is on a par with that of Hall of Fame players. "The best way to describe Roberto Clemente," says Bragan, "is to say, if he were playing in New York, they'd be comparing him to DiMaggio. I would say his greatness is limited only by the fact that he does not hit the long ball consistently and by the fact that he is not playing in New York, or even Chicago or Los Angeles."

In an age of power, the fact that Clemente has never hit more than 23 home

runs (and has never driven in more than 94 runs) weighs heavily against his prestige. There is no doubting that his muscular arms and outsize hands are capable of power, for one of his home runs—a shot over Wrigley Field's left-center bleachers—stands as one of the longest smashes ever hit out of the Cub ball park. Yet because he plays half the schedule in spacious Forbes Field, where the man who guns for home runs undergoes traumatic revelations of inadequacy, Roberto wisely has tailored his style of the line drive and the hard ground ball hit through a hole. Thus he

hit only 10 home runs last year, but he is certain he can hit 20 any season he pleases, Forbes Field notwithstanding.

"If I make up my mind I'm going to hit 20 homers this year," he bellows with indignation, "I bet you any amount of money I can hit 20." A change of style would do the trick, he claims, but what sort of change? Ah, Roberto becomes tight-lipped. He is one of baseball's most sinister practitioners of intrigue.

"Nothing," he replies. "A little change in the hands, that's all. I don't want to tell you what it is."

In baseball any player who obviously

exaggerates simple moves is labeled a hot dog, and on two counts Clemente seems to fall within this definition. First, he not only favors the basket catch made famous by Mays but lends to it an added element of risk by allowing fly balls to drop below his waist before catching them. Second, when fielding routine singles, he often underhands the ball to second base in a great, looping arc instead of pegging it on a line.

Hotly defending himself, Clemente points out that both the low basket catch and the underhand throw are nothing more than natural habits carried over from his youth, for until he was seventeen, he was a softball player, not a baseball player. Not until a softball coach named Roberto Marin persuaded Clemente that he might earn big money in baseball did he turn to the sport. From the outset he was a natural wonder, and yet a problem.

The Dodgers signed him for a $10,000 bonus but were not quite sure what to do with him. At the time, if a first-year player who received more than $4,000 was sent to the minors, he not only had to stay there for a full season but would be eligible to be drafted by another club in November. The Dodgers could have protected Clemente from the draft by making room for him on their own roster, but they were gunning for a third straight pennant and felt that an untested nineteen-year-old would be dead weight on their backs. In the end Walter O'Malley's brain trust assigned Roberto to Montreal but told the Montreal manager, Max Macon, to hide him—that is, play him sparingly lest enemy bird dogs take a fancy to him.

Roberto recalls that '54 season with a shudder. "If I struck out, I stay in the line-up," he says. "If I played well, I'm benched. One day I hit three triples and the next day I was benched. Another time they took me out for a pinch hitter with the bases loaded in the first inning. Much of the time I was used only as a pinch runner or for defense. I didn't know what was going on, and I was confused and almost mad enough to go home. That's what they wanted me to do. That way nobody could draft me."

By religiously discomposing him, Max Macon held Roberto's batting average to .257, but a Pirate scout named Clyde Sukeforth was on to Macon's act. One day in Richmond, Va., before a Montreal-Richmond game, Sukeforth had seen Clemente cut loose with a couple of eye-popping practice throws. He stayed in Richmond four days. Macon countered by keeping Clemente on the bench except for two pinch-hitting appearances, but Sukeforth saw enough of Clemente in batting and fielding practice to be satisfied.

"Take care of our boy," he said to Macon as he prepared to leave town. "You're kidding," Macon said, trying a last-ditch con. "You don't want that kid." Sukeforth smiled and said, "Now, Max, I've known you for a good many years. We're a cinch to finish last and get first draft choice, so don't let our boy get into any trouble." At $4,000, Sukeforth had the steal of the century.

From the Dodger viewpoint, such setbacks are all part of the game, but for reasons the Dodgers had no knowledge of, Roberto has regarded their failure to protect him from the draft as a betrayal of trust. The Dodgers had been his boyhood favorites. Right after he had made a gentleman's agreement to accept their $10,000 bonus, the Braves offered him $30,000, he says, but he turned it down. "It was hard," Roberto says, "but I said I gave the Dodgers my word." As he sees it, the Dodgers took a faithful servant and gambled with him in the draft pool as they would with a handful of casino chips. Teaching the Dodger front office the importance of ethics, Roberto in the past five seasons has hit .375 against the pitching staff of Koufax, Drysdale, Osteen, Podres, and company. The only way to pitch to him, guesses Koufax hyperbolically, is to roll him the ball.

By now one thing should be clear to Pittsburgh's opponents. For their own good, they ought to warm the cockles of Clemente's heart with praise, commiserate with him when he has a hangnail, elect him to the All-Star team with a landslide vote, punch any sportswriter who does not quote him as if he were Churchill on the floor of Parliament, and campaign for him to receive his first Most Valuable Player award. "If I would be happy, I would be a very bad player," Roberto himself says. "With me, when I get mad, it puts energy in my body."

This business of failing to elect him to the All-Star team (as was the case last year when the malaria and/or paratyphoid caused Roberto to get off to a poor start) only assured that he would win another batting championship. Moreover, he cannot forget that in 1960, when he batted .314 and the Pirates won the pennant, he finished a shabby eighth in the voting for MVP. Dick Groat hit .325 for the Pirates that year, leading the league and winning the MVP trophy, but Clemente drove in 94 runs to Groat's 50, and demands to know why, if he was not Pittsburgh's most valuable player, he was the one the pitchers most often knocked down? When told that Groat sparked the team, Roberto proves that his American idiom is on the upgrade by retorting, "Sparked, my foot!" The point is, however, that he hit .351 the following year. Lest he ever simmer down and acquire a happy disposition, his teammates call him No Votes.

Ignored and rebuffed by baseball's

In crowd, Clemente nevertheless leads all popularity polls where it counts—with the paying customers in Pittsburgh. They seem to grasp that, if he is a man who covets recognition, he would rather have it from Joe Doaks than from all the members of the Baseball Writers Association of America. "Winning the World Series in 1960 was not the biggest thrill I ever have in my life," he said not long ago, looking out on the lights of San Juan from his veranda. "The biggest thrill was when I come out of the clubhouse after the last Series game and saw all those thousands of fans in the streets. It was something you cannot describe. I did not feel like a player at the time. I feel like one of those persons, and I walked the streets among them."

Such utterances by Clemente are not a pose for public consumption. Behind closed doors he has urged his teammates to set their sights high, for the novel reason that "we owe these people another pennant." Says Pitcher Bob Friend, a Pirate until traded to the Yankees in December: "He gets pretty windy on the subject, and you wonder how to turn him off." A lot of players leave the game feeling the world owes them a living, but Clemente's an exception to that rule. He knows what baseball's done for him, and he expresses his appreciation.

Puerto Ricans, meanwhile, hold Clemente in an esteem they otherwise tender only to cellist Pablo Casals and elder statesman Luis Muñoz Marin. "He is a glory to the island," says a night-club guitarist named Frankie Ramirez, whose sentiments are echoed from San Juan to Mayagüez. One recent morning Roberto and his engineer friend, Libertario Avilés, drove into the countryside east of San Juan. Avilés steered his Wildcat convertible past the old sugar-cane fields that were now being bulldozed for factory sites. Roberto's father had owned a few acres himself once and at the same time had worked as a foreman of a great plantation and with his wife had run a grocery and meat market for the workers. "My mother and father, they worked like racehorses for me," said Roberto. He has the mid-Victorian morality of the old Spanish families, and his sense of obligation runs strong. "Anybody," he was saying now, "who have the opportunity to serve their country or their island and don't, God should punish them. If you can be good, why you should be bad?"

The Wildcat coursed through the seaside village of Fajardo, and not far beyond turned up a dirt road where lay a dream that had possessed Roberto's emotions all winter. He was negotiating with the government to lease a lush 20 acres on which he plans to construct a sports camp for boys, plowing the profits into camp scholarships for the under-privileged. He will call the camp Sports City. Tramping through the seaside forest where Sports City will rise, Roberto explained his ambition: "We are known as a good-sportsmanship people, and I'm proud to be part of that recognition. But today life is moving too fast for these kids. You see fifteen-year-old boys and girls holding hands. They hang out on street corners. Maybe if I can keep them interested in sports, they will not always be talking about stealing and about gangster movies. I'm proud to do good for my island."

As Roberto spoke of his dream, he seemed no longer the worrier on whose lips are complaints of headaches, back-aches, sore feet, sore arms, and tired blood. "I like to work with kids," he said. But then he added with a frown, "I'd like to work with kids all the time, if I live long enough."

THE FACT IS—

1. Roberto Clemente is beset by a list of ills that would stop a lesser man. Can you name some of them?

2. Despite his list of ills, Clemente has performed great feats on the baseball diamond. List those that impress you the most.

3. What is the evidence that Clemente's self-confidence is healthy despite his physical troubles?

4. When Clemente's playing days are over, what is he planning to do?

THE CHAMPION

1. Imagine you are asked to vote for an entrant for Baseball's Hall of Fame or the Most Valuable Player award. Write a brief paper or make a brief talk in behalf of Roberto Clemente.

2. If your school newspaper asked you to interview Roberto Clemente for a forthcoming sports profile, what five questions (not answered in the essay just read) would you ask him? How do you imagine he might answer each?

THINKING ABOUT THE WORLD OF SPORTS

HOW DO SPORTS ENRICH LIFE?

1. Of all the sports mentioned in this unit, which one has the greatest appeal for you? Why? If *you* had prepared this unit, which additional sport might you have had represented? What would you have omitted? Why?

2. Find out about the records achieved by Satchel Paige, Ben Hogan, and Roberto Clemente in their specialties. What interesting boxing and football records can you discover and list?

3. If there were a Hall of Fame for Sportsmanship, who in this unit would be your first, second, and third choices? Defend your answer.

4. From your reading of this unit, which would you want to see more of in this country: professional or amateur sports? school or intramural teams? spectator or participant sports? Explain.

5. The World of Sport has many awards: "The Coach of the Year," "The Most Valuable Player," and so on. Of the men and women you have met in these stories, who would deserve such recognition? Why?

6. What should sports do for you—help you fight, win, build muscles, compete fairly, grow in maturity? Explain your ideas in a paper of about 100 words.

7. Each of the statements below might have been said by or about one of the sports figures you have read about. Can you identify them?

    a. Oh, for the good old days of boxing.

    b. Father Time is on the mound!

    c. If you can't outplay them, outwork them.

    d. I have a future and it's with Youth.

8. When Ted Williams, the great Boston Red Sox star, was inducted into Baseball's Hall of Fame, he said, "I hope Satchel Paige and Josh Gibson . . . will be inducted here as symbols of the great Negro players who are not there because they were not given a chance." With the world of sports moving toward complete integration, who among players from minority groups will one day deserve an honored place in baseball, basketball, football, and other sports? Defend your choices.

Americans Look at Themselves

So far in this book you have read a lot about America and Americans. You have read about adventure, sports, show business, and science. You have read biographies of great Americans. Perhaps now we should take a look at ourselves. A great Greek philosopher once said, "The unexamined life is not worth living." In this unit Americans take a look at themselves. They examine their lives and the lives of their fellow Americans. Let's see how we look at ourselves.

Of course, some views are serious. Countee Cullen's poem pleads for more understanding than most of us are willing to give. A chilling eyewitness account of the hanging of John Brown is followed by a section from the American epic *John Brown's Body*, showing the fervor of the times that led to Brown's raid on Harpers Ferry and ultimately to the War Between the States. Henry Wadsworth Longfellow, when he wrote "The Ship of State," foresaw and feared that the Union would be split by the war; his poem shows what strength, wisdom, and courage went into the creation and the building of the Union.

You will find a number of poems in this unit, because poets often have the greatest insight into the minds and motives of men. One kind of insight is shown in the poem "Dream," with its surprise withheld till the very last word. Quite a different kind of poem is Robert Tristram Coffin's "Crystal Moment," which gives us an observation of sheer beauty.

But if there is a most important point in this section, it is that one of the healthiest ways to look at ourselves is to take that look with a sense of humor. Humor can drive home many a point, from the revelation of our heroes' clay feet in "The Wild, Wild West" to the education of the Destry Road Boys. Humor can deal calmly with the battle of the generations, as in "The Heyday of the Blood." You will laugh at and with other people in this unit, but at the same time, and perhaps best of all, you may laugh a little at yourself.

Any Human to Another

COUNTEE CULLEN

The ills I sorrow at
Not me alone
Like an arrow,
Pierce to the marrow,
Through the fat   5
And past the bone.

Your grief and mine
Must intertwine
Like sea and river,
Be fused and mingle,   10
Diverse yet single,
Forever and forever.

Let no man be so proud
And confident,
To think he is allowed   15
A little tent
Pitched in a meadow
Of sun and shadow
All his little own.

Joy may be shy, unique,   20
Friendly to a few,
Sorrow never scorned to speak
To any who
Were false or true.

Your every grief   25
Like a blade
Shining and unsheathed
Must strike me down.
Of bitter aloes wreathed,
My sorrow must be laid   30
On your head like a crown.

COUNTEE CULLEN (1903–1946).

Countee Cullen was one of the first American Negroes to make an impact on modern American poetry. Perhaps because of his educational advantages (he had degrees from both New York University and Harvard), his poetry does not strike the note of passionate racial protest that we find in Negro poetry today. Cullen's models were largely the great English poets, and his work is smoothly literary. "Most things I write," he said, "I do for the sheer love of the music in them. A number of times I have said I wanted to be a poet and known as such and not as a Negro poet. Somehow or other, however, I find my poetry of itself treating of the Negro, of his joys and his sorrows—mostly of the latter—and of the heights and depths of emotion which I feel as a Negro." Because of the strongly musical quality of Cullen's verse, some of it has been made into a series of song cycles.

THE POET'S PURPOSE

1. Look carefully at the title of this poem. What idea does it suggest? Express in your own words one message the poet offers.

2. Read again stanzas two and five. What word is repeated? What is the effect on the poem as a whole?

3. Now reread the third stanza, with particular reference to lines 15–19. What connection do you see between this point of view and the thought which appears in Ella Wheeler Wilcox's words: "Laugh, and the world laughs with you; /Weep, and you weep alone"? Write a paragraph explaining your conclusions.

A WORD TO REMEMBER: unique

In line 20 the poet speaks of joy as being "shy, unique." *Unique* means "single or sole, one of a kind." *Unique* is often used too freely; therefore you must be careful when using it. The plot of a movie is not unique, but the Statue of Liberty is. How is *unique* related to the following words: *uniform, unity, universe, university, United States?*

SAMUEL CHOTZINOFF

"Isn't it all wonderful—I mean what's happened to me?" she bubbles to her interviewer. The success story of a talented Negro girl who made it to the top in the exclusive world of opera is just that—"all wonderful."

Leontyne Price

Leontyne Price swept into the room like a Winged Victory. In the fullness of her colorful clothes, in the inverted tub of her purple hat, she was all glorious show. Her light chocolate skin and her large, deep, expressive eyes, liquid and soft, harmonized beautifully with her get-up; and her rich, creamy, Southern speaking voice seemed like the perfect rounding out of her warm personality.

I wondered if this was the same Leontyne Price I had first gotten to know six or seven years ago, when she was all but unknown. As it turned out, her basic character was the same, but her extraordinary successes had given her a self-confidence and a cheerfulness that were new. Success had liberated a hidden abundance of spirit, a native sense of humor, and a limitless enthusiasm for life. Although she makes no bones about enjoying her success, she is anything but the typical first lady of an opera. Tremendous acclaim in Vienna, London, Milan, and New York—rave reviews and fabulous publicity—has not had the effect of making her conceited. Essentially she was the Leontyne Price I first knew, now more joyous, released from the timidity and reluctance of the artist who had yet to make her mark.

She embraced me and then sat down breathlessly and looked about approvingly. "Isn't it all wonderful—I mean what's happened to me?" She seemed to be implying, "I'm happy, and I love you and everything and everybody."

Her speech is rapid and fluent, often torrential. And her pleasure in expressing her ideas and general optimism was so fresh and simple that I hesitated to interrupt her; I put in a word here and there only to keep her from straying from her fairy-tale story.

"You see," she said soberly, "when I was a child, I was always sort of the local 'thing.' In those days I think even my mother thought I was a child prodigy just because I learned to play the piano at a very early age."

"Did you have a piano?"

"Yes. My mother, at great sacrifice (she was kind of a midwife, I think), paid on the installment plan for a piano for me, an upright. I must have been about six. I remember, too, the Christmas of my life. A piano *and* a bicycle! That was difficult because of the low-economy wages, and I do mean the lowest, which is what my father earned. He was a sawmill worker, and while I can't quote what he made, it wasn't much. The weekly income was supplemented by my mother, so the home budget benefited from the fact that both of my parents worked, you see."

"How many children were you?" I asked.

"Just two of us. My brother and I. My brother was to me the handsomest, most intelligent boy or man, next to my father, I had every known. My parents were married going on thirteen and a half or fourteen years before they had children. My father is now eighty-two years old; but you wouldn't believe it because he is so well preserved. My mother is considerably younger—my mother, I think, this year [1964] will be seventy years old. She too had a beautiful voice. She sort of lifted it in the Methodist church choir at home; still does, as a matter of fact. She was always extremely protective about my having everything. You know, at times somebody in the house had to go without something in order for me to have a piano lesson, or to have a nicer dress at school, or something that she might not have had time to make for me herself had to be bought for me at the local store in Laurel, Mississippi; it was kind of a dollar down and a dollar a week deal, you know. In those days ten dollars was an enormous amount of money. But I remember *always* having this particular protective 'thing,' as if my mother maybe *knew* something was going to happen—or at least she wanted it to happen, I don't know. As soon as I began to show signs of any musical talent at all, via, I imagine, notes of enthusiasm or words of enthusiasm from my local piano teacher, whom I still adore, Mrs. Hattie V. J. McInnis, I think that's when my mother began to believe maybe I would become, you know, *some*thing."

"First you began the piano?"

"I started playing extremely well

quite early—by about ten or eleven—and I was playing for all the Sunday school functions; all sorts of social functions the ladies' club would give for benefits, and little social affairs, you know.

"In a way, I remember very much that my father was terribly old-fashioned (and I'm very glad, in this stage of my life, that he was) when I got to courtin' age—which was considerably later than nowadays. They used to start about sixteen, because you really should have been married by eighteen. This highfalutin' idea about going to college was a bit much, you know, so the idea that Mama had was that I was just not going to be in the local group; I was going to go through high school—preferably with honors, which I did. I was going to absorb as much as possible, if it meant mortgaging the house, which was the only thing my parents ever owned. Fortunately they didn't really have to go too far—well"—Leontyne corrected herself—"yes, they did, because there was my brother, who was frankly, I find extremely more intelligent than myself, who had to be fed, clothed, and go to school, too. So I used to make a little extra money doing little piano jobs and things around town, and hither and yon. That's when I began doing little soirée things up at the Chisholms'—in what they called the big house. In other words, on the hill; that's where the white citizens lived in Laurel—and I always played with three Chisholm girls. We were the same age. I remember the Chisholms had an enormously beautiful playground. My aunt's servant house was set on the premises."

"Is that how you got to know the Chisholms, through your aunt?"

"Yes. I used to go up to the Chisholm house and I would play for them and I think I was supposed to have a little thing going for me—I was rather bright, they said—and I used to dance or sing or I would play the piano."

"You sang, too?"

"I sang, too, but not much. You know, everybody sings down that way."

"But you showed no vocal talent?"

"I would think that was too early."

"You weren't a child soprano, or anything like that?"

"No, but I was a *good* piano player; I still play piano fairly well. I had a very happy childhood, in a word. I was poor, but I had enough to eat and I had enough clothes to wear. I *liked* the world I had as a child. The main thing is that there was so much love *inside* the home that I was raised in. My brother and I are very close. My parents were not the kind of people who were afraid to show us that they were pretty stuck on us, and I think that has been a very good thing for me.

"My brother, who is a major in the Army now, wrote me recently what I think is one of the most beautiful letters from a mature American male I have ever read, which said that of all the men he had ever met in his life—including some officers in the Army he really admired—he still thought the man he would like to be like most in his life is our dad, and I think it's because we were—well, it's kind of like the Italian families, the provincial families. There is so much warmth and sweetness in the home. If there were problems, and there must have been many, I'm sure, it was all arranged very maturely—I have never heard my parents argue with one another. I have always seen my father treat my mother with the greatest respect, and sometimes even now I can see the strength of his love. Perhaps because she was younger than he, I don't know, he treats her in a very special kind of way. We just had a nice time as children, we really did."

For a moment Leontyne lost herself in savoring her happy childhood.

"So you went to high school," I prompted.

"Yes. I graduated from Oak Park, a vocational high school. I got a scholarship to Central State College in Wilberforce, Ohio, and that's where I graduated from."

"How old were you when you entered?"

"I was seventeen."

"Had you sung then at all?"

"Yes. I hadn't studied, but I was quite a local success—playing and singing."

"What did you sing?"

Leontyne laughed out loud. "You'll die," she said. "Things like "Homing," you know . . . 'All things come home at eventide.' "Because" was really my hit tune; I was really the wedding and funeral girl of all time! Anytime anybody died or got married, you know (in those days I don't think we had a telephone), they would just run over and say: somebody's getting married, or somebody died."

"Did you get paid for this?"

"Well, not very much."

"Now, when did you begin to study singing?"

"I didn't really begin in earnest until September 1949, at Juilliard."

"How did you get there?"

"Well, my first two years at Central State in Wilberforce, I majored in music education, which meant I would be able to teach music in public schools—it was kind of a security."

"You could always get a job."

"That was the whole thing. I had to be that practical for my father. But by my third year I had started to sing for local things—in chapel, in the glee club—and I started singing more than I was playing, because . . . oh, I don't know . . . when I started to sing, people would listen. Then President Wesley started having me sing when the dignitaries would come—like the Ohio Board of Education members and visiting dignitaries from other colleges; I was always up there singing in my basic black dress. I'm afraid it was "Homing" again, but I had worked up "Vissi d'Arte" in English (I'd rather not go into the translation). And I never forget, I was always singing "Depuis le Jour" In English, and I sang things like, well, all the hit tunes from the *Messiah*, you know."

"You sang "Depuis le Jour" without having studied?"

"We had a coach there; her name was Catherine Van Buren." Leontyne is most careful to give credit to everybody who has ever helped her.

"Did anyone think you were a remarkable singer?"

"Doctor Wesley did. Technically, that's when I got my application for Juilliard because he sent for it himself. I graduated from college, fortunately with honors—I was *cum laude* in my class, 3.6 average—and by the first of my senior year, I had decided: 'OK, I'll take a chance on it.' The summer of my junior year, the Chisholms went down to my father—that's why I will always respect them—and asked him if it was all right for them to finance my going to New York, because I talked at great length about my future with my parents and with the Chisholms. Mrs. Chisholm by this time was really sort of my confidant—I listened to records at her house, and I was exposed to a lot of things."

"Were both Mr. and Mrs. Chisholm convinced that you had a fine voice?"

"They were very enthusiastic. In one word, the Chisholms said to my father that they did not feel that I should stay at home and teach in Oak Park School, and would my parents give their permission for them to finance me. My father is a very strange man. He does not like to owe anybody a nickel—and I respect the Chisholms tremendously because they came to know him as a person, and they spoke to him like an individual, and I think that is why that relationship has maintained itself. I graduated from Central State College in June 1948, and I came up to Juilliard because my application had been accepted.

"The Chisholms financed my trip and they paid for my board at International House—my food, my books. International House is across the street from Juilliard. It's a marvelous place. I'm a better person for having lived there. It has foreign students and American students living in the same building."

"So you had your audition and you got a scholarship?"

"Yes, I also received a job on the information desk at International House, which helped. I think I made about, after taxes, twenty bucks a week. That's enough to help you get by on."

"Then what happened?"

"Well, I got the opera bug when I came to New York; I remember the first performance of opera I ever saw was at the City Center. It was *Turandot*. Then the second performance I went to did it for me. I stood up at the Met to hear *Salomé*. I was completely gone then and I said to myself, 'I have got to be an opera singer!' It was very difficult to get into the Juilliard Opera Workshop, because you really have to have outstanding qualities; there's not that much room in an active opera workshop in a school. So sometimes students waited as long as three years to get in. Finally, in my second year I got into the Opera Workshop and I did my first role.

"You know something? Two of my biggest breaks came when two operatic sopranos had emergency appendectomies. In 1957, in the middle of the intermission, during something like the third performance of *The Dialogues*, at San Francisco, suddenly the manager came in looking kind of strange, saying Miss Antoinetta Stella had canceled for an emergency appendectomy. They had everything ready there for *Aïda*, with no Aïda, and they asked me did I know it, and I said yes, I did, because I did, I really did—and the next thing I knew I was on the stage doing *Aïda*.

"I also remember something that was funny. Wait till you hear this. I remember I had everything thought out in *Aïda*. I said to myself, 'I can't go wrong. This'll be the first time I've ever been out on a stage for this kind of thing,' and let's face it, my skin was in my favor for a change. 'I got that made, I can't lose! There's nothing to worry about. OK, fine: Molinari-Pradelli is not a heavy-handed conductor; I will be heard. The only thing I don't know is exactly—well—if I get on the wrong side of the stage, I *get* on the wrong side of the stage. I can't go wrong. When the Ethiopian slaves come in, I will just go where they go; and with Robert Merrill, the Amonasro, I'll just go with him.' But I couldn't figure out where the tomb was going to be. So I kept walking up to the director, during the night, you know, between the acts, and I kept saying, 'Maestro, where . . .?' but he acted as if he wasn't listening and said, 'You were wonderful, you are beautiful tonight, and you just go change the costume and it's going to be fine.' Finally I said, 'I have a question to ask you: Where is the tomb? Where am I going to die? I don't have the slightest idea where I am going to die!' And he broke up with laughter. Well, I did find the tomb."

"Now, what about the future?"

She did not speak at once, and I could see from her expression that she was no longer thinking about her career. Then she looked at me earnestly. "I would like to try to make a gap between this constant tearing at—no, that's not what I mean." She was struggling for words. "I would like to fulfill a little more of my personal life. By that I don't mean I want to find a knight in shining armor on a white charger, or something. I know that already I have made the choice I want to make. But I'm in my mid-thirties, and I'm a little bit too young to be quite so preoccupied and narrow-minded about what I am doing. I think I would like to, at sixty or let's say fifty, not be so preoccupied with whether my high C is going to come out or not, but really try to do something for somebody else. I have become very interested in doing something for the unfortunate youth of New York and sharing what I have without being paid for it, to be available for things that may help people."

"You think you have been a lucky gal, is that it?"

"I think I have had more than my share of luck, and I'm young enough to be able to enjoy the material things."

"But you would also like to pay back?"

"In some way I would like to show my thanks, I think maybe to God, for what He has done for me."

THE FACT IS—

1. What musical talent did Miss Price show even before her singing talent?

2. Who were the singer's earliest benefactors? How did they help?

3. In one or two sentences, describe the star's early family life.

4. When did the author first meet the singer? What was his first reaction to her? As a result of her success, how had Leontyne Price changed?

SUCCESS STORY

1. Leontyne Price's career and life have, it has been said, a "fairy-tale" quality. Do you agree? Why?

2. Operas are stories set to music. Learn the story of at least one of the operas mentioned here, as Miss Price herself undoubtedly had to before singing her role.

3. Visit your library—

    a. Compare this version of Miss Price's life and career with at least one other (for example, the account in *Current Biography*).

    b. Find the names of other Negro opera singers, both male and female.

4. Suppose your community is starting a talent search for singers. Write a letter introducing a classmate, schoolmate, friend, or relative whom you deem worthy of support.

"Hoods" I Have Known

SONDRA SPATT

"Perhaps I should explain about hoods," writes the star pupil who fell into disgrace—and in with dirty Danny Tooey. "Our seventh-grade hoods . . . never did much but loaf at the back of the class and throw spitballs." Read this story with an open mind.

Whenever I reminisce about old beaux, I begin with poor Larry Dinhofer, who sat behind me in the eighth grade and asked me to the P.S. 333 prom because I asked him to my graduation party. From gratitude for that first invitation, Larry's mother bought me a monstrous bottle of Sweet Primrose toilet water, which I have kept to this day. The primroses or whatever they were have become so fermented through the years that I now use it for rubbing alcohol and think "Dinhofer" whenever I have an ache in my back. But strictly speaking, although memorable, Larry was not my first but only my first respectable beau. Before Larry, I had an unrespectable romance, long suppressed, a seventh-grade affair with the dirty, untrustworthy Danny Tooey, who was a hood.

Perhaps I should explain about hoods. Hoods in Brooklyn are boys who go to school only by the grace of the truant officer, "hood" being short for "hoodlum." "Juvenile delinquent" is a much longer word and not half as piquant. Our seventh-grade hoods were comparatively unaggressive. They never did much but loaf at the back of the class and throw spitballs at each other, sometimes at the teacher. They wore dungarees or chartreuse pants with pistol pockets in imitation of the Avenue E Boys, who were model hoods and real court cases. Our hoods, although harmless, grew aggressive-looking sideburns and great masses of curly black or blond hair. All of them shaved. Danny Tooey was the biggest, tallest, hairiest of the lot and the one who had been left back most often. He was fifteen.

When Danny was first left back into our class, we ignored each other. Our social milieux, even in school, were different. I sat in the front of the room, covered my books, raised my hand in answer to all questions, and agreed with the teacher on all points. I had already set my eye on the General Excellence Award at graduation. Danny, as I have already pointed out, never did anything in school except pledge allegiance to the flag, proving that hoods were untrustworthy but not unpatriotic.

Danny did not cover books; he destroyed them. Miss Malcolm thought well-bound books in hoody hands a waste, so Danny scattered the leaves of his worn-out volumes like nuts in May, sometimes maliciously, more often from the sort of pure disinterest playboys show when they run their Jaguars off cliffs in the movies. No one had ever called upon Danny to read from these books, you see. It was *l'acte gratuit*.[1]

When I fell into disgrace, Danny was the first hood whose friendship I

[1] *l'acte gratuit* (lahkt grah·TWEE): French for *his own free will*.

won. I was in with the leader of the gang, so to speak. I had been the Winged Messenger of the seventh grade and scurried around corridors clutching notes from Miss Malcolm with the expression postmen have when they meet up with the sleet or snow or fog people have been telling them about. I took my messenger position seriously, even though the notes, whenever I paused to open them, revealed nothing more serious than a date for tea or a lift to the beauty parlor. One day Miss Malcolm decided to affix a postscript to a note that she'd dispatched with me and came around a corner unexpectedly, giving both of us a shock.

"Since you have proved yourself a criminal, I'm going to treat you that way," she announced pontifically before the class, and made me clean out my desk and remove my books and self to the back of the room.

As a criminal, I found myself in a peculiar position. It had only been a note asking for more toilet supplies for the teachers' rest room, and hardly worth the drastic punishment, I felt. It was a mundane confidence I'd broken, though Miss Malcolm had mysteriously underlined "toilet supplies" for some reason I could not fathom. Nevertheless, I was disgraced, not only with the teacher but with all my friends. From that day on, Miss Malcolm would not call on me in class, even though I was the only one who knew the three most important Atlantic fishing ports and waved my arm wildly like a drowning Atlantic fisherman. She instructed the class to ignore me too. My friends from the front of the room, oh, perfidy, had been waiting all these years, I found, praying that I would fall from grace. They simply would not turn their heads or accept my notes.

Instead of being crushed by my fate, I was confident and not at all apologetic.

After all, I was the star pupil. And what would Miss Malcolm do without me when we reached the difficult Middle Atlantic States? As for my friends, "those schmoey kids" as I called them, my contempt for them was boundless. I vowed if I ever achieved my pure state again, I'd make them suffer.

Miss Malcolm seated Danny and me in a double seat, thinking, dear woman, that close contact with a hood was the worst punishment anyone could inflict on a clean, well-brought-up little girl. She expected me to cry and beg to be let back, at least to the class middle. That was because Miss Malcolm herself was afraid of that hairy creature who slouched into class with disquieting tread and rumbled unintelligible answers deep in his throat. "Urghs" was Danny's favorite comment, and it frightened Miss Malcolm.

When I arrived at the last seat, last row, Danny didn't know quite what to think. I was obviously a pseudo-hood and not destined to stay very long. Danny didn't rumble anything at me but regarded me mildly, even amusedly, that first afternoon. "You staying here, little girl?" he asked sarcastically as I piled my books in the desk. His tone implied that I didn't look dangerous enough to merit such a position. I don't think Danny fully realized the moral turpitude of note-reading.

No, I didn't think I was going to stay with Danny long either, at first. But days went by, and Miss Malcolm's gaze never glided past the dividing line— Raymond de Fato, who occasionally threw a spitball but wore a tie. I began to grow more and more uncomfortable. The classroom was long and crowded. Because of scufflings and murmurings around me, I couldn't hear anything that was going on past Raymond; Raymond wouldn't tell me, and even if I did hear, no one would call on me. But I could not go to Miss Malcolm begging to be let back. I was proud.

I began to bring *Jane Eyre* [1] to school and spent the whole day reading ferociously. But even that splendid book couldn't make up for the fact that I was missing the Middle Atlantic States. Nor did snubbing Miss Malcolm every day in front of the coatroom bring the desired satisfaction. I couldn't complain at home because my mother thought I should beg for mercy. She said I was "a stubborn fool" and "just like your father." I was an outcast and everybody knew it.

I would have been completely miserable if Danny hadn't decided to take me into his group.

Danny began making the first overtures by looking on with me as I read *Jane Eyre*. Of course I was surprised. Until then it had been mere peaceful coexistence. I didn't even know Danny could read. He'd just sit for days looking at me sardonically from under his tousle of black curls. Occasionally he had cocked an eyebrow at me and his entire broad and grimy brow had moved.

"Dat looks like a good book," he said to me one day, looking interested, and I immediately lent him my four-color pencil to doodle with. From then on we were friends. Even the good girls in my class didn't read Brontë because they couldn't understand words like "choler" and "lineaments." Such praise from a hood made me glow with pleasure.

Our friendship was sealed next day, when we had an examination. Danny gave me his rabbit foot for keeps. It was for luck, he explained, and you could write the answers on a little piece of paper in the claw.

[1] **Jane Eyre:** a highly romantic novel by Charlotte Brontë.

"Are you sure you don't want it?" I remember asking diffidently. "You probably need it more than I do."

"Oh, I can copy off you—dat's all right," he said.

I really didn't want that rabbit foot. A crib sheet was a little too far out on the road to dishonesty for a former star pupil, and I knew my New England products backward and forward anyway. Still, I accepted the foot for luck and as a token. I still remember the softness of it, and the little sharpnesses that were the nails.

The next thing Danny did was introduce me to the boys. This was difficult, but he managed to get them to ask me to lend them pencils. They were the shiest hoods imaginable. There were really ten of us in the back, but I only got to know five: Danny, Harry la Marca, Alan Brodnik, Ronny Abry, and Jo-Jo Begoyne.

These were the Destry Road Boys. Because of his age, ability, and the fact that he had been approached by the Avenue E Boys for possible merger, Danny was definitely the leader. He ruled with an iron hand. Once Harry and Jo-Jo had a fight in the back of the room, and they might have ripped each other to pieces if Danny hadn't broken it up. They moved silently, slowly, crouching a little by the door to the gym. "You never seen a shiv fight before?" Danny asked when he saw my wonder afterward, and he showed me the knives, six inches long.

"Dose guys are gonna get into real trouble one day—dey're only tirteen—dey don't have any sense," he said. During the fight Miss Malcolm had gone on with the class in the front of the room as though nothing was happening. After twenty years of dealing with crime, Miss Malcolm had found her method—the silent, or you-don't-exist, treatment.

The boys got a great deal of pleasure out of telling me about shiv fights and how the Avenue E Boys got away with robbing a candy store. The Destry Road Boys had never gotten away with anything because they had never pulled anything, except turning in false alarms, which any five-year-old can do. They were a small-time bunch and they knew it. Our neighborhood, Newton Park, was just too quiet and genteel to start any trouble, and there wasn't any point going over to Avenue E to find some because Danny wouldn't let them. "You want to get your heads knocked off?" he asked. Danny was the most cautious, perhaps because he was the only gang leader I've ever known. He'd been around and he knew that it was safest to do nothing and if anybody asked you anything to just mumble along.

I found that I too could expound to the boys on topics they hadn't heard before, usually last month's lessons. I think I may have been more interesting than Miss Malcolm, because when I told them about Cortés in Mexico and killing the great chief Montezuma, their eyes gleamed and they clasped imaginary sword handles. Alan Brodnik expressed a desire to make a poniard or a rapier in shop that week. "Swords, dat's all you guys need," Danny said in disgust, but I could see that he was interested too.

"Why didn't dey make a deal wit Montezuma and get a percentage?" he asked me once when I got involved with the more intricate dealings. "A percentage is better. Dopey Spaniards." I could see that Danny had everything all figured out.

I had been sitting in the back of the room for a week and a half when I began to notice a perceptible change in Danny. He began to wear white polo shirts instead of his old, saggy yellow one, and smelled faintly of Ivory soap. His face was clean and his hair was somehow higher, pulled together into a compact pompadour. Danny even turned his club jacket inside out so that the plain black showed instead of the worn fuchsia silk with its huge black "Destry Boys" lettering. "'Stoo flashy," Danny said, and that afternoon, after lunch, all the boys had their jackets turned around too.

Soon, whenever Danny and I read together because of Danny's pageless volumes, his fingers curled around my white-clean covers were white-clean too. The fingers also turned the pages exactly right, which proved that Danny could actually read as fast as I did. I began to think that Danny wasn't really a hood, or was just pretending, or that being a hood wasn't so bad at all if only the teacher would notice you. If we listened very carefully, Danny and I, we could hear Miss Malcolm's voice reading *Evangeline* far off, and once, when we got to the part that goes

Black were her eyes as the berry that grows on the thorn by the wayside—
Black, yet how softly they gleamed beneath the brown shade of her tresses!
Sweet was her breath as the breath of kine that feed in the meadows . . .

Danny bent over and whispered, "She looks like you."

Since I was definitely blond and blue-eyed, and since Danny had never whispered before in his life, I began to think something was wrong. Or, if Danny was becoming poetic, something might be right. But anyway—something. Yes, I thought rather priggishly, Danny has probably never sat next to a good poetry-reading little girl in his life; my presence has probably opened the door to a whole new world of clean-smelling respectability.

It occurred to me that I might tame Danny and turn him into a star pupil, thus killing two birds with one stone and getting me a seat in Respectability,

too. Why, I could probably persuade Danny to take elocution lessons. Then he could learn to pronounce "th" and other things, and Miss Malcolm would understand him. I had a little difficulty myself sometimes. And if I could convince his mother to get him some crisp white shirts and a tie. . . . Maybe my mother would iron them for him if Mrs. Tooey was busy.

Ronny, Harry, Alan, and Jo-Jo, although they showed no immediate signs of conversion, might still follow their leader out of hood-hood and I would have a whole gang to my credit. I could learn to iron shirts myself. Soon I would walk down Destry Road to be pointed at and stared at by the citizenry. "There's the girl who saves hoods," ladies would say as they waited in line by the fruit counter at Willy's. "Can you come and talk to my boy after school?" "Dere's dat dame." The Avenue E Boys would scowl and lurk behind the gum machine in front of Harry's. "She's the one who's been takin' our best material. Why, Danny Tooey, he could've been the best hood in Brooklyn, he's studyin' for the ministry."

Yes, I would save Danny. I determined to bring my *Believe-It-or-Not!* Ripley book to school immediately so Danny could begin assimilating the mass of interesting facts so necessary to star pupils. We would sit in the first row, side by side.

Alas. While I had been making plans for reformation, I had overlooked the real reason for Danny's behavior, which was, of course, sex. Danny Tooey wanted me to be more than just a friend. On Friday morning, May 11, Danny asked me to go to the movies with him the next evening, May 12. Not in the afternoon. In the evening. It was a sword-fighting picture, he said, and I would like it. I was shocked. Respectable seventh-grade girls, especially me, didn't wear lipstick or go out with boys;

eighth-grade girls could wear lipstick and go out, if they didn't make too much fuss about it. But no decent girl ever went anywhere, morning or evening, with a hood.

Oh, yes, there were a few. But they were scrawny and inky-haired and went to P.S. 293 and only appeared hanging around outside by the homogenized-bagel man at three o'clock. They weren't decent either. Because when the boys didn't show up, they would flirt with the homogenized-bagel man, and when he wasn't there, they would go to Harry's and stand in front of the gum machine. And they would make remarks like "Look who's here," whenever someone passed. The Avenue E Dolls, an auxiliary of the Boys, set the fashion in this case, and any girl hood who didn't have long black hair had to grow it or dye it quick, or run the risk of not being à la mode hood. À la mode hood also meant doe eyes, ultrabright lipstick, gold bangle earrings, cheap, tight skirts, and black and white uniform: black bra and white sweater or white bra and black sweater. And no slip. These girls didn't need to wear bras and I did. Only I didn't, and always felt self-conscious when I passed Harry's Candy Store in my light lawn dresses.

No, I couldn't possibly go out with Danny. I might convert him, but I couldn't go out with him. He probably would want me to kiss him in the movies. I knew what went on in the Destry Theater; I went every Saturday night with my mother and father; I knew. Those hoods. Surely Danny with all his hoodish savoir-faire knew that a girl in a pinafore dress, long blond braids, and well-fed expression was highly inappropriate for the leader of a gang. It was just the lure of the unknown, and was, of course, impossible.

I told Danny politely that I appreciated the thought but didn't think my mother would let me go out since I was only eleven years old. I had skipped several grades, I explained. Danny was very understanding about it and said I certainly looked older. At the end of the day, I gave him my *Believe-It-or-Not!* Ripley book for keeps, saying that my mother had refused permission at lunchtime but that this was for him, blushing all the while, I suppose. Danny was very embarrassed. He didn't blush, at first only mumbled "Urghs," but later came over to me at the coatroom and said: "Tanks. I don't know how to make just retribution." He was sweet about the whole thing.

Actually, I hadn't told my mother about Danny's invitation at all. I doubted whether she'd think the connection savory. But I thought about this, my almost first date, all the way home from school and all weekend. In fact, I couldn't stop thinking about it. No sooner would I settle down with my favorite book than the name Tooey would intrude itself into my mental stream. I felt the irresistible urge to write Danny Tooey, Danny, or just plain D. T. on all my clean book covers. Finally, in desperation, I wrote Yeoot Ynnad very small in the top of my stationery box. Such a thing had never happened to me before.

I decided to look up similar occurrences in my library, my highest source of wisdom. But mine proved an unprecedented occurrence. Heathcliff had been bad and Cathy had decided to be his girl friend, but he hadn't reformed and they had both died. That was the best I could find. But still ... Jane Eyre wouldn't marry Mr. Rochester when he was already married to Bertha, so it didn't seem right for me to go out with Danny while he was still a hood. But after he reformed ... it would probably take till eighth grade and then we could go out legitimately. Girls in the eighth grade not only went out, they could kiss too.

My mother noticed my mood of sorrowful melancholy, interspersed with come-hither glances and a slight puckering motion of the lips, and wrongly attributed my strange behavior to worry about the Middle Atlantic States. She instructed me to sue for Miss Malcolm's favor immediately or she would come up to school herself. Poor Mamma. How was she to know? After all, I had been a terrible bookworm, and I was only eleven years old.

When I went to the movies Saturday night with my parents, I tried to reconstruct Danny's features. All that hair made it difficult; it was all I could reconstruct. Underneath, Danny was handsome, I decided, and the features of the man on the screen melted, dimmed, and turned Tooeyesque in the darkness. What if it had not been my father sitting next to me, wheezing slightly from the air conditioning? What if it had been . . . To this day I can give no accurate description of Danny. The years have blurred even that blurry face. No matter how handsome and hairy and suave the fifteen-year-old Danny may have been, I hardly think he could have looked as I still picture him today—the precise image of Clark Gable.

Coming out of the Destry after the show, I managed to walk into an embarrassing situation. There stood Alan Brodnik, leaning against the fire hydrant, his arms round a girl. Alan looked at me appealingly and removed his arms. I made no comment, walked by without turning my head. My heart was sad, though, oh, sad. For what if it had been Yeoot Ynnad?

When I arrived at school Monday morning, I found our back-seat idyl broken. No longer could we peruse the same book like lion and lamb. Danny and I breathed hard and stared in whatever direction was opposite; we both mumbled. At last I had enough courage to ask Danny if he had learned anything interesting from the *Believe-It-or-Not!* Ripley book. He only looked at me vaguely and mumbled "Urghs." He had retrogressed.

Danny continued shy all day and did not speak to me. But he gave long, piteous glances and drew girls' heads in ink on the backs of his hands. This was terrible. I decided to follow Danny after school and make him talk to me. It was only to find out something of his home life for future reform, I told myself. When three o'clock and Danny and Harry, Jo-Jo, Alan, and Ronny broke upon the homogenized-bagel man, I was there too.

The boys looked at me curiously. All the other little girls were retreating away from school as fast as they could go, backs straight and heads held high. Was it true? Was it true? Jo-Jo winked at Harry. Danny said nothing but asked me if I wanted salt on my bagel. No, don't buy me bagels, don't, I felt like crying out. I don't *want* to be your girl friend. I just want to find out about your home life. However, I took one with salt.

Danny seemed relaxed and at ease now. He spoke animatedly, even vivaciously, and I could catch nearly every word he was saying. He took my arm and headed me, yes, toward Harry's Candy Store. The boys followed. I would not go to Harry's Candy Store, I told myself firmly, I would not under any conditions go to Harry's Candy Store. . . .

On the way to the candy store, Danny told me about his job as utility man, whatever that was, on a small fishing boat out of Sheepshead Bay. The boat and Danny left every day at three in the morning and didn't return till eight-thirty, just in time to drop Danny off for school. "Dat's why I'm so sleepy in da mornings," Danny explains.

When he was sixteen, next year, he

wouldn't have to come to school any more and could be a full-time fisherman. How exciting, I thought, thinking of *Captains Courageous*, but then I re-membered. If Danny left school, he'd never reach eighth grade, and what would happen to his "th's" and his white shirts and . . . our date for the movies? Even if he became a fisher-man—? what if there were a fish famine or something? Without me Danny would have to go back to being a hood. I would not let that happen. I would persuade Danny not to leave school. I would go with him to Harry's Candy Store every day and stand around with him near the gum machine.

When we reached Harry's, there were no girls from 293 around, thank goodness. Danny did nothing worse than hitch himself up on the wooden rack that held the newspapers and let his feet dangle on the New York *Post*. He'd been working since he was ten, he said, and it was all right. Except when the weather was bad and he didn't get paid. Or just got paid in fish. His Aunt Bella didn't like fish, he added a little glumly; she hated fish.

Aunt Bella's strong aversion to fish was all I ever found out about Danny Tooey's home life. "Look who's here," Danny said next, and when I looked, there stood Miss Malcolm.

"I want to talk to you, dear," she said.

Miss Malcolm and I walked home together. We had a long, intimate con-versation on the way, though I couldn't imagine why. I still hadn't apologized, and I certainly wasn't going to. I sup-pose Miss Malcolm had come out of school at three and seen her ex-star pu-pil in informal conversation with a rec-ognized hood. Poor Miss Malcolm. She thought she'd been responsible for start-ing me on a life of crime.

"You don't know it, dear, but I've been watching you," she said. I clutched my stationery box, but she only took my arm as we crossed the street as though I was her little girl.

"I've noticed how unhappy you've been at the back of the room. You've just been moping around and moping around, haven't you?"

I made no reply. I wondered what Miss Malcolm wanted me to do for not telling my mother about Harry's Candy Store. Yes, blackmail was on my mind. I had the makings of a first-class hood.

"You've been unhappy because you've wanted to come up to me and apologize for reading my note, haven't you?"

We were nearing my home. I thought about walking Miss Malcolm right past it and right on down to Sheepshead Bay. We could go down to the pier and watch the fishing boats come in. My Lord, I really was a fiendish child, now that I think of it.

"But you've been afraid. You've been afraid I was going to say some-thing unkind, weren't you?"

She patted me kindly on the arm. I thought of how I had walked past her every morning on my way to the coat-room, my head held high.

"But you know, I wouldn't have said anything unkind. Because I like you, dear. I think you're my best pupil."

I still didn't say anything. I was her best pupil. I wondered what Miss Mal-colm was planning to study next. It must be something harder than the Middle Atlantic, because three people had raised their hands that day and she didn't need me.

"And because I know you've wanted to apologize for a long time, tomorrow morning I am going to let you come back to the first seat, first row."

I couldn't stop the pleasure that I felt.

I didn't know why I had been reinstated but I was glad. Justice, as I had always maintained, does triumph. And, oh, what I would do to all those schmoey kids. I was a nasty-good little girl.

Miss Malcolm came inside the house to meet my mother and we all had tea. I didn't mind taking the enemy inside. Danny would approve, I was sure. And from my influential position, what couldn't I do for my friends. Soon I would convince Miss Malcolm of Danny's merits—and then . . .

"Do you think seventh-grade girls are too young to go out?" I remember asking Miss Malcolm as Mamma poured tea.

Alas, again. All my plans were in vain. The end of the affair came next day.

As Miss Malcolm announced the happy news and I carried my books away from our scarred double seat to my honored one, Danny stared at me sullenly without saying a word. He didn't say good-by, but on my last trip to the front of the room, he piled his *Believe-It-or-Not!* Ripley book on top of my grammar and the stationery box with the secret Yeoot Ynnad. He looked at me as though from across a million rows of double seats. Then he turned back to carving his name on the desk.

Hurt and bewildered, I couldn't understand Danny's heartlessness. I followed him out of the school building at three, lingered shyly by the homogenized-bagel man, but he just walked away. His back was slouched and his hair was no longer kempt. He was whistling.

After this I never went near Danny or any of the other boys again. And when Larry Dinhofer asked me for a date to the senior prom, I pretended that he was the first. But I always kept track of the Destry Road Boys, secretly, ashamedly. I felt a strong sense of communion with them and liked to think that my short stay had done them all good. Alan and Ronny and Harry went on to high school with me, but were put in special RX classes where they could sit around all day and throw spitballs without being disturbed by anyone. They just had a happy, lazy time. Occasionally I'd glimpse them having refreshments in front of the school. It was a different, nonhomogenized-bagel man, but the same boys all right. When I passed, they would stare but never make any sign of recognition.

Although none of the Destry Boys ever made Honor Society or anything like that, they never got any more delinquent than they were. As it turned out, only one boy from P.S. 333 ever ended up in jail, and that was Larry Dinhofer. He robbed a liquor store, and he had always worn white cuffs and sat in the first row, and no one I know has ever found a logical explanation. So Larry does belong among the hoods I've known after all. Alan Brodnik, bless him, was the only Destry Boy whose degenerate career I followed after high school. I've lost touch with him since, but the last I heard he'd turned up at Brooklyn College carrying *Tropic of Capricorn* and wearing a neat black goatee and a red velvet cummerbund. I never could quite understand that one either.

As for Danny, I never saw him after graduation. In fact, I don't think he stayed around that long but left after his sixteenth birthday sometime in March. I believe he gave the Destry Road Boys to Jo-Jo because he was the smartest. By that time my wounded feelings had healed, since I'd decided what had motivated him. It was all due to Danny's pure moral philosophy or something, I deduced, that was stronger than mere romance. Hoods didn't do anything but pledge allegiance to the flag. Star pupils sat in the first row. We just couldn't be friends. It was against all established codes, and Danny supported codes. I had to admire that.

Someone I know says she thinks she saw someone who looked like Danny in a summer theater production in Woodstock last year. She said that he was still big and had a lot of hair but that he spoke English perfectly. She said he was sweet and looked like Marlon Brando. Despite what my friend says, I don't like to think Danny became an actor. I don't like to think that at all. It makes me sad and a little embarrassed, for that would mean after all my seventh-grade heartbreak and eleven-year old plans, somebody else had reformed Danny after all. I'd rather have him be a fisherman. I'd rather have him be a hood.

THE FACT IS—

1. What were the characteristics of the "hoods" in this story?

2. How did the Destry Road Boys differ from the Avenue E Boys?

3. What novel did the narrator use as an opening wedge in winning Danny's friendship?

4. What use did the girl make of the *Believe-It-or-Not!* Ripley book?

5. What was the reason for Danny's improved appearance?

6. Do we find out what finally happened to Danny? What is your guess?

LIVING CAN BE FUN

1. This story has been called a prize example of humor. The author generally gets her results by "deadpanning," that it, making unemotional statements of fact like "I think 'Dinhofer' whenever I have an ache in my back." List three or four other examples of deadpan humor.

2. Miss Malcolm was pictured as being "afraid of that hairy creature who slouched into class with disquieting tread. . . ." To the likes of him, she gave the "silent treatment." Write a paragraph describing her.

3. Does the author condemn "hoods"? Consider the gang of which Danny was the leader. Write a careful paragraph in which you state your opinion and give your reasons.

A WORD TO REMEMBER: coexistence

Danny and the narrator had been sitting beside each other in peaceful coexistence (ko·ig·ZIS·tens). The prefix *co–* means "together," *exist* means "to be"; therefore, we have "to be together peacefully."

Explain what is meant by the statement "Existence without peaceful coexistence leads to nonexistence."

The Wild, Wild West

You may accept or reject this startling attack on the "heroes" who made the Wild West colorful. What were Wild Bill Hickok, Billy the Kid, and Wyatt Earp *really* like?

PETER LYON

The world of the Wild West is an odd world, complete with a history, a morality, a language, wars, a code, and a costume. The history is compounded of lies; the morality was based on evil; the language was composed largely of slang; the wars were fought by gangs of greedy gunmen; and the code and costume were both designed to accommodate violence.

The most glamorous, the most permanent products of this odd and violent world were its Heroes. How did they come into existence? They did not roll off an assembly line. They were carefully fashioned by hand, individually, by men highly skilled in the manufacture of myths. To understand how they were produced requires some knowledge of the economics of the Wild West.

There were, broadly speaking, two ways of making money in the Wild West. One demanded hard, hard work of farmer, cowhand, railroader, or miner. But as always seems to be the case in this bad old world, there were some few men who did not care for hard work. Either they had tried it personally, for a day or two, and found it repugnant, or they had formed a distaste for it by watching others try it, or perhaps they had simply heard about others who had tried it and so come to a bad end. In any case, these men determined never to work but rather to rely on their wits.

Now, how could a quick-witted man get rich out on the bare, bleak plains? Clearly the first step was to head for those outposts of civilization where a little heap of wealth had been piled up through the labor of others. This meant the cow towns, the mining camps, and the slowly shifting railroad settlements. Here he could gamble with the chumps: few professional gamblers starve. Here he could buy a share of a dance hall or saloon; either enterprise was gilt-edged. Before long he would have found, as others have before and since, that these careers lead straight into politics. He might have concluded that it was cheaper to run for office himself than to pay tribute to some stupider, lazier politician. So were marshals and sheriffs born.

But what of the dull-witted man who didn't choose to work? He had behind him a life of violence bred by the Civil War; often his thick skull held no learning whatever save how to ride, shoot, kill, burn, rob, and run. With the end of the war, he doffed his blue blouse—or, more often, his gray—and headed west toward a short, gory life of bank and train robberies. So were outlaws born.

For the man who was unusually active and had no objection to a day in the outdoors, there was a third, coarsening, semilegal path to quick dollars: he could slaughter bison. Only the Indians would object, and who cared a hoot for the Indians? A treaty of 1867 guaranteed that no white man would hunt buffalo south of the Arkansas River; by 1870, when the army officer commanding at Fort Dodge was asked what he would do if this promise were broken, he laughed and said, "Boys, if I were hunting buffalo, I would go where buffalo are"; in 1871 the massacre began in earnest. One hunter bagged 5,855 in two months. It has been estimated that 4,373,730 bison were killed in the three years between 1872 and 1874. To shoot the placid beasts was no easier than shooting fish in a barrel, but it was certainly no more difficult. And splendid practice—as safe as on a target range— for the marksman who might later choose to shoot at riskier game—a stagecoach driver or the leader of a posse. So were killers trained.

For the purposes of American myth, it remained only to make over all these sheriffs, outlaws, killers, and assorted villains into heroes. Considering the material on hand to work with, strong magic was required to effect the change. The principal magician was a man named Richard K. Fox, editor of the *National Police Gazette,* a lively weekly that circulated into every self-respecting barbershop, billiard parlor, and barroom throughout the Republic. Fox developed a classic formula for the manufacture of heroes, one in which truth was considered not at all essential.

Analysis of this Fox formula for heroes reveals that it has ten ingredients, like a Chinese soup:

1. THE HERO'S ACCURACY WITH ANY WEAPON IS PRODIGIOUS.

2. HE IS A NONPAREIL OF BRAVERY AND COURAGE.

3. HE IS COURTEOUS TO ALL WOMEN, REGARDLESS OF RANK, STATION, AGE, OR PHYSICAL CHARM.

4. HE IS GENTLE, MODEST, AND UNASSUMING.

5. HE IS HANDSOME, SOMETIMES EVEN PRETTY; BUT HE IS OF COURSE VERY MASCULINE, AND EXCEEDINGLY ATTRACTIVE TO WOMEN.

6. HE IS BLUE–EYED. HIS PIERCING BLUE EYES TURN GRAY AS STEEL WHEN HE IS AROUSED; HIS ASSOCIATES WOULD HAVE BEEN WELL ADVISED TO KEEP A COLOR CHART HANDY, SO THAT THEY MIGHT HAVE DIVED FOR A STORM CELLAR WHEN THE BLUE TURNED TO TATTLETALE GRAY.

7. HE WAS DRIVEN TO A LIFE OF OUTLAWRY AND CRIME BY HAVING QUITE PROPERLY DEFENDED A LOVED ONE FROM AN INTOLERABLE INSULT— WITH LETHAL CONSEQUENCES. THEREAFTER, HOWEVER . . .

8. HE SHIELDS THE WIDOW AND ORPHAN, ROBBING ONLY THE BANKER OR RAILROAD MONOPOLIST.

9. HIS DEATH COMES ABOUT BY MEANS OF BETRAYAL OR TREACHERY, BUT—

10. IT IS RARELY A CONCLUSIVE DEATH, SINCE HE KEEPS ON BOBBING UP LATER ON, IN OTHER PLACES, FOR MANY YEARS. IT IS, INDEED, ARGUABLE WHETHER HE IS DEAD YET.

With these ingredients in mind, let us examine one of the greatest so-called heroes—a man narrow-waisted and wide-hipped, with small hands and feet, whose long curly hair tumbles to his shoulders. He is celebrated as Wild Bill Hickok.

James Butler (Wild Bill) Hickok was born on a farm in LaSalle County, Illinois, on May 27, 1827. He died on the afternoon of August 2, 1876, in Saloon No. 10, on the main street of Deadwood, in the Dakota Territory, when a bullet fired by Jack McCall plowed through the back of his head and smashed a bone in the left forearm of a Captain Massey, a riverboat pilot with whom Hickok had been playing poker. During his lifetime Hickok did some remarkable deeds, and they were even more remarkably embroidered by himself and by a corps of admiring tagtails and tufthunters. When he died, he held two pair—aces and eights—a legendary combination known ever since as "the dead man's hand." It is the least of the legends that has encrusted his reputation, like barnacles on an old hulk.

Was he brave? His most critical biographer, William E. Connelley, has said that fear "was simply a quality he lacked."

Was he handsome? He was "the handsomest man west of the Mississippi. His eyes were blue—but could freeze to a cruel steel-gray at threat of evil or danger."

Was he gallant? His morals were "much the same as those of Achilles, King David, and Lancelot. . . ."

Had he no minor vices? Very few: "Wild Bill found relaxation and enjoyment in cards, but he seldom drank."

Could he shoot? Once in Solomon, Kansas, a pair of murderers fled from him. "One was running up the street and the other down the street in the opposite direction. Bill fired at both men simultaneously and killed them both." Presumably with his eyes closed. Again, in Topeka, in 1870, Buffalo Bill Cody threw his hat into the air as a target. "Wild Bill shot an evenly spaced row of holes along the outside of the rim as it was falling, and before it touched the ground." To appreciate fully this miracle of marksmanship, one must remember that Hickok was shooting black-powder cartridges. (Smokeless powder did not come into general use until about 1893.) Each time he fired, therefore, he put a puff of black smoke between himself and his target. After his first shot, he could not have seen his target. But then, nothing is impossible to the gunslinger of the Wild West.

But surely he was modest? Yes, indeed. "Faced with admirers, he blushed and stammered and fled."

Was he a sure-enough killer? Once he was asked how many white men he had killed, to his certain knowledge (Indians didn't count). Wild Bill reflected. "I suppose," he said at last, "I have killed considerably over a hundred." But this was in 1866; he would have another ten years to improve his record. To another reporter, he remarked: "As to killing men, I never think much about it. . . . The killing of a bad man shouldn't trouble one any more than killing a rat or an ugly cat or a vicious dog." Of course, it helps if one is as good a judge as Hickok of the badness of a man, or the ugliness of a cat.

But was a good man not obliged to kill a bad man, to tame the Wild West? And, after all, was Wild Bill not a pillar or righteousness in those sinful times? What about his bright reputation as marshal of the Kansas cow towns?

Hickok was, perhaps, a United States deputy marshal operating out of Fort Riley in February, 1866, and charged with rounding up army deserters and horse thieves; but the record of his tenure is fuzzy.

In mid-August, 1869, he was elected sheriff of Ellis County—of which Hays was the biggest town—to fill an unexpired term. He failed of reelection in November. A brief time in which to tame a tough town—nor does the record show any notable success. He may have killed a man named Jack (or Sam) Strawhorn (or Strawhan) who tried to get the drop on him; he may have killed two soldiers who talked tough at him; he may have thrashed Tom Custer, a brother of General George Custer [1]; he may have killed three soldiers whom Custer had vengefully sicked on him—all the evidence bearing on these matters is likewise fuzzy. What is certain is that Hickok left Hays in a hurry one winter night, lest he be further beset by the Seventh Cavalry.

In April, 1871, Hickok was appointed marshal of Abilene, and now the picture grows sharper. Man and town were just right for each other: each was at the height of notoriety. As for the town, which was all of five years old, 1871 would be its peak year as a cow town; 600,000 cattle would pass through its yards on the way to eastern markets; and all summer, cowboys by the hundreds would jam its saloons and dance halls—the Alamo, the Bull's Head, the Mint, and the Gold Room—to squander a year's wages. As for the man, *Harper's Monthly* had published not long before a lurid account of Hickok's fatal skill in battle, as told by Wild Bill himself. There was, for instance, Hickok's version of the McCanles affair. In truth, Hickok had shot down Dave McCanles from behind a curtain, shot a second man from behind a door, and mortally wounded a third man who was running for his life. But as Wild Bill told the tale, he had been attacked by McCanles and a gang of nine "desperadoes, horse thieves, murderers, regular cutthroats," but had slain six men with six shots and

[1] **General George Custer:** commander of the Seventh Cavalry, killed by the Sioux at the Battle of the Little Bighorn in 1876—"Custer's Last Stand."

dispatched the other four "bloodthirsty devils" with his knife.

A man whose fame rested on such fabulous fibs was just the sort needed to put down the frequent riots of a wicked cow town. At least, so thought Joseph McCoy, the founder of Abilene and, in 1871, also the town's mayor. Moreover, McCoy knew where to find his man, for Hickok was right in town, gambling for a living at the Alamo. Wild Bill took the job. He slung two six-shooters at his hips; he thrust a knife in the red sash he affected. In this fashion, he occasionally patrolled the streets.

But only occasionally. Most hours of most evenings he could be found at the Alamo, gambling with the cowboys. Meantime the taxpayers of Abilene grew irritated. Nor were the cowboys happy; for they believed that Hickok wore the star only to protect the extortions of the professional gamblers and saloonkeepers.

Matters came to a head on the night of October 5. A bunch of cowboys had been hurrahing the town in their traditional and tiresome fashion—forcing merchants of clothing to outfit poorly clad strangers, obliging passers-by to stand drinks for all hands—and Hickok reportedly warned them to quiet down. Back in the Alamo, at his poker table, Wild Bill heard someone fire a shot. He plunged out into the darkness to confront a Texan named Phil Coe. Some say that Coe's gun was already back in its holster, some say that it was dangling in his hand. Whichever the case, Hickok fired, felling Coe, and then, when he heard someone running toward him, at once wheeled and plugged his own deputy, one Mike Williams, in a typical exhibition of coolness, calm, and nerve. He was relieved of his official duties six weeks later.

After that there was nothing left but to exploit his fame in show business. He jointed Buffalo Bill Cody's stock company, an ignoble enterprise, but quit before long. In June, 1876, a Kansas newspaper reported, from Fort Laramie, that Wild Bill "was arrested on several occasions as a vagrant, having no visible means of support."

Later that month he galloped into Deadwood. A little more than a month later Jack McCall shot him from behind, for no particular reason.

Hickok had been a brave army scout and an able Indian scout; he had also been a liar, a professional gambler, and a killer. His score, according to a conservative chronicler of his deeds, was thirty-six men killed, apart from his service in the Army and against the Indians. What could be more fitting for such a man than to enshrine him on television—during the children's hour?

Perhaps even more celebrated than Wild Bill was a slight, short, bucktoothed, narrow-shouldered youth whose slouch added to his unwholesome appearance. He looked like an idiot. He was called Billy the Kid.

It is safe to say that at least a thousand writers have used Billy the Kid as a vessel into which to pour their passions, prejudices, and opinions; but it is likely that no two portraits of him jibe. He has been credited with every imaginable personality; from the way he has been described, one could conclude that he was the original Man with a Thousand Faces; his alleged backgrounds were as various as were his names.

The best guess is that he was born November 23, 1859, in New York City, and called Henry McCarty. There was also Joe, a younger brother. Around 1863 the family went west to Kansas. The father may have died here; at all events, Mrs. Catherine McCarty was married on March 1, 1873, with her two sons as witnesses, to William H. Antrim, in Santa Fe, New Mexico. The newlyweds settled in Silver City, near the Arizona border, and here Mrs. Antrim died on September 16, 1874. Henry McCarty was not yet fifteen.

He killed for the first time three years later: a blacksmith called Windy Cahill, in a saloon near Camp Grant, Arizona. There follow some gambling and some horse stealing. He was next a principal figure in the celebrated Lincoln County War, an affair which, including skirmishes and at least one pitched battle, went on for more than a year. The villains of this "war" were politicians, involved in their customary struggle for power. The Kid seems to have been caught up in it chiefly because he wasn't old enough to know any better. Several persons were killed in the course of this "war," and the Kid may have killed one or more of them; none can say for sure. In any case, his side lost, and for the rest of his brief life, he was an outlaw, a hunted man.

He stole some more livestock. He killed a man named Joe Grant, who "had thought" to shoot first. He rode with some exceedingly case-hardened characters, including Hendry Brown, John Middleton, and Dave Rudabaugh. Sheriff Pat Garrett and a posse first caught the Kid near Stinking Springs. He stood trial for murder, was found guilty, and was sentenced to be hanged. There were two men guarding him in the jail at Lincoln, but the Kid managed to get hold of a gun, killed them both, and fled again, again a free man.

Garrett stubbornly continued his pursuit. One brightly moonlit night he shot and killed the Kid in Fort Sumner, New Mexico. It was July 14, 1881. Henry McCarty, alias William Bonney, alias Billy the Kid, was not yet twenty-two.

And now the fun began.

The first book to follow the Kid's death appeared a month later and was subtitled "The history of an outlaw who killed a man for every year in his

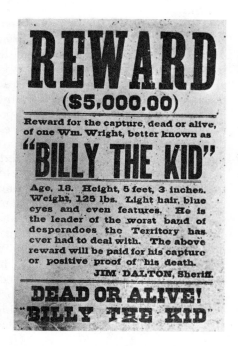

life," a fiction which was seized upon and inflated by nine out of every ten writers who followed. The author of this book was a man named Fable, appropriately enough, and he described the Kid as wearing "a blue dragoon jacket of the finest broadcloth, heavily loaded down with gold embroidery, buckskin pants, dyed a jet black, with small tinkling bells sewed down the sides . . . drawers of fine scarlet broadcloth . . . and a hat covered with gold and jewels. . . ."

The *Police Gazette* published a biography too, as did Pat Garrett. Both poured gore liberally over the Kid. Garrett added a nice touch: he said that Billy, to show his skill, once shot the heads off several snowbirds, one after another. (J. Frank Dobie has remarked tartly, of this story, that it didn't happen because it couldn't happen.)

By 1889, a Frenchman had written a wondrous book in which he reported how Billy the Kid killed his prison guard, a man named William Bonney. Other accounts appeared: the Kid had been a dishwasher in his youth; no, he had been a bootblack in New York City's Fourth Ward; no, he had gone to college in the East and was really an Ivy League type.

The number of his killings mounted steadily. Soon he had killed twenty-three men, one for each of his now twenty-three years, not counting seven Mexicans whom he shot "just to see them kick." A play about him opened in 1906 and ran for years. By 1918 its producers claimed it had been seen by ten million people. It was in 1906, too, that a dime novel appeared in which the Kid was described as an Apache who had been killed by Buffalo Bill, assisted by Wild Bill Hickok.

Then, oddly, the Kid dropped out of sight for a generation. When he reappeared, he was twenty-four years old,

and had killed twenty-four men. Walter Noble Burns sentimentalized him so successfully that Hollywood brought out the first of some twenty movies about him. Somebody made up the wonderful story that the gun Garrett had used to kill the Kid was the same gun worn by Wild Bill Hickok when he was shot in Deadwood.

The further away the mythmakers got from him, the more precisely they described him. He was "a boy of talent and exceptional intelligence," "good-natured and of a happy, carefree disposition," with "an unusually attractive personality." He was also called "an adenoidal moron." "He killed forty-five men." "He never killed anybody."

He was driven to a life of crime because, at the age of twelve, he killed a man who made a slurring remark to his mother. "His blue-gray eyes at times could turn cold and deadly." Pat Garrett never shot him at all, that night at Fort Sumner, for he was still alive in 1920, when he was known as Walk-Along Smith.

In one sense, it is perfectly true that Billy the Kid did not die. He is our most durable folk hero. Under his name there will always appear, whenever appropriate, the folk hero who fits the need of the hour: brutal killer, avenging angel, mama's boy, or gay, gallant cowpoke. The face is left blank, but it comes complete with a handy do-it-yourself kit so that the features may be easily filled in.

What, in summary, of the world of the Wild West? Clearly, it was an underworld, corrupt and rotten. Its heroes, vaunted for their courage, in fact showed only the rashness of the alcoholic or the desperation of the cornered rat. They were popularly supposed to have honored the Wild West's so-called code, which forbade the shooting of an unarmed man and likewise the shooting of an armed man until he had been faced and warned of the peril in which he stood. But look at the most celebrated heroes of all:

Hickok made his reputation by killing, from his hiding place, two unarmed men and then mortally wounding a third unarmed man who was running for his life.

Jesse James murdered at least two unarmed bank tellers, not because they had offered resistance, but when they were cowering at the bandit's feet.

Wyatt Earp and his brothers, shielded by police badges, provoked a fight, shot first, and killed men who, according to three eyewitnesses, were holding up their hands.

Bat Masterson is saved from any similar charge chiefly because he was such a poor shot.

Billy the Kid shot and killed from ambush, not once, but several times. Indeed, only the first of his authenticated killings seems to have come about in a man-to-man fight, and even on that occasion his opponent was unarmed.

What heroes, to be exalted by the Republic!

As outlaws, they were first adored because, it was argued, they robbed only the railroad monopolist and the banker, the men most heartily hated west of the Mississippi. As law officers, they were first adored because, it was said, they enforced the peace in dangerous circumstances, against overwhelming odds. Both suggestions are cockeyed. Outlaw or law officer, it made little difference; they were one brutal brotherhood. The so-called law officers more often caused than put down crime. Hendry Brown, an outlaw in New Mexico, could ride to Kansas and pin on a sheriff's star; Jim Younger, an outlaw in Missouri, could ride to Texas and pin on a deputy sheriff's star; even Billy the Kid rode for a time as a member of a bailiff's posse and, had his side won the Lincoln County War, might well have come down to us in folklore as a force for law and order. The whole boodle of them careened through lives of violence and vulgarity, to fetch up—where else? In the movies, the comics, and television.

But surely the producers of the popular entertainments do not pretend that they are reporting history? Surely they admit that their Wild West shows, especially on television, are at most so much embroidery basted onto the national folklore? Yet these producers persist in using names of real people and real places. They cite dates of real occurrences—usually, to be sure, absurdly wrong. They use such sly phrases as "based on actual events" or "a colorful look at our American heritage." Speaking of Wyatt Earp, they describe him as "one of the real-life heroes of yesterday . . . one of the greatest marshals in the annals of history . . . the famous straight-shootin', fast-ridin', fair-playin', clean-livin' lawman. . . ." They transform vicious, alcoholic gun fighters like Johnny Ringo and Clay Allison into sheriffs, symbols of justice and peace. They portray Jesse James as an innocent youth forced unfairly into a career of crime.

But even granting that the producers of this nonsense are not concerned with history but with legend, what a shameful and ghastly legend it is! Filled with ugly violence, and even uglier vulgarity.

The moral, of course, is that crime, when commercially exploited, does pay, and the more sadistic the better. The Wild West—portrayed by irresponsible men who care not a hang for the truth of history so long as they can count their audiences in the scores of millions—has become a permanent industry and has created for the world an enduring image of America.

Over it there hangs the stench of evil.

THE FACT IS—

1. "Men highly skilled in the manufacture of myths" created the heroes of the "Wild West." How did they do it?

2. What two or three types of men became heroes? What were their characteristics?

3. What two heroes are mentioned as being especially popular in the stories of the "Wild West"? What finally happened to each of them?

4. How do the producers of popular entertainments fool the public?

THE MAKING OF A "HERO"

1. Three concluding sentences in three consecutive paragraphs (page 315) begin with "So were." Why does the author use this device: for balance? building to a climax? emphasis?

2. Several times the author uses the words *legend* and *myth*. What do these two words mean? (Consult a dictionary.) What is the effect of using them? Do you know any other legends or myths?

3. This essay represents one type of humor. Reexamine it to find humorous phrases or sentences. Why is it amusing? What adjectives describe this type of humor?

4. Writing of this sort is sometimes called "debunking." (Consult a dictionary.) Write a paragraph to explain your reactions to this commentary on the "Wild West."

5. What movies or television programs use the "Wild West" as a form of popular entertainment? Do you enjoy them? Why, or why not?

A WORD TO REMEMBER: placid

"To shoot the placid beasts . . . was no more difficult than shooting fish in a barrel." This use of *placid* illustrates how the word is commonly used: to mean "unruffled, peaceful, calm." Thus it describes the nature of the beast (or person). The Latin root is *placere,* "to please." Related words are *placate, complacent,* and *implacable.* Can you see how *placid* and these related words retain the idea "to please"?

ing a shuffling fandango of triumph, he pushed me ahead of him to the stable, where old white Peggy, the only horse left at home, looked at us amazed.

"But it'll be twenty-eight miles, and Peg's never driven over eight!" I cried, my old-established world of rules and orders reeling before my eyes.

Eight—and—twenty-eight!
But I—am—eighty-eight!

Gran'ther improvised a sort of whooping chant of scorn as he pulled the harness from the peg. "It'll do her good to drink some pink lemonade—old Peggy! An' if she gits tired comin' home, I'll git out and carry her part way myself!"

His adventurous spirit was irresistible. I made no further objection and we hitched up together, I standing on a chair to fix the checkrein, and Gran'ther doing wonders with his one hand. Then, just as we were—Gran'ther in a hickory shirt, and with an old hat flopping over his wizened face, I barelegged, in ragged old clothes—so we drove out of the grassy yard, down the steep, stony hill that led to the main valley road, and along the hot, white turnpike, deep with the dust which had been stirred up by the teams on their way to the fair. Gran'-ther sniffed the air jubilantly and exchanged hilarious greetings with the people who constantly overtook old Peg's jogging trot. Between times he regaled me with spicy stories of the hundreds of thousands—they seemed no less numerous to me then—of county fairs he had attended in his youth. He was horrified to find that I had never been even to one.

"Why, Joey, how old be ye? 'Most eight, ain't it? When I was your age, I had run away and been to two fairs an' a hangin'."

"But didn't they lick you when you got home?" I asked shudderingly.

"You bet they did!" cried Gran'ther with gusto.

I felt the world changing into an infinitely larger place with every word he said.

"Now, this is somethin' like!" he exclaimed as we drew near to Granville and fell into a procession of wagons all filled with country people in their best clothes, who looked with friendly curiosity at the little, shriveled cripple, his face shining with perspiring animation, and at the little boy beside him, his bare feet dangling high above the floor of the battered buckboard, overcome with the responsibility of driving a horse for the first time in his life, and filled with such a flood of new emotions and ideas that he must have been quite pale.

Oh, that was a day! Never will I have such another! At the entrance to the grounds, Gran'ther stopped me while he solemnly untied the knot in his empty sleeve. I don't know what kind of harebrained vow he had tied up in it, but with the little ceremony disappeared every trace of restraint, and we plunged head over ears into the saturnalia of delights that was an old-time county fair.

People had little cash in those days, and Gran'ther's six dollars and forty-three cents lasted like the widow's cruse of oil. [1] We went to see the fat lady, who, if she was really as big as she looked to me then, must have weighed at least a ton. My admiration for Gran'ther's daredevil qualities rose to infinity when he entered into free-and-easy talk with her, about how much she ate, and could she raise her arms enough to do up her own hair, and how many yards of velvet it

[1] **widow's cruse of oil:** a widow with a small amount of oil and meal helped the prophet Elijah. No matter how much she used, her supply of meal and oil never gave out. Read the story in the Bible, I Kings 17:9–16.

took to make her gorgeous, gold-trimmed robe. She laughed a great deal at us, but she was evidently touched by his human interest, for she confided to him that it was not velvet at all, but furniture covering; and when he went away, she pressed on us a bag of peanuts. She said she had more peanuts than she could eat—a state of unbridled opulence which fitted in for me with all the other superlatives of that day.

We saw the dog-faced boy, whom we did not like at all; Gran'ther expressing with a candidly outspoken cynicism his belief that "them whiskers was glued to him." We wandered about the stock exhibit, gazing at the monstrous oxen, and hanging over the railings where the prize pigs lived to scratch their backs. In order to miss nothing, we even conscientiously passed through the Woman's Building, where we were very much bored by the serried ranks of preserve jars.

"Sufferin' Hezekiah!" cried Gran'ther irritably. "Who cares how gooseberry jel looks? If they'd give a felly a taste, now . . ."

This reminded him that we were hungry, and we went to a restaurant under a tent, where, after taking stock of the wealth that yet remained of Gran'ther's hoard, he ordered the most expensive things on the bill of fare.

After lunch we rode on the merry-go-round, both of us, Gran'ther clinging desperately with his one hand to his red camel's wooden hump, and crying out shrilly to me to be sure and not lose his cane. The merry-go-round had just come in at that time, and Gran'ther had never experienced it before. After the first giddy flight we retired to a lemonade stand to exchange impressions, and finding that we both alike had fallen completely under the spell of the new sensation, Gran'ther said that we sh'd keep on a-ridin' till we'd had enough! King

Solomon couldn't tell when we'd ever git a chance again! So we returned to the charge, and rode and rode and rode, through blinding clouds of happy excitement, so it seems to me now, such as I was never to know again. The sweat was pouring off from us, and we had tried all the different animals on the machine before we could tear ourselves away to follow the crowd to the race-track.

We took reserved seats, which cost a quarter apiece, instead of the unshaded ten-cent benches, and Gran'ther began at once to pour out to me a flood of horse talk and knowing racetrack aphorisms, which finally made a young fellow sitting next to us laugh superciliously. Gran'ther turned on him heatedly.

"I bet-che fifty cents I pick the winner in the next race!" he said sportily.

"Done!" said the other, still laughing.

Gran'ther picked a big black mare, who came in almost last, but he did not flinch. As he paid over the half dollar, he said: "Everybody's likely to make mistakes about some things; King Solomon was a fool in the head about women folks! I bet-che a dollar I pick the winner in this race!" and "Done!" said the disagreeable young man, still laughing. I gasped, for I knew we had only eighty-seven cents left, but Gran'ther shot me a command to silence out of the corner of his eyes, and announced that he bet on the sorrel gelding.

If I live to be a hundred and break the bank at Monte Carlo three times a week, I could not know a tenth part of the frantic excitement of that race or of the mad triumph when our horse won. Gran'ther cast his hat upon the ground, screaming like a steam calliope with exultation as the sorrel swept past the judges' stand ahead of all the others, and I jumped up and down in an agony of delight.

After that we went away, feeling that the world could hold nothing more glorious. It was five o'clock and we decided to start back. We paid for Peggy's dinner out of the dollar we had won on the race—I say "we," for by that time we were welded into one organism—and we still had a dollar and a quarter left. "While ye're about it, always go the whole hog!" said Gran'ther, and we spent twenty minutes in laying out that money in trinkets for all the folks at home. Then, dusty, penniless, laden with bundles, we bestowed our exhausted bodies and our uplifted hearts in the old buckboard, and turned Peg's head toward the mountains. We did not talk much during that drive, and though I thought at the time only of the carnival of joy we had left, I can now recall every detail of the trip—how the sun sank behind Indian Mountain, a peak I had known before only through distant views; then, as we journeyed on, how the stars came out above Hemlock Mountain—our own home mountain behind our house, and later, how the fireflies filled the darkening meadows along the river below us, so that we seemed to be floating between the steady stars of heaven and their dancing, twinkling reflection in the valley.

Gran'ther's dauntless spirit still surrounded me. I put out of mind doubts of our reception at home, and lost myself in delightful ruminatings on the splendors of the day. At first, every once in a while, Gran'ther made a brief remark, such as, "'Twas the hindquarters of the sorrel I bet on. He was the only one in the hull kit and bilin' of 'em that his quarters didn't fall away"; or, "You needn't tell me that them Siamese twins ain't unpinned every night as separate as you and me!" But later on, as the damp evening air began to bring on his asthma, he subsided into silence, only broken by great gasping coughs.

THE HEYDAY OF THE BLOOD   **329**

These were heard by the anxious, heartsick watchers at home, and, as old Peg stumbled wearily up the hill, Father came running down to meet us. "Where you be'n?" he demanded, his face pale and stern in the light of his lantern. "We be'n to the county fair!" croaked Gran'ther with a last flare of triumph, and fell over sideways against me. Old Peg stopped short, hanging her head as if she, too, were at the limit of her strength. I was frightfully tired myself, and frozen with terror of what Father would say. Gran'ther's collapse was the last straw. I began to cry loudly, but Father ignored my distress with an indifference which cut me to the heart. He lifted Gran'ther out of the buckboard, carrying the unconscious little old body into the house without a glance backward at me. But when I crawled down to the ground sobbing, I felt Mother's arms around me.

"Oh, poor, naughty little Joey!" she said. "Mother's bad, dear little boy!"

Well, that was the end of our day. I was so worn out that I fell asleep over my supper, in spite of the excitement in the house about sending for a doctor for Gran'ther, who was, so one of my awestruck sisters told me, having some kind of "fits." Mother must have put me to bed, for the next thing I remember, she was shaking me by the shoulder and saying, "Wake up, Joey. Your great-grandfather wants to speak to you. He's been suffering terribly all night, and the doctor thinks he's dying."

I followed her into Gran'ther's room, where the family was assembled about the bed. Gran'ther lay drawn up in a ball, groaning so dreadfully that I felt a chill like cold water at the roots of my hair; but a moment or two after I came in, all at once he gave a great sigh and relaxed, stretching out his legs and attempting to smile at me.

"Well, it was wuth it, warn't it, Joey?" he said gallantly, and closed his eyes peacefully to sleep.

Did he die? Gran'ther Pendleton? Not much! He came tottering down to breakfast the next morning, as white as an old ghost, with no voice left, his legs trembling under him, but he kept the whole family an hour and a half at the table, telling them in a loud whisper all about the fair, until Father said really he would have to take us to the one next year. Afterward he sat out on the porch watching old Peg graze around the yard. I thought he was in one of his absent-minded fits, but when I came out, he called me to him, and, setting his lips to my ear, he whispered:

"An' the seventh is a-goin' downhill fast, so I hear!" He chuckled to himself over this for some time, wagging his head feebly, and then he said: "I tell ye, Joey, I've lived a long time, and I've larned a lot about the way folks is made. The trouble with most of 'em is, they're 'fraid-cats! As Jeroboam Warner used to say—he was in the same regiment with me in 1812—the only way to manage this business of livin' is to give a hoop and let her rip! If ye just about half-live, ye just the same as half-die; and if ye spend yer time half-dyin', someday ye turn in and die all over, without rightly meanin' to at all—just a kind o' bad habit ye've got yerself inter." Gran'ther fell into a meditative silence for a moment. "Jeroboam, he said that the evenin' before the battle of Lundy's Lane, and he got killed the next day. Some live, and some die; but folks that live all over die happy, anyhow! Now I tell you what's my motto, an' what I've lived to be eighty-eight on. . . ."

This was the motto he told me: "Live while you live, and then die and be done with it!"

THE FACT IS—

1. What is the picture you get of Gran'ther Pendleton before his trip to the county fair?

2. What details of the journey to the fair made it a memorable adventure?

3. What features of the fair did Joey and Gran'ther enjoy most? Which did they enjoy least? Why was the horse racing especially exciting?

4. How does the trip home from the fair differ from the journey to the fair?

PEOPLE CAN BE FUNNY

1. "Gran'ther . . . withdrew himself into that incalculable distance . . . where very old people spend so many hours." Explain what the author means by this sentence.

2. Gran'ther said that "folks that live all over die happy." What does *living all over* mean? Does it include only enjoying the pleasant things in life?

3. *Heyday* means "a time of joy or high spirits." Does the title fit the story? Explain.

4. Why does the author wait until the very end of the story to tell the reader what Gran'ther's motto was?

5. Can you recall an exciting outing from your childhood? Describe it in a paragraph that shows what it meant to you.

6. Have you ever thought about a suitable motto to live by? Try writing down—for yourself alone—a statement that expresses your attitude toward school, toward work, toward people, toward God.

A WORD TO REMEMBER: meditative

Toward the end of this story, "Gran'ther fell into a meditative (MED-ih·tay·tiv) silence for a moment." *Meditative* means "dwelling in thought, musing," as in the sentence "Young people in high school are not naturally meditative." Can you imagine how else *meditative* might be used? For example, what is a meditative air? a meditative spell? Write a sentence or two illustrating different uses of this word.

John Brown's Last Day

DAVID HUNTER STROTHER

A man of strong beliefs, John Brown died with dignity and at peace with himself. Brown was—and is—controversial: some considered him an insane assassin; others thought him a martyr.

On Friday, December 2, the notorious John Brown [1] was executed at Charlestown, Virginia, according to the sentence of the law. . . .

As early as nine o'clock . . . the field (adjoining the town of Charlestown), which had been selected for the place of execution, was occupied by a considerable body of soldiers, horse, foot, and artillery. A line of sentinels encircled the enclosure preventing access by the fences, and a guard of infantry and artillery was posted at the gate by which spectators were required to enter.

[1] **John Brown:** A man who believed that some dramatic happening was needed to arouse the public and to bring an end to slavery. In 1859 he and a small band captured the United States arsenal at Harpers Ferry, Virginia (now West Virginia). A company of Marines under Colonel Robert E. Lee and Lieutenant J. E. B. Stuart recaptured the arsenal, killed ten of Brown's men—including two of his sons, and took John Brown prisoner.

I repaired to the field some time before the appointed hour that I might choose a convenient position to witness the final ceremony. The gibbet was erected on a gentle swell that commanded a view of the country for many miles around. From the scaffold which I ascended, the view was of surpassing beauty. On every side stretching away into the blue distance were broad and fertile fields dotted with corn shocks and white farmhouses glimmering through the leafless trees—emblems of prosperity and peace. Hard by was the pleasant village with its elegant suburban residences and bordering the picture east and west were the blue mountains thirty miles apart. In the Blue Ridge which lay to the eastward appeared the deep gap through which the Potomac and Shenandoah pour their united streams at Harpers Ferry, eight miles distant.

Near at hand stood long lines of soldiers resting on their arms while all the neighboring hills in sight were crowded with squadrons of cavalry. The balmy south wind was blowing, which covered the landscape with a warm and dreamy haze reminding one rather of May than December. "From hence," thought I, "the old man may see the spot where his enormous crime first took the form of action—he may see the beautiful land his dark plots had devoted to bloody ruin, he may see in the gleaming of a thousand swords and these serried lines of bayonets—what might be well calculated to make wiser men than he thoughtful."

At eleven o'clock, escorted by a strong column of soldiers, the prisoner entered the field. He was seated in a furniture wagon on his coffin with his arms tied down above the elbows, leaving the forearms free. The driver with two others occupied the front seat while the jailer sat in the afterpart of the wagon. I stood with a group of half a dozen gentlemen near the steps of the scaffold when the prisoner was driven up. He wore the same seedy and dilapidated dress that he had at Harpers Ferry and during his trial, but his rough boots had given place to a pair of particolored slippers and he wore a low-crowned broad-brimmed hat (the first time I had ever seen him with a hat). He had entirely recovered from his wounds and looked decidedly better and stronger than when I last saw him. As he neared the gibbet, his face wore a grim and grisly smirk which, but for the solemnity of the occasion, might have suggested ideas of the ludicrous. He stepped from the wagon with surprising agility and walked hastily toward the scaffold, pausing a moment as he passed our group to wave his pinioned arm and bid us good morning. I thought I could observe in this a trace of bravado—but perhaps I was mistaken, as his natural manner was short, ungainly, and hurried. He mounted the steps of the scaffold with the same alacrity; and there, as if by previous arrangement, he immediately took off his hat and offered his neck for the halter which was as promptly adjusted by Mr. Avis, the jailer. A white muslin cap or hood was then drawn over his face; and the sheriff, not remembering that his eyes were covered, requested him to advance to the platform. The prisoner replied in his usual tone, "You will have to guide me there."

The breeze disturbing the arrangement of the hood, the sheriff asked his assistant for a pin. Brown raised his hand and directed him to the collar of his coat where several old pins were quilted in. The sheriff took the pin and completed his work.

He was accordingly led forward to the drop, the halter hooked to the beam, and the officers, supposing that the execution was to follow immediately, took leave of him. In doing so, the sheriff inquired if he did not want a handkerchief to throw as a signal to cut the drop. Brown replied, "No, I don't care; I don't want you to keep me waiting unnecessarily."

These were his last words, spoken with that sharp nasal twang peculiar to him, but spoken quietly and civilly, without impatience or the slightest apparent emotion. In this position he stood for five minutes or more, while the troops that composed the escort were wheeling into the positions assigned them. I stood within a few paces of him and watched narrowly during these trying moments to see if there was any indication of his giving way. I detected nothing of the sort. He had stiffened himself for the drop and waited motionless till it came.

During all these movements no sound was heard but the quick, stern words of military command, and when these ceased, a dead silence reigned. Colonel Smith said to the sheriff in a low voice, "We are ready." The civil officers descended from the scaffold. One who stood near me whispered earnestly, "He trembles, his knees are shaking." "You are mistaken," I replied. "It is the scaffold that shakes under the footsteps of the officers." The sheriff struck the rope a sharp blow with a hatchet, the platform fell with a crash—a few convulsive struggles and a human soul had gone to judgment.

CLOSE TO ETERNITY

1. You notice that this report of John Brown's hanging is written in the first person. Why does this personal approach make the experience convincing?

2. The setting for the execution is pleasing to the senses. Select at least three phrases or sentences descriptive of the scene. How does this picture affect you as you follow the methodical steps leading to the hanging?

3. The careful reader realizes the nature of the man who is about to die. What qualities of character do you find? Write a paragraph presenting your ideas and support your conclusions by specific references.

4. How do you feel about this account of John Brown's death? What is the attitude of the author, a magazine reporter sent to witness the execution? Explain your reactions by offering several reasons.

A WORD TO REMEMBER: alacrity

To do something with *alacrity* (a·LAK·rih·tee) is to do it with cheerful readiness or briskness. John Brown "mounted the steps of the scaffold with . . . alacrity." Roget's *Thesaurus* gives as synonyms for *alacrity: rapidity, agility, eagerness,* and *animation.* Why do you suppose Strother chose *alacrity* rather than one of these words of similar meaning?

A different account of John Brown's last days, a companion piece
to the preceding selection, gives you opportunity for comparison.

John Brown's Speech

STEPHEN VINCENT BENÉT

I have, may it please the Court, a few words to say.

In the first place I deny everything but what I have all along admitted: of a design on my part to free slaves. . . .

Had I interfered in the matter which I admit, and which I admit has been fairly proved . . . had I so interfered in behalf of the rich, the powerful, the intelligent, or the so-called great . . . and suffered and sacrificed, what I have in this interference, it would have been all right. Every man in this Court would have deemed it an act worthy of reward rather than punishment.

I see a book kissed which I suppose to be the Bible, or at least the New Testament, which teaches me that all things whatsoever I would that men should do unto me, I should do even so to them. It teaches me further to remember them that are in bonds as bound with them. I endeavored to act up to that instruction. I say I am yet too young to understand that God is any respecter of persons. I believe that to have interfered as I have done, as I have always freely admitted I have done in behalf of His despised poor, I did no wrong, but right. Now, if it is deemed necessary that I should forfeit my life for the furtherance of the ends of justice and mingle my blood further with the blood of my children and with the blood of millions in this slave country whose rights are disregarded by wicked, cruel, and unjust enactments, I say, let it be done.

Let me say one word further. I feel entirely satisfied with the treatment I have received on my trial. Considering all the circumstances, it has been more generous than I expected. But I feel no consciousness of guilt. I have stated from the first what was my intention and what was not. I never had any design against the liberty of any person, nor any disposition to commit treason or incite slaves to rebel or make any general insurrection. I never encouraged any man to do so but always discouraged any idea of that kind.

Let me say also, in regard to the statements made by some of those connected with me, I hear it has been stated by some of them that I have induced them to join with me. But the contrary is true. I do not say this to injure them, but as regretting their weakness. Not one but joined me of his own accord, and the greater part at their own expense. A number of them I never saw, and never had a word of conversation with, till the day they came to me, and that was for the purpose I have stated.

Now I have done.

The voice ceased. There was a deep, brief pause.
The judge pronounced the formal words of death.
One man, a stranger, tried to clap his hands.
The foolish sound was stopped.
There was nothing but silence then.
         No cries in the court,
No roar, no slightest murmur from the thronged street,
As Brown went back to jail between his guards.
The heavy door shut behind them.
There was a noise of chairs scraped back in the courtroom,
And that huge sigh of a crowd turning back into men.

A month between the sentence and the hanging.
A month of endless visitors, endless letters.
A Mrs. Russell [1] came to clean his coat.
A sculptor sketched him.
       In the anxious North,
The anxious Dr. Howe [2] most anxiously
Denied all godly connection with the raid,
And Gerrit Smith [2] conveniently went mad
For long enough to sponge his mind of all
Memory of such an unsuccessful deed.
Only the tough, swart-minded Higginson [2]
Kept a grim decency, would not deny.
Pity the portly men, pity the pious,
Pity the fool who lights the powder-mine,
They need your counterfeit penny, they will live long.

[1] **Mrs. Russell:** wife of Judge Thomas Russell in whose home Brown had stayed while attempting to raise money for his cause in Boston.
[2] **Dr. Howe, Gerrit Smith,** and the Rev. Thomas Wentworth **Higginson** were among the backers of John Brown's raid. Dr. Samuel Gridley Howe was the husband of poet Julia Ward Howe.

In Charlestown meanwhile, there were whispers of rescue.
Brown told them,
"I am worth now infinitely more to die than to live."
And lived his month so, busily.
A month of trifles building up a legend
And letters in a pinched, firm handwriting
Courageous, scriptural, misspelt, and terse,
Sowing a fable everywhere they fell
While the town filled with troops.

                      The Governor came,
Enemies, friends, militia-cavaliers,
Old Border Foes.

             The month ebbed into days,
The wife and husband met for the last time,
The last letter was written:

"To be inscribed on the old family Monument at North Elba.
Oliver Brown born 1839 was killed at Harpers Ferry, Va. Nov.
   17th 1859
Watson Brown born 1835 was wounded at Harpers Ferry Nov.
   17th and died Nov. 19th 1859
(My Wife can) supply *blank* dates to above
John Brown born May 9th 1800 was executed at Charlestown
   Va. December 2nd 1859."

At last the clear warm day, so slow to come.
The North that had already now begun
To mold his body into crucified Christ's,
Hung fables about those hours—saw him move
Symbolically, kiss a negro child,
Do this and that, say things he never said,
To swell the sparse, hard outlines of the event
With sentimental omen.

                It was not so.
He stood on the jail-porch in carpet-slippers,
Clad in a loose ill-fitting suit of black,
Tired farmer waiting for his team to come.
He left one last written message:

"I, John Brown, am now quite *certain* that the crimes of this *guilty land: will* never be purged *away:* but with blood. I had *as I now think: vainly* flattered myself that without *very much* bloodshed; it might be done."

They did not hang him in the jail or the Square.
The two white horses dragged the rattling cart
Out of the town. Brown sat upon his coffin.
Beyond the soldiers lay the open fields
Earth-colored, sleepy with unfallen frost.
The farmer's eye took in the bountiful land.
"This *is* a beautiful country," said John Brown.

The gallows-stairs were climbed, the death-cap fitted.
Behind the gallows,
Before a line of red-and-gray cadets,
A certain odd Professor T. J. Jackson [1]
Watched disapprovingly the ragged militia
Deploy for twelve long minutes ere they reached
Their destined places.
The Presbyterian saber of his soul
Was moved by a fey breath.
      He saw John Brown,
A tiny blackened scrap of paper-soul
Fluttering above the Pit that Calvin [2] barred
With bolts of iron on the unelect;
He heard the just, implacable Voice speak out
"Depart ye wicked to eternal fire."
And sternly prayed that God might yet be moved
To save the predestined cinder from the flame.

Brown did not hear the prayer. The rough black cloth
Of the death-cap hid his eyes now. He had seen
The Blue Ridge Mountains couched in their blue haze.
Perhaps he saw them still, behind his eyes—

[1] **Professor T. J. Jackson:** later known as "Stonewall" Jackson, a general in the Confederate army.

[2] **Calvin:** John Calvin, sixteenth-century Protestant reformer, who believed that men were chosen by God to be saved or damned.

Perhaps just cloth, perhaps nothing any more.
"I shall look unto the hills from whence cometh my help."

The hatchet cut the cord. The greased trap fell.

Colonel Preston: [1]

"So perish all such enemies of Virginia,
   All such enemies of the Union,
   All such foes of the human race."

[1] **Colonel Preston:** commanding officer in charge of the execution.

THE FACT IS—

1. What was John Brown's attitude toward his accusers?
2. What did he say about statements made by his followers?
3. How much time passed between the pronouncement of sentence and his death? What happened during this time?
4. Where was John Brown hanged? Describe the place.

CLOSE TO ETERNITY

1. Explain how John Brown's speech in the courtroom affected his audience. Write a paragraph expressing your own reactions to it.
2. When John Brown heard "whispers of rescue," he replied, "I am worth now infinitely more to die than to live." What did he mean? Explain why he spoke these words.
3. Read again John Brown's last written message, beginning "I, John Brown, am now quite certain . . ." to "it might be done." How does this message influence your thinking about his place in history? Write your answer in a short paragraph.

A WORD TO REMEMBER: bountiful

John Brown described the countryside as a *bountiful* land. The word means "generous, abundant"; hence, it was a country that yielded a bountiful harvest. Look up the word *bounty* in an unabridged dictionary and note its various meanings. What connection do you find between these two words?

Crystal Moment

Robert P. Tristram Coffin

Once or twice this side of death
Things can make one hold his breath.

From my boyhood I remember
A crystal moment of September.

A wooded island rang with sounds   5
Of church bells in the throats of hounds.

A buck leaped out and took the tide
With jewels flowing past each side.

With his high head like a tree
He swam within a yard of me.   10

I saw the golden drop of light
In his eyes turned dark with fright.

I saw the forest's holiness
On him like a fierce caress.

Fear made him lovely past belief,   15
My heart was trembling like a leaf.

He leaned toward the land and life
With need above him like a knife.

In his wake the hot hounds churned,
They stretched their muzzles out and yearned.   20

They bayed no more, but swam and throbbed,
Hunger drove them till they sobbed.

Pursued, pursuers reached the shore
And vanished. I saw nothing more.

So they passed, a pageant such   25
As only gods could witness much,

Life and death upon one tether
And running beautiful together.

CRYSTAL MOMENT   **341**

Thief Jones

ROBERT P. TRISTRAM COFFIN

The people living round the place
Called him Thief Jones to his face,
Thief was like a Christian name,
It had lost the smut of shame.
Thief's house was black and let in weather,   5
The ridgepole hardly held together,
The doorway stood at a lee-lurch.
Men often opened it to search
Among the litter of net-corks there
For a lobster-buoy or pair   10
Of missing pants whose seat was sewn
With patches they could prove their own.
It got so, when a man lost track
Of anything, he took a tack
Down Thief's way and had a look.   15
The folks at Mundy's Landing took
Thief as they took foggy weather;
They'd learned to get on well together.

Thief never said a word if he
Happened to be in. He'd be   20
Glad to see the man and might
Help him straighten things out right—
"This rudder's yours, this anchor's mine."
He might invite the man to dine
On the hasty-pudding cooking   25
On his stove, after the looking.
Men liked to talk with Thief, he knew
Stories yellow, pink, and blue.
But though they liked to hear him lie,
They never halved a blueberry pie   30
From his cookstove's warming-shelf,
Thief ate his victuals by himself.

ROBERT P. TRISTRAM COFFIN (1892–1955).

"Poetry," wrote Robert P. Tristram Coffin, "is the art of putting different kinds of good things together: men and plows, boys and whistles, hounds and deer, sorrow and sympathy, life and death." The three last pairs are packed into "Crystal Moment." Like Longfellow and Nathaniel Hawthorne, Coffin was graduated from Maine's Bowdoin College. Almost all of his written work centered around the rugged beauty and granite-carved people of his native state. He reveled in the sharp changes of season and used his poet's eye to catch the beauty of the stark land and self-sufficient people. Since he wrote so much of Maine, we could call him a regional poet, But Coffin had a sense of nation as well as region and also a strong sense of his own worth. He wrote: "I have given upwards of a thousand lectures or readings across our country, carrying on my life-work of making poetry a center of the lives of the American people; and the response to my lectures has been most gratifying."

THE POET'S PURPOSE

Crystal Moment

1. Among the dictionary definitions of *crystal* are "clear," "transparent," and "pure." Can each of these fit the poet's meaning? Which do you think is best? Why?

2. Try to explain your reactions to the following lines: 5 and 6, 9 and 10, 19 and 20. Which of your senses is appealed to in each case?

3. Do the last two lines give the chief idea of the poem? If so, what is it?

4. This has been called Coffin's most appealing poem. Why could this poem be called appealing? Write a paragraph explaining why you did or did not find this poem appealing.

Thief Jones

1. What was your reaction to the title of this poem? Were you surprised? confused? disbelieving? Why doesn't Coffin give Jones's "Christian name"?

2. Explain the line: "It had lost the smut of shame." How does it contribute to your understanding of Jones?

3. Do you find pity or humor or both qualities in this poem? Give examples.

4. Read again the last four lines. Why did Thief eat "his victuals by himself"? What idea is implied in the last line?

Dream

DOROTHY VENA JOHNSON

I dreamed last night that you were married, love.
As proudly down the aisle you walked, all eyes
Sought you with echoes of such ardent sighs
I thought them strains of angels from above.
Attired in formal dress and fitted glove   5
You walked sedately. Many did arise
To see you splendent in your wedding guise,
Aglow and waiting for your new-found dove.

As branches droop from verdant willow tree
So drooped my weeping heart as you passed by,   10
Severing the ties of former destiny.
You were exuberant. How sad was I!
And only when the bride appeared, devout,
Was I triumphant—for your bride was stout!

THE POET'S PURPOSE

1. This poem is divided into two parts. Such an arrangement of eight lines and six lines with a definite rhyme scheme is called a sonnet. What does the poet say in the first part? What in the second part? Write in a single, well-developed sentence your understanding of the meaning of the whole poem.

2. What makes this poem amusing? Does the last line tie in with the theme of the poem? If you think so, explain how.

THE POET'S LANGUAGE

Many students think that poets speak a different language that ordinary people can understand only with difficulty. This is partly because much of the best poetry was written many years ago, and the English language has changed a great deal since those times. Another reason for this belief is that some poets deliberately reach out for difficult or unusual words to clothe difficult or unusual thoughts. Most poets today have moved in another direction and follow the lead of writers like Robert Frost, who set out to express himself in the familiar rhythms of everyday speech. Frost opened poems with simple lines like overheard conversations: "I'm going out to clean the pasture spring" and "Mary sat musing on the lamp flame at the table, / Waiting for Warren."

In "Dream" Dorothy Vena Johnson, capitalizing on our expectation that fancy language will clothe fancy thoughts, sneaks in the comic punch line: ". . . your bride was stout." Note the high tone of *devout,* the rhyme word for *stout;* this tone helps disarm us for the punch. The poet has laid her trap well with unusual words like *verdant* for "green" and expressions like *ardent sighs* and *wedding guise.* What other "poetic" words or expressions does this poet use? Would this poem have been as funny in everyday language? Why—or why not?

A WORD TO REMEMBER: sedately

By its very sound the word *sedately* (seh·DAYT·lee) suggests its meaning: "calmly, serenely." People should walk sedately to their seats in church. Where else should they walk sedately? Where should they *not* walk sedately?

GORDON PARKS

From bartender on a train to photographer of famous models and society folk is a long distance that the combination of ambition, courage, talent, and luck made possible for this man.

A
Choice
of
Weapons

We moved considerably farther from Joe Alvis's place this time. Our apartment was small, comfortable, and furnished on credit. Butch was almost five now; and in the spring the three of us began with the picnics, lake rides, and visits to the parks again. For some time I had been making a photographic collection of attractive girls, and Cecil Newman, the editor of the Minneapolis *Spokesman and Recorder*, began running them on the front page of his paper each week. There was no pay; I accepted the space for the pleasure of seeing my work published. It was good to see my name, in bold type, beneath the featured beauty each week; but I wasn't making money. So I told Cecil some sort of financial arrangement had to be made if we were to continue. His paper was in more financial trouble than I, but the two of us outtalked his wife, who resisted to the end, and raided her treasury for enough money to buy a press camera. Then Cecil appointed me official staff photographer—and circulation manager. My pay was a certain percentage of whatever amount of new circulation I could manage to get. Unfortunately I was a better photographer than circulation manager, so I tried to increase distribution by ignobly hinting to mothers that their *lovely* daughters might be photographed and put on the front page if they bought a subscription.

By September my commissions had become far less praiseworthy than my title. Winter, my bitter enemy, was coming; and so was another child, my wife informed me. So I began looking for a title that would have less prestige and more money attached to it. I had already made matters worse by going into debt for new photographic equipment to Harvey Goldstein, the dealer from whom we had bought the press camera. He had a blind faith in me, although he had no reason for such trust; I hadn't paid him a cent all summer. But he gave me everything I asked for, including plenty of helpful advice.

I was handed my new title on the twenty-third of September. It was not to be compared with the one Cecil had bestowed upon me. In fact I loathed it so much I refused to admit its existence. When the Chicago Northwestern Railway hired me on a bar car as a *porter,* I decided then and there that I was an *assistant bartender.* It had more dignity and sounded much better, I thought. I was not altogether a liar. I did serve drinks after the bartender had made them; but my specific duty was that of a porter—a title which I prefer not to mention again. But, most importantly, I had a regular salary and a source for tips.

The "400" was a fast, modern train that ran daily between Minneapolis, St. Paul, and Chicago. It was a good run for me because I was home every other night and in Chicago several days a week. There I photographed the skyscrapers and bridges, the boats moving up and down the canal. During the winter months I roamed the desolate areas along the river that cut through the heart of the city, photographing bums warming at bonfires, beggars wandering the windswept streets.

I worked hard at my double life, savoring with anticipation the day I could leave the railway forever. I would take it slower, learn my craft well, and then strike out. I felt my wife would be with me all the way. My conscience demanded that I hurry before time and a bigger family trapped me. I read every book on art and photography I could afford. I talked to painters, writers, and photographers whenever I discovered them on my car.

One day I saw the word *Life* in big red letters on a passenger's camera bag and discovered he was Bernard Hoffman, a photographer for that publication. We talked for a long time. "Come and work with us someday," he said when he got off in Chicago. And I laughed and promised him that I surely would. Then a few weeks later Bob Capa, the famous war photographer, came aboard, hoping to sleep the four hundred miles back to Chicago, only to be kept awake with my constant barrage of questions. And he said, "See you in Europe someday," when he stepped wearily off the car several hours later. The contact with these men transformed me into a dynamo.

Vogue was one of the magazines well-to-do passengers left on the train. I used to study the luxurious fashion photographs on its pages and the uncommon names of the photographers who took them—Steichen, Blumenfeld, Horst, Beaton, Hoyningen-Huene. How lucky they were, I thought. Daydreaming once, I printed my name under a Steichen portrait of Katharine Cornell. And my imagination assured me that it looked quite natural there.

No one could accuse me of being unaggressive now. I went to every large department store in the Twin Cities asking for a chance to photograph their merchandise. The manager of John

Thomas, a large women's store in Minneapolis, seemed astonished when I approached him. Looking at me curiously, he said, "But our photography is all done out in New York." Then he turned from me without another word.

But I kept trying, coming finally to Frank Murphy's, the most fashionable store in St. Paul. Frank Murphy had all but walked me out the door when his wife, a handsome woman with a shock of black hair, spoke to her husband. "What does he want, Frank?"

He gestured hopelessly. "To photograph fashions."

She was waiting on a customer but she looked me over and said, "Well, maybe he can." Frank Murphy looked back at his wife as though she had lost her wits. "But, darling . . ."

"Wait for me, young man. I'll be with you in a minute," she said. And by now I was as bewildered as her husband. For, aggressive as I was, I wasn't prepared for such a triumph. "Wait around; she'll talk to you," Frank Murphy said helplessly.

After her customer left, she turned to me. "Have you any samples of your work to show me?" she asked.

"No, I'm sorry."

"Why do you want to photograph fashion?"

"Because I know I can. That's all."

"Well, our clothes are photographed out East"—my spirits sank—"but I'm willing to give you a chance. I think it would be fun." She thought for a moment. "Can you be here tomorrow evening, right after we close? I'll have the models and dresses ready."

"Oh, sure. Yes, ma'm, I'll be here right on the dot," I said anxiously.

"All right." She was turning to another customer. "We'll be here waiting for you."

The ease and quickness of her decision stunned me. If I went on my regular run, I would be in Chicago the next evening. What's more, I suddenly realized I didn't even have lighting equipment or a camera suitable for fashion photography. But that evening I had Sally call the commissary and say that I was ill. Then I hurried to Harvey Goldstein and told him about my assignment; and he became as jittery as I, rushing about finding the necessary lamps, bulbs, films, and camera. We were both exhausted late that night after he had assembled the equipment and shown me how to use it.

The dresses and models were beautiful. And Mrs. Murphy seemed just as excited as I was about the whole thing. She went around buttoning the girls into the lovely evening dresses she had selected. And Frank Murphy stood by, watching us with a quizzical and skeptical eye. The models had more enthusiasm than talent; but they too were helpful and held the long tiring poses I demanded of them. My lighting, inspired by the pictures I had so often studied in the pages of *Vogue*, wasn't at all bad. The biggest problem came when the models appeared on the ground glass upside-down. Harvey hadn't warned me about this. And I went through the four-hour sitting with the awful feeling that there was something cockeyed about the lens or the camera. But I bluffed it through without anyone's being aware of my nervousness. And, when we were finished, Mrs. Murphy, obviously impressed with the way I had lighted and posed the models, asked me if I would like to continue shooting sports clothes at the country club the next day. I couldn't have been happier; and it must have shown on my face, for she bade me good night with a smile of deep satisfaction.

The big blow fell at exactly two o'clock the next morning when I developed the film. My wife was asleep when she heard the moaning and my head bumping against the kitchen wall. "What's the trouble?" she asked through the outer door.

"My life is ruined! Your life is ruined! The whole world is ruined!" I screamed, throwing open the room to her.

She stood, her hair up in curlers, bulky with our new child, looking at me in pity. "What's the trouble?"

I sat down dejectedly. "I've double-exposed every picture but one. After all that work—all that work. I can't face that woman tomorrow. I just can't face her."

"How'd it happen?" she asked.

"Those holders. I didn't turn the black side out after I exposed the film."

We were silent for what seemed like an age, sitting there in the dim light of the kitchen. I had been given my big chance and had muffed it. I kept groaning. "Why did this have to happen to me!"

"I'd blow up the good one, and show it to her," my wife suggested as she went off to bed. I sat for an hour before her suggestion sank in. Then I made a huge enlargement of the only good negative. It was elegantly framed and standing on an easel at the entrance to the country club when Mrs. Murphy arrived with the models the next afternoon. "My dear boy," she exclaimed, "it's absolutely beautiful. Where are the others? I just can't wait to see them."

I was tempted to lie. "But a woman like this deserves the truth—no matter what," I said to myself sadly. So I told the truth. "Forget it," she said cheerfully; "we've got more work to do." My heart lightened instantly. "But," she warned, "no more of those nasty double exposures." The next week my photographs were shown throughout her store and in all the front windows. And I must have walked up and down that street a hundred times that first night, feeling good every time someone stopped to look at one of them.

Marva Louis, the wife of the heavyweight champion of the world, Joe Louis, came to St. Paul while my photographs were still on display. And, as good luck would have it, someone took her by Murphy's to see them. And Marva, who was interested in fashion design, telephoned to compliment me before returning to Chicago. "This is Marva Louis," she said simply. "I saw your wonderful photographs at Frank Murphy's, and I think you are wasting your time here. Why don't you come to work in Chicago? I could get you a lot of work there."

I was overwhelmed, hardly knowing how to answer her. "I've been thinking about that, Mrs. Louis. Should I call you when I do come?"

"By all means," she said; and she gave me her address and phone number, not realizing, I am sure, the great joy she had brought to me. In my excitement I forgot to thank her for calling. I'll have to do that when I get to Chicago, I thought, and I hurried to the kitchen to give the news to my wife. She was frying potatoes when I burst in upon her. "Soon as the baby's born, we're going to Chicago," I shouted. Then I told her about the invitation Marva had extended me. Sally only smiled as she kept turning the potatoes. "Don't you understand what this means?" I said indignantly. I was crushed by her calmness.

"You're just restless again," she answered.

"Call it restlessness or whatever you want, but we're going to Chicago. I've made up my mind to that."

"We'll see," she said softly. And she kept turning the potatoes while I moved excitedly from room to room, feeling as if the eyes of the entire world were suddenly on me.

Our daughter was born shortly after that on November 4, while I was on a run to Chicago. My wife had named her Antoinette Stephanie by the time I reached the hospital; but after one look at that name on paper, I overruled her. A mild fight ensued but we eventually compromised on Toni. And that was what it would be.

For the rest of that winter, and the following spring and summer, all my thoughts were of moving to Chicago. Neither Sally nor I discussed it openly; her mother, we knew, would try to thwart my plan. Sally wasn't exactly enthusiastic about my giving up the railroad, and at times she allowed herself faint murmurings about the big chance we would be taking. But, knowing that I was fully determined, she finally decided to keep whatever doubts she had to herself. Her pessimism, however, was by no means groundless. I was spending almost everything, after food and rent, on new photographic equipment, preparing for the day when we would leave. I wouldn't have tolerated any objection to my spending. "How can I work without good equipment?" was to be my answer to any complaint. But the complaints never came.

An accidental meeting one day in Chicago with David Ross, the curator at the Southside Art Center, led to my abrupt departure from the Twin Cities that fall. It turned out, during our conversation in the gallery, that his wife Verlita and mine had struck up a friendship.

Our friendship was almost instantaneous. I thought he had some awfully big ideas about things, but then he probably thought the same thing about me. We both sounded off under the power of the strong Jamaican rum, expanding our dreams far beyond our capabilities. David was fair-skinned, thin, and dapper. His fingers were long and bony, and he used them freely to press his points.

I told him about Marva Louis's suggestion and my preparations for moving.

"Well, what's keeping you?" he asked.

"A studio or someplace to work from," I answered. I had never really considered this as a reason. But it came easily to my tongue, and it suddenly made sense. We parted with plans to see each other on my next run to Chicago. And I had already started across Michigan Avenue toward our rooming house when he caught up with me. He said, "We've been yakking all night and I've just realized that we can do each other some good."

"Like what?"

"Well, we've got a fully equipped darkroom at the Center, with nobody in it. We need a photographer and you need a place to work."

"Sounds great."

"We couldn't pay you anything but you wouldn't have to pay rent. We'd want you to photograph our activities now and then or an exhibit or things like that, and you could use one of the big rooms for your studio. How does it sound?"

"Sounds great," I repeated.

"It's a deal. Just let me know when you're coming. I'll start looking for an apartment for you." We pumped each other's hands happily and parted again. That night I lay awake till nearly dawn, trying to make the final decision, and two days later I gave the Chicago Northwestern notice. And, leaving the "400" on September 30, I swore never to ride it again except as a passenger.

The packing and storing of what little furniture we had were clandestine. My mother-in-law was suspicious, but she didn't know about our plans until three days before we were ready to go. Instead of declaring outright war, she took a just-you-wait-and-see attitude, predicting starvation for us before the winter was over.

Soon after, a letter came from David telling of a four-room furnished apartment someone had recommended. "I haven't seen it but it sounds pretty good and rents for $37.50 a month," he wrote.

"I'll take it. Arriving by car at ten Saturday morning," I wired back. But our battered Ford, filled to the corners with clothes, toys, sheets, blankets, developing trays, cameras, and even my enlarger, suffered two flat tires and a boiled-over radiator. We finally chugged up to David's house at three o'clock that afternoon, hungry and weary. We rested and ate some fried fish and potatoes Verlita fixed for us. Then, anxious about our new home, we drove over to see it.

The dreary brownstone sat next to a vacant lot in a rundown neighborhood just outside the South Side's black belt. Its ugly façade frowned down upon us when we got out of the car; and Sally, I noticed, was frowning back at it. The neighborhood, lying between the teeming black ghetto and the wealthy white residential section to the east, was in a sort of social limbo. An area where blacks were moving in and whites were moving out, it was a dwindling line of demarcation between the rich and the poor. The nondescript frame buildings surrounding ours had housed generations of Irish, Italians, Jews, and Poles; and they had taken on the architectural whims of these early immigrants, most of whom had prospered and moved on. "Property for Sale" signs were all over the neighborhood.

A small, graying, brown-skinned man opened the door when I knocked. He said, in a high squeaky voice, that his name was Mr. Reynolds, that he was the superintendent, and that he had been waiting around for us all day. I apologized for being late and asked him to show us the place. "I'll show it to you," he said, "but somebody better stay with that car. Half your stuff'd be gone by the time you got back."

Butch volunteered, being deliriously happy to sit alone at the steering wheel. Toni was asleep, but I threw her over my shoulder and carried her up the three flights through the gloomy hallway.

Mr. Reynolds took out a bunch of keys and started opening the door. "Need strong locks 'round here. Well, here's the living room," he said making a quick gesture with his hand.

I glanced at the dirty green walls, the worn carpeting, and the blistered ceiling. "Needs painting," I said, breaking the uncomfortable silence. I turned for a look at Sally. With Toni in her arms now, she stood in the doorway, unhappily observing the drab pieces of furniture.

Mr. Reynolds ignored my remark. "Here's the two bedrooms," he squeaked, pointing in their direction.

Sally didn't move. "Come on," I said, "take a look." She hesitated for a moment, then came over, and peeped into the dimly lit rooms. There was the same grease-splotched paper on all the walls, and its tawdry design, imitating the worst of the Victorian era, went well with the ornate brass beds and the credit-store dressers.

"The bathroom ain't much. Just a tub and a toilet stool. Look it over if you want to." Sally passed it up. But one quick look confirmed his description. There was an old-fashioned bathtub with claw feet and a primitive-looking stool. "And here's the kitchen. Comes with a gas stove and icebox." And a lot of grease and bugs, I thought, watching him squash a big cockroach with his foot. It was a darksome, dingy place, but my family was tired and needed someplace to sleep. I didn't dare ask Sally if she liked it. I just took $37.50 out of my pocket and paid the little man a month's rent. "It'll be fine," I assured her after he had gone; "just give me a week to fix it up and you won't know it."

"We'll see," she said; "we'll see."

The landlord gave in the next day and painted the place. Sally made new curtains for the windows; and with a few odds and ends we picked up at a secondhand store, our home began to brighten. So by the end of the first week, we had settled into the big city existence rather easily.

I began work at the Art Center right away. It was on South Michigan Avenue, nearly three miles north of where we lived, and quartered in an old red brick mansion, bought with solicited funds and proceeds from community benefits. There were about thirty employees on the staff, most of them teachers paid by the Federal Works Administration. Peter Pollack, a bustling curly-haired man, was the director and David was the assistant director and curator. There were three floors where the partitions had been cut away to make larger rooms. And the entire place, a haven for striving painters, sculptors, dancers, writers, and poets, was always alive with some sort of activity. My darkroom was located in the basement and it was complete with loading room, storage space, and good working facilities; and, as had been planned, I used a large room on the third floor for my studio. A good deal of Peter's and David's time was spent assuaging the feelings of opinionated officers and trustees, all of whom had different ideas for running the place. A revolt of some type was always at hand. At first my position was questioned, but at a tumultuous board meeting David shouted, "We don't pay him a red cent. He's doing as much for us as we are for him!" And that crisis was abruptly ended.

I did a brisk business from the very start. With the help of some of the influential board members and Marva Louis, whom I telephoned, I began gathering a steady clientele through a word-of-mouth campaign. The champion's beautiful wife had invited me to lunch at their Michigan Avenue apartment one afternoon. Before sitting down to eat, I was shown the large, mirrored, and elegantly overstuffed apartment from front to back. I gawked at closet after closet of dresses, drawers of gloves, a floor-to-ceiling rack filled with shoes of many patterns and colors—and there was one closet, nearly as large as my bedroom, where she kept her hats and coats. "You can use anything here you like for photographs," she said, "and I'll be delighted to pose for you." Over a nice but unfilling soufflé we talked of our hopes for the future. She was struck with the idea of being a designer, and it was easy to see where I fitted into her plans. I agreed to photograph her the following week. We flung ourselves into the effort with devotion. She was extremely photogenic and easy to work with. And clothes—room after room of them.

Our exertions were rewarded with a page of photographs in the Chicago *Sunday Tribune*, featuring Mrs. Louis and some of her new creations. And this brought me work from all over the city. At times I made as much as $150 a day. There were a number of talented young people who worked at the Center during those days, and one of the most promising was Charles White, a painter. He was mild-appearing, bespectacled, and blessed with humor, but his powerful, black figures pointed at the kind of photography that I knew I should be doing. We became close friends as the days went by. It was good to laugh and talk with him; and it was good to watch him strengthen an arm with a delicate brush stroke or give anguish to a face

with mixtures of coloring. We had great hopes, Charlie and I, and we spent hours talking to each other about them. "I've tried to get a Julius Rosenwald fellowship a couple of times," he complained sadly one day, "but they won't give me one."

"What's a Julius Rosenwald fellowship?" I asked.

"It's a fund set up for exceptionally able artists," he explained. "You oughta try for one next year."

"Has a photographer ever gotten one?"

"Not that I know of. Fact is I know they haven't. But that's all the more reason you should try."

"Man," Charlie said, "let's me and you get one of those in '42. What say?"

"I'm with you, buddy," I agreed. And we laughed and shook hands on it.

The Saturday morning I started poking around the South Side with my camera, I knew that more than anything else I wanted to strike at the evil of poverty. And here it was, under my feet, all around and above me. I could point the camera in any direction and record it. My own brush with it was motive enough, yet this landscape of ash piles, garbage heaps, tired tenements, and littered streets was worse than any I had seen. Everything looked wrecked and bombed out: this is what I would photograph and submit for the Rosenwald fellowship.

I hardly knew where to begin. So I walked along, pacing off this area where life and building alike had fallen into grave disrepair. Then I came to a vacant lot where a large Negro stood with a shovel in his hand and a woman and two children at his side. They were silent, looking as if they were at a graveside. A little girl, holding on to her mother's dress, was crying. I lifted my camera and shot the strange scene. As they made their way toward a tenement house, I followed them. And, passing the fresh grave, I saw a board stuck into the ashy earth. There was a crude crayon drawing of a dog on it. Beneath the drawing, printed also with crayon, and in a child's hand, were the words BUCKY, OUR FRIEND.

I was photographing this pathetic eulogy when the man looked back to me. "What you doin' there, fella?" he asked.

"Would the kids like a picture of the grave?"

They all looked at me strangely. "Yes, Poppa," the weeping girl said.

"What you chargin' for it?" the father asked.

"Nothing. Nothing at all. I'd just like for them to have it—if they want it."

"Yes, Poppa," the child repeated.

"How do we get it?" He seemed suspicious of me.

"Just give me your address and name, and I'll send it to you."

"That's all? We don't have to send you nothin'?"

"No, sir, not a thing," I said. "Have you got a pencil and paper?"

"In the house. We've got one in the house," the child said eagerly.

"Come on," the father said. I followed them over the lot to their building. We passed a sign on a large brick wall:

FIRST CLASS UNDERTAKER—HOME OF JENKINS FUNERAL SYSTEM ASSOCIATION —DON'T LET DEATH EMBARRASS YOUR LOVED ONES—JOIN TODAY—PREMIUMS AS LOW AS 10¢ PER WEEK.

I climbed a rickety stairway behind them to their third-floor room. The man invited me in, and after sizing me up properly, he asked me to sit down. The chair he offered was held together with baling wire. His wife sat on a stool and he stood up. "I thought you was some kind of inspector or somethin'," he said after we talked for a while. "They're always snoopin' round mindin' other people's business stead of cleanin' up this stinkin' place." And when I told him what I was trying to do with my camera, he pointed at his miserable quarters. "You won't find much worse'n this. Go ahead, take all the pictures you want. Just don't try to sell us none cause we're busted."

I started slowly, shooting first the one mattress where all of them slept on the floor. There was a small, round table covered with cracked oilcloth, and a greasy edition of *Cinderella* lay on it next to a stack of unwashed dishes. A wall shelf, covered with a piece of torn, dusty lace, held a framed picture of Christ and a Bible. There were a gas burner and a washtub with a chunk of ice in it, which served as their refrigerator; a fruit crate sat in the corner, filled with dirty clothes, and there was a sink, propped up with two broom handles. All the clothes the family owned hung above their heads on a rope that stretched across the room—overalls, gingham dresses, socks, and underwear. Most of the plaster had fallen from the walls, and the rotting laths showed through.

"This here is what they call a one-room kitchenette," the father went on. "Only about eight white families lived in this whole building once. When they cut out, the landlords chopped it up into the kinda holes you see I'm livin' in here. Now, there's more'n eight families on one floor alone. Gas and light free, they say. Well, we got two burners, and one of them works, and that one light bulb hangin' up there."

I broke in to ask him how much rent he paid.

"Seven bucks a week—when I can scrape it up. I got laid off from the slaughterhouse about six months ago. I get a odd job now and then. Most of the time I don't get nothin'."

I looked at the children. They sat wide-eyed on the mattress. The girl was about five, and she held her three-year-old brother's hand tightly. They watched their father as he talked.

"They're growin' children, good ones, but what's livin' like this gonna do to them down the line?"

I wrote down their address and promised to send them some of the pictures. I wanted to ask about the dog they had buried, but not before the children. I finally mentioned it to the father when he walked me outside. "He was the kids' pet. Nobody better not touch them while he was around, not even me. We got him to fight rats and keep guard round here. But my wife, she puts out some rat poison the other night and Bucky gets hold of it. And that's all of him."

This was only the beginning of weekend after weekend of tramping through the dismal acres of the South Side, photographing depressed people and the shacks and brick tenements that entombed them.

And there were the churches, big ones, little and middle-sized ones scattered among the taverns, butcher shops, and mortuaries. On Sunday mornings I turned my camera on those ardently religious folks as they went, in their Sunday best, to the storefront Bethels, God in Christs, African Methodists, and Pilgrim Baptists that they kept going with pennies, nickels, and dimes. "Religion is all we got left," an old missionary woman told me one day. I had asked her to pose for me, and she stood, a little white bonnet perched on top of her head, a Bible under her arm, looking into my camera. The lenses of her steel-rimmed glasses were like mirrors; focusing sharply on them, I caught a reflection of the desolation that surrounded us.

Being proud of that particular picture, I showed it to a society matron whom I photographed in her North-Side penthouse the next afternoon. She held up the picture in her jeweled white hands and observed it carefully. "A darling old lady," she purred, "an awful lot like the mammy we had as children," and in the same breath, "Oh, I do want so much for you to make me beautiful!" And, with deceit and guile, I told her what she wanted to hear, "You *are* beautiful." She shrieked with delight when I took her the finished photographs that Friday. And, with the handsome fee she paid me, I bought more film to expose in that frightful ghetto once again.

When the cold shock of that winter knifed in from the big lake, the South Side became desperate, and death stalked the side streets and dark alleyways. The robberies and slayings increased, and I walked the area with caution, aware of the danger in every block. There were always a lot of funerals during the winter months, and I photographed these sad rituals, catching when I could the despair on the faces of the mourners. The preachers' voices were always caressing to the families of the deceased, even when the deceased had died taking someone else's life. But sometimes, caught up in the emotion of their words, the preachers lost all feeling of time and the dead beneath their makeshift pulpits; and they lashed out with fury at the sin and corruption that hemmed them in. And, swaying with passion, they lifted the mourners into uncontrolled weeping, dancing, and shouting; the floors shook, the coffin shook, and it seemed that the one they had come to bury was forgotten. Once I followed a coffin to the baggage car. On the pine box it was shipped in was penciled the name Joshua Collins. He was going back to Natchez, Mississippi, where his life had started in a sharecropper's shack. "He wanted to be put away down there," his sister told me as the train pulled

out, "I don't know why. I don't want to ever see that place again. We had such a hard time gettin' out."

I worked hard the rest of that year and most of the next. The Art Center promised me a show in the early fall of 1941; this, Pollack and Ross thought, would give the Rosenwald people a chance to see my work at its very best. Charlie White worked hard too, and at times we got together and talked about our chances. Meanwhile we set out to bag sponsors, as required by the fellowship fund. My list eventually included Alain Locke, the first Negro Rhodes Scholar; Horace Cayton, the writer; Pollack and Ross. I spent most of August printing the things I had shot. For an amateur, I had a well-rounded selection to choose from—the South-Side series, landscapes, seascapes, fashions I had shot at Frank Murphy's, and some of the wealthy ladies who sat for me in Chicago.

Fall came quicker than usual, it seemed; but by working day and night I was able to meet the deadline. David hung the show, and we spent the final hours changing or readjusting the order of the pictures for what he called "impact." By the time Sally and I arrived, the gallery was already filling. And, if attendance had anything to do with it, the show was a success. It seemed that half of Chicago was there. The elite, dressed in their furs and finery, rubbed elbows with some of the people I had photographed in the poor quarter; I had invited as many of them as I could find. Jack Delano, the FSA photographer whose work had inspired me years before, attended; and the Rosenwald Fund was represented by Edwin R. Embree, its director, and William C. Haygood, a white Southerner who was his assistant. There were tables full of dainty sandwiches and cocktails with white-jacketed waiters to serve them. It was a grand affair. But my warmest moment came when the little missionary woman I had photographed walked into the gallery wearing her bonnet. Her photograph was one of the largest in the room and, subconsciously, I suppose, I had hung it next to that of the bejeweled lady who thought she resembled her "mammy." It was odd to see the two of them standing beneath their respective portraits with newsmen's flashbulbs popping in their faces. Despite the gathering of beautiful ladies and other affluent people, she was the most sought after. Nearly everyone in the place shook her hand before she finally went home in a taxi I called for her.

Embree and Haygood said glowing things about the exhibition before they left, and I went home glowing in presumptuous confidence; then, a couple of days later, realizing they weren't judges, I started to sweat it out. I had done all I could. The question was: had I done enough?

Things gradually returned to normal, and I settled back into my daily work. Now and then I imagined myself as a successful Rosenwald fellow, but just as often I felt the pangs of reading the letter that would come one day—saying I had not been accepted. At times I tried to forget the whole business, but this was impossible. Nearly a month had passed when Peter Pollack told me that a jury of photographers, selected to judge my work, had turned me down flat. All this was in strict confidence; the information had been leaked out to Pollack. Terribly disappointed with the news, we sat around for a while, enveloped in gloom. I had given up altogether. "I don't think I'll ever try again," I said, thinking back over the hard work I had put in.

"Just a minute," Pollack said. He was dialing the phone. "Hello. Mr. Haygood, please. Hello, Billy. Pete Pollack speaking. Billy, why did they let photographers judge Parks's work? The man's an artist. Artists should have judged his work." They talked for a few minutes and Pollack hung up. "I have a hunch you'll get another chance. Haygood might put your work before the artists' jury." And for the next few weeks Pollack sweated with me.

Finally one morning an envelope came from the fund. I was still in bed when Sally brought it to me, and I lay there for a few seconds, afraid to open it. "Here," I said, handing it back to her, "give me the bad news." She fumbled with the envelope for a long moment;

then, beginning at last to read, her anxious face softened. Then she said weakly, "You made it." She sat down on the bed and we remained there, quiet in our happiness, for several minutes. I wondered about Charlie White, afraid he might not have been so fortunate. I didn't know it then, but he was thinking the same way about me. The two of us were cautiously reserved when I finally got him on the phone.

"Charlie?"

"Gordon?" His voice couldn't hide the joy, and neither could mine.

"We made it! We made it!" we both shouted at the top of our voices.

THE FACT IS—

1. Mr. Parks's career included some lucky as well as unlucky breaks. Name one of each.

2. How did the author take advantage of his job on a train to advance his career as a photographer?

3. Where in this account did following the motto "Honesty is the best policy" help the author?

4. The author was a man whom people were glad to help. Name five who did help him and tell what help each gave.

A CHOICE OF WEAPONS

1. In Shakespeare's *Hamlet* a father advises his son, "This above all: to thine own self be true." Does the career of Gordon Parks support this idea? How?

2. Find evidence that Parks's family did not always support the author enthusiastically.

3. Why, if Mr. Parks wanted to become a fashion photographer, did he take so many shots of the poor in the slums?

4. What guidance for your own vocational future can you find in this autobiographical excerpt?

5. The selection here ends with Parks shouting, "We made it!" How successful did he become? What new challenges did he meet and survive? Visit your library for answers to these questions.

THINKING ABOUT AMERICANS LOOKING AT THEMSELVES

AMERICAN EXPERIENCES

1. Many writers have the great ability to describe a character in a sentence: "In the fullness of her colorful clothes, in the inverted tub of her purple hat, she was all glorious show." "Only the tough, swart-minded Higginson kept a grim decency." In which selections do these two characters appear? Choose characters from three other selections. Write a well-developed sentence describing each of the three characters you selected.

2. The story "Heyday of the Blood" leaves the reader with an idea. What is it? Select three poems which offer other ideas and for each write a well-developed sentence expressing the thought.

3. Using the two selections on John Brown, write a comparison to show how two authors treat one subject. What similarities and differences do you see? Consider each author's point of view.

4. You want, let us say, to experience the artistry of a Leontyne Price or a Gordon Parks. Think of where in your school or community you might find an example of their work. Report on your findings.

DO YOU REMEMBER THESE WORDS?

Give the meaning of each of the italicized words in the following sentences; then try using each word in a substantial, original sentence.

1. A *placid* disposition sometimes suggests a colorless personality.

2. Members of large families should enjoy lives of happy *coexistence.*

3. Although he did not openly *gloat* at his opponent's misfortune, he smiled with satisfaction.

4. People behave more *sedately* at a formal dance than at a football game.

5. The students fell into a *meditative* mood when the news was announced.

6. With *alacrity* she accepted a "bid" to the Junior Prom, since she had no date.

7. Our country has sent *bountiful* supplies of food to foreign lands.

8. Edgar Allan Poe's short stories have been called *unique* among horror tales.

PART TWO

The great writers of America are a mixed crew. Among them we find the world-renowned Ben Franklin, at home alike in the printer's shop or at the diplomat's ball; Emily Dickinson, shy and mousy, hiding from family guests; Mark Twain, who once styled himself "The Wild Humorist of the Pacific Slope"; Stephen Crane, who began his "artistic education on the Bowery"; the doomed Poe; and the long-lived, long-respected modern poets, Robert Frost and Carl Sandburg. One common bond of these uncommon people is a feeling for America, its land and its people. Franklin helped to create this nation; Walt Whitman celebrated it in such poems as "Leaves of Grass" and "I Hear America Singing"; Lincoln died to keep it whole; John Steinbeck pleaded for its homeless poor in *The Grapes of Wrath*. Frost stated our semihistorical, semimystical relation to our land in his poem "The Gift Outright."

> "The land was ours before we were the land's,
> She was our land more than a hundred years
> Before we were her people. . . ."

For a people whose literary heritage was borrowed at best and who had produced little of note before 1770, we have built up a remarkable body of literature. Herman Melville with *Moby Dick* and Mark Twain with *Huckleberry Finn* produced novels that stand with the world's best. Poe and Whitman, Frost and Steinbeck are read in dozens of languages. Americans in recent years have carried home five Nobel prizes for literature.

Imagination and experience are curiously mixed in American literature. If we are told that Senator Daniel Webster once told the

AMERICAN WRITERS

Devil, "By the thirteen original colonies I'd go to the Pit itself to save the Union!" we accept it; just as we accept Ralph Waldo Emerson's statement that the embattled farmers at Concord "fired the shot heard round the world." We may be startled by the dark world of Poe's imaginings, but we enter it willingly; just as we enter the now-distant world of Franklin's Philadelphia or Mark Twain's boyhood home, Hannibal, Missouri. It is the mark of Poe's genius that he can create a fantasy world as "real" as Philadelphia or Hannibal or Steinbeck's painful but hopeful view of today's "America and the Americans."

Many writers in this section of ADVENTURES FOR AMERI–CANS combine their immediate experience and the world of the imagination. It is hardly possible to read a poem by Robert Frost or Carl Sandburg without realizing that what they write is based upon a sharp, direct experience which they share with you, the reader. Even the closed world of Emily Dickinson is a world related to ours. In common with all the writers in this section, she has the capacity, through her gift of a soaring imagination, to bring you into her world and to show you something about your own world as she leads you into hers.

Imagination is one of man's greatest possessions. If you should wish to test this statement, read Stephen Crane's *The Red Badge of Courage*. This book is usually described as a "realistic" novel, and yet it was written by a young man who had never experienced battle, had never seen war. Or read the poetry and prose of Melville and Whitman, whose experience with Americans led them to dwell on plain people, men described by historian Van Wyck Brooks as "full-blooded, magnanimous, genial, large, and deep."

Or read the selections from Mark Twain's *Autobiography,* selections in which the imagination of a mature and wise man colors the remembered events of youth.

This part of ADVENTURES FOR AMERICANS contains eleven great American writers in nine units. Each writer stands alone as a literary giant; you will see when you read Units Three and Eight why we paired Melville and Whitman, Frost and Sandburg. All eleven are writers against whom the other writers are measured.

Although these writers appear in roughly historical order, we are not presenting a history of American literature. We do not pretend that these are the only great American writers, nor even the greatest of the great. In "American Scenes" appear writers many critics would rank with some we include here—Ralph Waldo Emerson and Henry Wadsworth Longfellow, for example. In "American Scenes" also are modern writers who may some day be rated as high as those included here—John Updike, perhaps, or Pearl S. Buck.

Any student of American history or any student who wants to relate literature to history will find interesting material here. Franklin and Lincoln, of course, made history. Poe, in addition to originating the American short story, is the father both of the detective story and of American literary criticism. Melville and Whitman were born the same year, shared a common American experience, formed similar views of their fellow Americans, and died about a year apart. Crane and Frost, on the other hand, although born only four years apart, seem to represent completely different generations of American life and experience. Franklin took part in the negotiations following the French and Indian War more than two hundred years ago; Steinbeck served as a reporter during the war in Vietnam.

Above all, you will learn from these writers a great deal about what it was—and is—like to be an American. These writers, in their lives as in their writing, sum up the American experience, the taking in of immigrants and the moving west. Franklin and Poe were born in Boston, while Frost and Steinbeck were born in California; the fathers of both Franklin and Sandburg were foreigners in our land. These eleven are writers whose thoughts have crystallized the American experience for generations of our fellow countrymen—and for us.

Benjamin Franklin, First Typical American

The eighteenth century in America can almost be called the century of Benjamin Franklin. Franklin lived from 1706 to 1790 and was better known throughout the world than any other American except George Washington. Thomas Jefferson called Franklin "the greatest man and ornament of the age and country in which he lived."

It should be easy to talk about Franklin, but which Franklin are we to talk about? Benjamin Franklin, the poor boy who arrived in Philadelphia with little more than enough money to buy three puffy rolls but went on to make his personal fortune by forty? or Benjamin Franklin, the brilliant painter who at seventeen was editing a journal and later founded his own magazine which became *The Saturday Evening Post*? or the ambassador who charmed and impressed courts in England and in France? We could also mention Franklin, the public benefactor, who devoted great time and energy to the good of Philadelphia and its people; Franklin, the prolific inventor and gadgeteer; Franklin, who loved the ladies as they loved him; Franklin, the writer, whose wit and wisdom have come down through the decades in *Poor Richard's Almanac* and whose *Autobiography* has been called the "one indisputable literary classic" written by an American before 1800.

Benjamin Franklin was an almost unbelievably versatile man. Only Thomas Jefferson could rival him in the breadth and depth of his interests. And yet this very versatility makes Franklin a paradox. Here was a man who dressed plainly, whose speech was earthy and witty; but who found himself admired by the lords and ladies in the greatest and most glittering court in the world, that of Louis XVI of France. Here was a man of frugality, prudence, and simplicity, who lived much of his life among magnificence and luxury. Although Franklin gained his experience by dealing with his own personal affairs and the simple problems of the colonists, he proved to be a skillful negotiator, triumphing over the most subtle and cunning diplomats in Europe.

Here was a man any of whose careers would have been a full-time occupation for most other men. But Franklin could take time from these careers to experiment with electricity, to champion daylight-saving time, to invent a type of eyeglasses and a stove. (Perhaps you're sitting right now in a student chair with a writing arm; this type of chair is another Franklin invention.)

Here is a public benefactor, founder of the academy that later became the University of Pennsylvania, originator of a pioneer fire department, organizer and fund raiser of the first great hospital in Philadelphia and the first public library.

How did he find time for all these achievements? How could he bring into harmony all these activities and endeavors? No one can ever really answer these questions in dealing with as complex a character as Franklin, but we can examine some of the traits of his personality to seek the answers. First, Franklin was practical. Had he not been practical, he could not have survived the necessity of making his own way from his early teens. That he survived so well is a tribute to his natural genius. Second, he was curious. He was willing to spend much of his time reading to inform himself. Also he had the capacity to learn from people. In order to learn from the best minds in Philadelphia, he formed a society of the most intelligent men to meet regularly and exchange ideas and information. He was curious also about the world in which he lived. He experimented with electricity to find out the nature of the physical world. He invented a portable stepladder to make living in that physical world easier and more convenient. (Mr. Franklin was very fond of convenience!)

Franklin combined with these traits a more important attribute, tolerance, or moderation. You could call it taking a broad view or sometimes just the ability to see the other fellow's side. In his autobiography Franklin calls this trait "humility" and he describes very well how that virtue applies to him.

I made it a rule to forbear all direct contradiction to the sentiments of others, and all positive assertion of my own.... When another asserted something that I thought an error, I denied myself the pleasure of contradicting him abruptly, and of showing immediately some absurdity in his proposition. ... I soon found the advantage of this change in my manner.... The modest way in which I proposed my opinions procured them a readier reception and less contradiction; I had less mortification when I was found to be in the wrong, and I more easily prevailed with others to give up their mistakes and join with me when I happened to be in the right. And this mode, which I at first put on with some violence to natural inclination, became at length so easy, and so habitual to me, that perhaps for these fifty years past no one has ever heard a dogmatic expression escape me. And to this habit ... I think it principally owing that I had early so much weight with my fellow citizens ...; for I was but a bad speaker, never eloquent, subject to much hesitation in my choice of words, hardly correct in language, and yet I generally carried my points.

Can you see how effective Franklin must have been in the intense debates and disagreements which surrounded our Declaration of Independence and how eagerly his services must have been sought after in order that his persuasive "humility" would help achieve compromise? It was perhaps this same quality which made him so effective in dealing with France. First of all, he had to persuade the French to become our allies in fact. Then he had to beg the necessary loans to keep our revolutionary army in the field. Finally he was incredibly astute in arranging the terms of the peace, as important to a nation as victory in the war.

But during all this period of negotiation, when his subtle skill helped our cause so much, his practicality was quite as important. Franklin was hardheaded enough to realize that nothing less would satisfy the Americans who had fought and sacrificed for so many years. This practicality gave him the steel to resist all the compromises which would have taken away from our ultimate American triumph—a new country founded on new principles. This kind of practicality, for Franklin, was also a kind of idealism.

Perhaps the final answer to his complexity is that with all his talent for coming to terms with others, Franklin had come to terms with himself. Although he lived his life in an age of great turbulence, although he faced one crisis after another, he maintained a serenity and an inner peace. It made his life a happy one—happy because he was able to do so much for others; but happy, too, because what he had done for others gave him deep satisfaction for himself.

From the Autobiography

In Which Franklin Flees Boston

My brother had, in 1720 or 1721, begun to print a newspaper. It was the second that appeared in America, and was called the *New England Courant*.[1] The only one before it was the *Boston News-Letter*. I remember his being dissuaded by some of his friends from the undertaking, as not likely to succeed, one newspaper being, in their judgment, enough for America. At this time (1771) there are not less than five-and-twenty. He went on, however, with the undertaking, and after having

worked in composing the types and printing off the sheets, I was employed to carry the papers through the streets to the customers.

He had some ingenious men among his friends, who amused themselves by writing little pieces for this paper, which gained it credit and made it more in demand, and these gentlemen often visited us. Hearing their conversations and their accounts of the approbation their papers were received with, I was excited to try my hand among them; but being still a boy, and suspecting that my brother would object to printing anything of mine in his paper if he knew it to be mine, I contrived to disguise my hand, and, writing an anonymous paper, I put it in at night under the door of the printing house. It was found in the morning and communicated to his writing friends when they called in as usual.

[1] ***New England Courant:*** Actually the fourth newspaper in the English colonies, it was the first to do more than reprint reports from Europe.

They read it, commented on it in my hearing, and I had the exquisite pleasure of finding it met with their approbation, and that, in their different guesses at the author, none were named but men of some character among us for learning and ingenuity. I suppose now that I was rather lucky in my judges, and that perhaps they were not really so very good ones as I then esteemed them.

Encouraged, however, by this, I wrote and conveyed in the same way to the press several more papers which were equally approved; and I kept my secret till my small fund of sense for such performances was pretty well exhausted, and then I discovered it, when I began to be considered a little more by my brother's acquaintance, and in a manner that did not quite please him, as he thought, probably with reason, that it tended to make me too vain. And, perhaps, this might be one occasion of the differences that we began to have about this time. Though a brother, he considered himself as my master, and me as his apprentice, and, accordingly, expected the same services from me as he would from another, while I thought he demeaned me too much in some he required of me, who from a brother expected more indulgence. Our disputes were often brought before our father, and I fancy I was either generally in the right, or else a better pleader, because the judgment was generally in my favor. But my brother was passionate, and had often beaten me, which I took extremely amiss; and, thinking my apprenticeship very tedious, I was continually wishing for some opportunity of shortening it, which at length offered in a manner unexpected.

One of the pieces in our newspaper on some political point, which I have now forgotten, gave offense to the Assembly. He was taken up, censured, and imprisoned for a month, by the speaker's warrant, I suppose, because he would not discover his author. I too was taken up and examined before the council; but, though I did not give them any satisfaction, they contented themselves with admonishing me, and dismissed me, considering me, perhaps, as an apprentice, who was bound to keep his master's secrets.

During my brother's confinement, which I resented a good deal, notwithstanding our private differences, I had management of the paper; and I made bold to give our rulers some rubs in it, which my brother took very kindly, while others began to consider me in an unfavorable light, as a young genius that had a turn for libeling and satire. My brother's discharge was accompanied with an order of the House (a very odd one), that *"James Franklin should no longer print the paper called the New England Courant."*

There was a consultation held in our printing house among his friends, what he should do in this case. Some proposed to evade the order by changing the name of the paper; but my brother, seeing inconveniences in that, it was finally concluded on as a better way, to let it be printed for the future under the name of BENJAMIN FRANKLIN; and to avoid the censure of the Assembly, that might fall on him still printing it by his apprentice, the contrivance was that my old indenture should be returned to me, with a full discharge on the back of it, to be shown on occasion: but to secure him the benefit of my service, I was to sign new indentures for the remainder of the term, which were to be kept private. A very flimsy scheme it was; however, it was immediately executed, and the paper went on accordingly, under my name for several months.

At length, a fresh difference arising

between my brother and me, I took upon me to assert my freedom, presuming that he would not venture to produce the new indentures. It was not fair in me to take this advantage, and this I therefore reckon one of the first errata of my life; but the unfairness of it weighed little with me when under the impressions of resentment for the blows his passion too often urged him to bestow upon me, though he was otherwise not an ill-natured man: perhaps I was too saucy and provoking.

When he found I would leave him, he took care to prevent my getting employment in any other printing house of the town, by going round and speaking to every master, who accordingly refused to give me work. I then thought of going to New York, as the nearest place where there was a printer; and I was rather inclined to leave Boston when I reflected that I had already made myself a little obnoxious to the governing party, and, from the arbitrary proceedings of the Assembly in my brother's case, it was likely I might, if I stayed, soon bring myself into scrapes; and further, that my indiscrete disputations about religion began to make me pointed at with horror by good people as an infidel or atheist. I determined on the point, but my father now siding with my brother, I was sensible that, if I attempted to go openly, means would be used to prevent me. My friend Collins, therefore, undertook to manage a little for me. He agreed with the captain of a New York sloop for my passage. . . . So I sold some of my books to raise a little money, was taken on board privately, and as we had a fair wind, in three days I found myself in New York, near 300 miles from home, a boy of but seventeen, without the least recommendation to or knowledge of any person in the place, and with very little money in my pocket.

Three-Penny Worth of Bread

We met with a squall that tore our rotten sails to pieces, prevented our getting into the Kill,[1] and drove us upon Long Island. In our way, a drunken Dutchman, who was a passenger too, fell overboard. When he was sinking, I reached through the water to his shock pate [2] and drew him up, so that we got him in again. His ducking sobered him a little, and he went to sleep, taking first out of his pocket a book which he desired I would dry for him. It proved to be my old favorite author Bunyan's *Pilgrim's Progress* in Dutch, finely printed on good paper, with copper cuts, a dress better than I had ever seen it wear in its own language. . . .

When we drew near the island, we found it was at a place where there could be no landing, there being a great surf on the stony beach. So we dropped anchor and swung round toward the shore. Some people came down to the water edge and hallowed to us, as we did to them; but the wind was so high, and the surf so loud, that we could not hear so as to understand each other. There were canoes on the shore, and we made signs and hallowed that they should fetch us. But they either did not understand us, or thought it impracticable, so they went away. With night coming on, we had no remedy but to wait till the wind should abate. In the meantime, the boatman and I concluded to sleep, if we could; and so crowded into the scuttle with the Dutchman, who was still wet, and the spray beating over the head of our boat leaked through to us, so that we were soon almost as wet as he. In this manner we lay

[1] **Kill:** channel or stream between Staten Island and Bergen Neck, New Jersey.
[2] **shock pate:** hair on top of the head.

all night, with very little rest. But, the wind abating the next day, we made shift to reach Amboy before night, having been thirty hours on the water, without victuals, or any drink but a bottle of filthy rum, and the water we sailed on being salt.

In the evening I found myself very feverish and went in to bed; but having read somewhere that cold water drank plentifully was good for a fever, I followed the prescription, sweat plentiful most of the night. My fever left me, and in the morning, crossing the ferry, I proceeded on my journey on foot, having fifty miles to Burlington, where I was told I should find boats that would carry me the rest of the way to Philadelphia.

It rained very hard all the day. I was thoroughly soaked, and by noon a good deal tired, so I stopped at a poor inn, where I stayed all night, beginning now to wish that I had never left home. I cut so miserable a figure, too, that I found, by the questions asked me, I was suspected to be some runaway servant and in danger of being taken up on that suspicion. However, I proceeded the next day and got in the evening to an inn within eight or ten miles of Burlington, kept by one Dr. Brown. He entered into conversation with me while I took some refreshment, and, finding I had read a little, became very sociable and friendly. Our acquaintance continued as long as he lived. He had been, I imagine, an itinerant doctor, for there was no town in England, or country in Europe, of which he could not give a very particular account. . . .

At his house I lay that night, and the next morning reached Burlington, but had the mortification to find that the regular boats were gone a little before my coming, and no other expected to go before Tuesday, this being Saturday. I returned to an old woman in the town, of whom I had bought gingerbread to eat on the water, and asked her advice. She invited me to lodge at her house till a passage by water should offer; and being tired with my foot traveling, I accepted the invitation. She, understanding I was a printer, would have had me stay at that town and follow my business, being ignorant of the stock necessary to begin with. She was very hospitable, gave me a dinner of oxcheek with great good will, accepting only a pot of ale in return; and I thought myself fixed till Tuesday should come. However, walking in the evening by the side of the river, a boat came by, which I found was going toward Philadelphia with several people in her. They took me in, and, as there was no wind, we rowed all the way. About midnight, not having yet seen the city, some of the company were confident we must have passed it, and would row no farther. The others knew not where we were. So we put toward the shore, got into a creek, landed near an old fence, with the rails of which we made a fire, the night being cold, in October, and there we remained till daylight. Then one of the company knew the place to be Cooper's Creek, a little above Philadelphia, which we saw as soon as we got out of the creek, and arrived there about eight or nine o'clock on the Sunday morning and landed at the Market Street wharf.

I have been the more particular in this description of my journey, and shall be so of my first entry into that city, that you may in your mind compare such unlikely beginnings with the figure I have since made there. I was in my working dress, my best clothes being to come round by sea. I was dirty from my journey, my pockets were stuffed out with shirts and stockings, and I knew no soul nor where to look for lodging. I was fatigued with traveling, rowing, and want of rest. I was very hungry, and my whole stock of cash consisted of a Dutch dollar and about a shilling in copper. The latter I gave the people of the boat for my passage, who at first refused it on account of my rowing. But I insisted on their taking it, a man being sometimes more generous when he has but a little money than when he has plenty, perhaps through fear of being thought to have but little.

Then I walked up the street, gazing about till near the market house I met a boy with bread. I had many a meal on bread, and, inquiring where he got it, I went immediately to the baker's he directed me to in Second Street and asked for biscuit, intending such as we had in Boston; but they, it seems, were not made in Philadelphia. Then I asked for a three-penny loaf and was told they had none such. So not considering or knowing the difference of money, and the greater cheapness nor the names of his bread, I bade him give me three-penny worth of any sort. He gave me, accordingly, three great puffy rolls. I was surprised at the quantity, but took it and, having no room in my pockets, walked off with a roll under each arm, and eating the other. Thus I went up Market Street as far as Fourth Street,

passing by the door of Mr. Read, my future wife's father; when she, standing at the door, saw me, and thought I made, as I certainly did, a most awkward, ridiculous appearance. Then I turned and went down Chestnut Street and part of Walnut Street, eating my roll all the way, and, coming round, found myself again at Market Street wharf, near the boat I came in, to which I went for a draft of the river water; and being filled with one of my rolls, gave the other two to a woman and her child that came down the river in the boat with us and were waiting to go farther.

Thus refreshed, I walked again up the street, which by this time had many clean-dressed people in it, who were all walking the same way. I joined them, and thereby was led into the great meetinghouse of the Quakers near the market. I sat down among them, and after looking round awhile and hearing nothing said, being very drowsy through labor and want of rest the preceding night, I fell fast asleep, and continued so till the meeting broke up, when one was kind enough to rouse me. This was, therefore, the first house I was in, or slept in, in Philadelphia.

THE FACT IS—

1. Why did Benjamin Franklin submit his first "little pieces" anonymously?

2. Why was James Franklin arrested? For what offense was he sent to prison?

3. Why did James print his paper under his brother Benjamin's name?

4. Benjamin Franklin wrote that he was "rather inclined to leave Boston." Why?

5. Make a list of the hardships Franklin had on his journey.

6. Why was Franklin so interested in the Dutchman's copy of *Pilgrim's Progress?*

7. Which incident in this selection illustrates Franklin's willingness to work? Which illustrates his friendliness?

8. What was the reaction of Franklin's future wife to her first sight of Ben?

A BOY OF BUT SEVENTEEN

1. In reading Franklin's description, what differences do you notice between newspapers then and now? Do you think a paper like the *New England Courant* would sell many copies today? Why, or why not?

2. There are more than twice as many people in New York City today as there were in the colonies in 1771. When a newspaper quit publishing in May 1967, New York was left with only three daily papers; yet Franklin says there were at least twenty-five papers in the colonies in 1771. Write a paragraph in which you give reasons to explain this remarkable difference.

3. Benjamin Franklin wrote that from his brother he "expected more indulgence." Assume that you are young Benjamin about to flee Boston. Write a letter to James detailing your grievances.

AN ITINERANT PRINTER

1. Have you ever taken a long, uncomfortable journey? Jot down a list of the discomforts. Taking special care with the descriptions of your discomforts, write an account of the journey.

2. After Franklin had insisted that the people in the boat take his shilling, he said, "a man being sometimes more generous when he has but a little money than when he has plenty, perhaps through fear of being thought to have but little." Do you agree?

3. Write a short dramatic sketch in which Franklin converses with his future wife that day on Market Street. (If you want to review the dramatic form, check any selection listed under "Drama" at the end of the Table of Contents.)

A WORD TO REMEMBER: diligent

Another word that is used to describe Franklin is *diligent* (DIL·ih·j'nt), which means "steady and earnest in doing a job." Franklin worked diligently at his printing; he was even more diligent about educating himself. In his letters and in his almanac, he advised people to be careful, industrious, and attentive workers. Laziness and carelessness often cause a man to fail; diligence helps him to succeed.

From Franklin's Letters

We now make a great leap from Franklin, the seventeen-year-old printer, to Franklin, the elder statesman and scientist. You will note that he is still traveling and carefully observing everything.

A Whirlwind

Philadelphia, August 25, 1775

Dear Sir:

As you have my former papers on Whirlwinds, etc., I now send you an account of one which I had lately an opportunity of seeing and examining myself.

Being in Maryland, riding with Colonel Tasker and some other gentlemen to his country seat, where I and my son were entertained by that amiable and worthy man with great hospitality and kindness, we saw in the vale below us a small whirlwind beginning in the road and showing itself by the dust it raised and contained. It appeared in the form of a sugar loaf, spinning on its point, moving up the hill toward us, and enlarging as it came forward. When it passed by us, its smaller part near the ground appeared not bigger than a common barrel, but widening upward, it seemed, at forty or fifty feet high, to be twenty or thirty feet in diameter.

The rest of the company stood looking after it, but my curiosity being stronger, I followed it, riding close by its side, and observed its licking up in its progress all the dust that was under its smaller part. As it is a common opinion that a shot fired through a waterspout will break it, I tried to break this little whirlwind by striking my whip frequently through it, but without any effect. Soon after, it quitted the road and took to the woods, growing every moment larger and stronger, raising, instead of dust, the old, dry leaves with which the ground was thick covered, and making a great noise with them and the branches of the trees, bending some tall trees round in a circle swiftly and very surprisingly. Though the progressive motion of the whirl was not so swift but that a man on foot might have kept pace with it, the circular motion was amazingly rapid. By the leaves it was now filled with, I could plainly perceive that the current of air they were driven by moved upward in a spiral line. When I saw the trunks and bodies of large trees enveloped in the passing whirl, which continued entire after it had left them, I no longer wondered that my whip had no effect on it in its smaller state.

I accompanied it about three quarters of a mile, till some limbs of dead trees, broken off by the whirl, flying about and falling near me, made me more apprehensive of danger. Then I stopped, looking at the top of it as it went on, which was visible by means of the leaves contained in it for a very great height above the trees. Many of the leaves, as they got loose from the upper and widest part, were scattered in the wind; but so great was their height in the air that they appeared no bigger than flies. My son, who was by this time come up with me, followed the whirlwind till it left the woods and crossed an old tobacco field, where, finding neither dust nor leaves to take up, it gradually became invisible below as it went away over that field.

The course of the general wind then blowing was along with us as we traveled, and the progressive motion of the whirlwind was in a direction nearly opposite, though it did not keep a straight line, nor was its progressive motion uniform, it making little sallies on either hand as it went, proceeding sometimes faster and sometimes slower, and seeming sometimes for a few seconds almost stationary, then starting forward pretty fast again. When we rejoined the company, they were admiring the vast height of the leaves, now brought by the common wind over our heads. These leaves accompanied us as we traveled, some falling now and then round about us, and some not reaching the ground till we had gone near three miles from the place where we first saw the whirlwind begin. Upon my asking Colonel Tasker if such whirlwinds were common in Maryland, he answered pleasantly, "No, not at all common; but we got this on purpose to treat Mr. Franklin." And a very high treat it was, to,

Dear Sir,
Your affectionate friend,
and humble servant,

B. F.

Not Worth
the Whistle

When I was a child seven years old, my friends on a holiday filled my pocket with coppers. I went directly to a shop where they sold toys for children; and being charmed with the sound of a whistle that I met by the way in the hands of another boy, I voluntarily offered and gave all my money for one. I then came home and went whistling all over the house, much pleased with my whistle, but disturbing all the family. My brothers and sisters and cousins, understanding the bargain I had made, told me I had given four times as much for it as it was worth; put me in mind what good things I might have bought with the rest of my money; and laughed at me so much for my folly that I cried with vexation; and the reflection gave me more chagrin than the whistle gave me pleasure.

This, however, was afterward of use to me, the impression continuing on my mind; so that often, when I was tempted to buy some unnecessary thing, I said to myself, "Don't give too much for the whistle"; and so I saved my money.

As I grew up, came into the world, and observed the actions of men, I thought I met with many, very many, who *gave too much for the whistle*.

When I saw one too ambitious of court favor, sacrificing his time in attendance on levees, his repose, his liberty, his virtue, and perhaps his friends to attain it, I said to myself, "This man gives too much for his whistle."

When I saw another fond of popularity, constantly employing himself in political bustles, neglecting his own affairs and ruining them by that neglect, "He pays, indeed," said I, "too much for his whistle."

If I knew a miser who gave up every kind of comfortable living, all the pleasure of doing good to others, all the esteem of his fellow citizens, and the joys of benevolent friendship for the sake of accumulating wealth, "Poor man," said I, "you pay too much for your whistle."

When I met with a man of pleasure, sacrificing every laudable improvement of the mind or of his fortune, to mere corporeal sensations, and ruining his health in their pursuit, "Mistaken man," said I, "you are providing pain for yourself, instead of pleasure; you give too much for your whistle."

If I see one fond of appearance or fine clothes, fine houses, fine furniture, fine equipages, all above his fortune, for which he contracts debts and ends his career in a prison, "Alas!" say I, "he has paid dear, very dear, for his whistle."

When I see a beautiful, sweet-tempered girl married to an ill-natured brute of a husband, "What a pity," say I, "that she should pay so much for a whistle!"

In short, I conceive that a great part of the miseries of mankind are brought upon them by the false estimates they have made of the value of things, and by their *giving too much for their whistles*.

A New Look at the Indians

Savages we call them, because their manners differ from ours, which we think the perfection of civility; they think the same of theirs.

Perhaps if we could examine the manners of different nations with impartiality, we would find no people so rude as to be without rules of politeness; nor any so polite as not to have some remains of rudeness.

The Indian men, when young, are hunters and warriors; when old, counselors; for all their government is by the counsel or advice of the sages. There is no force; there are no prisons; no officers to compel obedience or inflict punishment. Hence they generally study oratory, the best speaker having the most influence. The Indian women till the ground, dress the food, nurse and bring up the children, and preserve and hand down to posterity the memory of public transactions. These employments of men and women are accounted natural and honorable. Having few artificial wants, they have abundance of leisure for improvements of conversation. Our laborious manner of life compared with theirs they esteem slavish and base; and the learning on which we value ourselves they regard as frivolous and useless. An instance of this occurred at the Treaty of Lancaster in Pennsylvania, Anno 1774, between the government of Virginia and the Six Nations.[1] After the principal business was settled, the commissioner from Virginia acquainted the Indians by a speech that there was at Williamsburg a college with a fund for educating Indian youth, and that if the chiefs of the Six Nations would send down half a dozen of their sons to that college, the government would take care that they should be well provided for and instructed in all the learning of the white people. It is one of the Indian rules of politeness not to answer a public proposition the same day that it is made. They think it would be treating it as a light matter and that they show it respect by taking time to consider it, as of a matter important. They therefore deferred their answer till the day following, when their speaker began by expressing their deep sense of kindness of the Virginia government in making them that offer. "For we know," says he, "that you highly esteem the kind of learning taught in those colleges, and that the maintenance of our young men while with you would be very expensive to you. We are convinced, therefore, that you mean to do us good by your proposal, and we thank you heartily. But you who are wise must know that different nations have different conceptions of things; and you will therefore not take it amiss if our ideas of this kind of education happen not to be the same with yours. We have had some experience of it. Several of our young people were formerly brought up at the colleges of the northern provinces. They were instructed in all your sciences. But when they came back to us, they were bad runners, ignorant of every means of living in the woods, unable to bear either cold or hunger, knew neither how to build a cabin, take a deer, or kill an enemy, spoke our language imperfectly; were therefore neither fit for hunters, warriors, nor counselors. They were totally good for nothing. We are however not the less obliged by your kind offer, though we decline accepting it; and to show our grateful sense of it, if the gentlemen of Virginia will send us a dozen of their sons, we will take great

[1] **Six Nations:** a league of six Iroquois Indian tribes that lived chiefly in New York State.

care of their education, instruct them in all we know, and make *men* of them."

The politeness of these savages in conversation is indeed carried to excess, since it does not permit them to contradict or deny the truth of what is asserted in their presence. By this means they indeed avoid disputes, but then it becomes difficult to know their minds or what impression you make upon them. The missionaries who have attempted to convert them to Christianity all complain of this as one of the great difficulties of their mission. The Indians hear with patience the truths of the gospel explained to them, and give their usual tokens of assent and approbation: you would think they were convinced. No such matter. It is mere civility.

A Swedish minister, having assembled the chiefs of the Susquehanna Indians,[1] made a sermon to them, ac-

---

[1] **Susquehanna** (sus·kwe·HAN·ah) **Indians:** a tribe of Indians living along the Susquehanna River in Pennsylvania.

quainting them with the principal historical facts on which our religion is founded, such as the fall of our first parents by eating an apple, the coming of Christ to repair the mischief, his miracles and suffering, etc. When he had finished, an Indian orator stood up to thank him. "What you have told us," says he, "is all very good. It is indeed bad to eat apples. It is better to make them all into cider. We are much obliged by your kindness in coming so far to tell us those things which you have heard from your mothers. In return I will tell you some of those we have heard from ours.

"In the beginning our fathers had only the flesh of animals to subsist on, and if their hunting was unsuccessful, they were starving. Two of our young hunters, having killed a deer, made a fire in the woods to broil some parts of it. When they were about to satisfy their hunger, they beheld a beautiful young woman descend from the clouds and seat herself on that hill which you see yonder among the blue mountains. They said to each other, 'It is a spirit that perhaps has smelled our broiling venison and wishes to eat of it: let us offer some to her.'

"They presented her with the tongue; she was pleased with the taste of it and said, 'Your kindness shall be rewarded. Come to this place after thirteen moons, and you shall find something that will be of great benefit in nourishing you and your children to the latest generations.'

"They did so, and to their surprise found plants they had never seen before, but which from that ancient time have been constantly cultivated among us to our great advantage. Where her right hand had touched the ground, they found maize; where her left hand had touched it, they found kidney beans; and where her backside had sat on it, they found tobacco."

The good missionary, disgusted with this idle tale, said, "What I delivered to you were sacred truths; but what you tell me is mere fable, fiction, and falsehood." The Indian, offended, replied, "My brother, it seems your friends have not done you justice in your education. They have not well instructed you in the rules of common civility. You saw that we who understand and practice these rules believed all your stories; why do you refuse to believe ours?"

THE FACT IS—

1. Tell three observations Franklin made about this whirlwind.

2. Why did Franklin stop following the whirlwind?

3. In the story of the whistle, Franklin discusses people's sense of values. What are some of the examples of bad bargains?

4. Have you ever "given too much for the whistle"? Write a paper telling how you profited from the experience.

5. Are there times in life when we find that we have given too much for the whistle, whether we want to or not? Give an example from your own experience of such a time.

6. Name three differences in the way the Indians and the colonists lived.

7. What was the Indian way of acting on a public proposal?

8. Why did the Indians refuse the offer to send their young men to the college at Williamsburg?

9. What are some of the things the Indians thought an educated man should be able to do?

FRANKLIN AS A SCIENTIST

1. "The rest of the company stood looking after it [the whirlwind], but my curiosity being stronger, I followed it. . . ." What does this sentence tell about Franklin?

2. In a modern encyclopedia, read an article on whirlwinds. Compare the facts given in the encyclopedia with Franklin's observations. Then write a paper with the title "How Good a Scientist Was Benjamin Franklin?"

3. Try watching something very carefully—a storm, a pet, a man at work, an experiment. Then write your observations in a letter to a friend.

"NO PEOPLE SO RUDE...."

1. How did the Indian and the missionary differ in their reaction to each other's story? Although Franklin was a Christian, his sympathies appear to be with the Indian. Why?

2. The white frontiersmen claimed that the Indians were thieves and liars. Getting your evidence from Franklin's essay, defend the Indians from these charges.

3. What remarks and conclusions of Franklin's make him sound like an ideal ambassador to the United Nations? Write a short speech that Franklin might deliver regarding a current international problem.

4. Try to find some more information about the customs and way of life of the American Indians. The class might work in committees to find out about the government, religion, art, and daily life of various tribes. Were they savages or were they civilized? Discuss this question.

WORDS TO REMEMBER: sagacity and civil

No word picture of Franklin is complete without the word *sagacity* (sah·GAS·ih·tee). From his studies of men and of books and from his varied experiences, Franklin developed sagacity, which is good judgment and practical wisdom. He was sagacious (wise) in his recommendations for improving Philadelphia and in his advice in Poor Richard's sayings.

We can tell that Franklin was very conscious of people's manners, for he often used the words *civil* and *civilities* in his writings. A civil person is one who shows respect for others in his speech and actions. A civil answer is a courteous answer, and civil behavior is polite behavior. Civilities are acts of courtesy. Is "civil disobedience" a contradiction in terms? Discuss the connection between *civil* and *civilization*.

Sayings
of
Poor Richard

To build up his printing business, Franklin wrote an almanac under the name of "Richard Saunders"—Poor Richard. The famous sayings were originally fillers, items just the right length to chink the spaces around monthly calendars and zodiac readings.

1. One today is worth two tomorrows.

2. A truly great man will neither trample on a worm nor sneak to an emperor.

3. If you would know the value of money, go and try to borrow some; he that goes a-borrowing goes a-sorrowing.

4. He that is of the opinion that money will do everything may well be suspected of doing everything for money.

5. If a man empties his purse into his head, no man can take it away from him. An investment in knowledge always pays the best interest.

6. People who are wrapped up in themselves make small packages.

7. The eye of a master will do more work than both his hands.

8. Fools make feasts, and wise men eat them.

9. 'Tis hard for an empty bag to stand upright.

10. He that lives on hope will die fasting.

11. If a man could have half his wishes, he would double his troubles.

12. They that won't be counseled can't be helped.

13. Love your neighbor; yet don't pull down your hedge.

14. Three may keep a secret if two of them are dead.

15. Glass, china, and reputation are easily cracked and never well mended.

16. The rotten apple spoils his companions.

17. Be slow in choosing a friend, slower in changing.

18. Fish and visitors smell in three days.

THE FACT IS—

1. Which of Poor Richard's sayings show that Franklin valued time?
2. Which sayings show his sense of humor?
3. Do any sayings give advice that you consider valuable to your life?

POOR RICHARD'S PIRACY

"Franklin, in his always piratical manner, stole this and rephrased." A modern biographer of Franklin points out that Franklin borrowed and altered sayings of Titan Leeds, a Philadelphia rival.

Franklin defended his "piracy" by admitting it. He had Poor Richard say: "Not a tenth part of the wisdom was my own, . . . but rather the gleanings I had made of the sense of all ages and nations." Do you think this is a good defense? Why, or why not?

THINKING ABOUT FRANKLIN

1. Benjamin Franklin has been called the first typical American. Do you agree? Write a short poem in which, by citing specific examples, you either defend or attack the thesis.

2. If Franklin were living today, do you think he would have been able to do as many different things as he did two centuries ago? Discuss.

3. One biographer wrote that Franklin "matched wits with the best brains of Europe and never lost a trick." Read a recent historical or biographical work to see just how good a diplomat Franklin was. Write a short paper on this subject.

4. The Franklin exploit that most amazed Europeans was his experiment with the kite and the key. Can you see why? Read about the experiment and discover what—if anything—Franklin added to the world's knowledge of electricity.

5. Most of Franklin's vocations depended on the skillful use of language—printer, Poor Richard, autobiographer, constitutional delegate, diplomat, and so forth. Write a short paper on Franklin and "the power of words."

6. Do you know of any of today's leaders who have a wide variety of interests and accomplishments? See if you can find one whose range approximates Franklin's, and write a short paper praising your subject as a modern Benjamin Franklin.

The Dark World of Poe

Edgar Allan Poe was considered by many of his friends and biographers to be possessed of a devil—not a sly mischievous devil, nor yet a huge devil striding through the world and leading men to their destruction, but rather a melancholy fallen angel who spent his life mourning a lost paradise.

Poe was born in Boston, Massachusetts, on January 19, 1809, less than a month before Abraham Lincoln was born in a log cabin in Kentucky. Poe's parents were actors. When he was one year old, Poe's father abandoned his young wife and three small children. When Poe was two, his mother died of tuberculosis.

Then he had what seemed an extraordinary turn of good luck: he became the ward of John Allan, a wealthy and childless tobacco merchant in Richmond, Virginia. Poe's every wish was gratified; it was generally believed that Allan would adopt Poe and leave him his large fortune. At first Poe justified the devotion which Allan's wife lavished upon him. He became a superb horseman, a strong swimmer, a brilliant and conscientious student. He read French and Latin fluently and claimed some knowledge of German and Italian. His intense interest in music led to the lyric quality of his best poetry. His one year at the University of Virginia and a later year at West Point were marked by continued scholastic brilliance but marred by escapades and opposition to authority.

Shortly before dismissal from West Point for "gross neglect of duty" and disobedience of orders," Poe wrote Allan a letter in which he correctly prophesied his life of poverty and sorrow: "My future life (which, thank God, will not endure long) must be passed in indigence and sickness." Mrs. Allan had died, depriving Poe of her love and indulgence. John Allan, whose remarriage to a younger wife killed Poe's last hope of being his heir, practically threw Poe out and left him to fend for himself, refusing to pay even the trifling personal expenses that the Spartan life of a cadet demanded. At the University of Virginia, Poe had begun to gamble and to drink heavily. Poe gambled not for excitement but because he hoped to make the little money he needed—but he always lost. So began the pathetic slide that was to end in his early death.

It was as if Poe's heredity had overtaken the good fortune of his surroundings. His father had drunk himself out of work, his mother had always played wildly emotional parts, his sister was considered mad, and his brother was a tubercular drunkard. Poe found little comfort in love. His courtship of a Baltimore girl ended when her parents intervened and married her off to a wealthy suitor. Later he married a pretty, ineffectual cousin. They were so poor that there was no furniture in the house, and the teenage wife slept on a straw mattress wrapped in Poe's overcoat with a cat in her arms to keep warm. She died of tuberculosis at the age of twenty-four. Toward the end of his life, Poe again courted his first love, who was by this time a wealthy widow. According to romantic legend, they planned to be married, but before the wedding Poe died.

So great was Edgar Allan Poe's talent and so varied his capabilities that, in spite of his catalog of personal misfortune and woe, he was able to leave us one of our greatest literary legacies. He has left some of our finest poetry, some of our greatest short stories. He was a brilliant editor, a clear-headed and influential literary critic.

Like most creative geniuses, Poe wrote from a combination of his own personal experience, his reading, his study of the works of other men of talent, and the total effect of all these on his own unique imagination.

As a boy on the plantation of his foster parents, he had sat enthralled as he heard weird stories of voodoo, apparitions, corpses, and graveyards. He knew the languages of chemistry, botany, medicine, music, and mathematics. He read widely in learned magazines from other parts of the world. All of these different experiences were transformed by the magic of his imagination and made part of our experience by the precise craftsmanship of his art.

Of particular appeal to us, living in the space age, is Poe's tremendous interest in astronomy. He had his own telescope and stayed up for many hours scanning the skies. He shared our hope of reaching the moon. After reading a book on astronomy, he said, "I longed to give free rein . . . in depicting my daydreams about the scenery of the moon." In his own way he did just this in his story "The Unparalleled Adventure of One Hans Pfall."

It is the final irony of Poe's life that he perhaps has been appreciated in other countries more than he has here at home—particularly in France and Russia. The French must have been pleased that Poe, who invented the detective story, made his detective in "Murders in the Rue Morgue," "The Purloined Letter," and other tales a Frenchman, C. Auguste Dupin. Perhaps they were attracted to the "far-out" aspect of his horror stories, but probably the main reason the French liked Poe was the mysterious, musical quality of his poetry. As for the Russians, they discovered Poe even before the French did, and the great pianist and composer Sergei Rachmaninoff set "The Bells" to a tone poem for chorus and orchestra.

But in his own country, too, Edgar Allan Poe is honored for his unique imagination, the distinction of his varied talents, and the precision of his craftsmanship. His poetry is loved for its romantic, mystic aloofness and its spellbinding rhythm, qualities shown in the opening stanza of "Annabel Lee." His most memorable tales drive the reader on, impelled by a single mood, often horror or mystery, as in "The Black Cat" and "The Sphinx." Poe died in poverty, rags, sickness, and filth, not even dimly aware that the world would rate him high among the first and foremost of America's poets and storytellers.

Eldorado

Gaily bedight,
A gallant knight,
In sunshine and in shadow,
Had journeyed long,
Singing a song,   5
In search of Eldorado.

But he grew old—
This knight so bold—
And o'er his heart a shadow
Fell as he found   10
No spot of ground
That looked like Eldorado.

And, as his strength
Failed him at length,
He met a pilgrim shadow—   15
"Shadow," said he,
"Where can it be—
This land of Eldorado?"

"Over the Mountains
Of the Moon,   20
Down the Valley of the Shadow,
Ride, boldly ride,"
The shade replied,—
"If you seek for Eldorado!"

Annabel Lee

It was many and many a year ago,
  In a kingdom by the sea,
That a maiden there lived whom you may know
  By the name of Annabel Lee;
And this maiden she lived with no other thought   5
  Than to love and be loved by me.

I was a child and *she* was a child,
  In this kingdom by the sea,
But we loved with a love that was more than love,
  I and my Annabel Lee,   10
With a love that the wingèd seraphs of heaven
  Coveted her and me.

And this was the reason that, long ago,
  In this kingdom by the sea,
A wind blew out of a cloud, chilling   15
  My beautiful Annabel Lee;
So that her highborn kinsmen came
  And bore her away from me,
To shut her up in a sepulcher
  In this kingdom by the sea.   20

The angels, not half so happy in heaven,
  Went envying her and me;
Yes, that was the reason (as all men know,
  In this kingdom by the sea)
That the wind came out of the cloud by night,   25
  Chilling and killing my Annabel Leè.

But our love it was stronger by far than the love
  Of those who were older than we,
  Of many far wiser than we;
And neither the angels in heaven above,   30

EDGAR ALLAN POE   **385**

Nor the demons down under the sea,
Can ever dissever my soul from the soul
    Of the beautiful Annabel Lee:

For the moon never beams, without bringing me dreams
    Of the beautiful Annabel Lee;   35
And the stars never rise, but I feel the bright eyes
    Of the beautiful Annabel Lee;
And so, all the nighttide, I lie down by the side
Of my darling, my darling, my life and my bride
    In her sepulcher there by the sea,   40
    In her tomb by the sounding sea.

THE FASCINATION OF THE UNKNOWN

1. What is "Eldorado"? What is the literal meaning of the word, and what is its figurative meaning? Consult a large dictionary.

2. Each of the four stanzas of "Eldorado" has a different mood or atmosphere. In the first stanza expressions like "gaily," "gallant knight," "in sunshine," and "singing a song" indicate that the mood is light, happy, optimistic. Describe the mood of each of the other three stanzas. What words or phrases determine the mood in these three stanzas?

3. In one or two well-constructed sentences, state the meaning of this poem. What is the poet saying?

4. In "Annabel Lee" the phrase "this kingdom by the sea" is repeated several times. What other phrases are repeated? Explain why.

5. The last stanza of "Annabel Lee" establishes the poet's feeling or mood. Select several words and phrases which convey this mood, and write a statement showing how.

6. Poe once wrote that the death of a beautiful woman is "the most poetical topic in the world." Many critics disagree; they say that such fascination with death is unhealthy. What do you think?

A WORD TO REMEMBER: covet

Covet means "to wish for enviously," "to feel great desire for what belongs to another." In the poem, the angels of heaven "coveted her and me" (line 12). What did they covet and why? Explain how the word might apply to you.

The Black Cat

"A guilty conscience never feels secure." In this horror story a man experiences the truth of this statement.

For the most wild yet most homely narrative which I am about to pen, I neither expect nor solicit belief. Mad indeed would I be to expect it in a case where my very senses reject their own evidence. Yet, mad am I not, and very surely do I not dream. But tomorrow I die, and today I would unburden my soul. My immediate purpose is to place before the world plainly, succinctly, and without comment a series of mere household events. In their conse-

EDGAR ALLAN POE   **387**

quences these events have terrified, have tortured, have destroyed me. Yet I will not attempt to expound them. To me they have presented little but horror; to many they will seem less terrible than baroques. Hereafter, perhaps, some intellect may be found which will reduce my phantasm to the commonplace—some intellect more calm, more logical, and far less excitable than my own, which will perceive in the circumstances I detail with awe nothing more than an ordinary succession of very natural causes and effects.

From my infancy I was noted for the docility and humanity of my disposition. My tenderness of heart was even so conspicuous as to make me the jest of my companions. I was especially fond of animals, and was indulged by my parents with a great variety of pets. With these I spent most of my time and never was so happy as when feeding and caressing them. This peculiarity of character grew with my growth and in my manhood I derived from it one of my principal sources of pleasure. To those who have cherished an affection for a faithful and sagacious dog, I need hardly be at the trouble of explaining the nature or the intensity of the gratification thus derivable. There is something in the unselfish and self-sacrificing love of a brute, which goes directly to the heart of him who has had frequent occasion to test the paltry friendship and gossamer fidelity of mere *man*.

I married early and was happy to find in my wife a disposition not uncongenial with my own. Observing my partiality for domestic pets, she lost no opportunity of procuring those of the most agreeable kind. We had birds, goldfish, a fine dog, rabbits, a small monkey, and *a cat*.

This latter was a remarkably large and beautiful animal, entirely black, and sagacious to an astonishing degree. In speaking of his intelligence, my wife, who at heart was not a little tinctured with superstition, made frequent allusion to the ancient popular notion which regarded all black cats as witches in disguise. Not that she was ever *serious* upon this point, and I mention the matter at all for no better reason than that it happens just now to be remembered.

Pluto—this was the cat's name—was my favorite pet and playmate. I alone fed him, and he attended me wherever I went about the house. It was even with difficulty that I could prevent him from following me through the streets.

Our friendship lasted in this manner for several years, during which my general temperament and character, through the instrumentality of the fiend Intemperance, had (I blush to confess it) experienced a radical alteration for the worse. I grew day by day more moody, more irritable, more regardless of the feelings of others. I suffered myself to use intemperate language to my wife. At length I even offered her personal violence. My pets, of course, were made to feel the change in my disposition. I not only neglected but ill-used them. For Pluto, however, I still retained sufficient regard to restrain me from maltreating him as I made no scruple of maltreating the rabbits, the monkey, or even the dog when by accident or through affection they came in my way. But my disease grew upon me, for what disease is like alcohol! and at length even Pluto, who was now becoming old and consequently somewhat peevish—even Pluto began to experience the effects of my ill temper.

One night, returning home much intoxicated from one of my haunts about town, I fancied that the cat avoided my presence. I seized him, when, in his fright at my violence, he inflicted a slight wound upon my hand with his teeth. The fury of a demon instantly possessed me. I knew myself no longer. My original soul seemed at once to take its flight from my body, and a more than fiendish malevolence, gin-nurtured, thrilled every fiber of my frame. I took from my waistcoat pocket a penknife, opened it, grasped the poor beast by the throat, and deliberately cut one of its eyes from the socket! I blush, I burn, I shudder while I pen the damnable atrocity.

When reason returned with the morning, when I had slept off the fumes of the night's debauch, I experienced a sentiment half of horror, half of remorse, for the crime of which I had been guilty, but it was at best a feeble and equivocal feeling, and the soul remained untouched. I again plunged into excess and soon drowned in wine all memory of the deed.

In the meantime the cat slowly recovered. The socket of the lost eye presented, it is true, a frightful appearance, but he no longer appeared to suffer any pain. He went about the house as usual but, as might be expected, fled in extreme terror at my approach. I had so much of my old heart left as to be at first grieved by this evident dislike on the part of a creature which had once so loved me. But this feeling soon gave place to irritation. And then came, as if to my final and irrevocable overthrow, the spirit of Perverseness. Of this spirit, philosophy takes no account. Yet I am not more sure that my soul lives than I am that perverseness is one of the primitive impulses of the human heart, one of the indivisible primary faculties, or sentiments, which give direction to the character of man. Who has not a hundred times found himself committing a vile or a silly action for no other rea-

son than because he knows he should *not?* Have we not a perpetual inclination in the teeth of our best judgment to violate that which is *law,* merely because we understand it to be such? This spirit of Perverseness, I say, came to my final overthrow. It was this unfathomable longing of the soul *to vex itself,* to offer violence to its own nature, to do wrong for the wrong's sake only that urged me to continue and finally to consummate the injury I had inflicted upon the unoffending brute. One morning in cool blood I slipped a noose about its neck and hung it to the limb of a tree; hung it with the tears streaming from my eyes and with the bitterest remorse at my heart; hung it *because* I knew that it had loved me and *because* I felt it had given me no reason of offense; hung it *because* I knew that in so doing I was committing a sin, a deadly sin that would so jeopardize my immortal soul as to place it—if such a thing were possible—even beyond the reach of the infinite mercy of the Most Merciful and Terrible God.

On the night of the day on which this cruel deed was done, I was aroused from sleep by the cry of fire. The curtains of my bed were in flames. The whole house was blazing. It was with great difficulty that my wife, a servant, and myself made our escape from the conflagration. The destruction was complete. My entire worldly wealth was swallowed up, and I resigned myself thenceforward to despair.

I am above the weakness of seeking to establish a sequence of cause and effect between the disaster and the atrocity. But I am detailing a chain of facts and wish not to leave even a possible link imperfect. On the day succeeding the fire, I visited the ruins. The walls, with one exception, had fallen in. This exception was found in a compart-

ment wall, not very thick, which stood about the middle of the house and against which had rested the head of my bed. The plastering had here in great measure resisted the action of the fire—a fact which I attributed to its having been recently spread. About this wall a dense crowd was collected, and many persons seemed to be examining a particular portion of it with very minute and eager attention. The words "strange!" "singular!" and other similar expressions excited my curiosity. I approached and saw as if graven in bas-relief upon the white surface the figure of a gigantic *cat*. The impression was given with an accuracy truly marvelous. There was a rope about the animal's neck.

When I first beheld this apparition—for I could scarcely regard it as less—my wonder and my terror were extreme. But at length reflection came to my aid. The cat, I remembered, had been hung in a garden adjacent to the house. Upon the alarm of fire, this garden had been immediately filled by the crowd, by some one of whom the animal must have been cut from the tree and thrown, through an open window into my chamber. This had probably been done with the view of arousing me from sleep. The falling of other walls had compressed the victim of my cruelty into the substance of the freshly spread plaster, the lime of which, with the flames and the ammonia from the carcass, had then accomplished the portraiture as I saw it.

Although I thus readily accounted to my reason, if not altogether to my conscience, for the startling fact just detailed, it did not the less fail to make a deep impression upon my fancy. For months I could not rid myself of the phantasm of the cat, and during this period there came back into my spirit a half-sentiment that seemed, but was not, remorse. I went so far as to regret the loss of the animal and to look about me among the vile haunts which I now habitually frequented for another pet of the same species and of somewhat similar appearance with which to supply its place.

One night as I sat, half-stupefied, in a den of more than infamy, my attention was suddenly drawn to some black object reposing upon the head of one of the immense hogsheads of gin or of rum which constituted the chief furniture of the apartment. I had been looking steadily at the top of this hogshead for some minutes, and what now caused me surprise was the fact that I had not sooner perceived the object thereupon. I approached it and touched it with my hand. It was a black cat, a very large one, fully as large as Pluto and closely resembling him in every respect but one. Pluto had not a white hair upon any portion of his body, but this cat had a large although indefinite splotch of white covering nearly the whole region of the breast.

Upon my touching him, he immediately arose, purred loudly, rubbed against my hand, and appeared delighted with my notice. This, then, was the very creature of which I was in search. I at once offered to purchase it of the landlord; but this person made no claim to it, knew nothing of it, had never seen it before.

I continued my caresses, and when I prepared to go home, the animal evinced a disposition to accompany me. I permitted it to do so, occasionally stooping and patting it as I proceeded. When it reached the house, it domesticated itself at once and became immediately a great favorite with my wife.

For my own part, I soon found a dislike to it arising within me. This was just the reverse of what I had anticipated, but I know not how or why it was, its evident fondness for myself rather disgusted and annoyed. By slow degrees these feelings of disgust and annoyance rose into the bitterness of hatred. I avoided the creature, a certain sense of shame and the remembrance of my former deed of cruelty preventing me from physically abusing it. I did not for some weeks strike or otherwise violently ill use it, but gradually—very gradually—I came to look upon it with unutterable loathing, and to flee silently from its odious presence as from the breath of a pestilence.

What added, no doubt, to my hatred of the beast was the discovery on the morning after I brought it home that, like Pluto, it also had been deprived of one of its eyes. This circumstance, however, only endeared it to my wife, who, as I have already said, possessed in a high degree that humanity of feeling which had once been my distinguishing trait and the source of many of my simplest and purest pleasures.

With my aversion to this cat, however, its partiality for myself seemed to increase. It followed my footsteps with a pertinacity which it would be difficult to make the reader comprehend. Whenever I sat, it would crouch beneath my chair or spring upon my knees, covering me with its loathsome caresses. If I arose to walk, it would get between my feet and thus nearly throw me down or, fastening its long and sharp claws in my dress, clamber in this manner to my breast. At such times, although I longed to destroy it with a blow, I was yet withheld from so doing partly by a memory of my former crime, but chiefly—let me confess it at once— by absolute *dread* of the beast.

This dread was not exactly a dread of physical evil, and yet I should be at a loss how otherwise to define it. I am almost ashamed to own—yes, even in this felon's cell, I am almost ashamed to own—that the terror and horror with which the animal inspired me had been heightened by one of the merest chimeras it would be possible to conceive. My wife had called my attention, more than once to the character of the mark of white hair of which I have spoken and which constituted the sole visible difference between the strange beast and the one I had destroyed. The reader will remember that this mark, although large, had been originally very indefinite, but by slow degrees, degrees nearly imperceptible and which for a long time my reason struggled to reject as fanciful, it had at length seemed a rigorous distinctness of outline. It was now the representation of an object that I shudder to name, and for this, above all, I loathed and dreaded and would have rid myself of the monster *had I dared*—it was now, I say, the image of a hideous, of a ghastly thing—of the Gallows!—oh, mournful and terrible engine of horror and of crime, of agony and of death!

And now was I indeed wretched beyond the wretchedness of mere humanity. And *a brute beast*, whose fellow I had contemptuously destroyed—*a brute beast* to work out for *me*, for me, a man fashioned in the image of the High God, so much of insufferable woe! Alas! neither by day nor by night knew I the blessing of rest any more! During the former the creature left me no moment alone, and in the latter I started hourly from dreams of unutterable fear to find the hot breath of *the thing* upon my face, and its vast weight, an incarnate nightmare that I had no power to shake off, incumbent eternally upon my heart!

Beneath the pressure of torments such as these, the feeble remnant of the good within me succumbed. Evil thoughts became my sole intimates— the darkest and most evil of thoughts. The moodiness of my usual temper increased to hatred of all things and of all mankind, while from the sudden, frequent, and ungovernable outbursts of a fury to which I now blindly abandoned myself, my uncomplaining wife, alas! was the most usual and the most patient of sufferers.

One day she accompanied me upon some household errand into the cellar of the old building which our poverty compelled us to inhabit. The cat followed me down the steep stairs, and nearly throwing me headlong, exasperated me to madness. Uplifting an axe and forgetting in my wrath the childish dread which had hitherto stayed my hand, I aimed a blow at the animal which, of course, would have proved instantly fatal had it descended as I wished. But this blow was arrested by the hand of my wife. Goaded by the interference into a rage more than demoniacal, I withdrew my arm from her grasp and buried the axe in her brain. She fell dead upon the spot without a groan.

This hideous murder accomplished, I set myself forthwith and with entire deliberation to the task of concealing the body. I knew that I could not remove it from the house either by day or by night without the risk of being observed by the neighbors. Many projects entered my mind. At one period I thought of cutting the corpse into minute fragments and destroying them by fire. At another I resolved to dig a grave for it in the floor of the cellar. Again I deliberated about casting it in the well in the yard, about packing it in a box as if merchandise, with the usual arrangements, and so getting a porter to take it from the house. Finally I hit upon what

I considered a far better expedient than either of these. I determined to wall it up in the cellar.

For a purpose such as this, the cellar was well adapted. Its walls were loosely constructed and had lately been plastered throughout with a rough plaster which the dampness of the atmosphere had prevented from hardening. Moreover, in one of the walls was a projection, caused by a false chimney or fireplace, that had been filled up and made to resemble the rest of the cellar. I made no doubt that I could readily displace the bricks at this point, insert the corpse, and wall the whole up as before so that no eye could detect anything suspicious.

And in this calculation I was not deceived. By means of a crowbar, I easily dislodged the bricks, and having carefully deposited the body against the inner wall, I propped it in that position, while with little trouble I relaid the whole structure as it originally stood. Having procured mortar, sand, and hair with every possible precaution, I prepared a plaster which could not be distinguished from the old, and with this I very carefully went over the new brickwork. When I had finished, I felt satisfied that all was right. The wall did not present the slightest appearance of having been disturbed. The rubbish on the floor was picked up with the minutest care. I looked around triumphantly and said to myself, "Here at least, then, my labor has not been in vain."

My next step was to look for the beast which had been the cause of so much wretchedness, for I had at length firmly resolved to put it to death. Had I been able to meet with it at the moment, there could have been no doubt of its fate, but it appeared that the crafty animal had been alarmed at the violence of my previous anger and forbore to present itself in my present mood. It is impossible to describe or to imagine the deep, the blissful sense of relief which the absence of the detested creature occasioned in my bosom. It did not make its appearance during the night, and thus for one night at least, since its introduction into the house, I soundly and tranquilly slept, aye, *slept* even with the burden of murder upon my soul!

The second and the third day passed, and still my tormentor came not. Once again I breathed as a free man. The monster, in terror, had fled the premises forever! I should behold it no more! My happiness was supreme! The guilt of my dark deed disturbed me but little. Some few inquiries had been made, but these had been readily answered. Even a search had been instituted, but, of course, nothing was to be discovered. I looked upon my future felicity as secured.

Upon the fourth day of the assassination, a party of the police came very unexpectedly into the house and proceeded again to make rigorous investigation of the premises. Secure, however, in the inscrutability of my place of concealment, I felt no embarrassment whatever. The officers bade me accompany them in their search. They left no nook or corner unexplored. At length, for the third or fourth time, they descended into the cellar. I quivered not in a muscle. My heart beat calmly as that of one who slumbers in innocence. I walked the cellar from end to end. I folded my arms upon my bosom and roamed easily to and fro. The police were thoroughly satisfied and prepared to depart. The glee at my heart was too strong to be restrained. I burned to say if but one word by way of triumph and to render doubly sure their assurance of my guiltlessness.

"Gentlemen," I said at last, as the party ascended the steps. "I delight to have allayed your suspicions. I wish you all health and a little more courtesy. By the by, gentlemen, this—this is a very well constructed house." (In the rabid desire to say something easily, I scarcely knew what I uttered at all.) "I may say an *excellently* well constructed house. These walls—are you going, gentlemen?—these walls are solidly put together." And here, through the mere frenzy of bravado, I rapped heavily, with a cane which I held in my hand, upon that very portion of the brickwork behind which stood the corpse of the wife of my bosom.

But may God shield and deliver me from the fangs of the archfiend! No sooner had the reverberation of my blows sunk into silence than I was answered by a voice from within the tomb! by a cry at first muffled and broken, like the sobbing of a child, and then quickly swelling into one long, loud, and continuous scream, utterly anomalous and inhuman—a howl—a wailing shriek, half of horror and half of triumph, such as might have arisen only out of hell, conjointly from the throats of the damned in their agony and of the demons that exult in the damnation.

Of my own thoughts it is folly to speak. Swooning, I staggered to the opposite wall. For one instant the party upon the stairs remained motionless, through extremity of terror and of awe. In the next a dozen stout arms were toiling at the wall. It fell bodily. The corpse, already greatly decayed and clotted with gore, stood erect before the eyes of the spectators. Upon its head, with red extended mouth and solitary eye of fire, sat the hideous beast whose craft had seduced me into murder and whose informing voice had consigned me to the hangman. I had walled the monster up within the tomb!

THE FACT IS—

1. What led the narrator to unburden his soul by telling his story?

2. Who or what is the fiend Intemperance?

3. What is Perverseness?

4. What was "graven in bas-relief" upon the one remaining wall of the house after the fire?

5. What drove the narrator to kill his wife?

6. What gave him self-confidence when the police appeared?

"THE DISEASE OF AN EVIL CONSCIENCE"

1. The narrator values highly the friendship of animals, especially of a black cat. Have you ever been deeply attached to an animal? If so, describe and illustrate your friendship with this animal.

2. Pluto was the cat's name. In mythology who was Pluto? Write a careful paragraph explaining how this name applies to the events of the story.

3. "Who has not a hundred times found himself committing a vile or a silly action for no other reason than because he knows he should *not?*" Illustrate this statement from your own experiences. Did conscience make you suffer? How?

4. Explain how superstition contributes to the effectiveness of this story.

5. This story is typical of Poe's tales of horror and terror. Write a paragraph explaining why you think one of these two characteristics is more important than the other.

A WORD TO REMEMBER: incumbent

Poe describes "an incarnate nightmare" as "incumbent eternally upon my heart." *Incumbent* is an adjective meaning "lying or resting on something else"; "imposed as a duty: obligatory"; "bent over so as to rest on or touch an underlying surface." Which meaning applies in the quotation above? Write sentences illustrating the two other meanings.

This word *incumbent* is also a noun, as in "The present incumbent is running for reelection."

The Sphinx

An overactive imagination can destroy a man's sense of reality. See how fear and brooding affected one man.

During the dread reign of cholera in New York, I had accepted the invitation of a relative to spend a fortnight with him in the retirement of his *cottage ornée* on the banks of the Hudson. We had here around us all the ordinary means of summer amusement, and what with rambling in the woods, sketching, boating, fishing, bathing, music, and books, we should have passed the time pleasantly enough, but for the fearful intelligence which reached us every morning from the populous city. Not a day elapsed which did not bring us news of the decease of some acquaintance. Then as the fatality increased, we learned to expect daily the loss of some friend. At length we trembled at the approach of every messenger. The very air from the south seemed to us redolent with death. That palsying thought, indeed, took entire possession of my soul. I could neither speak, think, nor dream of anything else. My host was of a less excitable temperament and, although greatly depressed in spirits, exerted himself to sustain my own. His richly philosophical intellect was not at any time affected by unrealities. To the substances of terror, he was sufficiently alive, but of its shadows he had no apprehension.

His endeavors to arouse me from the condition of abnormal gloom into which I had fallen were frustrated in great measure by certain volumes which I had found in his library. These were of a character to force into germination whatever seeds of hereditary superstition lay latent in my bosom. I had been reading these books without his knowledge, and thus he was often at a loss to account for the forcible impressions which had been made upon my fancy.

A favorite topic with me was the popular belief in omens—a belief which at this one epoch of my life I was almost seriously disposed to defend. On this subject we had long and animated discussions, he maintaining the utter groundlessness of faith in such matters, I contending that a popular sentiment arising with absolute spontaneity—that is to say, without apparent traces of suggestion—had in itself the unmistakable elements of truth and was entitled to much respect.

The fact is that soon after my arrival at the cottage, there had occurred to myself an incident so entirely inexplicable, and which had in it so much of the portentous character that I might well have been excused for regarding it as an omen. It appalled and at the same time

so confounded and bewildered me that many days elapsed before I could make up my mind to communicate the circumstances to my friend.

Near the close of an exceedingly warm day, I was sitting, book in hand, at an open window, commanding, through a long vista of the riverbanks, a view of a distant hill, the face of which nearest my position had been denuded, by what is termed a landslide, of the principal portion of its trees. My thoughts had been long wandering from the volume before me to the gloom and desolation of the neighboring city. Uplifting my eyes from the page, they fell upon the naked face of the hill and upon an object —upon some living monster of hideous conformation which very rapidly made its way from the summit to the bottom, disappearing finally in the dense forest below. As this creature first came in sight, I doubted my own sanity—or at least the evidence of my own eyes, and many minutes passed before I succeeded in convincing myself that I was neither mad nor in a dream. Yet when I describe the monster (which I distinctly saw and calmly surveyed through the whole period of its progress), my readers, I fear, will feel more difficulty in being convinced of these points than even I did myself.

Estimating the size of the creature by comparison with the diameter of the large trees near which it passed—the few giants of the forest which had escaped the fury of the landslide—I concluded it to be far larger than any ship of the line in existence. I say ship of the line because the shape of the monster suggested the idea—the hull of one of our seventy-four's might convey a very tolerable conception of the general outline. The mouth of the animal was situated at the extremity of a proboscis some sixty or seventy feet in length and about as thick as the body of an ordinary ele-

phant. Near the root of this trunk was an immense quantity of black, shaggy hair, more than could have been supplied by the coats of a score of buffaloes; and projecting from the hair downwardly and laterally sprang two gleaming tusks not unlike those of the wild boar, but of infinitely greater dimension. Extending forward, parallel with the proboscis and on each side of it, was a gigantic staff, thirty or forty feet in length, formed seemingly of pure crystal and in shape a perfect prism—it reflected in the most gorgeous manner the rays of the declining sun. The trunk was fashioned like a wedge with the apex to the earth. From it there were outspread two pairs of wings, each wing nearly one hundred yards in length, one pair being placed above the other, and all thickly covered with metal scales, each scale apparently some ten or twelve feet in diameter. I observed that the upper and lower tiers of wings were connected by a strong chain. But the chief peculiarity of this horrible thing was the representation of a *Death's head,* which covered nearly the whole surface of its breast and which was as accurately traced in glaring white upon the dark ground of the body as if it had been there carefully de-

signed by an artist. While I regarded this terrific animal, and more especially the appearance on its breast, with a feeling of horror and awe, with a sentiment of forthcoming evil which I found it impossible to quell by any effort of the reason, I perceived the huge jaws at the extremity of the proboscis suddenly expand themselves, and from them there proceeded a sound so loud and so expressive of woe that it struck upon my nerves like a knell, and as the monster disappeared at the foot of the hill, I fell at once, fainting, to the floor.

Upon recovering, my first impulse, of course, was to inform my friend of what I had seen and heard, and I can scarcely explain what feeling of repugnance it was which in the end operated to prevent me.

At length, one evening some three or four days after the occurrence, we were sitting together in the room in which I had seen the apparition, I occupying the same seat at the same window and he lounging on a sofa near at hand. The association of the place and time impelled me to give him an account of the phenomenon. He heard me to the end, at first laughed heartily, and then lapsed into an excessively grave demeanor, as if my insanity was a thing beyond suspicion. At this instant I again had a distinct view of the monster, to which, with a shout of absolute terror, I now directed his attention. He looked eagerly, but maintained that he saw nothing, although I designated minutely the course of the creature as it made its way down the naked face of the hill.

I was now immeasurably alarmed, for I considered the vision either as an omen of my death, or, worse, as the forerunner of an attack of mania. I threw myself passionately back in my chair and for some moments buried my face in my hands. When I uncovered my eyes, the apparition was no longer visible.

My host, however, had in some degree resumed the calmness of his demeanor and questioned me very rigorously in respect to the conformation of the visionary creature. When I had fully satisfied him on this head, he sighed deeply, as if relieved of some intolerable burden, and went on to talk with what I thought a cruel calmness of various points of speculative philosophy which had heretofore formed subjects of discussion between us. I remember his insisting very especially (among other things) upon the idea that the principal source of error in all human investigations lay in the liability of the understanding to underrate or to overvalue the importance of an object through mere misadmeasurement of its propinquity. "To estimate properly, for example," he said, "the influence to be exercised on mankind at large by the thorough diffusion of democracy, the distance of the epoch at which such diffusion may possibly be accomplished should not fail to form an item in the estimate. Yet can you tell me one writer on the subject of government who has ever thought this particular branch of the subject worthy of discussion at all?"

He here paused for a moment, stepped to a bookcase, and brought forth one of the ordinary synopses of natural history. Requesting me then to exchange seats with him that he might the better distinguish the fine print of the volume, he took my armchair at the window and, opening the book, resumed his discourse very much in the same tone as before.

"But for your exceeding minuteness," he said, "in describing the monster, I might never have had it in my power to demonstrate to you what it was. In the first place, let me read to you a schoolboy account of the genus *Sphinx*, of the family *Crepuscularia*, of the order *Lepidoptera*, of the class of *Insecta*—or insects. The account runs thus:

Four membranous wings covered with little colored scales of metallic appearance; mouth forming a rolled proboscis, produced by an elongation of the jaws, upon the sides of which are found the rudiments of mandibles and downy palpi; the inferior wings retained to the superior by a stiff hair; antennae in the form of an elongated club, prismatic; abdomen pointed, the Death's-headed Sphinx has occasioned much terror among the vulgar, at times, by the melancholy kind of cry which it utters and the insignia of death which it wears upon its corselet.

He here closed the book and leaned forward in the chair, placing himself accurately in the position which I had occupied at the moment of beholding "the monster."

"Ah, here it is," he presently exclaimed. "It is reascending the face of the hill, and a very remarkable-looking creature I admit it to be. Still, it is by no means so large or so distant as you imagined it, for the fact is that as it wriggles its way up this thread which some spider has wrought along the window sash, I find it to be about the sixteenth of an inch distant from the pupil of my eye."

THE FACT IS—

1. What disaster provided a background for the experience related in this story?

2. What pastime encouraged the narrator's natural tendency to believe in omens?

3. How did the narrator determine the size of the "monster" he thought he saw on the hillside?

4. What is a *Death's head?*

5. How did the narrator's friend lead him to realize that what he saw was not a monster?

DO YOU BELIEVE IN FANTASY?

1. The narrator was stricken by an "abnormal gloom." What combination of circumstances caused this condition?

2. The narrator looked out upon the "naked face of the hill" (page 397) from his armchair by the window. How does this view contribute to making the appearance of a "living monster" acceptable? In a careful paragraph, explain the relationship between the background and the events of the story.

3. What is a delusion? How does it differ from an illusion? Which word better describes the narrator's state of mind? Explain.

4. How does the paragraph from "a schoolboy account of the genus *Sphinx*" explain the conclusion of this tale? What final impression of the narrator does it give you?

A WORD TO REMEMBER: portentous

The word *portentous* means "threatening, eliciting amazement or wonder," as in the expression "a portentous sign or omen." What is an antonym for this word? Use both "portentous" and its antonym in original sentences.

Alone

From childhood's hour I have not been
As others were—I have not seen
As others saw—I could not bring
My passions from a common spring—
From the same source I have not taken   5
My sorrow—I could not awaken
My heart to joy at the same tone—
And all I lov'd—*I* lov'd alone.
Then—in my childhood—in the dawn
Of a most stormy life—was drawn   10
From ev'ry depth of good and ill
The mystery which binds me still—
From the torrent, or the fountain—
From the red cliff of the mountain—
From the sun that round me roll'd   15
In its autumn tint of gold—
From the lightning in the sky
As it pass'd me flying by—
From the thunder, and the storm—
And the cloud that took the form   20
(When the rest of Heaven was blue)
Of a demon in my view.

ONE MAN'S CONFESSION

1. Poe says that from childhood "I could not bring/My passions from a common spring—" (lines 3 and 4). Explain the meaning of this quotation. What one quality of his character does it suggest?

2. "The mystery which binds me still—" (line 12). The "mystery" is his awareness of being alone in life. Why do you think he feels this way?

3. "Of a demon in my view" (line 22). What is the demon? How does it indicate the poet's outlook on life? What is the predominant mood of the poem?

4. This poem is a brief self-portrait of Poe. In a careful paragraph which includes at least one quotation from the poem, describe this man.

THINKING ABOUT EDGAR ALLAN POE

1. The two short stories in this unit have certain qualities in common, such as terror. Name two or three other characteristics which would apply to them, and arrange the characteristics in order of their effectiveness.

2. Poe's use of the narrator in his short stories is effective. Why? Try your hand at writing a story with the "I" an imaginary person—not you.

3. Poe's poems are remembered more for their musical qualities than for their meaning; for example, the musical sound in line 34 of "Annabel Lee" is caused, in part, by rhyming of the words "beams" and "dreams." Which one of the three poems in this unit is most musical? How did the poet create this effect?

4. Which of the ideas in these three poems do you think might apply to human experience in general? Choose two of the poems and state the idea which might apply to many men.

5. Poe said that one chief purpose of literature is to give pleasure. Do these stories and poems illustrate successfully this statement? Write a paragraph to explain how and why.

Melville and Whitman, Voyagers in Imagination

In 1820, when Herman Melville and Walt Whitman were a year old, a British writer scoffed, "Who reads an American book?" When Melville and Whitman died seventy years later, almost every literate person in the world read American books. Two of the books most widely read—both now considered American epics—were *Moby Dick,* a novel of the sea by Herman Melville, and *Leaves of Grass,* a volume of poems by Walt Whitman.

Americans are a people on the move. A better life is always over the next hill; adventure is around the next bend of the river. Faraway places have cast a spell, sometimes only because they were "far away"; sometimes because "far away" represented a dream of new worlds and new freedoms, perhaps of Paradise.

Herman Melville

No call has been more persistent than the cry of the sea. From the first Phoenician sailor who set out to explore the mysteries of what Homer called the "wine-dark sea" to the fisherman who tends his lobster pots off the coast of Maine, the sea, peaceful and turbulent, savagely destructive and richly bountiful, has cast a spell. Herman Melville was a man who heeded the call of the sea. For him the sea always represented romance and mystery; and the deeper meanings of his greatest novel, *Moby Dick,* will always excite the speculation of literary critics and the curiosity of the ordinary person who reads it for its exciting whale hunt and its stormy human beings.

Growing up near the New York waterfront, Melville had been filled with sailor's stories from his childhood, and at nineteen he signed on a ship bound for Europe. Here he had to learn the arduous duties of a man who had chosen to serve under sail. In tempestuous winds and in the rigors of biting cold, he had to learn to climb 100 feet into the rigging of a ship, to edge himself out on a slender rope, and to take in or let out canvas which might be coated with ice. He had to bear the rough toughness of his shipmates and to endure the humiliation of being cheated out of his entire salary by the captain. The brutal realism of this life only strengthened Melville's romantic notions about the sea.

After teaching school a few months, Melville again found the call of the sea too much. He went to New Bedford, Massachusetts, and signed on the crew of the whaler *Acushnet.* Much more time aboard a whaler was spent in weathering the storms—both natural and human—and in the bloody, slimy work of cutting up the whale than in exciting chases or close contests with the savage prey. Conditions became so bad that in the Marquesas Islands seven of the crew, including Melville, jumped the ship. Here in the South Pacific, Melville found himself among a handsome, primitive people, whose innocence and simple life he admired. You will find his picture of earthly paradise in faraway places both in *Typee,* the partly fictional story of his stay in the Marquesas, and in *Omoo,* which tells of the once lovely and unspoiled island of Tahiti.

Later Melville was to come to feel that man would never find this ideal life even though he might seek it forever.

In the obsessive search by Captain Ahab for the white whale in *Moby Dick*, we see how terrible a quest for an ideal can be.

After marrying the daughter of a prominent jurist, Melville spent three years in New York. Then, for thirteen years he lived with his family on a farm in the beautiful Berkshire hills near Pittsfield, Massachusetts. During a part of that time, Nathaniel Hawthorne was his neighbor; Melville's masterpiece, *Moby Dick,* was dedicated to Hawthorne. Both men, living essentially solitary lives away from their former literary circles, derived pleasure and stimulation from each other. Although Melville in 1863 took a relatively obscure job in the New York customs house, he did not remove himself from the "actions and passions" of his fellowmen who were completely caught up in the Civil War.

The romantic views of Melville's novels have no place in his poetry. He was one of the first of our poets and literary artists to write about war the way most of us know it: as a grinding, dirty business of machines as well as men. He was a prophet foretelling the mean, bloody mechanics of future wars, as in these lines from a poem about the fight between the *Monitor* and the *Merrimac,* the first battle between ironclad ships:

> The ringing of those plates on plates
> Still ringeth round the world—
> The clangor of that blacksmiths' fray
>> The anvil-din
>> Resounds this message from the
>> Fates. . . .

Walt Whitman

Whitman, who was almost an exact contemporary of Melville, was more deeply involved in the Civil War. In search of his brother who had been wounded, he came to a battlefield torn

by the Army of the Potomac and the Army of Northern Virginia. Once he found his brother and had a chance to see at first hand how crude hospitals were in those days before antiseptics and antibiotics, he spent his time working in hospitals and in trying to help the suffering, helpless wounded men. Some of Walt Whitman's most moving prose and poetry reflects his deep personal compassion for the agony of these soldiers. Because of this experience, he became personally involved with the Union cause and developed a deep feeling for Lincoln and for the anguish he endured as President of a divided country.

Perhaps only Whitman and Lincoln had his vision of the *whole* of America: its plains, its mountains, its rivers, its lakes, and the encompassing sea. Whitman's most important volume of poetry bore the title *Leaves of Grass*, because grass was to him a symbol of the richness and fullness, the variety and opportunity of our life. And it was *our life* which he celebrated with a verve and enthusiasm no American poet has ever matched. No part of our landscape, our bodies, or our lives failed to evoke in Whitman reverence and exhilaration.

One might think that a man who wanted to celebrate all of America would choose to express his feelings by conventional means, ways his fellow Americans would readily understand because they were the familiar rhymes and rhythms of classical poetry, but Whitman sought out the new and unconventional not only in his subjects but also in his methods. He wrote unrhymed verse. He wrote what came to be called *free verse*. Whitman's poetry is not the for-

mal rhyme and music of meter that you find in Poe, but the poetry of free, strong images that make you see, and perhaps more importantly, make you feel. He wrote free verse deliberately because he believed that poetry—like land, air, and water—should be for all the people in a democracy. At first only a select few (Emerson was an outstanding example) appreciated his poetry; it was not for many years that he attained the unique place he occupies among all American poets. Whitman's joy in all the natural aspects of life seemed to be reflected in his personality. Most of those who knew him, whether they were intellectuals or common people, were attracted to him and found him to be hearty and happy, a good fellow.

In common with many serious writers, Whitman made his living first as a newspaperman, working in Brooklyn, on Long Island, and in New York. In his early years he did not show that love for the whole country which was to make his reputation. After he traveled to New Orleans, where he edited the New Orleans *Crescent*, he journeyed widely throughout the United States. During these travels he had an opportunity to meet all kinds of men and women, most of them forced to work long and hard to earn a living. Before he traveled throughout the United States, he tended to dress very much as a dude; but when he got back to New York, he always dressed in rough clothing and tried to identify himself as much as possible with the ordinary person living an ordinary life. He met and made friends with laborers, carpenters, seamen, and others who lived by long hours and hard work.

MELVILLE

From Redburn

He Is Initiated

Redburn went to sea to "cut his mother's apron strings" and to live the life of adventure, danger, glamor boys so often dream about. He found that dreams are one thing; life another.

By the time I got back to the ship, everything was in an uproar. The pea-jacket man was there, ordering about a good many men in the rigging, and people were bringing off chickens, and pigs, and beef, and vegetables from the shore. Soon after, another man, in a striped calico shirt, a short blue jacket, and beaver hat, made his appearance, and went to ordering about the man in the big pea jacket. And at last the captain came up the side and began to order about both of them.

These two men turned out to be the first and second mates of the ship.

Thinking to make friends with the second mate, I took out an old tortoise-shell snuffbox of my father's, in which I had put a piece of Cavendish tobacco, to look sailorlike, and offered the box to him very politely. He stared at me a moment and then exclaimed, "Do you think we take snuff aboard here, youngster? No, no, no time for snuff-taking at sea. Don't let the 'old man' see that snuffbox; take my advice and pitch it overboard as quick as you can."

I told him it was not snuff, but tobacco, when he said he had plenty of tobacco of his own and never carried any such nonsense about him as a tobacco box. With that, he went off about his business and left me feeling foolish enough. But I had reason to be glad he had acted thus. For if he had not, I think I should have offered my box to the chief mate, who in that case, from what I afterward learned of him, would have knocked me down or done something else equally uncivil.

As I was standing looking around me, the chief mate approached in a great hurry about something, and seeing me in his way, cried out, "Ashore with you, you young loafer! There's no stealings here. Sail away, I tell you, with that shooting jacket!"

Upon this I retreated, saying that I was going out in the ship as a sailor.

"A sailor!" he cried, "a barber's clerk, you mean; *you* going out in the ship? what, in that jacket? Hang me, I hope the old man hasn't been shipping any more greenhorns like you—he'll make a shipwreck of it if he has. But this is the way nowadays; to save a few dollars in seamen's wages, they think nothing of shipping a parcel of farmers and clodhoppers and baby boys. What's your name, Pillgarlic?"

"Redburn," said I.

"A pretty handle to a man, that; scorch you to take hold of it; haven't you got any other?"

"Wellingborough," said I.

"Worse yet. Who had the baptizing of ye? Why didn't they call you Jack, or Jill, or something short and handy? But I'll baptize you over again. D'ye hear, sir, henceforth your name is *Buttons*. And now do you go, Buttons, and clean out that pigpen in the longboat; it has not been cleaned out since last voyage. And bear a hand about it, d'ye hear; there's them pigs there waiting to be put in. Come, be off about it, now."

Was this then the beginning of my sea career? set to cleaning out a pigpen, the very first thing?

But I thought it best to say nothing. I had bound myself to obey orders, and it was too late to retreat. So I only asked for a shovel, or spade, or something else to work with.

"We don't dig gardens here," was the reply; "dig it out with your teeth!"

After looking around, I found a stick and went to scraping out the pen, which was awkward work enough, for another boat called the "jolly-boat" was capsized right over the longboat, which brought them almost close together. These two boats were in the middle of the deck. I managed to crawl inside of the longboat; and after barking my shins against the seats and bumping my head a good many times, I got along to the stern, where the pigpen was.

While I was hard at work, a drunken sailor peeped in and cried out to his comrades, "Look here, my lads, what sort of a pig do you call this? Hallo! inside there! What are you 'bout there? Trying to stow yourself away to steal a passage to Liverpool? Out of that! out of that, I say." But just then the mate came along and ordered this drunken rascal ashore.

The pigpen being cleaned out, I was set to work picking up some shavings which lay about the deck; for there had been carpenters at work on board. The mate ordered me to throw these shavings into the longboat at a particular place between two of the seats. But as I found it hard work to push the shavings through in that place, and as it looked wet there, I thought it would be better for the shavings, as well as myself, to thrust them where there was a larger opening and a dry spot. While I was thus employed, the mate, observing me, exclaimed with an oath, "Didn't I tell you to put those shavings somewhere else? Do what I tell you, now, Buttons, or mind your eye!"

Stifling my indignation at his rudeness, which by this time I found was my only plan, I replied that that was not so good a place for the shavings as that which I myself had selected, and asked him to tell me *why* he wanted me to put them in the place he designated. Upon this, he flew into a terrible rage, and without explanation reiterated his order like a clap of thunder.

This was my first lesson in the discipline of the sea, and I never forgot it. From that time I learned that sea officers never give reasons for anything they order to be done. It is enough that they command it, so that the motto is *"Obey orders, though you break owners."*

I now began to feel very faint and sick again, and longed for the ship to be leaving the dock; for then I made no doubt we would soon be having something to eat. But as yet, I saw none of the sailors on board, and as for the men at work in the rigging, I found out that they were "riggers," that is, men living ashore who worked by the day in getting ships ready for sea. And this I found out to my cost, for yielding to the kind blandishment of one of these riggers, I had swapped away my jackknife with him for a much poorer one of his own, thinking to secure a sailor friend for the voyage.

At last I watched my chance, and while people's backs were turned, I seized a carrot from several bunches lying on deck, and clapping it under the skirts of my shooting jacket, went forward to eat it; for I had often eaten raw carrots, which taste something like chestnuts. This carrot refreshed me a good deal, though at the expense of a little pain in my stomach. Hardly had I disposed of it when I heard the chief mate's voice crying out for "Buttons." I ran after him, and received an order to go aloft and "slush down the maintop mast."

This was all Greek to me, and after receiving the order, I stood staring about me, wondering what it was that was to be done. But the mate had turned on his heel and made no explanations. At length I followed after him and asked what I must do.

"Didn't I tell you to slush down the maintop mast?" he shouted.

"You did," said I, "but I don't know what that means."

"Green as grass! A regular cabbage head!" he exclaimed to himself. "A fine time I'll have with such a greenhorn aboard. Look you, youngster. Look up to that long pole there—d'ye see it? That piece of a tree there, you timberhead—well—take this bucket here, and go up the rigging—that rope ladder there—do you understand?—and dab this slush all over the mast, and look out for your head if one drop falls on deck. Be off now, Buttons."

The eventful hour had arrived. For the first time in my life, I was to ascend a ship's mast. Had I been well and hearty, perhaps I should have felt a little shaky at the thought; but as I was then, weak and faint, the bare thought appalled me.

But there was no hanging back. It would look like cowardice, and I could not bring myself to confess that I was suffering for want of food; so rallying again, I took up the bucket.

It was a heavy bucket with strong iron hoops, and might have held per-

haps two gallons. But it was only half-full now of a sort of thick lobbered gravy, which I afterward learned was boiled out of the salt beef used by the sailors. Upon getting into the rigging, I found it was no easy job to carry this heavy bucket up with me. The rope handle of it was so slippery with grease that although I twisted it several times about my wrist, it would be still twirling round and round, and slipping off. Spite of this, however, I managed to mount as far as the "top," the clumsy bucket half the time straddling and swinging about between my legs, and in momentary danger of capsizing. Arrived at the "top," I came to a dead halt, and looked up. How to surmount that overhanging impediment completely posed me for the time. But at last, with much straining, I contrived to place my bucket in the "top"; and then, trusting to Providence, swung myself up after it. The rest of the road was comparatively easy; though whenever I incautiously looked down

toward the deck, my head spun round so from weakness that I was obliged to shut my eyes to recover myself. I do not remember much more. I only recollect my safe return to the deck.

In a short time the bustle of the ship increased; the trunks of cabin passengers arrived, and the chests and boxes of the steerage passengers, besides baskets of wine and fruit for the captain.

At last we cast loose, and swinging out into the stream, came to anchor, and hoisted the signal for sailing. Everything, it seemed, was on board but the crew, who in a few hours after, came off, one by one, in Whitehall boats, their chests in the bow, and themselves lying back in the stern like lords; and showing very plainly the complacency they felt in keeping the whole ship waiting for their lordships.

"Ay, ay," muttered the chief mate, as they rolled out of their boats and swaggered on deck, "it's your turn now, but it will be mine before long. Yaw about while you may, my hearties; I'll do the yawing after the anchor's up."

Several of the sailors were very drunk, and one of them was lifted on board insensible by his landlord, who carried him down below and dumped him into a bunk. And two other sailors, as soon as they made their appearance, immediately went below to sleep off the fumes of their drink.

At last, all the crew being on board, word was passed to go to dinner fore and aft, an order that made my heart jump with delight, for now my long fast would be broken. But though the sailors, surfeited with eating and drinking ashore, did not then touch the salt beef and potatoes which the black cook handed down into the forecastle, and though this left the whole allowance to me, to my surprise I found that I could eat little or nothing, for now I only felt deadly faint, but not hungry.

He Calls on the Captain

What reminded me most forcibly of my ignominious condition was the widely altered manner of the captain toward me. I had thought him a fine, funny gentleman, full of mirth and good humor and good will to seamen, and one who could not fail to appreciate the difference between me and the rude sailors among whom I was thrown. Indeed, I had made no doubt that he would in some special manner take me under his protection and prove a kind friend and benefactor to me; as I had heard that some sea captains are fathers to their crew. And so they are; but such fathers as Solomon's precepts tend to make—severe and chastising fathers, fathers whose sense of duty overcomes the sense of love, and who every day, in some sort, play the part of Brutus, who ordered his son away to execution, as I have read in our old family Plutarch.

Yes, I thought that Captain Riga, for Riga was his name, would be attentive and considerate to me and strive to cheer me up and comfort me in my lonesomeness. I did not even deem it at all impossible that he would invite me down into the cabin of a pleasant night to ask me questions concerning my parents and prospects in life; besides obtaining from me some anecdotes touching my great-uncle, the illustrious senator; or give me a slate and pencil, and teach me problems in navigation; or perhaps engage me at a game of chess. I even thought he might invite me to dinner on a sunny Sunday and help me plentifully to the nice cabin fare, as knowing how distasteful the salt beef and pork and hard biscuit of the forecastle must at first be to a boy like me, who had always lived ashore and at home.

And I could not help regarding him with peculiar emotions, almost of tenderness and love, as the last visible link in the chain of associations which bound me to my home. For, while yet in port, I had seen him and Mr. Jones, my brother's friend, standing together and conversing; so that from the captain to my brother there was but one intermediate step; and my brother and mother and sisters were one.

And this reminds me how often I used to pass by the places on deck where I remembered Mr. Jones had stood when we first visited the ship lying at the wharf; and how I tried to convince myself that it was indeed true that he had stood there, though now the ship was so far away on the wide Atlantic Ocean, and he perhaps was walking down Wall Street or sitting reading the newspaper in his counting room, while poor I was so differently employed.

When two or three days had passed without the captain's speaking to me in any way or sending word into the forecastle that he wished me to drop into the cabin to pay my respects, I began to think whether I should not make the first advances, and whether indeed he did not expect it of me, since I was but a boy, and he a man; and perhaps that might have been the reason why he had not spoken to me yet, deeming it more proper and respectful for me to address him first. I thought he might be offended, too, especially if he were a proud man, with tender feelings. So one evening a little before sundown, in the second dogwatch, when there was no more work to be done, I concluded to call and see him.

After drawing a bucket of water, and having a good washing to get off some of the chicken-coop stains, I went down into the forecastle to dress myself as neatly as I could. I put on a white shirt in place of my red one, and got into a pair of cloth trousers instead of my duck ones, and put on my new pumps, and then carefully brushing my shooting jacket, I put that on over all; so that upon the whole I made quite a genteel figure, at least for a forecastle, though I would not have looked so well in a drawing room.

When the sailors saw me thus employed, they did not know what to make of it, and wanted to know whether I was dressing to go ashore. I told them no, for we were then out of sight of land; but that I was going to pay my respects to the captain. Upon which they all laughed and shouted, as if I were a simpleton; though there seemed nothing so very simple in going to make an evening call upon a friend. Then some of them tried to dissuade me, saying I was green and raw; but Jackson, who sat looking on, cried out with a hideous grin, "Let him go, let him go, men—he's a nice boy. Let him go. The captain has some nuts and raisins for him." And so he was going on when one of his violent fits of coughing seized him and he almost choked.

As I was about leaving the forecastle, I happened to look at my hands, and seeing them stained all over of a deep yellow, for that morning the mate had set me to tarring some strips of canvas for the rigging, I thought it would never do to present myself before a gentleman that way. So for want of kids, I slipped on a pair of woolen mittens, which my mother had knit for me to carry to sea. As I was putting them on, Jackson asked me whether he shouldn't call a carriage; and another bade me not forget to present his best respects to the skipper. I left them all tittering, and coming on deck was passing the cookhouse when the old cook called after me, saying I had forgot my cane.

But I did not heed their impudence, and was walking straight toward the cabin door on the quarter-deck when the chief mate met me. I touched my hat and was passing him, when, after staring at me till I thought his eyes would burst out, he all at once caught me by the collar and with a voice of thunder wanted to know what I meant by playing such tricks aboard a ship that he was mate of? I told him to let go of me or I would complain to my friend the captain, whom I intended to visit that evening. Upon this he gave me such a whirl around that I thought the Gulf Stream was in my head, and then shoved me forward, roaring out I know not what. Meanwhile the sailors were all standing around the windlass looking aft, mightily tickled.

Seeing I could not effect my object that night, I thought it best to defer it for the present; and returning among the sailors, Jackson asked me how I had found the captain and whether the next time I went, I would not take a friend along and introduce him.

The upshot of this business was that before I went to sleep that night, I felt well satisfied that it was not customary for sailors to call on the captain in the cabin, and I began to have an inkling of the fact that I had acted like a fool; but it all arose from my ignorance of sea usages.

And here I may as well state that I never saw the inside of the cabin during the whole interval that elapsed from our sailing till our return to New York, though I often used to get a peep at it through a little pane of glass set in the house on deck just before the helm, where a watch was kept hanging for the helmsman to strike the half-hours by with his little bell in the binnacle,[1] where the compass was. And it used to

---

[1] **binnacle** (BIN·a·k'l): a stand containing the ship's compass.

be the great amusement of the sailors to look in through the pane of glass when they stood at the wheel, and watch the proceedings in the cabin, especially when the steward was setting the table for dinner, or the captain was lounging over a decanter of wine on a little mahogany stand, or playing the game called solitaire, at cards, of an evening.

The day following my attempt to drop in at the cabin, I happened to be making fast a rope on the quarter-deck when the captain suddenly made his appearance, promenading up and down and smoking a cigar. He looked very good-humored and amiable, and it being just after his dinner, I thought that this, to be sure, was just the chance I wanted.

I waited a little while, thinking he would speak to me himself, but as he did not, I went up to him and began by saying it was a very pleasant day, and hoped he was very well. I never saw a man fly into such a rage. I thought he was going to knock me down. But after standing speechless awhile, he all at once plucked his cap from his head and threw it at me. I don't know what impelled me, but I ran to the lee scuppers where it fell, picked it up, and gave it to him with a bow; then the mate came running up and thrust me forward again; and after he had got me as far as the windlass, he wanted to know whether I was crazy or not, for if I was, he would put me in irons right off and have done with it.

But I assured him I was in my right mind and knew perfectly well that I had been treated in the most rude and ungentlemanly manner both by him and Captain Riga. Upon this he rapped out a great oath and told me if I ever repeated what I had done that evening or ever again presumed so much as to lift my hat to the captain, he would tie me into the rigging and keep me there un-

til I learned better manners. "You are very green," said he, "but I'll ripen you." Indeed this chief mate seemed to have the keeping of the dignity of the captain, who, in some sort, seemed too dignified personally to protect his own dignity.

I thought this strange enough, to be reprimanded and charged with rudeness for an act of common civility. However, seeing how matters stood, I resolved to let the captain alone for the future, particularly as he had shown himself so deficient in the ordinary breeding of a gentleman. And I could hardly credit it that this was the same man who had been so very civil and polite and witty when Mr. Jones and I called upon him in port.

But this astonishment of mine was much increased when, some days after, a storm came upon us and the captain rushed out of the cabin in his nightcap and nothing else but his shirt on; and leaping up on the poop, began to jump up and down and curse and swear and call the men aloft all manner of hard names, just like a common loafer in the street.

Besides all this, too, I noticed that while we were at sea, he wore nothing but old shabby clothes, very different from the glossy suit I had seen him in at our first interview, and after that on the steps of the City Hotel, where he al-ways boarded when in New York. Now he wore nothing but old-fashioned snuff-colored coats with high collars and short waists; and faded, short-legged pantaloons, very tight about the knees; and vests that did not conceal his waistbands, owing to their being so short, just like a little boy's. And his hats were all caved in and battered, as if they had been knocked about in a cellar, and his boots were sadly patched. Indeed, I began to think that he was but a shabby fellow after all, particularly as his whiskers lost their gloss and he went days together without shaving, and his hair, by a sort of miracle, began to grow of a pepper and salt color, which might have been owing, though, to his discontinuing the use of some kind of dye while at sea. I put him down as a sort of impostor, and while ashore, a gentleman on false pretenses. For no gentleman would have treated another gentleman as he did me.

THE FACT IS—

1. What were Redburn's first three tasks on board the ship?

2. Why did Redburn feel sick and faint before the ship sailed?

3. Why did Redburn decide to make his social call on the captain? What happened?

BEFORE THE MAST

1. Redburn started his new job with very little preparation and no idea of what to expect or how to conduct himself. Tell about some of your experiences in a new job or situation.

2. The headlines say that juvenile delinquency is on the rise. If men like Captain Riga were in control of young people, do you think the problem would increase or lessen? Give the reasons for your opinion.

3. Suppose you were a newspaper reporter posing as a seaman on Captain Riga's ship. Write the story you would submit to your newspaper about life on board the ship and the treatment of sailors.

From Typee

A Day in
the Typee Valley

Have you ever dreamed of living on a tropical island in the South Seas? In *Typee,* Melville wrote about the simple life, the beautiful women and strong men he found when he lived in the Marquesas between voyages.

Nothing can be more uniform and undiversified than the life of the Typees. One tranquil day of ease and happiness follows another in quiet succession; and with these unsophisticated savages the history of a day is the history of a life. I will, therefore, as briefly as I can, describe one of our days in the valley.

To begin with the morning. We were not very early risers—the sun would be shooting his golden spikes above the Happar mountain ere I threw aside my tapa robe and, girding my long tunic about my waist, sallied out with Faya-way and Kory-Kory and the rest of the household, and bent my steps toward the stream. Here we found congregated all those who dwelt in our section of the valley, and here we bathed with them. The fresh morning air and the cool flowing waters put both soul and body in a glow, and after a half-hour employed in this recreation, we sauntered back to the house—Tinor and Marheyo gathering dry sticks by the way for firewood, some of the young men laying the coconut trees under contribution as they passed beneath them, while Kory-Kory played his outlandish pranks for my particular diversion, and Fayaway and I, not arm in arm to be sure, but sometimes hand in hand, strolled along with feelings of perfect charity for all the world and especial good will toward each other.

Our morning meal was soon prepared. The islanders are somewhat abstemious at this repast, reserving the more powerful efforts of their appetite to a later period of the day. For my own part, with the assistance of my valet, who always officiated as spoon on these occasions, I ate sparingly from one of Tinor's trenches of *poi-poi* which was devoted exclusively for my own use, being mixed with the milky meat of ripe coconut. A section of a roasted breadfruit, a small cake of *amar,* or a mess of *cokoo,* two or three bananas, or a *mawmee* apple, an *annuee,* or some other agreeable and nutritious fruit served from day to day to diversify the meal, which was finished off by tossing off the liquid contents of a young coconut or two.

While partaking of this simple repast, the inmates of Marheyo's house, after the style of the indolent Romans, reclined in sociable groups upon the divan of mats, and digestion was promoted by cheerful conversation.

After the morning meal was concluded, pipes were lighted, and among them my own especial pipe, a present from the noble Mehevi. The islanders, who only smoke a whiff or two at a time, and at long intervals, and who keep their pipes going from hand to hand continually, regarded my systematic smoking of four or five pipefuls of tobacco in succession as something quite wonderful. When two or three pipes had circulated freely, the company gradually broke up. Marheyo went to the little hut he was forever building. Tinor began to inspect her rolls of tapa or employed her busy fingers in plaiting grass mats. The girls anointed themselves with their fragrant oils, dressed their hair, or looked over their curious finery and compared together their ivory trinkets, fashioned out of boars' tusks or whales' teeth. The young men and warriors produced their spears, paddles, canoe gear, battle clubs, and war conchs, and occupied themselves in carving all sorts of figures upon them with pointed bits of shell or flint, and adorning them, especially the war conchs, with tassels of braided bark and tufts of human hair. Some, immediately after eating, threw themselves once more upon the inviting mats and resumed the employment of the previous night, sleeping as soundly as if they had not closed their eyes for a week. Others sallied out into the groves for the purpose of gathering fruit or fibers of bark and leaves, the last two being in constant requisition and applied to a hundred uses. A few, perhaps, among the girls, would slip into the woods after flowers or repair to the stream with small calabashes and coconut shells in order to polish them by friction with a smooth stone in the water. In truth these innocent people seemed to be at no loss for something to occupy their time; and it would be no light task to enumerate all their employments, or rather pleasures.

My own mornings I spent in a variety of ways. Sometimes I rambled about from house to house, sure of receiving a cordial welcome wherever I went, or from grove to grove, and from one shady place to another, in company with Kory-Kory and Fayaway and a rabble rout of merry young idlers. Sometimes I was too indolent for exercise, and accepting one of the many invitations I was continually receiving, stretched myself out on the mats of some hospitable dwelling and occupied myself pleasantly either in watching the proceedings of those around me or taking part in them myself. Whenever I chose to do the latter, the delight of the islanders was boundless, and there was always a throng of competitors for the honor of instructing me in any particular craft. I soon became quite an accomplished hand at making tapa— could braid a grass sling as well as the best of them—and once, with my knife, carved the handle of a javelin so exquisitely that I have no doubt to this day Karnoonoo, its owner, preserves it as a surprising specimen of my skill. As noon approached, all those who had wandered forth from our habitation began to return, and when midday was fairly come, scarcely a sound was to be heard in the valley: a deep sleep fell upon all. The luxurious siesta was hardly ever omitted, except by old Marheyo, who was so eccentric a character that he seemed to be governed by no fixed principles whatever, but, acting just according to the humor of the moment, slept, ate, or tinkered away at his little hut without regard to the proprieties of time or place. Frequently he might have been seen taking a nap in the sun at noonday, or a bath in the stream at midnight. Once I beheld him perched eighty feet from the ground in the tuft of a coconut tree, smoking, and often I saw him standing up to the waist in water, engaged in plucking out the stray hairs of his beard, using a piece of mussel shell for tweezers.

The noontide slumber lasted generally an hour and a half, very often longer, and after the sleepers had arisen from their mats, they again had recourse to their pipes, and then made preparations for the most important meal of the day.

I, however, like those gentlemen of leisure who breakfast at home and dine at their club, almost invariably, during my intervals of health, enjoyed the afternoon repast with the bachelor chiefs of the Ti, who were always rejoiced to see me, and lavishly spread before me all the good things which their larder afforded. Mehevi generally produced among other dainties a baked pig, an article which I have every reason to suppose was provided for my sole gratification.

The Ti was a right jovial place. It did my heart, as well as my body, good to visit it. Secure from female intrusion, there was no restraint upon the hilarity of the warriors, who, like the gentlemen of Europe after the cloth is drawn and the ladies retire, freely indulged their mirth.

After spending a considerable portion of the afternoon at the Ti, I usually found myself, as the cool of the evening came on, either sailing on the little lake with Fayaway or bathing in the waters of the stream with a number of the savages, who at this hour always repaired thither. As the shadows of night approached, Marheyo's household were once more assembled under his roof: tapers were lit, long and curious chants were raised, interminable stories were told (for which one present was little the wiser), and all sorts of social festivities served to while away the time.

One day, in company with Kory-Kory, I had repaired to the stream for the purpose of bathing when I observed a woman sitting upon a rock in the midst of the current and watching with the liveliest interest the gambols of something, which at first I took to be an uncommonly large species of frog that was sporting in the water near her.

Attracted by the novelty of the sight, I waded toward the spot where she sat, and could hardly credit the evidence of my senses when I beheld a little infant, the period of whose birth could not have extended back many days, paddling about as if it had just risen to the surface after being hatched into existence at the bottom. Occasionally the delighted parent reached out her hands toward it when the little thing, uttering a faint cry and striking out its tiny limbs, would sidle for the rock and the next moment be clasped to its mother's bosom. This was repeated again and again, the baby remaining in the stream about a minute at a time. Once or twice it made wry faces at swallowing a mouthful of water, and choked and spluttered as if on the point of strangling. At such times, however, the mother snatched it up, and by a process scarcely to be mentioned obliged it to eject the fluid. For several weeks afterward I observed this woman bringing her child down to the stream regularly every day in the cool of the morning and evening and treating it to a bath. No wonder that the South Sea Islanders are so amphibious a race, when they are thus launched into the water as soon as they see the light. I am convinced that it is as natural for a human being to swim as it is for a duck. And yet in civilized communities how many able-bodied individuals die, like so many drowning kittens, from the occurrence of the most trivial accidents!

Fishing Parties

There was no instance in which the social and kindly dispositions of the Typees were more forcibly evinced than in the manner they conducted their great fishing parties. Four times during my stay in the valley, the young men assembled near the full of the moon and went together on these excursions. As they were generally absent about forty-eight hours, I was led to believe that they went out toward the open sea, some distance from the bay. The Polynesians seldom use a hook and line, almost always employing large well-made nets, most ingeniously fabricated from the twisted fibers of a certain bark. I examined several of them which had been spread to dry upon the beach at Nuku-heva. They resemble very much our own seines, and I should think are very nearly as durable.

All the South Sea Islanders are passionately fond of fish; but none of them can be more so than the inhabitants of Typee. I could not comprehend, therefore, why they so seldom sought it in their waters, for it was only at stated times that the fishing parties were formed, and these occasions were always looked forward to with no small degree of interest.

During their absence the whole population of the place was in a ferment, and nothing was talked of but *pehee, pehee* (fish, fish). Toward the time when they were expected to return, the vocal telegraph was put into operation—the inhabitants, who were scattered throughout the length of the valley, leaped upon rocks and into trees, shouting with delight at the thoughts of the anticipated treat. As soon as the approach of the party was announced, there was a general rush of the men toward the beach, some of them remaining, however, about the Ti, in order to get matters in readiness for the reception of the fish, which were brought to the taboo groves in immense packages of leaves, each one of them being suspended from a pole carried on the shoulders of two men.

I was present at the Ti on one of these occasions, and the sight was most interesting. After all the packages had arrived, they were laid in a row under the veranda of the building and opened. The fish were all quite small, generally about the size of a herring, and of every variety of color. About one-eighth of the whole being reserved for the use of the Ti itself, the remainder was divided into numerous smaller packages, which were immediately dispatched in every direction to the remotest parts of the valley. Arrived at their destination, these were in turn portioned out and equally distributed among the various houses of each particular district. The fish were under a strict taboo until the distribution was completed, which seemed to be effected in the most impartial manner. By the operation of this system, every man, woman, and child in the vale were at one and the same time partaking of this favorite article of food.

Once I remember the party arrived at midnight, but the unseasonableness of the hour did not repress the impatience of the islanders. The carriers dispatched from the Ti were to be seen hurrying in all directions through the deep groves, each individual preceded by a boy bearing a flaming torch of dried coconut boughs, which from time to time was replenished from the materials scattered along the path. The wild glare of these enormous flambeaux, lighting up with a startling brilliancy the innermost recesses of the vale and seen moving rapidly along beneath the canopy of leaves, the savage shout of the excited messengers sounding the news of their approach, which was answered on all sides, and the strange appearance of their naked bodies, seen against the gloomy background, produced altogether an effect upon my mind that I shall long remember.

It was on this same occasion that Kory-Kory awakened me at the dead hour of night, and in a sort of transport communicated the intelligence con-

tained in the words *pehee perni* (fish come). As I happened to have been in a remarkably sound and refreshing slumber, I could not imagine why the information had not been deferred until morning; indeed, I felt very much inclined to fly into a passion and box my valet's ears; but on second thoughts I got quietly up, and on going outside the house was not a little interested by the moving illumination which I beheld.

When old Marheyo received his share of the spoils, immediate preparations were made for a midnight banquet; calabashes of *poi-poi* were filled to the brim, green breadfruit were roasted, and a huge cake of *amar* was cut up with a sliver of bamboo and laid out on an immense banana leaf.

At this supper we were lighted by several of the native tapers, held in the hands of young girls. These tapers are most ingeniously made. There is a nut abounding in the valley, called by the Typees *armor,* closely resembling our common horse chestnut. The shell is broken and the contents extracted whole. Any number of these are strung at pleasure upon the long elastic fiber that traverses the branches of the coconut tree. Some of these tapers are eight and ten feet in length, but being perfectly flexible, one end is held in a coil while the other is lighted. The nut burns with a fitful bluish flame, and the oil that it contains is exhausted in about ten minutes. As one burns down, the next becomes ignited, and the ashes of the former are knocked into a coconut shell kept for the purpose. This primitive candle requires continual attention and must be constantly held in the hand. The person so employed marks the lapse of time by the number of nuts consumed, which is easily learned by counting the bits of tapa distributed at regular intervals along the string.

I grieve to state so distressing a fact, but the inhabitants of Typee were in the habit of devouring fish much in the same way that a civilized being would eat a radish, and without any more previous preparation. They eat it raw: scales, bones, gills, and all the inside. The fish is held by the tail, and the head being introduced into the mouth, the animal disappears with a rapidity that would at first nearly lead one to imagine it had been launched bodily down the throat.

Raw fish! Shall I ever forget my sensations when I first saw my island beauty devour one? Oh, heavens! Fayaway, how could you ever have contracted so vile a habit? However, after the first shock had subsided, the custom grew less odious in my eyes, and I soon accustomed myself to the sight. Let no one imagine, however, that the lovely Fayaway was in the habit of swallowing great vulgar-looking fishes: oh, no; with her beautiful small hand she would clasp a delicate, little, golden-hued love of a fish and eat it as elegantly and as innocently as though it were a Naples biscuit. But, alas! it was after all a raw fish; and all I can say is that Fayaway ate it in a more ladylike manner than any other girl of the valley.

When in Rome, do as the Romans do, I held to be so good a proverb that being in Typee I made a point of doing as the Typees did. Thus I ate *poi-poi* as they did, I walked about in a garb striking for its simplicity, and I reposed on a community of couches, besides doing many other things in conformity with their peculiar habits. But the farthest I ever went in the way of conformity was on several occasions to regale myself with raw fish. These being remarkably tender and quite small, the undertaking was not so disagreeable in the main, and after a few trials I positively began to relish them; however, I subjected them to a slight operation with my knife previously to making my repast.

THE FACT IS—

1. How did the narrator spend his mornings in Typee?

2. Who was Fayaway? Who was Kory-Kory?

3. How did the natives of Typee learn to swim?

4. What foods were mentioned in the selection? How were these eaten?

5. After the fish was caught, how was it distributed?

SOUTH PACIFIC

1. What lessons for living do you think we could learn from the natives of the Typee valley? What could they learn from us that would benefit them?

2. The narrator described life on the island as "little else than an often interrupted and luxurious nap." What did he like and dislike about this way of life? Why do you suppose he decided to leave the island and return to the United States?

3. Melville decided that he would follow the customs of the islanders in accordance with the old saying, "When in Rome, do as the Romans do." What do you think of this idea? Are there any customs of the Typees which you would not have followed? Which ones? Why?

A WORD TO REMEMBER: taboo

When we say that something is taboo, we mean that it is forbidden. Although *taboo* was originally a Polynesian word meaning "sacred," its meaning has been broadened.

1. Describe one school taboo you have discovered.

2. Complete the sentence: One taboo at home that I like is ____.

3. Write a paragraph with the title "Taboos I Can Live Without."

WHITMAN

Whitman loved life and he loved people. He could spend hours on the beach listening to the pounding surf or swapping yarns with fishermen, and he was completely happy pushing his way through crowded city streets, in all the hustle and noise and confusion. Whitman's joy and zest for living is shown in these selections.

From *Song of Myself*

I think I could turn and live with animals, they are so placid and
    self-contained,
I stand and look at them long and long.

They do not sweat and whine about their condition,
They do not lie awake in the dark and weep for their sins,
They do not make me sick discussing their duty to God,   5
Not one is dissatisfied, not one is demented with the mania of own-
    ing things,
Not one kneels to another, nor to his kind that lived thousands of
    years ago,
Not one is respectable or unhappy over the whole earth.

. . . . .

I saw a marriage of the trapper in the open air in the far west, the
    bride was a red girl,
Her father and his friends sat near cross-legged and dumbly smok-
    ing, they had moccasins to their feet and large thick blankets
    hanging from their shoulders,   10
On a bank lounged the trapper, he was dressed mostly in skins, his
    luxuriant beard and curls protected his neck, he held his bride
    by the hand,
She had long eyelashes, her head was bare, her coarse straight
    locks descended upon her voluptuous limbs and reached to her
    feet.

When I Heard the Learned Astronomer

When I heard the learned astronomer,
When the proofs, the figures, were ranged in columns before me,
When I was shown the charts and diagrams, to add, divide, and
    measure them,
When I sitting heard the astronomer where he lectured with much
    applause in the lecture room,
How soon unaccountable I became tired and sick,   5
Till rising and gliding out I wandered off by myself,
In the mystical moist night air, and from time to time,
Looked up in perfect silence at the stars.

Miracles

Why, who makes much of a miracle?
As to me I know of nothing else but miracles,
Whether I walk the streets of Manhattan,
Or dart my sight over the roofs of houses toward the sky,
Or wade with naked feet along the beach just in the edge of the water,   5
Or stand under trees in the woods,
Or talk by day with anyone I love, or sleep in the bed at night with
    anyone I love,
Or sit at table at dinner with the rest,
Or look at strangers opposite me riding in the car,°
Or watch honeybees busy around the hive of a summer forenoon,   10
Or animals feeding in the fields,
Or birds, or the wonderfulness of insects in the air,
Or the wonderfulness of the sundown, or of stars shining so quiet
    and bright,
Or the exquisite delicate thin curve of the new moon in spring;

These with the rest, one and all, are to me miracles,   15
The whole referring, yet each distinct and in its place.

To me every hour of the light and dark is a miracle,
Every cubic inch of space is a miracle,
Every square yard of the surface of the earth is spread with the same,
Every foot of the interior swarms with the same.   20

To me the sea is a continual miracle,
The fishes that swim—the rocks—the motion of the waves—the
    ships with men in them,
What stranger miracles are there?

9. **car:** streetcar or railroad car.

ON FURTHER THOUGHT

Song of Myself

1. What qualities does the poet find attractive in animals? Does he find these qualities in most human beings?
2. What qualities does the poet find attractive in the marriage of the trapper and the Indian girl?
3. Although the first excerpt from "Song of Myself" is about animals and the second about people, it is logical to place them together. Why?

When I Heard the Learned Astronomer

1. Why did Whitman leave the astronomer's lecture?
2. Why did looking at the stars mean more to him than listening to the lecture?
3. Do you think the astronomer could have appreciated the stars as Whitman did? Discuss.

Miracles

Whitman lists a number of separate items which he calls miracles. Taking all together, what to him was a miracle?

TWO WRITERS IN WARTIME

"Glorious," "thrilling," "wondrous" may be how some writers describe war. To Melville and Whitman, both of whom lived through the American Civil War, although neither fought in it, the war was ghastly, terrible, a time of woe for fighting men, parents, and the country at large. From enlistment to the battlefield, from the hospital to the cemetery, the war meant for many Americans anxiety, hurt, death. Melville and Whitman tell us how they saw the Civil War; but Whitman concludes, "The real war will never get in the books." His reason may surprise you.

These three poems by Walt Whitman carry you from the excitement of recruiting in "Beat! Beat! Drums!" through the calm interlude of the bivouac to the final fearful moments as an army corps moves toward battle.

Beat! Beat! Drums!

WALT WHITMAN

Beat! beat! drums!—blow! bugles! blow!
Through the windows—through doors—burst like a ruthless force,
Into the solemn church, and scatter the congregation,
Into the school where the scholar is studying;
Leave not the bridegroom quiet—no happiness must he have now
    with his bride,   5
Nor the peaceful farmer any peace, plowing his field or gathering
    his grain,
So fierce you whir and pound, you drums—so shrill you bugles,
    blow.

Beat! beat! drums!—blow! bugles! blow!
Over the traffic of cities—over the rumble of wheels in the streets;
Are beds prepared for sleepers at night in the houses? no sleepers
    must sleep in those beds,   10

No bargainers' bargains by day—no brokers or speculations—
    would they continue?
Would the talkers be talking? would the singer attempt to sing?
Would the lawyer rise in the court to state his case before the judge?
Then rattle quicker, heavier drums—you bugles wilder blow.

Beat! beat! drums!—blow! bugles! blow!   15
Make no parley—stop for no expostulation,
Mind not the timid—mind not the weeper or prayer,
Mind not the old man beseeching the young man,
Let not the child's voice be heard, nor the mother's entreaties,
Make even the trestles to shake the dead where they lie awaiting
    the hearses,   20
So strong you thump O terrible drums—so loud you bugles blow.

Bivouac on a Mountainside

WALT WHITMAN

I see before me now a traveling army halting,
Below a fertile valley spread, with barns and the orchards of summer,
Behind, the terraced sides of a mountain, abrupt, in places rising
    high,
Broken, with rocks, with clinging cedars, with tall shapes dingily
    seen,
The numerous campfires scatter'd near and far, some away up on the
    mountain,   5
The shadowy forms of men and horses, looming, large-sized, flicker-
    ing,
And over all the sky—the sky! far, far out of reach, studded, breaking
    out, the eternal stars.

An Army Corps on the March

WALT WHITMAN

With its cloud of skirmishers in advance,
With now the sound of a single shot snapping like a whip, and now an
    irregular volley,
The swarming ranks press on and on, the dense brigades press on,
Glittering dimly, toiling under the sun—the dust-cover'd men,
In columns rise and fall to the undulations of the ground,   5
With artillery interspers'd—the wheels rumble, the horses sweat,
As the army corps advances.

BEFORE THE BATTLE

1. In "Beat! Beat! Drums!" what do you think the drums and bugles represent?

2. To make you hear the drums and bugles, Whitman has used a number of words that represent sounds. "Whir" (line 7) is one example. Select several of these sound words and explain how each one changes the sound of the drums or bugles.

3. This is a good poem to read aloud. Before you read, decide which lines should be read faster than others, and where the voice should be louder and more excited.

4. In "Bivouac on a Mountainside" and "An Army Corps on the March," Whitman conveys both the heat of the march and the comparative coolness of the campsite selected for the overnight rest. Which words or phrases in the first poem help you feel the coolness of the campsite? which in the second, the heat of the march?

5. Could either picture shown in these two poems apply to a modern army? Why, or why not?

At the battle of Shiloh, Tennessee, General U. S. Grant rallied the Union army after an initial rout and drove the Confederates from the field. The battle of Malvern Hill was the climax of a series of battles on the Virginia Peninsula. During the Seven Days' Battles, the Confederates under General Robert E. Lee forced the invading Union army under General George B. McClellan away from Richmond, the Confederate capital.

Shiloh

A Requiem

(April, 1862)

HERMAN MELVILLE

Skimming lightly, wheeling still,
  The swallows fly low
Over the field in clouded days,
  The forest-field of Shiloh—
Over the field where April rain   5
Solaced the parched ones stretched in pain
Through the pause of night
That followed the Sunday fight
  Around the church of Shiloh—
The church so lone, the log-built one,   10
That echoed to many a parting groan
    And natural prayer
Of dying foemen mingled there—
Foemen at morn, but friends at eve—
  Fame or country least their care: 15
(What like a bullet can undeceive!)
  But now they lie low,
While over them the swallows skim,
  And all is hushed at Shiloh.

Malvern Hill

(July, 1862)

HERMAN MELVILLE

Ye elms that wave on Malvern Hill
  In prime of morn and May,
Recall ye how McClellan's men
    Here stood at bay?
While deep within yon forest dim   5
  Our rigid comrades lay—
Some with the cartridge in their mouth,
Others with fixed arms lifted South—
    Invoking so
The cypress glades? Ah wilds of woe!   10

The spires of Richmond, late beheld
  Through rifts in musket-haze,
Were closed from view in clouds of dust
    On leaf-walled ways,
Where streamed our wagons in caravan;   15
  And the Seven Nights and Days

Of march and fast, retreat and fight,
Pinched our grimed faces to ghastly plight—
  Does the elm wood
Recall the haggard beards of blood?   20

The battle-smoked flag, with stars eclipsed,
 We followed (it never fell!)—
In silence husbanded our strength—
  Received their yell;
Till on this slope we patient turned   25
 With cannon ordered well;
Reverse we proved was not defeat;
But ah, the sod what thousands meet!—
  Does Malvern Wood
Bethink itself, and muse and brood?   30

 We elms of Malvern Hill
  Remembered every thing;
 But sap the twig will fill:
 Wag the world how it will,
  Leaves must be green in Spring.   35

THE BATTLE

1. In "Shiloh," how do you explain the line, "Foemen at morn, but friends at eve"?

2. What does Melville mean by the "natural prayer" of dying men? How different is this from the regular prayer of the living?

3. How do you interpret Melville's "What like a bullet can undeceive"?

4. Without referring to a history book for the full details, reconstruct the battle of Malvern Hill as you think Melville wants you to see it, and include the topography (physical features) of the battlefield.

5. Throughout the poem, the poet addresses himself to the elms. Why? What questions does he ask of them? What is their answer?

After every war the veterans come home; the wounded and the dead come home. In the North after the Civil War, an added sorrow to those shown in Melville's "The College Colonel" and "Come Up from the Fields, Father" was the assassination of Abraham Lincoln in the very moment of victory. Walt Whitman's "O Captain! My Captain!" expresses the country's shock and agony.

The College Colonel

HERMAN MELVILLE

He rides at their head;
   A crutch by his saddle just slants in view,
One slung arm is in splints, you see,
   Yet he guides his strong steed—how coldly too.
He brings his regiment home—   5
   Not as they filed two years before,
But a remnant half-tattered, and battered, and worn,
Like castaway sailors, who—stunned
     By the surf's loud roar,
   Their mates dragged back and seen no more—   10
Again and again breast the surge,
   And at last crawl, spent, to shore.

A still rigidity and pale—
   And Indian aloofness lones his brow;
He has lived a thousand years   15
Compressed in battle's pains and prayers,
   Marches and watches slow.
There are welcoming shouts, and flags;
   Old men off hat to the Boy,
Wreaths from gay balconies fall at his feet,   20
   But to *him*—there comes alloy.

It is not that a leg is lost,
   It is not that an arm is maimed,
It is not that the fever has racked—
   Self he has long disclaimed.   25
But all through the Seven Days' Fight,
   And deep in the wilderness grim,
And in the field-hospital tent,
   And Petersburg crater, and dim
Lean brooding in Libby, there came—   30
   Ah heaven!—what *truth* to him.

Come Up from the Fields, Father

WALT WHITMAN

Come up from the fields, Father, here's a letter from our Pete,
And come to the front door, Mother, here's a letter from thy dear
   son.

Lo, 'tis autumn,
Lo, where the trees, deeper green, yellower and redder,
Cool and sweeten Ohio's villages with leaves fluttering in the
   moderate wind,   5
Where apples ripe in the orchards hang and grapes on the trellised
   vines,
(Smell you the smell of grapes on the vines?
Smell you the buckwheat where the bees were lately buzzing?)
Above all, lo, the sky so calm, so transparent after the rain, and with
   wondrous clouds,
Below too, all calm, all vital and beautiful, and the farm prospers
   well.   10

Down in the fields all prospers well,
But now from the fields come, Father, come at the daughter's call,
And come to the entry, Mother, to the front door come right away.

Fast as she can she hurries, something ominous, her steps trembling,
She does not tarry to smooth her hair nor adjust her cap.   15

Open the envelope quickly,
O this is not our son's writing, yet his name is signed,
O a strange hand writes for our dear son, O stricken mother's soul!
All swims before her eyes, flashes with black, she catches the main
    words only,
Sentences broken, *gunshot wound in the breast, cavalry skirmish,*
    taken to hospital,   20
At present low, but will soon be better.

Ah, now the single figure to me,
Amid all teeming and wealthy Ohio with all its cities and farms,
Sickly white in the face and dull in the head, very faint,
By the jamb of a door leans.   25

Grieve not so, dear Mother (the just-grown daughter speaks through
    her sobs,
The little sisters huddle around speechless and dismayed).
See, dearest Mother, the letter says Pete will soon be better.

Alas, poor boy, he will never be better (nor maybe needs to be
    better, that brave and simple soul),
While they stand at home at the door he is dead already,   30
The only son is dead.

But the mother needs to be better,
She with thin form presently dressed in black,
By day her meals untouched, then at night fitfully sleeping, often
    waking,
In the midnight waking, weeping, longing with one deep longing,   35
O that she might withdraw unnoticed, silent from life escape and
    withdraw,
To follow, to seek, to be with her dear dead son.

O Captain! My Captain!

WALT WHITMAN

O Captain! my Captain! our fearful trip is done,
The ship has weathered every rack, the prize we sought is won,
The port is near, the bells I hear, the people all exulting,
While follow eyes the steady keel, the vessel grim and daring;
        But O heart! heart! heart!   5
         O the bleeding drops of red,
           Where on the deck my Captain lies,
           Fallen cold and dead.

O Captain! my Captain! rise up and hear the bells;
Rise up—for you the flag is flung—for you the bugle trills,   10
For you bouquets and ribboned wreaths—for you the shores a-crowding,
For you they call, the swaying mass, their eager faces turning;
        Here Captain! dear father!
         This arm beneath your head!
           It is some dream that on the deck,   15
           You've fallen cold and dead.

My Captain does not answer, his lips are pale and still,
My father does not feel my arm, he has no pulse nor will,
The ship is anchored safe and sound, its voyage closed and done,
From fearful trip the victor ship comes in with object won: 20
        Exult O shores, and ring O bells!
        But I with mournful tread,
         Walk the deck my Captain lies,
           Fallen cold and dead.

AFTER THE BATTLE

1. In stanza 1 of "The College Colonel," Melville compares a returning regiment to castaway sailors. How accurate is this comparison? Explain.

2. What, in your opinion, was the "truth" that came to the College Colonel (last line, last stanza)? Has the fact that he is a "college" (not just an "ordinary") colonel helped him come to this "truth"?

3. Select in "Come Up from the Fields, Father" some words or phrases that help you to picture the peace of the farm. How is that peace broken?

4. What does the poet know that the family doesn't? Where in the poem does he reveal this knowledge?

5. In "O Captain! My Captain!" explain the "fearful trip," "the prize we sought," and "the port is near." Clue: Lee had surrendered only a few days before Lincoln's death.

6. What are the various emotions expressed in "O Captain! My Captain!"? For example, the second four lines express sorrow at Lincoln's death. How does the mood of the first four lines of each stanza contrast with the mood of the last four lines of the stanza? How does the poet indicate this difference to the reader?

A FIGURE OF SPEECH

A metaphor is a figure of speech in which two different things are compared by saying that one *is* the other. For example, in the poem you have just read, the United States is called a ship and President Lincoln is called its captain. The things that are said about the ship and its captain are also said about the nation and the President. You and your classmates often use metaphors in everyday speaking. Listen for some and report them to the class.

"The Real War Will Never Get in the Books"

WALT WHITMAN

It is not the better bullet or the shrewder general that deserves a nation's admiration in wartime.

The movements of the late Secession War and their results, to any sense that studies well and comprehends them, shows that popular democracy, whatever its faults and dangers, practically justifies itself beyond the proudest claims and wildest hopes of its enthusiasts. Probably no future age can know, but I well know how the gist of this fiercest and most resolute of the world's warlike contentions resided exclusively in the unnamed, unknown rank and file; and how the brunt of its labor of death was, to all essential purposes, volunteered. The people, of their own choice, fighting, dying for their own idea, insolently attacked by the Secession slave power and its very existence imperiled.

Descending to detail, entering any of the armies, and mixing with the private soldiers, we see and have seen august spectacles. We have seen the alacrity with which the American-born populace, the peaceablest and most good-natured race in the world, and the most personally independent and intelligent, and the least fitted to submit to the irksomeness and exasperation of regimental discipline, sprang, at the first tap of drum, to arms—not for gain, not for glory, nor to repel invasion—but for an emblem, a mere abstraction—for the life, *the safety, of the flag.* We have seen the unequaled docility and obedience of these soldiers. We have seen them tried long and long by hopelessness, mismanagement, and by defeat; have seen the incredible slaughter toward or through which the armies (as at First Fredericksburg, and afterward at the Wilderness) still unhesitatingly obeyed orders to advance.

We have seen them in trench, or crouching behind breastwork, or tramping in deep mud, or amid pouring rain or thick-falling snow, or under forced marches in hottest summer (as on the road to get to Gettysburg)—vast suffocating swarms, divisions, corps, with every man so grimed and black with sweat and dust his own mother would not have known him—his clothes all dirty, stained, and torn, with sour, accumulated sweat for perfume—many a comrade, perhaps a brother, sunstruck, staggering out, dying by the roadside of exhaustion—yet the great bulk bearing steadily on, cheery enough, hollow-bellied from hunger, but sinewy with unconquerable resolution.

We have seen this race proved wholesale by drearier yet more fearful tests—the wound, the amputation, the shattered face or limb; the slow, hot fever; long impatient anchorage in bed; and all the forms of maiming, operation, and disease.

Alas! America we have seen, though only in her early youth, already to hospital brought. There have we watched these soldiers, many of them only boys in years—marked their decorum, their religious nature and fortitude, and their sweet affection. Wholesale, truly. For at the front and through the camps in countless tents stood the regimental, brigade, and division hospitals; while everywhere amid the land, in or near cities, rose clusters of huge, white-washed, crowded, one-story wooden barracks; and there ruled agony with bitter scourge, yet seldom brought a cry; and there stalked death by day and night along the narrow aisles between the rows of cots or by the blankets on the ground, and touched lightly many a poor sufferer, often with blessed, welcome touch.

I know not whether I shall be understood, but I realize that it is finally from what I learned personally mixing in such scenes that I am now penning these pages.

One night in the gloomiest period of the war, in the Patent Office Hospital in Washington City, as I stood by the bed-side of a Pennsylvania soldier who lay conscious of quick-approaching death yet perfectly calm and with noble, spiritual manner, the veteran surgeon, turning aside, said to me that though he had witnessed many, many deaths of soldiers and had been a worker at Bull Run, Antietam, Fredericksburg, etc., he had not seen yet the first case of man or boy that met the approach of dissolution with cowardly qualms or terror. My own observation fully bears out these remarks.

What have we here if not, towering above all talk and argument, the plentifully supplied, last-needed proof of democracy, in its personalities? Curiously enough, too, the proof on this point comes, I should say, every bit as much from the South as from the North. Although I have spoken only of the latter, yet I deliberately include all. Grand, common stock! To me the accomplished and convincing growth, prophetic of the future; proof, undeniable to sharpest sense, of perfect beauty; tenderness and pluck that never feudal lord nor Greek nor Roman breed yet rivaled.

Let no tongue ever speak in disparagement of the American races, north or south, to one who has been through the war in the great army hospitals.

THE "REAL WAR"

1. What, according to Whitman, was the major reason for which men fought in the Union Army?

2. Where does he express his admiration for the man at the front?

3. What evidence have we here that Whitman felt no prejudice against the South?

4. What is the "real war" that Whitman thinks will never get into the books? Do you agree with him? Why?

5. Examine more of Whitman's poetry for examples of how he has sung the praises of the "unnamed, unknown rank and file."

THINKING ABOUT HERMAN MELVILLE AND WALT WHITMAN

1. There are startling similarities in the lives and work of Herman Melville and Walt Whitman. Both were born in the New York City area in 1819; each achieved success with his first published book but later suffered loss of popularity; each wrote a book described as "an American epic"; both died at the age of seventy-two. What other similarities do you discover in their lives and work? Can you discover any outstanding differences?

2. One literary historian (George F. Whicher) writes: "Musing on his country's ills, 'On the world's fairest hope linked with man's foulest crime,' Melville cannot convince himself that a spiritual regeneration will necessarily follow the resort to the sword. . . . [but Whitman] was ready to chant a greater supremacy, confident that 'affection shall solve the problems of Freedom yet.'" What is "the world's fairest hope"? What is "man's foulest crime"? Who more accurately predicted the American future, Melville or Whitman?

3. Although he was a very serious man, Melville also had a sense of humor. Point out some passages in his writing that you found amusing.

4. Suppose that the editor of *Holiday*, a magazine about vacation and travel, wanted to advertise his magazine by making a pamphlet containing quotations from some famous American writers. Select some of Melville's passages about foreign lands that could be included in this pamphlet.

5. What similarities and differences do you see between the urge of young people in Melville's day to go to sea and their present yearning for flight into space?

6. From your reading of Whitman's poetry and prose, do you think he might have made a good teacher or politician; a worker in some other profession? Select one, and by reference to the works just read, defend your choice.

7. Imagine that Walt Whitman, Abraham Lincoln, and Herman Melville had met to discuss why men fight and how peace can be won. Select one member of the class to represent each man and act out a conversation that might have taken place. You may quote literally from the materials in this (and in the Lincoln) section.

8. Many Civil War battles are mentioned by name in this section. Select one or more that you think you'd like to know more about, and prepare a written (or oral) report on the battle (or battles) you have researched.

Abraham Lincoln, Tragic Hero of the Republic

Of all our presidents, Abraham Lincoln has the strongest place in the affections of Americans. He was the President who brought our country through its most tragic days, and he also claims our devotion for his human warmth and compassion. Unlike most writers in this book, Lincoln neither thought of himself as a literary figure nor wrote for literary effect. What he wrote or what he said was usually prepared for some particular occasion, but it reached the people's minds and hearts. His clear mind and his human sympathy created some of the most memorable utterances ever made by an American. His Second Inaugural Address is remembered for its dignity and its "charity for all"; his Gettysburg Address, memorized and delivered by generations of Americans, has often been called the perfect speech.

Lincoln's all-embracing compassion is perhaps best shown in his letter to Mrs. Bixby, a Massachusetts mother who was said to have lost five sons in Union service. The Bixby letter is now generally regarded as a unique expression of sympathy in time of deep personal sorrow. Lincoln's concern was not for history's opinion; his concern was that Mrs. Bixby should know he shared her grief and sense of loss.

Abraham Lincoln's life has a storybook quality. He went to five different schools but had less than a year of formal schooling. He read everything he could lay his hands on. The Bible was always available; he learned much from it, including simplicity and majesty of style in writing. Lincoln educated himself so well

that he could pass the Illinois bar examination and become a lawyer.

Lincoln bore all his troubles with vast patience. His personal trials were many. His six feet four inches of height called attention to his awkward figure and homely face; opponents called him a "baboon" and a "gorilla." His wife had three half-brothers in the Confederate Army. Moreover, she was half-mad and she nagged him. During the war his beloved son Willie died. But it was a war; and Lincoln, as Commander in Chief, kept a clear head.

For longer than two years he struggled with ineffective generals. Only after painfully gathered experience did he raise to highest command the Union's most successful general, Ulysses S. Grant, whom many accused of being a drunkard. Grant's history was questionable enough to make his appointment an act of courage by the President. Lincoln's difficulty with generals is shown by his relationship with George B. McClellan. "Little Mac" cut a dashing figure; the men were wildly enthusiastic about him. He was one of the most brilliant organizers and trainers of an army that the United States had even seen. Twice, after the Union Army had suffered disastrous defeats, he was made commander of the Army of the Potomac. McClellan could always find a thousand excuses for not engaging the enemy and for opposing the President. After Lincoln finally removed him from high command, the vain and egotistic McClellan even ran against Lincoln for the presidency. Following the failure of a series of commanding generals, Lincoln

brought Grant east to run the war because he knew Grant would fight.

In his politics and as President, Lincoln was opposed to slavery but saw that his main task was the preservation of the Union. To open the war with a statement freeing the slaves would be politically impossible; so he waited until the Union victory of Antietam to issue the Emancipation Proclamation.

In most statues Lincoln is a brooding figure weighed down by the sorrows and responsibilities of his people and his country. This is only part of Lincoln. He was a laughing man too. He delighted in the time he could spend with his children. He had a rich, salty wit which came directly from his background on the frontier. He was an entertaining storyteller who could use both his storytelling and his wit to advantage in the rough and tumble of politics. The assassin's bullet in Ford's Theatre on Good Friday in 1865 ended the life of a man of the people, a man whose loss was mourned in both the North and the South.

The First Time I Saw Lincoln

WALT WHITMAN

"I shall not easily forget the first time I ever saw Abraham Lincoln," wrote Whitman of a vivid memory when Lincoln visited New York in an atmosphere of strange and unfriendly silence.

I shall not easily forget the first time I ever saw Abraham Lincoln. It must have been about the eighteenth or nineteenth of February, 1861. It was a rather pleasant afternoon in New York City as he arrived there from the West to remain a few hours and then pass on to Washington to prepare for his inauguration. I saw him in Broadway, near the site of the present post office. He came down, I think from Canal Street, to stop at the Astor House.

The broad spaces, sidewalks, and streets in that neighborhood and for some distance were crowded with solid masses of people—many thousands. The omnibuses and other vehicles had all been turned off, leaving an unusual hush in that busy part of the city. Presently two or three shabby hack barouches made their way with difficulty through the crowd and drew up at the Astor House entrance.

A tall figure stepped out of the center of these barouches, paused leisurely on the sidewalk, looked up at the granite walls and looming architecture of the grand old hotel—then, after a relieving stretch of arms and legs, turned around for over a minute to slowly and good-humoredly scan the appearance of the vast and silent crowds.

There were no speeches, no compliments, no welcome—as far as I could hear, not a word said. Still, much anxiety was concealed in that quiet. Cautious persons had feared some marked insult or indignity to the President-elect—for he possessed no personal popularity at all in New York City and very little political. But it was evidently tacitly agreed that if the few political supporters of Mr. Lincoln present would entirely abstain from any demonstration on their side, the immense majority—who were anything but supporters—would abstain on their side also. The result was a sulky, unbroken silence, such as certainly never before characterized a New York crowd.

From the top of an omnibus (driven up one side, close by, and blocked by the curbstone and the crowds), I had, I say, a capital view of it all and especially of Mr. Lincoln: his looks and gait; his perfect composure and coolness; his unusual and uncouth height; his dress of complete black, stovepipe hat pushed back on his head; dark brown complexion; seamed and wrinkled yet canny-looking face; black, bushy head of hair; disproportionately long neck; and his hands held behind, as he stood observing the people.

He looked with curiosity upon that immense sea of faces, and the sea of faces returned the look with similar curiosity. In both there was a dash of comedy, almost farce, such as Shakespeare puts in his blackest tragedies. The crowd that hemmed around consisted, I should think, of thirty to forty thousand men, not a single one his personal friend, while, I have no doubt (so frenzied were the ferments of the time) many an assassin's knife and pistol lurked in hip or breast pocket there—ready, soon as break and riot came.

But no break or riot came. The tall figure gave another relieving stretch or two of arms and legs; then, with moderate pace, and accompanied by a few unknown-looking persons, ascended the portico steps of the Astor House, disappeared through its broad entrance—and the dumb show ended.

THE FACT IS—

1. Why was Lincoln visiting New York?

2. Why was he met by almost total silence?

3. Whenever a President appears, anxiety for his safety runs high. Why was this an especially tense time for a President-elect to be exposed to large masses?

FIRST IMPRESSIONS

1. Write a paper under the title "I shall not easily forget the first time I ever saw ____."

2. Compare this word portrait of Lincoln with actual photographs, paintings, or drawings you have seen of him.

3. Compare Whitman's impressions of Lincoln with others that you have read.

Abe Lincoln Grows Up

CARL SANDBURG

"He'll never come to much,"
Dennis Hanks said of his
day-old cousin, Abraham
Lincoln. Little did the cousin
(or the world) then know how
wrong the prediction was.

One morning in February of the year 1809, Tom Lincoln came out of his cabin to the road, stopped a neighbor, and asked him to tell "the granny woman," Aunt Peggy Walters, that Nancy would need help soon.

On the morning of February 12, a Sunday, the granny woman was there at the cabin. And she and Tom Lincoln and the moaning Nancy Hanks welcomed into a world of battle and blood, of whispering dreams and wistful dust, a new child, a boy.

A little later that morning Tom Lincoln threw some extra wood on the fire and an extra bearskin over the mother, went out of the cabin, and walked two miles up the road to where the Sparrows, Tom and Betsy, lived. Dennis Hanks, the nine-year-old boy adopted by the Sparrows, met Tom at the door.

In his slow way of talking—he was a slow and a quiet man—Tom Lincoln told them, "Nancy's got a boy baby." A half-sheepish look was in his eyes, as though maybe more babies were not wanted in Kentucky just then.

The boy, Dennis Hanks, took to his feet, down the road to the Lincoln cabin. There he saw Nancy Hanks on a bed of poles cleated to a corner of the cabin, under warm bearskins.

She turned her dark head from looking at the baby to look at Dennis and threw him a tired, white smile from her mouth and gray eyes. He stood by the bed, his eyes wide open, watching the even, quiet breaths of this fresh, soft red baby.

"What you goin' to name him, Nancy?" the boy asked.

"Abraham," was the answer, "after his grandfather."

Soon came Betsy Sparrow. She washed the baby, put a yellow petticoat and a linsey shirt on him, cooked dried berries with wild honey for Nancy, put the one-room cabin in better order, kissed Nancy and comforted her, and went home.

Little Dennis rolled up in a bearskin and slept by the fireplace that night. He listened for the crying of the newborn child once in the night and the feet of the father moving on the dirt floor to help the mother and the little one. In the morning he took a long look at the baby and said to himself, "Its skin looks just like red cherry pulp squeezed dry, in wrinkles."

He asked if he could hold the baby. Nancy, as she passed the little one into Dennis' arms, said, "Be keerful, Dennis, fur you air the fust boy he's ever seen."

And Dennis swung the baby back and forth, keeping up a chatter about how tickled he was to have a new cousin to play with. The baby screwed up the muscles of its face and began crying with no letup.

Dennis turned to Betsy Sparrow, handed her the baby, and said to her, "Aunt, take him! He'll never come to much."

So came the birth of Abraham Lincoln that twelfth of February in the year 1809—in silence and pain from a wilderness mother on a bed of cornhusks and bearskins—with an early laughing child prophecy he would never come to much.

And though he was born in a house with only one door and one window, it was written he would come to know many doors, many windows; he would read many riddles and doors and windows.

The Lincoln family lived three crop years on the farm where baby Abraham was born. It was a discouraging piece of land with yellow and red clay, stony soils, thick underbrush, land known as "barren."

The baby grew, learning to sit up, to crawl over the dirt floor of the cabin; the gristle became bone; the father joked about the long legs getting longer; the mother joked about how quick he grew out of one shirt into another.

Sparrows and Hankses who came visiting said, "He's solemn as a papoose." An easy and a light bundle he was to carry when the family moved to a farm on Knob Creek, eight miles from Hodgenville, on the main highway from Louisville to Nashville.

During the year 1817 little Abe Lincoln, eight years old, going on nine, had an ax put in his hands and helped his father cut down trees and notch logs for the corners of their new cabin, forty yards from the pole shed where the family was cooking, eating, and sleeping.

Wild turkey, ruffed grouse, partridge, coon, rabbit, were to be had for the shooting of them. Once Abe took the gun as a flock of wild turkeys came toward the new log cabin, and, standing inside, shot through a crack and killed one of the big birds; and after that, somehow, he never felt like pulling the trigger on game birds. A mile from the cabin was a salt lick where deer came; there the boy could have easily shot the animals as they stood rubbing their tongues along the salty slabs or tasting of a saltish ooze. His father did the shooting; the deer killed gave them meat for Nancy's skillet; and the skins were tanned, cut, and stitched into shirts, trousers, mitts, moccasins. They wore buckskin; their valley was called the Buckthorn Valley.

After months the cabin stood up, four walls fitted together with a roof, a one-room house eighteen feet square, for a family to live in. A stick chimney plastered with clay ran up outside. The floor was packed and smoothed dirt. A log fire lighted the inside; no windows were cut in the walls. For a door there was a hole cut to stoop through. Bedsteads were cleated to the corners of the cabin; pegs stuck in the side of a wall made a ladder for young Abe to climb up in a loft to sleep on a hump of dry leaves; rain and snow came through chinks of the roof onto his bearskin cover. A table and three-legged stools had the top sides smoothed with an ax, and the bark side under, in the style called "puncheon."

A few days of this year in which the cabin was building, Nancy told Abe to wash his face and hands extra clean; she combed his hair, held his face between her two hands, smacked him a kiss on the mouth, and sent him to school— nine miles and back—Abe and Sally hand in hand hiking eighteen miles a day.

He learned to spell words he didn't know the meaning of, spelled the words before he used them in sentences. In a list of "words of eight syllables accented upon the sixth" was the word "incomprehensibility." He learned that first, and then such sentences as "Is he to go in?" and "Ann can spin flax."

Some neighbors said, "It's a pore make-out of a school," and Tom complained it was a waste of time to send the children nine miles just to sit with a lot of other children and read out loud all day in a "blab" school. But Nancy, as she cleaned Abe's ears in corners where he forgot to clean them, and as she combed out the tangles in his coarse, sandy black hair, used to say, "Abe, you go to school now, and larn all you kin." And he kissed her and said, "Yes, Mammy," and started with his sister on the nine-mile walk through timberland where bear, deer, coon, and wildcats ran wild.

Fall time came with its early frost, and they were moved into the new cabin, when horses and a wagon came breaking into the clearing one day. It was Tom and Betsy Sparrow and their seventeen-year-old boy, Dennis Hanks, who had come from Hodgenville, Kentucky, to cook and sleep in the pole shed of the Lincoln family till they could locate land and settle. Hardly a year had passed, however, when both Tom and Betsy Sparrow were taken down with the "milk sick," beginning with a whitish coat on the tongue. Both died and were buried in October on a little hill in a clearing in the timbers nearby.

Soon after, there came to Nancy Hanks Lincoln that white coating of the tongue; her vitals burned; the tongue turned brownish; her feet and hands grew cold and colder, her pulse slow and slower. She knew she was dying, called for her children, and spoke to them her last choking words. Sarah and Abe leaned over the bed. A bony hand of the struggling mother went out, putting its fingers into the boy's sandy black hair; her fluttering, guttural words seemed to say he must grow up and be good to his sister and father.

So, on a bed of poles cleated to the corner of the cabin, the body of Nancy Hanks Lincoln lay, looking tired . . . tired . . . with a peace settling in the pinched corners of the sweet, weary mouth, silence slowly etching away the lines of pain and hunger drawn around the gray eyes where now the eyelids closed down in the fine pathos of unbroken rest, a sleep without interruption settling about the form of the stooped and wasted shoulder bones; looking to the children who tiptoed in, stood still, cried their tears of want and longing, whispered "Mammy, Mammy," and heard only their own whispers answering; looking to these little ones of her brood as though new secrets had come to her in place of the old secrets given up with the breath of life.

Tom Lincoln took a log left over from the building of the cabin, and he and Dennis Hanks whipsawed the log into planks, planed the planks smooth, and made them of a measure for a box to bury the dead wife and mother in. Little Abe, with a jackknife, whittled pinewood pegs. And then, while Dennis and Abe held the planks, Tom bored holes and stuck the whittled pegs through the bored holes. This was the coffin, and they carried it the next day to the same little timber clearing nearby, where a few weeks before they had buried Tom and Betsy Sparrow. It was in the way of the deer run leading to the saltish water; light feet and shy hoofs ran over those early winter graves.

So the woman, Nancy Hanks, died, thirty-six years old, a pioneer sacrifice, with memories of monotonous, endless everyday chores, of mystic Bible verses read over and over for their promises, and with memories of blue wistful hills and a summer when the crab-apple blossoms flamed white and she carried a boy child into the world.

The farm boys in their evenings at Jones's store in Gentryville talked about how Abe Lincoln was always reading, digging into books, stretching out flat on his stomach in front of the fireplace, studying till midnight and past midnight, picking a piece of charcoal to write on the fire shovel, shaving off what he wrote, and then writing more—till midnight and past midnight. The next thing Abe would be reading books between the plow handles, it seemed to them. And once, trying to speak a last word, Dennis Hanks said, "There's suthin' peculiarsome about Abe."

He wanted to learn, to know, to live, to reach out; he wanted to satisfy hungers and thirsts he couldn't tell about, this big boy of the backwoods. And some of what he wanted so much, so deep down, seemed to be in the books. Maybe in books he would find the answers to dark questions pushing around in the pools of his thoughts and the drifts of his mind. He told Dennis and other people, "The things I want to know are in books; my best friend is the man who'll get me a book I ain't read." And sometimes friends answered, "Well, books ain't as plenty as wildcats in these parts o' Indianny."

This was one thing meant by Dennis when he said there was "suthin' peculiarsome" about Abe. It seemed that Abe made the books tell him more than they told other people. All the other farm boys had gone to school and read *The Kentucky Preceptor,* but Abe picked out questions from it, such as "Who has the most right to complain, the Indian or the Negro?" and Abe would talk about it, up one way and down the other, while they were in the cornfield pulling fodder for the winter. After Abe read poetry, especially Bobby Burns's poems, Abe began writing rhymes himself. When Abe sat with a girl, with their bare feet in the creek water, and she spoke of the moon rising, he explained to her it was the earth moving and not the moon—the moon only seemed to rise.

He liked to explain to other people what he was getting from books; explaining an idea to someone else made it clearer to him. The habit was growing on him of reading out loud; words came more real if picked from the silent page of the book and pronounced on the tongue; new balance and values of words stood out if spoken aloud. When writing letters for his father or the neighbors, he read the words out loud as they got written. Before writing a letter, he asked questions such as "What do you want to say in the letter? How do you want to say it? Are you sure that's the best way to say it? Or do you think we can fix up a better way to say it?"

As he studied his books, his lower lip stuck out; Josiah Crawford noticed it was a habit and joked Abe about the "stuck-out lip." This habit, too, stayed with him.

What he got in the schools didn't satisfy him. He went to three different schools in Indiana, besides two in Kentucky—altogether about four months of school. He learned his A B C; how to spell, read, write. And he had been with the other barefoot boys in butternut jeans learning "manners" under the schoolteacher, Andrew Crawford, who had them open a door, walk in, and say "Howdy do?" Yet what he tasted of books in school was only a beginning, only made him hungry and thirsty, shook him with a wanting and a wanting of more and more of what was hidden between the covers of books.

He kept on saying, "The things I want to know are in books; my best friend is the man who'll get me a book I ain't read." He said that to Pitcher, the lawyer over at Rockport, nearly twenty miles away, one fall afternoon, when he walked from Pigeon Creek to Rockport and borrowed a book from Pitcher. Then when fodder-pulling time came a few days later, he shucked corn from early daylight till sundown along with his father and Dennis Hanks and John Hanks; but after supper he read the book till midnight, and at noon he hardly knew the taste of his cornbread because he had the book in front of him. It was a hundred little things like these which made Dennis Hanks say there was "suthin' peculiarsome" about Abe.

Besides reading the family Bible and figuring his way through the old arithmetic they had at home, he got hold of *Aesop's Fables, The Pilgrim's Progress, Robinson Crusoe,* and Weems's *The Life of Francis Marion.* The book of fables, written or collected thousands of years ago by the Greek slave known as Aesop, sank deep in his mind. As he read through the book a second and third time, he had a feeling there were fables all around him, that everything he touched and handled, everything he saw and learned had a fable wrapped in it somewhere. One fable was about a bundle of sticks and a farmer whose sons were quarreling and fighting.

There was a fable in two sentences which read: "A coachman, hearing one of the wheels of his coach make a great noise, and perceiving that it was the worst one of the four, asked how it came to take such a liberty. The wheel answered that from the beginning of time creaking had always been the privilege of the weak." And there were shrewd, brief incidents of foolery such as this: "A waggish, idle fellow in a country town, being desirous of playing a trick on the simplicity of his neighbors and at the same time putting a little money in his pocket at their cost, advertised that he would on a certain day show a wheel carriage that should be so contrived as to go without horses. By silly curiosity the rustics were taken in, and each succeeding group who came out from the show were ashamed to confess to their neighbors that they had seen nothing but a wheelbarrow."

The style of the Bible, of Aesop's fables, the hearts and minds back of those books, were much in his thoughts. His favorite pages in them he read over and over. Behind such proverbs as "Muzzle not the ox that treadeth out the corn" and "He that ruleth his own spirit is greater than he that taketh a city," there was a music of simple wisdom and a mystery of common everyday life that touched deep spots in him, while out of the fables of the ancient Greek slave, he came to see that cats, rats, dogs, horses, plows, hammers, fingers, toes, people—all had fables connected with their lives, characters, places. There was, perhaps, an outside for each thing as it stood alone, while inside of it was its fable.

One book came, titled *The Life of George Washington,* by M. L. Weems, formerly rector of Mt. Vernon Parish. It pictured men of passion and proud ignorance in the government of England driving their country into war on the American colonies. It quoted the far-visioned warning of Chatham [1] to the British parliament, "For God's sake, then, my lords, let the way be instantly opened for reconciliation. I say instantly; or it will be too late forever."

The book told of war, as at Saratoga.[2] "Shrill and terrible, from rank to rank, resounds the clash of bayonets—frequent and sad the groans of the dying."

The Weems book reached some deep spots in the boy. He asked himself what it meant that men should march, fight, bleed, go cold and hungry for the sake of what they called "freedom."

"Few great men are great in everything," said the book. And there was a cool sap in the passage: "His delight was in that of the manliest sort, which, by stringing the limbs and swelling the muscles, promotes the kindliest flow of blood and spirits. At jumping with a long pole, or heaving heavy weights, for his years he hardly had an equal."

Such book talk was a comfort against the same thing over again, day after day, so many mornings the same kind of water from the same spring, the same fried pork and cornmeal to eat, the same drizzles of rain, spring plowing, summer weeds, fall fodder pulling, each coming every year, with the same tired feeling at the end of the day, so many days alone in the woods or the fields or else the same people to talk with, people from whom he had learned all they could teach him. Yet there ran through his head the stories and sayings of other people, the stories and sayings of books, the learning his eyes had caught from books; they were a comfort; they were good to have because they were good by themselves; and they were still better to have because they broke the chill of the lonesome feeling.

He was thankful to the writer of Aesop's fables because that writer stood by him and walked with him, an invisible companion, when he pulled fodder or chopped wood. Books lighted lamps in the dark rooms of his gloomy hours. . . . Well—he would live on; maybe the time would come when he would be free from work for a few weeks, or a few months, with books, and then he would read. . . . Yes, then he would read. . . . Then he would go and get at the proud secrets of his books.

His father—would he be like his father when he grew up? He hoped not. Why should his father knock him off a fence rail when he was asking a neighbor, passing by, a question? Even if it was a smart question, too pert and too quick, it was no way to handle a boy in front of a neighbor. No, he was going to be a man different from his father. The books—his father hated the books. His father talked about "too much eddication"; after readin', writin', 'rithmetic, that was enough, his father said. He, Abe Lincoln, the boy, wanted to know more than the father, Tom Lincoln, wanted to know. Already Abe knew more than his father; he was writing letters for the neighbors; they hunted out the Lincoln farm to get young Abe to find his bottle of ink with blackberry-brier root and copperas in it, and his pen

---

[1] **Chatham:** William Pitt, the earl of Chatham.
[2] **Saratoga** (sar·a·TOH·gah), New York: Revolutionary War battles were fought here.

made from a turkey-buzzard feather, and write letters. Abe had a suspicion sometimes his father was a little proud to have a boy that could write letters, and tell about things in books, and outrun and outwrestle and rough-and-tumble any boy or man in Spencer County. Yes, he would be different from his father: he was already so; it couldn't be helped.

In growing up from boyhood to young manhood, he had survived against lonesome, gnawing monotony and against floods, forest and prairie fires, snakebites, horse kicks, ague, chills, fever, malaria, "milk sick."

A comic outline against the sky he was, hiking along the roads of Spencer and other counties in southern Indiana in those years when he read all the books within a fifty-mile circuit of his home. Stretching up on the long legs that ran from his moccasins to the body frame with its long, gangling arms, covered with linsey-woolsey, then the lean neck that carried the head with its surmounting coonskin cap or straw hat —it was, again, a comic outline—yet with a portent in its shadow. His laughing "howdy," his yarns and drollery, opened the doors of men's hearts.

THE FACT IS—

1. Describe the home in which Lincoln was born.

2. What were some of the problems a boy growing up like Abe had to face? How many of these problems would he have to face if he lived today?

3. Which one of his parents was the more insistent that Abe get an education? What interpretation do you have for why there was a difference?

4. What was Abe's first school like? How did he and his sister go to school?

"THE THINGS I WANT TO KNOW..."

1. Life for the Lincoln family was difficult, without many advantages. Yet Abe had a "peculiarsome" something inside him that helped him rise above his surroundings. What was this peculiarsome something? How did it help him?

2. What signs can you see in the boy Lincoln that he would become a spokesman for the weak and unprotected? an independent thinker? a Bible quoter?

3. Explain what Sandburg means by "Books lighted lamps in the dark rooms of his gloomy hours." List the books which did that for Lincoln. Which books, if any, have done that for you?

4. Investigate the card catalogue and the shelves of your school and local library to see how many of the books that influenced Lincoln's youth are still available to you now. Read and report on one.

The Lincoln
Who Lives in Anecdote

Lincoln was not only a great

storyteller; he was also an

excellent subject for stories.

What he said and did has

been recorded by those who

remembered him, lest we

forget what a wise, witty,

and humane man he was.

The young men in and around the frontier village of New Salem sized Abe up and decided to see what stuff he had in him. First, he was to run a foot race with a man from Wolf. "Trot him out," said Abe. Second, he was to wrestle with a man from Little Grove. "All right," said Abe. Third, he must fight a man from Sand Ridge. "Nothing wrong about that," said Abe.

The foot racer from Wolf couldn't pass Abe. The man from Little Grove, short and heavy, ran at Abe like a battering ram. Abe stepped aside, caught him by the neck, threw him heels over head, and gave him a fall that nearly broke his bones. Abe was now getting mad. "Bring on your man from Sand Ridge," he hooted. But a committee came up, gave him the right hand of fellowship, and told him, "You have sand in your craw. We will take you into our crowd."

—CARL SANDBURG

A rich man in Springfield had been vindictively pursuing a poor man for an alleged debt of $2.50. When the poor man denied the debt and refused to pay, the rich man asked Lincoln to enter suit. At first Lincoln was disinclined. Then he consented, stipulating that his fee would be $10, cash down.

The client readily produced the $10. Whereupon Lincoln went to the poor man and gave him $5 on condition that he would immediately pay the alleged debt. Thus Lincoln made $5, the poor man gained $2.50, and the claim was satisfied.　　　　—EMANUEL HERTZ

After listening for some time one day to a would-be client's statement, Lincoln suddenly swung around in his chair and exclaimed: "Well, you have got a good case in technical law, but a pretty bad one in equity and justice. You'll have to get some other fellow to win it for you.

I couldn't do it. All the time while standing talking to that jury, I'd be thinking, 'Lincoln, you're a liar,' and I believe I should forget myself and say it out loud."　　—JOHN H. LITTLEFIELD

When it came to Lincoln's attention that a fourteen-year old boy had been sentenced to be shot, he wrote to Stanton suggesting a more appropriate punishment:

"My Dear Sir: Hadn't we better spank this drummer boy and send him back home? A. Lincoln."

　　　　　　　　　　—H. JACK LANG

An elderly woman in a reception room flashed a question, "How can you speak kindly of your enemies when you should rather destroy them?" "Madam," he said, as he gazed slowly into her face, "do I not destroy them when I make them my friends?"

　　　　　　　　　　—CARL SANDBURG

A WORD TO REMEMBER: anecdote

The word *anecdote* has undergone a most remarkable change. Originally it was a secret, private matter—something not to give out. Anecdotes were "the unpublished details of history." Since, however, readers and listeners were often intrigued by just these little details—about people, places and things—*anecdote* became what was revealed, not concealed. Even more, anecdotes now serve to tell a story that illustrates a particular point about a person, a place, or a thing.

1. If the first anecdote may be said to illustrate the point that "You stand your ground when you're being tested," what can we learn about Lincoln through each of the other anecdotes in this section?

2. Reread "Abe Lincoln Grows Up." Select three anecdotes from this essay and be prepared to read each one to the class with an explanation of the precise point Sandburg seeks to make about Lincoln through each of these anecdotes.

3. Many prominent Americans (Presidents and the less famous) live, as Lincoln has, "in anecdote." Find and report on an anecdote which tells us something about one such prominent American.

From Lincoln's Writings

One of the reasons that Lincoln is still alive to us today is that his own writings beautifully express his thought and feelings. The following selections are part of every American's literary heritage.

From The First Inaugural Address

Physically speaking, we cannot separate. We cannot remove our respective sections from each other, nor build an impassable wall between them. A husband and wife may be divorced, and go out of the presence and beyond the reach of each other; but the different parts of our country cannot do this. They cannot but remain face to face, and intercourse, either amicable or hostile, must continue between them. It is impossible, then, to make that intercourse more advantageous or more satisfactory after separation than before. Can aliens

ABRAHAM LINCOLN   **453**

make treaties easier than friends can make laws? Can treaties be more faithfully enforced between aliens than laws can among friends? Suppose you go to war; you cannot fight always, and when after much loss on both sides and no gain on either, you cease fighting, the identical old questions as to terms of intercourse are again upon you.

This country, with its institutions, belongs to the people who inhabit it. Whenever they shall grow weary of the existing government, they can exercise their constitutional right of amending it, or their revolutionary right to dismember or overthrow it. I cannot be ignorant of the fact that many worthy and patriotic citizens are desirous of having the national Constitution amended. . . . I understand a proposed amendment to the Constitution—which amendment, however, I have not seen—has passed Congress, to the effect that the federal government shall never interfere with the domestic institutions of the states, including that of persons held to service. To avoid misconstruction of what I have said, I depart from my purpose not to speak of particular amendments, so far as to say that, holding such a provision now to be implied constitutional law, I have no objections to its being made express and irrevocable.

The chief magistrate derives all his authority from the people, and they have conferred none upon him to fix terms for the separation of the states. The people themselves can do this also if they choose, but the executive, as such, has nothing to do with it. His duty is to administer the present government as it came to his hands, and to transmit it, unimpaired by him, to his successor. Why should there not be a patient confidence in the ultimate justice of the people? Is there any better or equal hope in the world? In our present differences is either party without faith of being in the right? If the Almighty Ruler of nations, with his eternal truth and justice, be on your side of the North, or yours of the South, that truth and that justice will surely prevail, by the judgment of this great tribunal of the American people. By the frame of the government under which we live, the same people have wisely given their public servants but little power for mischief, and have with equal wisdom provided for the return of that little to their own hands at very short intervals. While the people retain their virtue and vigilance, no administration, by any extreme of wickedness or folly, can very seriously injure the government in the short space of four years.

My countrymen, one and all, think calmly and well upon this whole subject. Nothing valuable can be lost by taking time. If there be an object to hurry any of you in hot haste to a step which you would never take deliberately, that object will be frustrated by taking time; but no good object can be frustrated by it. Such of you as are now dissatisfied still have the old Constitution unimpaired, and on the sensitive point, the laws of your own framing under it; while the new administration will have no immediate power, if it would, to change either. If it were admitted that you who are dissatisfied hold the right side in this dispute, there is still no single good reason for precipitate action. Intelligence, patriotism, Christianity, and a firm reliance on Him who has never yet forsaken this favored land are still competent to adjust in the best way all our present difficulty. In your hands, my dissatisfied fellow countrymen, and not in mine, are the momentous issues of civil war. The government will not assail you. You can have no conflict without being yourselves the aggressors. You have no oath registered in heaven to destroy the government, while I shall have the most solemn one to "preserve, protect, and defend" it.

I am loath to close. We are not enemies, but friends. We must not be enemies. Though passion may have strained, it must not break our bonds of affection. The mystic chords of memory stretching from every battlefield and patriot grave to every living heart and hearthstone all over this broad land will yet swell the chorus of the Union when again touched, as surely they will be, by the better angels of our nature.

The Gettysburg Address

Four score and seven years ago our fathers brought forth on this continent a new nation, conceived in liberty, and dedicated to the proposition that all men are created equal.

Now we are engaged in a great civil war, testing whether that nation, or any nation so conceived and so dedicated, can long endure. We are met on a great battlefield of that war. We have come to dedicate a portion of that field as a final resting place for those who here gave their lives that that nation might live. It is altogether fitting and proper that we should do this.

But in a larger sense we cannot dedicate, we cannot consecrate, we cannot hallow this ground. The brave men, living and dead, who struggled here have consecrated it far above our poor power to add or detract. The world will little note nor long remember what we say here, but it can never forget what they did here. It is for us, the living, rather, to be dedicated here to the unfinished work which they who fought here have thus far so nobly advanced. It is rather for us to be here dedicated to the great task remaining before us—that from these honored dead we take increased devotion to that cause for which they gave the last full measure of devotion; that we here highly resolve that these dead shall not have died in vain; that this nation, under God, shall have a new birth of freedom; and that government of the people, by the people, and for the people, shall not perish from the earth.

From The Second Inaugural Address

... Neither party expected for the war the magnitude or the duration which it has already attained. Neither anticipated that the cause of the conflict might cease with, or even before, the conflict itself should cease. Each looked for an easier triumph and a result less fundamental and astounding. Both read the same Bible, and pray to the same God; and each invokes His aid against the other. It may seem strange that any men should dare to ask a just God's assistance in wringing their bread from the sweat of other men's faces; but let us judge not, that we be not judged. The prayers of both could not be answered—that of neither has been answered fully....

With malice toward none; with charity for all; with firmness in the right, as God gives us to see the right, let us strive on to finish the work we are in; to bind up the nation's wounds; to care for him who shall have borne the battle, and for his widow and his orphan—to do all which may achieve and cherish a just and lasting peace among ourselves, and with all nations.

ABRAHAM LINCOLN   **455**

A Letter to Mrs. Bixby

Executive Mansion
Washington, November 21, 1864

Mrs. Bixby, Boston, Massachusetts

Dear Madam:

I have been shown in the files of the War Department a statement of the Adjutant-General of Massachusetts that you are the mother of five sons who have died gloriously on the field of battle. I feel how weak and fruitless must be any words of mine which should attempt to beguile you from the grief of a loss so overwhelming. But I cannot refrain from tendering to you the consolation that may be found in the thanks of the Republic they died to save. I pray that our heavenly Father may assuage the anguish of your bereavement, and leave you only the cherished memory of the loved and lost, and the solemn pride that must be yours to have laid so costly a sacrifice upon the altar of freedom.

Yours very sincerely and respectfully,

Abraham Lincoln

UNION FOREVER

1. What does Lincoln mean when he says that divorce between husband and wife is possible but not between parts of the country?

2. What argument does Lincoln support by the contrast he draws between aliens and friends?

3. What recommendations for change does Lincoln make to those who are dissatisfied with the conduct of their government?

4. How can one defend a President's idea that the people once dissatisfied with government may exercise . . . "their revolutionary right to dismember or overthrow it"?

5. In which approach, constitutional amendment or violent revolutionary action, does Lincoln have greater faith for a better country? Which of these, in your view, spells greater hope for a better land?

6. The Civil Rights issue in our time, just as the slavery issue in Lincoln's, has divided Americans sharply. Could the ideas of Lincoln, as expressed in any of these excerpts from his writings, serve to unite the people today?

7. What is the major theme of the Gettysburg Address? the Second Inaugural Address?

8. Unnecessary repetition can weaken an essay, oral or written. Yet Lincoln uses repetition. Give an example. Does the repetition weaken or strengthen his message? Explain.

9. How could the message in the Second Inaugural Address be applied at home or abroad in the world you live in today?

10. Presidents often delegate to others the task of composing letters. Do you think Lincoln did that in his letter to Mrs. Bixby?

A Tree
Is Best
Measured
When
It's Down

CARL SANDBURG

On an early morning streetcar in Philadelphia, a good Quaker unrolled a morning newspaper, stared at it, and broke out: "My God! What is this? Lincoln is assassinated!" In the gray dawn on this streetcar, men cupped their faces in their hands, and on the straw-covered floor fell hot tears. The driver of the streetcar came in to make sure of what he heard. Then he went out and took the bells off his horses. And he drove on with his car filled with mourners, some silent, some sobbing.

Newsboys at their stands cried no headlines, handed the damp sheets from the press to the buyers, one boy noticed as he brushed with his dirty hand the tears from his dirty cheeks. In thousands of stores, the merchant told the clerks they would close for the day; in many schools the sobbing teacher could only tell the children, "Go home. There will be no school today." The father, the children coming home unexpected, the mother asked what was wrong and heard, "Mama, they've killed the President" or "Our President is dead." Then the family hunted up crepe or black cloth for the front doorway. . . .

In Charleston, South Carolina, one old woman walked a street looking straight ahead, wringing her hands and crying, "O Lawd! O Lawd! Marse Sam's dead! O Lawd! Uncle Sam's dead!"

There was a funeral. It took long to pass its many given points. Many millions of people saw it and personally moved in it and were part of its procession. The line of march ran seventeen hundred miles. As a dead march nothing like it had ever been attempted before. Like the beginning and end of the Lincoln Administration, it had no precedents to go by. It was garish, vulgar, massive, bewildering, chaotic. Also it was simple, final, majestic, august. . . .

From his White House in Washington—where it began—they carried his coffin and followed it nights and days for twelve days. By night, bonfires and torches lighted the right of way for a slow-going railroad train. By day, troops with reversed arms, muffled drums, multitudinous feet seeking the pivotal box with the silver handles. By day, bells tolling, bells sobbing the requiem, the salute guns, cannons rumbling their inarticulate thunder. . . .

Then to Springfield, Illinois, the old home town, the Sangamon nearby, the New Salem hilltop nearby, for the final rest of cherished dust. Thus the route and the ceremonial rites in epitome. The weather was April and May but the smoke and haze was October and the feeling of the hour silent snow on the January earth of a hard winter.

THINKING ABOUT ABRAHAM LINCOLN

1. Imagine that you have been chosen to deliver a Lincoln Day assembly talk to your school. Prepare an outline for your talk based on what you have learned from your readings here.

2. Lincoln once said of a long-winded lawyer, "He can compress the most words into the smallest ideas of any man I ever met." How was Lincoln's method of speaking and writing almost exactly the opposite? Why have so many speakers and writers looked to Lincoln as their model for crispness and concreteness, the balanced sentence, and the pointed anecdote? Find some of Lincoln's sentences that illustrate each of these.

3. Write a paper titled "If Lincoln were President of the United States Today." Think of two major problems facing the United States today and tell how you think Lincoln would handle them.

4. "Abe Lincoln Grows Up" suggests that even as a boy and a young man, there was promise of what Mr. Lincoln would become as a mature man. What evidence do you see in the speeches, the letter, and the anecdotes that the promise was fulfilled?

The Closed World of Emily Dickinson

These words, written as an appeal for a new genius to write for the *Atlantic Monthly*, attracted four small poems by a writer of genius, Emily Dickinson.

What can we say of Miss Emily Dickinson? Of what you and I might call her *real life*, we can say very little. She was born in the small Massachusetts town of Amherst in 1830 and died at the age of fifty-six in the house where she was born. Most of her life was lived in solitude. She was a recluse. She was an eccentric.

No one knows why the part of Emily Dickinson's life which is significant to the world was lived alone. Her girlhood seemed to be normal. Her father was an important man in Amherst and in the state. He brought her up as any young girl might have been brought up at that time. Although she was educated largely at home, she did attend the Mount Holyoke Female Seminary (now called Mount Holyoke College). She disliked it, but no more than young people today are apt to dislike school. As far as we know, she left Massachusetts only once: she went on a trip with her father to Washington and came back by way of Philadelphia.

There is a story that in Philadelphia she met a married clergyman and fell in love with him. Because her love was not returned, she became a recluse. We know that she did meet such a man, but

there is no evidence of a love affair. There is some evidence that his spiritual counsels were sometimes interpreted by Emily as declarations of love. Beyond that there seems little to support the many rumors in the many biographies of this woman who was to lead a life so strange to us. She wrote a great many letters, but she had her sister, Lavinia, address the letters and send them. They were usually short notes that did not demand answers. In her years of solitude, she was never seen in public. She dressed always in white, but the dressmaker who came to the house had to fit the dresses on her sister, who passed them on to Emily. She liked children and liked to give them cookies. She was so anxious not to be seen that she would lower the cookies in a basket from a bedroom window. She spent most of her time in her bedroom, and there she wrote hundreds of poems. Only seven of her poems were published in her lifetime. Her family knew she wrote poetry, but they were completely unaware of the staggering quantity of verse she was turning out.

Only after her death did Emily Dickinson gain her reputation as a poet. The executors of her estate were astounded to find the number of poems which she had written, hidden away in bureau drawers, written on the backs of envelopes, on old bills, on any piece of paper she could find. Some she had wrapped up in tubes, tied in ribbons, and put away. She seemed to have little desire to communicate with anyone but herself. Hers was a private life and her poetry seems to express individual im-

pressions of the world circumscribed by the house and gardens of her family's home in Amherst.

In one short poem she seems to be telling us this truth about herself:

The soul selects her own society,
Then shuts the door.
To her divine majority
Present no more.

There is a legend that the first of her poetry published after her death was neglected, but this is not true. Her sister, Lavinia, was responsible for getting the poems edited and bringing them out. Her first volume of poetry went through six printings in the first few weeks. However, for some thirty years thereafter, her word disappeared from public notice, and it was not until 1924 that it was rediscovered. Since then her family have discovered more and more poetry. Although we are not sure we have it all, there is now a con-

siderable body of her published work including in all more than eighteen hundred poems.

Emily Dickinson knew where heaven was and that she would go there. She spoke intimately to God—intimately and sometimes impertinently. Sometimes she spoke to a mysterious "you," but the reader doesn't know who that "you" might be.

She was not always serene in her seeming self-reliance.

Nor try to tie the butterfly;
Nor climb the bars of ecstasy.
In insecurity to lie
Is joy's insuring quality.

Truly, Colonel Thomas Wentworth Higginson was, although he didn't know it, describing Emily Dickinson's poetry when he said, "There may be years of crowded passion in a word and half a life in a sentence."

EMILY DICKINSON **461**

A Word

A word is dead
When it is said,
  Some say.
I say it just
Begins to live   5
  That day.

I Never Saw a Moor

I never saw a moor,
  I never saw the sea;
Yet know I how the heather looks
  And what a wave must be.

I never spoke with God,   5
  Nor visited in heaven;
Yet certain am I of the spot
  As if the chart were given.

To Make a Prairie

To make a prairie it takes a clover
And one bee—
One clover, and a bee,
And reverie.
The reverie alone will do   5
If bees are few.

Like Rain It Sounded

Like rain it sounded till it curved,
And then I knew 'twas wind;
It walked as wet as any wave
But swept as dry as sand.

When it had pushed itself away   5
To some remotest plain
A coming as of hosts was heard—
That was indeed the rain!

It filled the wells, it pleased the pools,
It warbled in the road,   10
It pulled the spigot from the hills
And let the floods abroad;

It loosened acres, lifted seas,
The sites of centers stirred,
Then like Elijah° rode away   15
Upon a wheel of cloud.

15. **Elijah** (ee·LY·juh): Old Testament prophet
carried to heaven in a fiery chariot.

I Like to See It Lap the Miles

I like to see it lap the miles,
And lick the valleys up,
And stop to feed itself at tanks;
And then, prodigious, step

Around a pile of mountains,   5
And, supercilious, peer
In shanties by the sides of roads;
And then a quarry pare

To fit its sides, and crawl between,
Complaining all the while   10
In horrid, hooting stanza;
Then chase itself down hill

And neigh like Boanerges;°
Then, punctual as a star,
Stop—docile and omnipotent—   15
At its own stable door.

13. **Boanerges** (boh·ah·NUR·jeez): thunderous
preacher.

A Narrow Fellow in the Grass

A narrow fellow in the grass
Occasionally rides;
You may have met him—did you not,
His notice sudden is.

The grass divides as with a comb,   5
A spotted shaft is seen;

And then it closes at your feet
And opens further on.

He likes a boggy acre,
A floor too cool for corn. 10
Yet when a child, and barefoot,
I more than once, at morn,

Have passed, I thought, a whiplash
Unbraiding in the sun,—
When, stooping to secure it, 15
It wrinkled, and was gone.

Some Keep the Sabbath

Some keep the Sabbath going to church;
   I keep it staying at home,
With a bobolink for a chorister,
   And an orchard for a dome.

Some keep the Sabbath in surplice; 5
   I just wear my wings;
And instead of tolling the bell for church,
   Our little sexton sings.

God preaches—a noted clergyman—
   And the sermon is never long; 10
So instead of getting to heaven at last,
   I'm going all along!

We Never Know How High

We never know how high we are
   Till we are called to rise;
And then, if we are true to plan,
   Our statures touch the skies.

The heroism we recite   5
   Would be a daily thing,
Did not ourselves the cubits warp
   For fear to be a king.

As Old As Woe

As old as Woe—
How old is that?
Some eighteen thousand years.
As old as Bliss—
How old is that?   5
They are of equal years.

Together chiefest they are found,
But seldom side by side;
From neither of them though he try
Can human nature hide.   10

EMILY DICKINSON   **467**

THOUGHTS ON LIFE

A Word

1. What kind of word is the poet talking about? Give several examples.
2. Have you ever regretted uttering some words that might "live"? Explain.

I Never Saw a Moor

1. How do the moor and the prairie suggest the idea of faith?
2. Explain the last line of this poem. How does it emphasize the main idea?

To Make a Prairie

1. What is a "prairie"? Make up a dictionary-style definition from the information Miss Dickinson gives. Do you think this is a satisfactory definition? Why, or why not?
2. What quality in the poet's personality is emphasized in this poem?

Like Rain It Sounded

1. What comparison is the basis for understanding this poem? Name characteristics common to the elements in this comparison. What is the main contrast?
2. From the poem, select three verbs which appeal strongly to the imagination. Explain clearly how each arouses your sense of sight or sound.

I Like to See It Lap the Miles

1. Personification is giving to things or ideas the characteristics of living creatures. Explain three or more illustrations from this poem.
2. In the last stanza to what creature is the train likened and what qualities do they have in common?
3. Explain "punctual as a star" (line 14). What does this comparison add to the total impression of the train?

A Narrow Fellow in the Grass

1. What creature is being described in this poem? From the first two verses, select three details which identify it.

2. The last verse offers a vivid comparison. Explain it. What does "wrinkled" contribute?

Some Keep the Sabbath

1. Explain the following lines:

> **a.** "I just wear my wings;" (line 6)
>
> **b.** "Our little sexton sings." (line 8)

2. What does the poet worship?

3. Is she religious? In two or three sentences, explain what religion means to her.

We Never Know How High

1. Whose plan is referred to in the expression "if we are true to plan"?

2. "The cubits" in line 7 means "our growth." Summarize the ideas in the second verse. Do you agree with this viewpoint?

3. From what you know of her life, would you say Miss Dickinson practiced what she preaches here?

As Old as Woe

1. Why are "Woe" and "Bliss" seldom found "side by side"? Illustrate from your own experience.

2. What is the main idea of this poem?

THINKING ABOUT EMILY DICKINSON

1. "I Like to See It Lap the Miles" and "A Narrow Fellow in the Grass" have generally been popular with students. What do they have in common? Do you like them? Why, or why not? If you don't like them, select one or two other poems in this collection which you like better and indicate why.

2. "We Never Know How High" is a poem which emphasizes an idea or thought. What two or three poems other than "As Old as Woe" have a similar emphasis? Name them and state the idea for each.

3. Emily Dickinson's poems are different from Poe's. Which type of poetry do you prefer and why? Reread quickly Poe's poems with a view to writing a well-planned paragraph or two in which you point out the similarities and dissimilarities between his poems and Miss Dickinson's.

4. How do you think the townspeople of Amherst reacted to Emily's odd way of living? Write an imaginary conversation in which she is discussed. Reread the Introduction and find a chapter or two in a biography to use as a basis for this conversation.

5. These poems by Emily Dickinson offer an opportunity for describing her character. Write a careful paragraph using specific quotations from poems to give a picture of this poet.

Mark Twain, the Wild Humorist

Mark Twain was a complicated man whose humor sometimes masked a low opinion of mankind. It is difficult to laugh at such observations as: "If you pick up a starving dog and make him prosperous, he will not bite you. This is the principal difference between a dog and a man."

Although famed as the creator of Tom Sawyer and Huckleberry Finn, boys from the simple, rural American West, Twain lived out his life in eastern cities, seeking the company and approval of wealthy and important people. Although he wrote classics, he scoffed at literary art and claimed he wrote only for money. (He defined a classic as "something everybody wants to have read and nobody wants to read.") He scoffed at money and man's gullibility. He was a man from Missouri and needed to be shown—but he lost a huge fortune on publishing schemes and inventions. In typical Twain fashion, the greatest writer in America recouped his losses not by writing but by a world-girdling lecture tour.

The famous Mark Twain of Hannibal was born Samuel Langhorne Clemens in Florida, Missouri, some thirty miles in from the Mississippi River. When Sam was four, the family moved to Hannibal, another small town. But for Sam Clemens it was an extremely exciting place because it was directly on the river, the main artery of commerce for the country. The young boy could see floating down this turbulent and unpredictable stream a procession of steamboats, some gaudy and shiny, with rich men and women in fine clothes parading their decks; he could see the flat barges loaded with produce, logs,

or lumber, and handled by rough workmen. The arrival of a steamboat was an event in Hannibal.

In his famous *Life on the Mississippi*, he describes the response to the cry "Steamboat a-comin'!"

Drays, carts, men, boys, all go hurrying from many quarters to a common center, the wharf. Assembled there, the people fasten their eyes upon the coming boat as upon a wonder they are seeing for the first time. And the boat *is* rather a handsome sight, too. She is long and sharp and trim and pretty; she has two tall, fancy-topped chimneys with a gilded device of some kind swung between them; a fanciful pilothouse, all glass and "gingerbread," perched on top of the "texas" deck behind them; the paddle boxes are gorgeous with a picture or with gilded rays above the boat's name. . . .

The heroes of the river were not the captains of these crafts but rather the pilots. The pilot was the man who knew the river so well that he could even anticipate its changes. What might be true of a trip down the river one day might not be true the next. Snags, emerging islands, changes of course always made every Mississippi passage perilous and exciting.

Twain, like all boys of his time and place, dreamed of being a river pilot. Unlike most, he succeeded. He wrote graphically of his experiences from his days as a "cub" until the time when he became the greatest of all great men, a Mississippi River pilot. Twain's books about the river are exciting for two reasons: because life on the river was exciting and because Mark Twain had remarkable gifts of perception. He could describe *accurately* and in a highly personal fashion the handling of boats, the life on the river, and—more important than anything else—the people who made that life so exciting. During this exhilarating period in Mark Twain's life, he got to know an extraordinary variety of types and classes of people.

As Twain wrote in *Life on the Mississippi,* he "got personally and familiarly acquainted with about all the different types of human nature that are to be found in fiction, biography, or history." When he began to write professionally, he took Mark Twain as his penname. (Boatmen periodically cast a weighted line over the side of the boat to determine how much water she had under her. "Mark twain" meant two fathoms, or twelve feet, which was safe water.)

Like Herman Melville and Walt Whitman, Carl Sandburg and John Steinbeck, Twain traveled all over America. Leaving his native Missouri, he roamed the United States from the Nevada mining claims and Gold Rush streets of San Francisco to newspaper offices in New York and a quiet home in Connecticut. He even spent some time in Hawaii, where he found the native dances "strange and unpleasant." He was fascinated by the glitter and sophistication of New York.

Mark Twain's first best seller was *Innocents Abroad,* a collection of sketches based on his trip to Europe and the Holy Land aboard the steamer *Quaker City.* He was sent by a San Francisco paper and, because of his feeling of western freedom and irresponsibility, termed himself "The Wild Humorist of the Pacific Slope." But before he left for Europe, there is plenty of evidence that Twain had come to a deep understanding of the American spirit. In one of his travel letters, he wrote this:

It is a toiling determined nation, this of ours, and little given to dream. Our Alexanders do not sit down and cry because there are no more worlds to conquer, but snatch off their coats and fall to shinning around and raising corn and cotton and improving sewing machines.

In *Innocents Abroad,* Twain deliberately acted the dumb American and debunked the cultural glories of Europe. He "galloped through the Louvre," and as a lordly Mississippi River pilot, he remarked that Italy's "historical creek," the Arno, would have to have water pumped into it to make it a river.

Many of his remarks now seem merely provincial and in bad taste, but they served to help America break away from Europe, upon which she had been overly dependent in arts and manners.

Mark Twain made many excursions into different worlds, but always he remained democratic and a spokesman for America with all its various types of people, land, and work. Most of this feeling is distilled into his two best-known works, *Tom Sawyer* and *Huckleberry Finn.* So important is *Huckleberry Finn* in literary history that one of our greatest modern writers, Ernest Hemingway, said, "All modern America literature comes from *Huckleberry Finn.*"

Mark Twain was one of our true geniuses and one of the most vivid portrayers of American life. He was one of the very first to bring to the attention of the whole world the fact that there was a particularly American character, unique to us, with many precious and admirable attributes.

Everything Happened to Sam

Mark Twain's humor often reflected the boyish pranks of his childhood. He enjoyed recalling those carefree days, and used the incidents in his fiction.

My mother had a good deal of trouble with me, but I think she enjoyed it. She had none at all with my brother Henry, who was two years younger than I, and I think that the unbroken monotony of his goodness and truthfulness and obedience would have been a burden to her but for the relief and variety which I furnished in the other direction. I was a tonic. I was valuable to her. I never thought of it before but now I see it. I never knew Henry to do a vicious thing toward me or toward anyone else—but he frequently did righteous ones that cost me as heavily. It was his duty to report me, when I needed reporting and neglected to do it myself, and he was very faithful in discharging that duty. He is Sid in *Tom Sawyer*. But Sid was not Henry. Henry was a very much finer and better boy than Sid ever was.

It was Henry who called my mother's attention to the fact that the thread with which she had sewed my collar together to keep me from going in swimming had changed color. My mother would not have discovered it but for that, and she was manifestly piqued when she recognized that that prominent bit of circumstantial evidence had escaped her sharp eye. That detail probably added a detail to my punishment. It is human. We generally visit our shortcomings on somebody else when there is a possible excuse for it—but no matter. I took it out of Henry. There is always compensation for such as are unjustly used. I often took it out of him—sometimes as an advance payment for something which I hadn't yet done. These were occasions when the opportunity was too strong a temptation, and I had to draw on the future. I did not need to copy this idea from my mother and probably didn't. It is most likely that I invented it for myself. Still, she wrought upon that principle upon occasion.

If the incident of the broken sugar bowl is in *Tom Sawyer*—I don't remember whether it is or not—that is an example of it. Henry never stole sugar. He took it openly from the bowl. His mother knew he wouldn't take sugar when she wasn't looking, but she had her doubts about me. Not exactly doubts, either. She knew very well I would. One day when she was not present, Henry took sugar from her prized and precious old-English sugar bowl, which was an heirloom in the family, and he managed to break the bowl. It was the first time I had ever had a chance to tell on him, but he was not disturbed. When my mother came in and saw the bowl lying on the floor in fragments, she was speechless for a minute. I was waiting for her to ask "Who did that?"—so that I could fetch out my news. But it was an error of calculation. When she got through with her silence, she didn't ask anything about it—she merely gave me a crack on the skull with her thimble that I felt all the way down to my heels. Then I broke out with my injured innocence, expecting to make her very sorry that she had punished the wrong one. I expected her to do something remorseful and pathetic. I told her that I

was not the one—it was Henry. But there was no upheaval. She said, without emotion, "It's all right. It isn't any matter. You deserve it for something that you are going to do that I shan't hear about."

There was a stairway outside the house, which led up to the rear part of the second story. One day Henry was sent on an errand, and he took a tin bucket along. I knew he would have to ascend those stairs, so I went up and locked the door on the inside and came down into the garden, which had been newly plowed and was rich in choice, firm clods of black mold. I gathered a generous equipment of these and ambushed him. I waited till he had climbed the stairs and was near the landing and couldn't escape. Then I bombarded him with clods, which he warded off with his tin bucket the best he could, but without much success, for I was a good marksman. The clods smashing against the weather-boarding fetched my mother out to see what was the matter, and I tried to explain that I was amusing Henry. Both of them were after me in a minute, but I knew the way over that high board fence and escaped for that time. After an hour or two, when I ventured back, there was no one around and I thought the incident was closed. But it was not so. Henry was ambushing me. With an unusually competent aim for him, he landed a stone on the side of my head which raised a bump there which felt like the Matterhorn.[1] I hurried to my mother straightaway for sympathy, but she was not strongly moved. It seemed to be her idea that incidents like this would eventually reform me if I harvested enough of them. So the matter was only educational. I had had a sterner view of it than that before.

[1] **Matterhorn** (MAT·er·horn): a mountain in the Swiss Alps.

It was not right to give the cat the "Pain-Killer"; I realize it now. I would not repeat it in these days. But in those "Tom Sawyer" days it was a great and sincere satisfaction to me to see Peter perform under its influence—and if actions do speak as loud as words, he took as much interest in it as I did. It was a most detestable medicine, Perry Davis's Pain-Killer. Mr. Pavey's Negro man, who was a person of good judgment and considerable curiosity, wanted to sample it and I let him. It was his opinion that it was made of hellfire.

Those were cholera days of 1849. The people along the Mississippi were paralyzed with fright. Those who could run away did it. And many died of fright in the flight. Fright killed three persons where the cholera killed one. Those who couldn't flee kept themshelves drenched with cholera preventives, and my mother chose Perry Davis's Pain-Killer for me. She was not distressed about herself. She avoided that kind of preventive. But she made me promise to take a teaspoonful of Pain-Killer every day. Originally it was my intention to keep the promise, but at that time I didn't know as much about Pain-Killer as I knew after my first experiment with it. She didn't watch Henry's bottle—she could trust Henry. But she marked my bottle with a pencil on the label every day and examined it to see if the teaspoonful had been removed. The floor was not carpeted. It had cracks in it and I fed the Pain-Killer to the cracks with very good results—no cholera occurred down below.

It was upon one of these occasions that that friendly cat came waving his tail and supplicating for Pain-Killer— which he got—and then went into those hysterics which ended with his colliding with all the furniture in the room and finally going out of the open win-

dow and carrying the flowerpots with him, just in time for my mother to arrive and look over her glasses in petrified astonishment and say, "What in the world is the matter with Peter?"

I don't remember what my explanation was, but if it is recorded in that book, it may not be the right one.

Whenever my conduct was of such exaggerated impropriety that my mother's extemporary punishments were inadequate, she saved the matter up for Sunday and made me go to church Sunday night—which was a penalty sometimes bearable, perhaps. But as a rule it was not, and I avoided it for the sake of my constitution. She would never believe that I had been to church until she had applied her test. She made me tell her what the text was. That was a simple matter—caused me no trouble. I didn't have to go to church to get a text. I selected one for myself. This worked very well until one time when my text and the one furnished by a neighbor, who had been to church, didn't tally. After that my mother took other methods; I don't know what they were now.

In those days men and boys wore rather long cloaks in the wintertime. They were black and were lined with very bright and showy Scotch plaids. One winter's night when I was starting to church to square a crime of some kind committed during the week, I hid my cloak near the gate and went off and played with the other boys until church was over. Then I returned home. But in the dark I put the cloak on wrong side out, entered the room, got along very well until the temperature of the church was mentioned. My mother said, "It must have been impossible to keep warm there on such a night."

I didn't see the art of that remark and was foolish enough to explain that I wore my cloak all the time that I was in church. She asked if I kept it on from church home, too. I didn't see the bearing of that remark. I said that that was what I had done. She said, "You wore it with that red Scotch plaid outside and glaring? Didn't that attract any attention?"

Of course to continue such a dialogue would have been tedious and unprofitable, and I let it go and took the consequences.

That was about 1849. Tom Nash was a boy of my own age, the postmaster's son. The Mississippi was frozen across and he and I went skating one night, probably without permission. I cannot see why we should go skating in the night unless without permission, for there could be no considerable amusement to be gotten out of skating at midnight if nobody was going to object to it. About midnight, when we were more than half a mile out toward the Illinois shore, we heard some ominous rumbling and grinding and crashing going on between us and the home side of the river, and we knew what it meant: the river was breaking up. We started for home, pretty badly scared. We flew along at full speed whenever the moonlight sifting down between the clouds enabled us to tell which was ice and which was water. In the pauses we waited, started again whenever there was a good bridge of ice, paused again when we came to naked water, and waited in distress until a floating vast cake should bridge that place. It took us an hour to make the trip—a trip which we made in a misery of apprehension all the time. But at last we arrived within a very brief distance of the shore. We waited again. There was another place that needed bridging. All about us the ice was plunging and grinding along and piling itself up in mountains on the shore and the dangers were increasing, not diminishing. We grew very impatient to get to solid ground, so we started too early and went springing from cake to cake. Tom made a miscalculation and fell short. He got a bitter bath, but he was so close to shore that he only had to swim a stroke or two—then his feet struck hard bottom and he crawled out. I arrived a little later, without accident. We had been in a drenching perspiration and Tom's bath was a disaster for him. He took to his bed, sick, and had a procession of diseases. The closing one was scarlet fever and he came out of it stone deaf. Within a year or two speech departed. . . . But some years later he was taught to talk, after a fashion—one couldn't always make out what it was he was trying to say. Of course he could not modulate his voice, since he couldn't hear himself talk. When he supposed he was talking low and confidentially, you could hear him in Illinois.

Four years ago I was invited by the University of Missouri to come out there and receive the honorary degree of LL.D.[1] I took that opportunity to spend a week in Hannibal—a city now, a village in my day. It had been fifty-

[1] LL.D.: Doctor of Laws.

five years since Tom Nash and I had had that adventure. When I was at the railway station ready to leave Hannibal, there was a great crowd of citizens there. I saw Tom Nash approaching me across a vacant space and I walked toward him, for I recognized him at once. He was old and white-headed, but the boy of fifteen was still visible in him. He came up to me, made a trumpet of his hands at my ear, nodded his head toward the citizens, and said confidentially—in a yell like a foghorn—"Same darned fools, Sam."

THE FACT IS—

1. How was Sam a "tonic" for his mother?

2. In what three ways did Sam dispose of Davis's Pain-Killer to avoid taking it himself?

3. How did Sam's mother try to discover whether or not Sam had been to church on Sunday?

HAPPY MEMORIES

1. "We generally visit our shortcomings on somebody else when there is a possible excuse for it." How did Sam demonstrate this human characteristic? From your own experience, give an example.

2. Select two or three incidents in this story, such as the sugar-bowl incident, and explain what the humor is.

3. The story of Tom Nash and Sam and their midnight adventure on the ice recalls vividly an unforgettable boyhood experience. Write a paragraph describing an event which you will always remember, and explain why.

A WORD TO REMEMBER: tedious

Tedious, an adjective, means "tiresome because of length or dullness; boring." The dialogue between Sam and his mother about the "red Scotch plaid" is described as tedious. Any task, such as homework, may sometimes become boring. Give two antonyms for *tedious*.

Jim Wolf
and the Cats

Shyness has embarrassed many young people. Did you

—or anyone you know—ever have as much trouble as

Jim Wolf did because of this human peculiarity?

It was back in those far-distant days that Jim Wolf came to us. He was from Shelbyville, a hamlet thirty or forty miles back in the country, and he brought all his native sweetness and gentleness and simplicities with him. He was approaching seventeen, a grave and slender lad, trustful, honest, honorable, a creature to love and cling to. And he was incredibly bashful. He was with us a good while but he could never conquer that peculiarity. He could not be at ease in the presence of any woman, not even in my good and gentle mother's; and as to speaking to any girl, it was wholly impossible.

It is to this kind that untoward things happen. My sister gave a "candy-pull" on a winter's night. I was too young to be of the company and Jim was too diffident. I was sent up to bed early and Jim followed of his own motion. His room was in the new part of the house and his window looked out on the roof of the L annex. That roof was six inches deep in snow and the snow had an ice crust upon it which was as slick as glass. Out of the comb of the roof projected a short chimney, a common resort for sentimental cats on moonlight nights—and this was a moonlight night. Down at the eaves below the chimney, a canopy of dead vines spread away to some posts, making a cozy shelter. And after an hour or two the rollicking crowd of young ladies and gentlemen grouped themselves in its shade, with their saucers of liquid and piping-hot candy disposed about them on the frozen ground to cool. There was joyous chaffing and joking and laughter—peal upon peal of it.

About this time a couple of old, disreputable tomcats got up on the chimney and started a heated argument about something; also about this time I gave up trying to get to sleep and went visiting to Jim's room. He was awake and fuming about the cats and their intolerable yowling. I asked him, mockingly, why he didn't climb out and drive them away. He was nettled and said overboldly that for two cents he *would*.

It was a rash remark and was probably repented of before it was fairly out of his mouth. But it was too late—he was committed. I knew him; and I knew he would rather break his neck than back down, if I egged him on judiciously.

"Oh, of course you would! Who's doubting it?"

It galled him and he burst out, with sharp irritation, "Maybe *you* doubt it!"

"I? Oh, no! I shouldn't think of such a thing. You are always doing wonderful things, with your mouth."

He was in a passion now. He snatched on his yarn socks and began to raise the window, saying in a voice quivering with anger, "*You* think I dasn't—you do! Think what you blame please. I don't care what you think. I'll show you!"

The window made him rage; it wouldn't stay up.

I said, "Never mind, I'll hold it."

Indeed, I would have done anything to help. I was only a boy and was already in a radiant heaven of anticipation. He climbed carefully out, clung to the window sill until his feet were safely placed, then began to pick his perilous way on all fours along the glassy comb, a foot and a hand on each side of it.

I believe I enjoy it now as much as I did then; yet it is nearly fifty years ago. The frosty breeze flapped his short shirt about his lean legs; the crystal roof shone like polished marble in the intense glory of the moon; the unconscious cats sat erect upon the chimney, alertly watching each other, lashing their tails, and pouring out their hollow grievances. And slowly and cautiously Jim crept on, flapping as he went, the gay and frolicsome young creatures under the vine canopy unaware, and outraging these solemnities with their misplaced laughter. Every time Jim slipped, I had a hope; but always on he crept and disappointed it. At last he was within reaching distance. He paused, raised himself carefully up, measured his distance deliberately, then made a frantic grab at the nearest cat—and missed it. Of course he lost his balance. His heels flew up; he struck on his back; and like a rocket he darted down the roof feet first, crashed through the dead vines and landed in a sitting position in fourteen saucers of red-hot candy in the midst of all that party—and dressed as *he* was—this lad who could not look a girl in the face with his clothes on. There was a wild scramble and a storm of shrieks and Jim fled up the stairs, dripping broken crockery all the way.

The incident was ended. But I was not done with it yet, though I supposed I was. Eighteen or twenty years later I arrived in New York from California, and by that time I had failed in all my other undertakings and had stumbled into literature without intending it. This was early in 1867. I was offered a large sum to write something for the *Sunday Mercury* and I answered with the tale of "Jim Wolf and the Cats." I also collected the money for it— twenty-five dollars. It seemed overpay, but I did not say anything about that, for I was not so scrupulous then as I am now.

THE FACT IS—

1. How did Sam, the narrator, get Jim to crawl out onto the roof?
2. How did Jim happen to land on the ground during the party?
3. What use did Sam make of this story years later?

JAMES FENIMORE COOPER, MARK TWAIN, AND YOU: AMERICAN WRITERS

Writing styles change; some writers seem frozen in their periods as hard as the ice crust Jim Wolf crawled out onto. (Not long ago, for example, most respectable writers would have avoided ending a sentence with *onto*, because their rule said, "Don't end a sentence with a preposition.") Mark Twain, great student of writing styles, was highly critical of James Fenimore Cooper, who wrote *The Last of the Mohicans* and other famous adventure stories about seventy years before Twain set up a list of "rules governing literary art." According to Twain, Cooper violated all the rules, especially Rule 18: "Employ a simple and straightforward style."

Another seventy years have passed since Mark Twain's essays on Cooper. Perhaps you, judging by modern standards, don't think Twain's style gave him the right to criticize anyone else's. Can you rewrite the following description from "Jim Wolf and the Cats" in a more "simple and straightforward style"?

> The frosty breeze flapped his short shirt about his lean legs; the crystal roof shone like polished marble in the intense glory of the moon; the unconscious cats sat erect upon the chimney, alertly watching each other, lashing their tails, and pouring out their hollow grievances.

Choose from the story another sentence, one you consider complicated and roundabout. Rewrite the sentence and compare your rewriting with your classmates. Did anyone improve on Mark Twain?

A WORD TO REMEMBER: diffident

Some people, like Jim in the story, are diffident. Because Jim was timid and lacked confidence in himself, he wouldn't join the young people at the candy-pull. Also, because of this extreme diffidence—or shyness—he was painfully embarrassed when he "crashed" the party.

In a substantial original sentence, show your understanding of *diffident*. Give one or two antonyms for *diffident*.

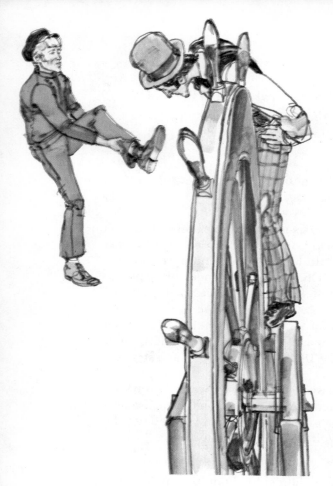

Sam Squares His Long Account with His Boss

Young Sam Clemens sailed under a master pilot, Horace Bixby. He realized his dream of becoming a riverboat pilot in spite of many obstacles, one of which was a boss named Brown.

"When I was a boy, there was but one permanent ambition among my comrades in our village on the west bank of the Mississippi River. That was to be a steamboatman. We had transient ambitions of other sorts, but they were only transient. When a circus came and went, it left us all burning to become clowns; the first Negro minstrel show that ever came to our section left us all suffering to try that kind of life. Now and then we had a hope that if we lived and were good, God would permit us to be pirates. These ambitions faded out, each in its turn; but the ambition to be a steamboatman always remained."

During the two or two and a half years of my apprenticeship, I served under many pilots, and had experience of many kinds of steamboatmen and many varieties of steamboats. For it was not always convenient for Mr. Bixby to have me with him, and in such cases he sent me with somebody else. I am to this day profiting somewhat by that experience; for in that brief, sharp schooling, I got personally and familiarly acquainted with about all the different types of human nature that are to be found in fiction, biography, or history. The fact is daily borne in upon me that the average shore-employment requires as much as forty years to equip a man with this sort of an education. When I say I am still profiting by this thing, I do not mean that it has constituted me a judge of men. No, it has not done that, for judges of men are born, not made. My profit is various in kind and degree, but the feature of it which I value most is the zest which that early experience has given to my later reading. When I find a well-drawn character in fiction or biography, I generally take a warm personal interest in him, for the reason that I have known him before—met him on the river.

The figure that comes before me oftenest, out of the shadows of that vanished time, is that of Brown, of the steamer *Pennsylvania*, . . . whose memory was so good and tiresome. He was a middle-aged, long, slim, bony, smooth-shaven, horse-faced, ignorant, stingy, malicious, snarling, fault-hunting, mote-magnifying tyrant. I early got the habit of coming on watch with dread at my heart. No matter how good a time I might have been having with the off-watch below, and no matter how high my spirits might be when I started aloft, my soul became lead in my body the moment I approached the pilothouse.

I still remember the first time I ever entered the presence of that man. The boat had backed out from St. Louis and was "straightening down." I ascended to the pilothouse in high feather, and very proud to be semiofficially a member of the executive family of so fast and famous a boat. Brown was at the wheel. I paused in the middle of the room, all fixed to make my bow, but Brown did not look around. I thought he took a furtive glance at me out of the corner of his eye, but as not even this notice was repeated, I judged I had been mistaken. By this time he was picking his way among some dangerous "breaks" abreast the woodyards; therefore it would not be proper to interrupt him; so I stepped softly to the high bench and took a seat.

There was silence for ten minutes. Then my new boss turned and inspected me deliberately and painstakingly from head to heel for about—as it seemed to me—a quarter of an hour. After which he removed his countenance and I saw it no more for some seconds; then it came around once more, and this question greeted me:

"Are you Horace Bixby's cub?"

"Yes, sir."

After this there was a pause and another inspection. Then:

"What's your name?"

I told him. He repeated it after me. It was probably the only thing he ever forgot; for although I was with him many months, he never addressed himself to me in any other way than "Here!" and then his command followed.

"Where was you born?"

"In Florida, Missouri."

A pause. Then:

"Dern sight better stayed there!"

By means of a dozen or so of pretty direct questions, he pumped my family history out of me.

The leads [1] were going now in the first crossing. This interrupted the inquest. When the leads had been laid in, he resumed:

"How long you been on the river?"

I told him. After a pause:

"Where'd you get them shoes?"

I gave him the information.

"Hold up your foot!"

---

[1] **leads** (LEDZ): weighted lines used to measure the depth of water. They are handled by the leadsman.

I did so. He stepped back, examined the shoe minutely and contemptuously, scratching his head thoughtfully, tilting his high sugar-loaf hat well forward to facilitate the operation, then ejaculated, "Well, I'll be dod derned!" and returned to his wheel.

What occasion there was to be dod derned about it is a thing which is still as much of a mystery to me now as it was then. It must have been all of fifteen minutes—fifteen minutes of dull, homesick silence—before that long horseface swung round upon me again —and then what a change! It was as red as fire, and every muscle in it was working. Now came this shriek:

"Here! You going to set there all day?"

I lit in the middle of the floor, shot there by the electric suddenness of the surprise. As soon as I could get my voice, I said apologetically, "I have had no orders, sir."

"You've had no *orders*! My, what a fine bird we are! We must have *orders*! Our father was a *gentleman*—and *we've* been to *school*. Yes, *we* are a gentleman, *too*, and got to have *orders*! Orders, is it? ORDERS is what you want! Dod dern my skin, *I'll* learn you to swell yourself up and blow around *here* about your dod-derned *orders*! G'way from the wheel!" (I had approached it without knowing it.)

I moved back a step or two and stood as in a dream, all my senses stupefied by this frantic assault.

"What you standing there for? Take that ice pitcher down to the texas-tender! Come, move along, and don't you be all day about it!"

The moment I got back to the pilot-house Brown said:

"Here! What was you doing down there all this time?"

"I couldn't find the texas-tender; I had to go all the way to the pantry."

"Derned likely story! Fill up the stove."

I proceeded to do so. He watched me like a cat. Presently he shouted:

"Put down that shovel! Derndest numskull I ever saw—ain't even got sense enough to load up a stove."

All through the watch this sort of thing went on. Yes, and the subsequent watches were much like it during a stretch of months. As I have said, I soon got the habit of coming on duty with dread. The moment I was in the presence, even in the darkest night, I could feel those yellow eyes upon me, and knew their owner was watching for a pretext to spit out some venom on me. Preliminarily he would say:

"Here! Take the wheel."

Two minutes later:

"*Where* in the nation you going to? Pull her down! Pull her down!"

After another moment:

"Say! you going to hold her all day? Let her go—meet her! meet her!"

Then he would jump from the bench, snatch the wheel from me, and meet her himself, pouring out wrath upon me all the time.

George Ritchie was the other pilot's cub. He was having good times now; for his boss, George Ealer, was as kind-hearted as Brown wasn't. Ritchie had steered for Brown the season before; consequently, he knew exactly how to entertain himself and plague me, all by one operation. Whenever I took the wheel for a moment on Ealer's watch, Ritchie would sit back on the bench and play Brown, with continual ejaculations of "Snatch her! snatch her! Derndest mudcat I ever saw!" "Here! Where are you going *now*? Going to run over that snag?" "Pull her *down*! Don't you hear me? Pull her down!" "There she goes! *Just* as I expected! I *told* you not to cramp that reef. G'way from the wheel!"

So I always had a rough time of it, no matter whose watch it was; and sometimes it seemed to me that Ritchie's good-natured badgering was pretty nearly as aggravating as Brown's dead-earnest nagging.

I often wanted to kill Brown, but this would not answer. A cub had to take everything his boss gave in the way of vigorous comment and criticism; and we all believed that there was a United States law making it a penitentiary offense to strike or threaten a pilot who was on duty. However, I could *imagine* myself killing Brown. There was no law against that; and that was the thing I used always to do the moment I was abed. Instead of going over my river in my mind, as was my duty, I threw business aside for pleasure and killed Brown. I killed Brown every night for months; not in old, stale, commonplace ways, but in new and picturesque ones—ways that were sometimes surprising for freshness of design and ghastliness of situation and environment.

Brown was *always* watching for a pretext to find fault; and if he could find no plausible pretext, he would invent one. He would scold you for shaving a shore, and for not shaving it; for hugging a bar, and for not hugging it; for "pulling down" when not invited, and for *not* pulling down when not invited, for firing up without orders, and for waiting *for* orders. In a word, it was his invariable rule to find fault with everything you did; and another invariable rule of his was to throw all his remarks (to you) into the form of an insult.

One day we were approaching New Madrid, bound-down and heavily laden. Brown was at one side of the wheel, steering; I was at the other, standing by to "pull down" or "shove up." He cast a furtive glance at me every now and then. I had long ago learned what that meant; viz., he was trying to invent a trap for me. I wondered what shape it was going to take. By and by he stepped back from the wheel and said in his usual snarly way:

"Here! See if you've got gumption enough to round her to."

This was simply *bound* to be a success. Nothing could prevent it, for he had never allowed me to round the boat to before. Consequently, no matter how I might do the thing, he could find free fault with it. He stood back there with his greedy eye on me, and the result was what might have been foreseen: I lost my head in a quarter of a minute, and didn't know what I was about. I started too early to bring the boat around, but detected a green gleam of joy in Brown's eye, and corrected my mistake. I started around once more while too high up, but corrected myself again in time. I made other false moves and still managed to save myself. But at last I grew so confused and anxious that I tumbled into the very worst blunder of all—I got too far *down* before beginning to fetch the boat around. Brown's chance was come.

His face turned red with passion; he made one bound, hurled me across the house with a sweep of his arm, spun the wheel down, and began to pour out a stream of vituperation upon me which lasted till he was out of breath. In the course of this speech, he called me all the different kinds of hard names he could think of, and once or twice I thought he was even going to swear—but he had never done that, and he didn't this time. "Dod dern" was the nearest he ventured to the luxury of swearing, for he had been brought up with a wholesome respect for future fire and brimstone.

That was an uncomfortable hour; for there was a big audience on the hurricane deck. When I went to bed that

night, I killed Brown in seventeen different ways—all of them new.

Two trips later I got into serious trouble. Brown was steering; I was "pulling down." My younger brother [Henry] appeared on the hurricane deck and shouted to Brown to stop at some landing or other, a mile or so below. Brown gave no intimation that he had heard anything. But that was his way: he never condescended to take notice of an underclerk. The wind was blowing; Brown was deaf (although he always pretended he wasn't), and I very much doubted if he had heard the order. If I had had two heads, I would have spoken; but as I had only one, it seemed judicious to take care of it. So I kept still.

Presently, sure enough, we went sailing by that plantation. Captain Klinefelter appeared on the deck, and said:

"Let her come around, sir, let her come around. Didn't Henry tell you to land here?"

"*No,* sir!"

"I sent him up to do it."

"He *did* come up; and that's all the good it done, the dod-derned fool. He never said anything."

"Didn't *you* hear him?" asked the captain of me.

Of course I didn't want to be mixed up in this business, but there was no way to avoid it; so I said:

"Yes, sir."

I knew what Brown's next remark would be, before he uttered it. It was:

"Shut your mouth! You never heard anything of the kind."

I closed my mouth, according to instructions. An hour later Henry entered the pilothouse, unaware of what had been going on. He was a thoroughly inoffensive boy, and I was sorry to see him come, for I knew Brown would have no pity on him. Brown began straightaway:

"Here! Why didn't you tell me we'd got to land at that plantation?"

"I did tell you, Mr. Brown."

"It's a lie!"

I said:

"You lie yourself. He did tell you."

Brown glared at me in unaffected surprise; and for as much as a moment, he was entirely speechless. Then he shouted at me:

"I'll attend to your case in a half a minute!" then to Henry, "And you leave the pilothouse. Out with you!"

It was pilot law, and must be obeyed. The boy started out and even had his foot on the upper step outside the door, when Brown, with a sudden access of fury, picked up a ten-pound lump of coal and sprang after him. But I was between, with a heavy stool, and I hit Brown a good honest blow which stretched him out.

I had committed the crime of crimes —I had lifted my hand against a pilot on duty! I supposed I was booked for the penitentiary sure, and couldn't be booked any surer if I went on and squared my long account with this person while I had the chance. Consequently I stuck to him and pounded him with my fists a considerable time. I do not know how long, the pleasure of it probably made it seem longer than it really was. But in the end he struggled free and jumped up and sprang to the wheel: a very natural solicitude, for, all this time, here was this steamboat tearing down the river at the rate of fifteen miles an hour and nobody at the helm! However, Eagle Bend was two miles wide at this bank-full stage and correspondingly long and deep: and the boat was steering herself straight down the middle and taking no chances. Still, that was only luck—a body *might* have found her charging into the woods.

Perceiving at a glance that the *Pennsylvania* was in no danger, Brown gathered up the big spyglass, war-club fashion, and ordered me out of the pilot-house with more than Comanche bluster. But I was not afraid of him now; so, instead of going, I tarried, and criticized his grammar. I reformed his ferocious speeches for him and put them into good English, calling his attention to the advantage of pure English over the dialect of the Pennsylvania collieries whence he was extracted. He could have done his part to admiration in a crossfire of mere vituperation, of course, but he was not equipped for this species of controversy. So he presently laid aside his glass and took the wheel, muttering and shaking his head; and I retired to the bench. The racket had brought everybody to the hurricane deck, and I trembled when I saw the old captain looking up from amid the crowd. I said to myself, "Now I *am* done for!" for although, as a rule, he was so fatherly and indulgent toward the boat's family, and so patient of minor shortcomings, he could be stern enough when the fault was worth it.

I tried to imagine what he *would* do to a cub pilot who had been guilty of such a crime as mine, committed on a boat guard deep with costly freight and alive with passengers. Our watch was nearly ended. I thought I would go and hide somewhere till I got a chance to slide ashore. So I slipped out of the pilothouse and down the steps and around to the texas door, and was in the act of gliding within when the captain confronted me! I dropped my head, and he stood over me in silence a moment or two, then said impressively:

"Follow me."

I dropped into his wake; he led the way to his parlor in the forward end of the texas. We were alone now. He closed the after door; then moved slowly to the forward one and closed that. He sat down; I stood before him.

He looked at me some little time, then said:

"So you have been fighting Mr. Brown?"

I answered meekly:

"Yes, sir."

"Do you know that that is a very serious matter?"

"Yes, sir."

"Are you aware that this boat was plowing down the river fully five minutes with no one at the wheel?"

"Yes, sir."

"Did you strike him first?"

"Yes, sir."

"What with?"

"A stool, sir."

"Hard?"

"Middling, sir."

"Did it knock him down?"

"He—he fell, sir."

"Did you follow it up? Did you do anything further?"

"Yes, sir."

"What did you do?"

"Pounded him, sir."

"Pounded him?"

"Yes, sir."

"Did you pound him much? That is, severely?"

"One might call it that, sir, maybe."

"I'm deuced glad of it! Hark ye, never mention that I said that. You have been guilty of a great crime; and don't you ever be guilty of it again, on the boat. *But*—lay for him ashore! Give him a good sound thrashing, do you hear? I'll pay the expenses. Now, go—and mind you, not a word of this to anybody. Clear out with you! You've been guilty of a great crime, you whelp!"

I slid out, happy with the sense of a close shave and a mighty deliverance; and I heard him laughing to himself and slapping his fat thighs after I had closed his door.

When Brown came off watch, he

went straight to the captain, who was talking with some passengers on the boiler deck, and demanded that I be put ashore in New Orleans—and added:

"I'll never turn a wheel on this boat again while that cub stays."

The captain said:

"But he needn't come round when you are on watch, Mr. Brown."

"I won't even stay on the same boat with him. *One* of us has got to go ashore."

"Very well," said the captain, "let it be yourself," and resumed his talk with the passengers.

During the brief remainder of the trip, I knew how an emancipated slave feels, for I was an emancipated slave myself. While we lay at landings, I listened to George Ealer's flute, or to his readings from his two Bibles, that is to say, Goldsmith and Shakespeare, or I played chess with him—and would have beaten him sometimes, only he always took back his last move and ran the game out differently.

THE FACT IS—

1. What was a "cub" in Mark Twain's day? Who were the two cubs on the *Pennsylvania?*

2. How did Twain benefit throughout his life from his youthful experiences on the river?

3. How did George Ritchie entertain himself in the pilothouse?

4. What was "the crime of crimes" on a riverboat? Who committed such an act?

"ORDERS IS ORDERS"

1. Was Mr. Brown a bully? Why, or why not? Explain your answer.

2. Why did Brown hate Mark? Describe a situation in your own life, or one you have read about in which a person like Brown has resented another person, and explain why.

3. The captain was delighted to learn that the young "cub" had "pounded" Brown, even though Mark Twain was "guilty of a great crime." Write a careful paragraph describing the character of the captain. Use references to the story.

A WORD TO REMEMBER: contemptuously

Brown "examined the shoe . . . contemptuously," that is, scornfully or disdainfully. *Contemptuous* and *contemptible* are easily confused, though they have different meanings. Look up both words in a reliable dictionary and use each one in a sentence.

Mrs. Clemens—
an Expression
of Appreciation

In the beginning of February 1870, I was married to Miss Olivia L. Langdon, and I took up my residence in Buffalo, New York. Tomorrow will be the thirty-sixth anniversary of our marriage. My wife passed from this life one year and eight months ago in Florence, Italy, after an unbroken illness of twenty-two months' duration.

I saw her first in the form of an ivory miniature in her brother Charley's stateroom in the steamer *Quaker City* in the Bay of Smyrna, in the summer of 1867, when she was in her twenty-second year. I saw her in the flesh for the first time in New York in the following December. She was slender and beautiful and girlish—and she was both girl and woman. She remained both girl and woman to the last day of her life. Under a grave and gentle exterior burned inextinguishable fires of sympathy, energy, devotion, enthusiasm, and absolutely limitless affection. She was always frail in body, and she lived upon her spirit, whose hopefulness and courage were indestructible.

She became an invalid at sixteen through a partial paralysis caused by falling on the ice, and she was never strong again while her life lasted. After that fall she was not able to leave her bed during two years, nor was she able to lie in any position except upon her back. All the great physicians were brought to Elmira, one after another during that time, but there was no helpful result. In those days both worlds were well acquainted with the name of Doctor Newton, a man who was regarded in both worlds as a quack. He moved through the land in state, in magnificence, like a potentate, like a circus. Notice of his coming was spread upon the dead walls in vast colored posters, along with his formidable portrait, several weeks beforehand.

One day Andrew Langdon, a relative of the Langdon family, came to the house and said, "You have tried everybody else; now try Doctor Newton, the quack. He is downtown at the Rathbun House, practicing upon the well-to-do at war prices and upon the poor for nothing. I saw him wave his hands over Jake Brown's head and take his crutches away from him and send him about his business as good as new. I saw him do the like with some other cripples. They may have been 'temporaries' instituted for advertising purposes, and not genuine. But Jake is genuine. Send for Newton."

Newton came. He found the young girl upon her back. Over her was suspended a tackle from the ceiling. It had been there a long time but unused. It was put there in the hope that by its steady motion she might be lifted to a sitting posture, at intervals, for rest. But it proved a failure. Any attempt to raise her brought nausea and exhaustion and had to be relinquished. Newton opened the windows—long darkened—and delivered a short, fervent prayer. Then he put an arm behind her shoulders and said, "Now we will sit up, my child."

The family were alarmed and tried to stop him, but he was not disturbed and raised her up. She sat several minutes without nausea or discomfort. Then Newton said, "Now we will walk a few steps, my child." He took her out of bed and supported her while she walked several steps. Then he said, "I have reached the limit of my art. She is not cured. It is not likely that she will ever be cured. She will never be able to walk far, but after a little daily practice she will be able to walk one or two hundred yards, and she can depend on being able to do that for the rest of her life."

His charge was fifteen hundred dollars and it was easily worth a hundred thousand. For from the day that she was eighteen until she was fifty-six, she was always able to walk a couple of hundred yards without stopping to rest; and more than once I saw her walk a quarter of a mile without serious fatigue.

Newton was mobbed in Dublin, in London, and in other places. He was rather frequently mobbed in Europe and in America but never by the grateful Langdons and Clemenses. I met Newton once, in after years, and asked him what his secret was. He said he didn't know but thought perhaps some subtle form of electricity proceeded from his body and wrought the cures.

Perfect truth, perfect honesty, perfect candor, were qualities of my wife's character which were born with her. Her judgments of people and things were sure and accurate. Her intuitions almost never deceived her. In her judgments of the characters and acts of both friends and strangers, there was always room for charity, and this charity never failed. I have compared and contrasted her with hundreds of persons and my conviction remains that hers was the most perfect character I have ever met. And I may add that she was the most winningly dignified person I have ever known. Her character and disposition were of the sort that not only invite worship but command it. No servant ever left her service who deserved to remain in it. And as she could choose with a glance of her eye, the servants she selected did in almost all cases deserve to remain, and they did remain. She was always cheerful and she was always able to communicate her cheerfulness to others. During the nine years that we spent in poverty and debt, she was always able to reason me out of my despairs and find a bright side to the clouds and make me see it. In all that time I never knew her to utter a word of regret concerning our altered circumstances, nor did I ever know her children to do the like. For she had taught them and they drew their fortitude from her. The love which she bestowed upon those whom she loved took the form of worship, and in that form it was returned—returned by relatives, friends, and the servants of her household.

It was a strange combination which wrought into one individual, so to speak, by marriage—her disposition and character and mine. She poured out her prodigal affections in kisses and caresses and in a vocabulary of endearments whose profusion was always an astonishment to me. I was born reserved as to endearments of speech and caresses, and hers broke upon me as the summer waves break upon Gibraltar. I was reared in that atmosphere of reserve. As I have already said, I never knew a member of my father's family to kiss another member of it except once, and that at a deathbed. And our village was not a kissing community. The kissing and caressing ended with courtship—along with the deadly piano-playing of that day.

She had the heart-free laugh of a girl. It came seldom, but when it broke upon the ear, it was as inspiring as music. I heard it for the last time when she had been occupying her sickbed for more than a year and I made a written note of it at the time—a note not to be repeated.

Tomorrow will be the thirty-sixth anniversary. We were married in her father's house in Elmira, New York, and went next day by special train to Buffalo, along with the whole Langdon family and with the Beechers and the Twichells, who had solemnized the marriage. We were to live in Buffalo, where I was to be one of the editors of the Buffalo *Express* and a part owner of the paper. I knew nothing about Buffalo, but I had made my household arrangements there through a friend, by letter. I had instructed him to find a boardinghouse of as respectable a character as my light salary as editor would command. We were received at about nine o'clock at the station in Buffalo and were put into several sleighs and driven all over America, as it seemed to me— for apparently we turned all the corners in the town and followed all the streets there were—I scolding freely and characterizing that friend of mine in very uncomplimentary ways for securing a boardinghouse that apparently had no definite locality. But there was a conspiracy—and my bride knew of it, but I was in ignorance. Her father, Jervis Langdon, had bought and furnished a new house for us in the fashionable street, Delaware Avenue, and had laid in a cook and housemaids and a brisk

and electric young coachman, an Irishman, Patrick McAleer. And we were being driven all over that city in order that one sleighful of these people could have time to go to the house and see that the gas was lighted all over it and a hot supper prepared for the crowd. We arrived at last, and when I entered that fairy place, my indignation reached high-water mark, and without any reserve I delivered my opinion to that friend of mine for being so stupid as to put us into a boardinghouse whose terms would be far out of my reach. Then Mr. Langdon brought forward a very pretty box and opened it and took from it a deed of the house. So the comedy ended very pleasantly and we sat down to supper.

The company departed about midnight and left us alone in our new quarters. Then Ellen, the cook, came in to get orders for the morning's marketing —and neither of us knew whether beefsteak was sold by the barrel or by the yard. We exposed our ignorance and Ellen was full of Irish delight over it. Patrick McAleer, that brisk young Irishman, came in to get his orders for next day—and that was our first glimpse of him.

It sounds easy and swift and unobstructed but that was not the way of it. It did not happen in that smooth and comfortable way. There was a deal of courtship. There were three or four proposals of marriage and just as many declinations. I was roving far and wide on the lecture beat, but I managed to arrive in Elmira every now and then and renew the siege. Once I dug an invitation out of Charley Langdon to come and stay a week. It was a pleasant week but it had to come to an end. I was not able to invent any way to get the invitation enlarged. No schemes that I could contrive seemed likely to deceive. They did not even deceive me, and when a person cannot deceive himself, the chances are against his being able to deceive other people. But at last help and good fortune came and from a most unexpected quarter. It was one of those cases so frequent in the past centuries, so infrequent in our day—a case where the hand of Providence is in it.

I was ready to leave for New York. A democrat wagon stood outside the main gate with my trunk in it and Barney, the coachman, in the front seat with the reins in his hand. It was eight or nine in the evening and dark. I bade good-by to the grouped family on the front porch, and Charley and I went out and climbed into the wagon. We took our places back of the coachman on the remaining seat, which was aft toward the end of the wagon and was only a temporary arrangement for our accommodation and was not fastened in its place; a fact which, most fortunately for me, we were not aware of. Charley was smoking. Barney touched up the horse with the whip. He made a sudden spring forward. Charley and I went over the stern of the wagon backward. In the darkness the red bud of fire on the end of his cigar described a curve through the air which I can see yet. This was the only visible thing in all that gloomy scenery. I struck exactly on the top of my head and stood up that way for a moment, then crumbled down to the earth unconscious. It was a very good unconsciousness for a person who had not rehearsed the part. It was a cobblestone gutter and they had been repairing it. My head struck in a dish formed by the conjunction of four cobblestones. That depression was half full of fresh new sand and this made a competent cushion. My head did not touch any of those cobblestones. I got not a bruise. I was not even jolted. Nothing was the matter with me at all.

Charley was considerably battered, but in his solicitude for me, he was substantially unaware of it. The whole family swarmed out, Theodore Crane in the van with a flask of brandy. He poured enough of it between my lips to strangle me and make me bark but it did not abate my unconsciousness. I was taking care of that myself. It was very pleasant to hear the pitying remarks trickling around over me. That was one of the happiest half-dozen moments of my life. There was nothing to mar it—except that I had escaped damage. I was afraid that this would be discovered sooner or later and would shorten my visit. I was such a dead weight that it required the combined strength of Barney and Mr. Langdon, Theodore and Charley to lug me into the house, but it was accomplished. I was there. I recognized that this was victory. I was there. I was safe to be an incumbrance for an indefinite length of time—but for a length of time, at any rate, and a Providence was in it.

They set me up in an armchair in the parlor and sent for the family physician. Poor old creature, it was wrong to rout him out but it was business, and I was too unconscious to protest. Mrs. Crane —dear soul, she was in this house. three days ago, gray and beautiful and as sympathetic as ever—Mrs. Crane brought a bottle of some kind of liquid fire whose function was to reduce contusions. But I knew that mine would deride it and scoff at it. She poured this on my head and pawed it around with her hand, stroking and massaging, the fierce stuff dribbling down my backbone and marking its way, inch by inch, with the sensation of a forest fire. But I was satisfied. When she was getting worn out, her husband, Theodore, suggested that she take a rest and let Livy carry on the assuaging for a while. That was very pleasant. I should have been obliged to recover presently if it hadn't been for that. But under Livy's manipulations— if they had continued—I should probably be unconscious to this day. It was very delightful, those manipulations. So delightful, so comforting, so enchanting, that they even soothed the fire out of that fiendish successor to Perry Davis's "Pain-Killer."

Then that old family doctor arrived and went at the matter in an educated and practical way—that is to say, he started a search expedition for contusions and humps and bumps and announced that there were none. He said that if I would go to bed and forget my adventure, I would be all right in the morning—which was not so. I was not all right in the morning. I didn't intend to be all right and I was far from being all right. But I said I only needed rest and I didn't need that doctor any more.

I got a good three days' extension out of that adventure and it helped a good deal. It pushed my suit forward several steps. A subsequent visit completed the matter and we became engaged conditionally; the condition being that the parents should consent.

In a private talk Mr. Langdon called my attention to something I had already noticed—which was that I was an almost entirely unknown person; that no one around about knew me except Charley, and he was too young to be a reliable judge of men; that I was from the other side of the continent and that only those people out there would be able to furnish me a character in case I had one —so he asked me for references. I furnished them and he said we would now suspend our industries and I could go away and wait until he could write to those people and get answers.

In due course answers came. I was sent for and we had another private conference. I had referred him to six prominent men, among them two clergymen (these were all San Franciscans), and he himself had written to a bank cashier who had in earlier years been a Sunday-School superintendent in Elmira and well known to Mr. Langdon. All those men were frank to a fault. They not only spoke in disapproval of me but they were quite unnecessarily and exaggeratedly enthusiastic about it. One clergyman (Stebbins) and the ex-Sunday-School superintendent (I wish I could recall his name) added to their black testimony the conviction that I would fill a drunkard's grave. It was just one of those usual long-distance prophecies. There being no time limit, there is no telling how long you may have to wait. I have waited until now and fulfillment seems as far away as ever.

The reading of the letters being finished, there was a good deal of pause and it consisted largely of sadness and solemnity. I couldn't think of anything to say. Mr. Langdon was apparently in the same condition. Finally he raised his handsome head, fixed his clear and candid eye upon me, and said, "What kind of people are these? Haven't you a friend in the world?"

I said, "Apparently not."

Then he said, "I'll be your friend myself. Take the girl. I know you better than they do."

Thus dramatically and happily was my fate settled. Afterward, hearing me talking lovingly, admiringly, and fervently of Joe Goodman, he asked me where Goodman lived. I told him out on the Pacific coast. He said, "Why, he seems to be a friend of yours! Is he?"

I said, "Indeed he is; the best one I ever had."

"Why, then," he said, "what could you have been thinking of? Why didn't you refer me to him?"

I said, "Because he would have lied just as straightforwardly on the other side. The others gave me all the vices; Goodman would have given me all the virtues. You wanted unprejudiced testimony, of course. I knew you wouldn't get it from Goodman. I did believe you would get it from those others and possibly you did. But it was certainly less complimentary than I was expecting."

The date of our engagement was

February 4, 1869. The engagement ring was plain and of heavy gold. That date was engraved inside of it. A year later I took it from her finger and prepared it to do service as a wedding ring by having the wedding date added and engraved inside of it—February 2, 1870. It was never again removed from her finger for even a moment.

In Italy when death had restored her vanished youth to her sweet face and she lay fair and beautiful and looking as she had looked when she was girl and bride, they were going to take that ring from her finger to keep for the children. But I prevented that sacrilege. It is buried with her.

In the beginning of our engagement, the proofs of my first book, *Innocents Abroad*, began to arrive and she read them with me. She also edited them. She was my faithful, judicious, and painstaking editor from that day forth until within three or four months of her death—a stretch of more than a third of a century.

THE FACT IS—

1. How long were Sam and Olivia married?
2. Who was Doctor Newton? How did he help Olivia?
3. What surprise awaited the newly married couple in Buffalo?
4. How did Sam extend his week's visit at the Langdon home?
5. What was Mark Twain's first book?

"TILL DEATH DO US PART"

1. Sam Clemens describes his wife Olivia as "the most perfect character I have ever met." He emphasizes her charity. What does this word mean as he uses it? Do you like Olivia? Why, or why not?
2. Although this is a serious tribute to his wife, Twain includes many light passages, such as "neither of us knew whether beefsteak was sold by the barrel or by the yard." Can you find other light passages? Are such passages out of place in a tribute like this? Explain.
3. Write an appreciation of a person you know. Use specific events or circumstances to illustrate the person's character.

A WORD TO REMEMBER: fortitude

Fortitude means "strength of mind that enables a person to encounter danger or bear pain or adversity (i.e., misfortune) with courage." A person who is ill for a long time but remains cheerful and complains little shows fortitude; that is, he endures his hardship bravely. Mark Twain said that his family accepted their change of fortune with fortitude. Name two or three people in history who have displayed fortitude.

THINKING ABOUT MARK TWAIN

DO YOU REMEMBER THESE WORDS?

Give the meaning of each of the italicized words in the following sentences; then give at least one antonym for each word.

1. Exercises which develop physical and mental strength may become *tedious* unless you keep in mind their value.

2. At social functions a *diffident* person may be unhappy.

3. Kidnaping, a *contemptible* act among civilized people, sometimes carries the death penalty.

4. With a *contemptuous* gesture she stalked out of the room.

5. When our way of life has been threatened, we Americans have shown great *fortitude* in fighting for freedom.

A RARE PERSONALITY

1. Some people found Mark Twain a lovable person and some found him just the opposite. From what you have read select an incident that illustrates the first point of view and one that illustrates the second. Write a paragraph on each.

2. "Sam Squares His Long Account with His Boss" illustrates particularly well Mark Twain's ability to describe a character. What selection *other than* his tribute to his wife shows the same ability? Explain your answer.

3. Read chapters from Mark Twain's *Roughing It* and *Innocents Abroad* for your own amusement or to share with the class.

Stephen Crane, American Realist

Stephen Crane's entire career was jammed into the last ten years of the nineteenth century. He died in 1900, only twenty-eight years old, but famous as a war correspondent, an adventurer, a novelist, and a poet. Before his early death he gave us one of the great American classics and a body of work which commands universal respect.

Crane spent most of his adult life as a newspaper reporter. His search for realism was almost an obsession; his passion was to view and write "the real thing." Yet his great masterpiece, *The Red Badge of Courage,* is a completely imaginative work about a battle which he had never seen, in a war which he had not taken part. To create what may be the greatest war story ever told, Crane relied on his imagination and the tall tales of old soldiers. No less an authority than General Omar N. Bradley, one of the great generals of World War II, has said that it is a completely accurate picture of the young recruit in battle. Crane himself saw actual combat two years after his imaginative novel came out and reported with relief, "*The Red Badge* is all right."

As a newspaper reporter Crane sought the most difficult and dangerous assignments. He tried to report what he saw with absolute fidelity. A superb reporter, he was in constant demand as a newspaperman. For Pulitzer and Hearst, the leading newspapermen of his day, Crane filed dispatches from the West, from Mexico and Cuba, from England and Greece. He was a star reporter whose presence anywhere was news in itself.

Although *The Red Badge of Courage* gained for Crane at twenty-four instant recognition as a great writer, his literary works were always subject to controversy. Some of his work was so far ahead of his time that many publishers would not publish it and booksellers would not handle it. Readers and editors alike rejected Crane's occasional use of profanity and his argument: "But that's the way such men talk!"

Stephen Crane covered wars and disasters. He was shipwrecked and shot at. He wore himself out in his uncompromising search for truth, for "the real thing." He was not happy that so much that he wanted to say was not accepted in his time; perhaps this unhappiness is reflected in these few lines from a short poem, "The Heart," in which he describes a man who holds his heart in his hand and eats it:

I said, "Is it good, friend?"
"It is bitter-bitter," he answered;
"But I like it
Because it is bitter,
And because it is my heart."

When Crane tried to enlist in the Spanish-American War, he found he had tuberculosis. In debt and in poor health, he covered the war with suicidal bravery. But bravery was not enough. At long last, Stephen Crane decided to take the rest which his frantic life and weakened body demanded. When he reached his chosen resting-place, the Black Forest, in Germany, he died.

The First Taste of Battle

"Here they come! Here they come!" went the cry through the lines. To the veteran it was a familiar warning. To the youth it was new and strange.

There were moments of waiting. The youth thought of the village street at home before the arrival of the circus parade on a day in the spring. He remembered how he had stood, a small, thrillful boy, prepared to follow the dingy lady upon the white horse, or the band in its faded chariot. He saw the yellow road, the lines of expectant people, and the sober houses. He particularly remembered an old fellow who used to sit upon a cracker box in front of the store and feign to despise such exhibitions. A thousand details of color and form surged in his mind. The old fellow upon the cracker box appeared in middle prominence.

Someone cried, "Here they come!"

There was rustling and muttering among the men. They displayed a feverish desire to have every possible cartridge ready to their hands. The boxes were pulled around into various positions, and adjusted with great care. It was as if seven hundred new bonnets were being tried on.

The tall soldier, having prepared his rifle, produced a red handkerchief of some kind. He was engaged in knotting it about his throat with exquisite attention to its position, when the cry was repeated up and down the line in a muffled roar of sound.

"Here they come! Here they come!" Gun locks clicked.

Across the smoke-infested fields came a brown swarm of running men who were giving shrill yells. They came

STEPHEN CRANE   **499**

on, stooping and swinging their rifles at all angles. A flag, tilted forward, sped near the front.

As he caught sight of them, the youth was momentarily startled by a thought that perhaps his gun was not loaded. He stood trying to rally his faltering intellect so that he might recollect the moment when he had loaded, but he could not.

A hatless general pulled his dripping horse to a stand near the colonel of the 304th. He shook his fist in the other's face. "You've got to hold 'em back!" he shouted savagely; "you've got to hold em back!"

In his agitation the colonel began to stammer. "A-all r-right, General, all right! We-we'll do our—we-we'll d-d-do—do our best, General." The General made a passionate gesture and galloped away. The colonel, perchance to relieve his feelings, began to scold like a wet parrot. The youth, turning swiftly to make sure that the rear was unmolested, saw the commander regarding his men in a highly resentful manner, as if he regretted above everything his association with them.

The man at the youth's elbow was mumbling, as if to himself: "Oh, we're in for it now! oh, we're in for it now!"

The captain of the company had been pacing excitedly to and fro in the rear. He coaxed in schoolmistress fashion, as to a congregation of boys with primers. His talk was an endless repetition. "Reserve your fire, boys—don't shoot till I tell you—save your fire—wait till they get close up—don't be fools—"

Perspiration streamed down the youth's face, which was soiled like that of a weeping urchin. He frequently, with a nervous movement, wiped his eyes with his coat sleeve. His mouth was still a little way open.

He got the one glance at the foe-swarming field in front of him, and instantly ceased to debate the question of his piece being loaded. Before he was ready to begin—before he had announced to himself that he was about to fight—he threw the obedient, well-balanced rifle into position and fired a first wild shot. Directly he was working at his weapon like an automatic affair.

He suddenly lost concern for himself, and forgot to look at a menacing fate. He became not a man but a member. He felt that something of which he was a part—a regiment, an army, a cause, or a country—was in a crisis. He was welded into a common personality which was dominated by a single desire. For some moments he could not flee any more than a little finger can commit a revolution from a hand.

If he had thought the regiment was about to be annihilated, perhaps he could have amputated himself from it. But its noise gave him assurance. The regiment was like a firework that, once ignited, proceeds superior to circumstances until its blazing vitality fades. It wheezed and banged with a mighty power. He pictured the ground before it strewn with the discomfited.

There was a consciousness always of the presence of his comrades about him. He felt the subtle battle brotherhood more potent even than the cause for which they were fighting. It was a mysterious fraternity born of the smoke and danger of death.

He was at a task. He was like a carpenter who has made many boxes, making still another box, only there was furious haste in his movements. He, in his thought, was careering off in other places, even as the carpenter who as he works whistles and thinks of his friend or his enemy, his home or a saloon. And these jolted dreams were never perfect to him afterward, but remained a mass of blurred shapes.

Presently he began to feel the effects of the war atmosphere—a blistering sweat, a sensation that his eyeballs were about to crack like hot stones. A burning roar filled his ears.

Following this came a red rage. He developed the acute exasperation of a pestered animal, a well-meaning cow worried by dogs. He had a mad feeling against his rifle, which could only be used against one life at a time. He wished to rush forward and strangle with his fingers. He craved a power that would enable him to make a world-sweeping gesture and brush all back. His impotency appeared to him, and made his rage into that of a driven beast.

Buried in the smoke of many rifles, his anger was directed not so much against the men who he knew were rushing toward him as against the swirling battle phantoms which were choking him, stuffing their smoke robes down his parched throat. He fought frantically for respite for his senses, for air, as a babe being smothered attacks the deadly blankets.

There was a blare of heated rage mingled with a certain expression of intentness on all faces. Many of the men were making low-toned noises with their mouths, and these subdued cheers, snarls, imprecations, prayers made a wild, barbaric song that went as an undercurrent of sound, strange and chant-like with the resounding chords of the war march. The man at the youth's elbow was babbling. In it there was something soft and tender like the monologue of a babe. The tall soldier was swearing in a loud voice. From his lips came a black procession of curious oaths. Of a sudden another broke out in a querulous way like a man who has mislaid his hat. "Well, why don't they support us? Why don't they send supports? Do they think—"

The youth in his battle sleep heard this as one who dozes hears.

There was a singular absence of heroic poses. The men bending and surging in their haste and rage were in every impossible attitude. The steel ramrods clanked and clanged with incessant din as the men pounded them furiously into the hot rifle barrels. The flaps of the cartridge boxes were all unfastened, and bobbed idiotically with each movement. The rifles, once loaded, were jerked to the shoulder and fired without apparent aim into the smoke or at one of the blurred and shifting forms which upon the field before the regiment had been growing larger and larger like puppets under a magician's hand.

The officers, at their intervals, rearward, neglected to stand in picturesque attitudes. They were bobbing to and fro roaring directions and encouragements. The dimensions of their howls were extraordinary. They expended their lungs with prodigal wills. And often they nearly stood upon their heads in their anxiety to observe the enemy on the other side of the tumbling smoke.

The lieutenant of the youth's company had encountered a soldier who had fled screaming at the first volley of his comrades. Behind the lines these two were acting a little isolated scene. The man was blubbering and staring with sheeplike eyes at the lieutenant, who had seized him by the collar and was pommeling him. He drove him back into the ranks with many blows. The soldier went mechanically, dully, with his animallike eyes upon the officer. Perhaps there was to him a divinity expressed in the voice of the other—stern, hard, with no reflection of fear in it. He tried to reload his gun, but his shaking hands prevented. The lieutenant was obliged to assist him.

The men dropped here and there like bundles. The captain of the youth's company had been killed in an early part of the action. His body lay stretched out in the position of a tired man resting, but upon his face there was an astonished and sorrowful look, as if he thought some friend had done him an ill turn. The babbling man was grazed by a shot that made the blood stream widely down his face. He clapped both hands to his head. "Oh!" he said, and ran. Another grunted suddenly as if he had been struck by a club in the stomach. He sat down and gazed ruefully. In his eyes there was mute, indefinite reproach. Farther up the line a man, standing behind a tree, had had his knee joint splintered by a ball. Immediately he had dropped his rifle and gripped the tree with both arms. And there he remained, clinging desperately and crying for assistance that he might withdraw his hold upon the tree.

At last an exultant yell went along the quivering line. The firing dwindled from an uproar to a last vindictive popping. As the smoke slowly eddied away, the youth saw that the charge had been repulsed. The enemy were scattered into reluctant groups. He saw a man climb to the top of the fence, straddle the rail, and fire a parting shot. The waves had receded, leaving bits of dark debris upon the ground.

Some in the regiment began to whoop frenziedly. Many were silent. Apparently they were trying to contemplate themselves.

After the fever had left his veins, the youth thought that at last he was going to suffocate. He became aware of the foul atmosphere in which he had been struggling. He was grimy and dripping like a laborer in a foundry. He grasped his canteen and took a long swallow of the warmed water.

A sentence with variations went up and down the line. "Well, we've helt 'em back. We've helt 'em back; derned if we haven't." The men said it blissfully, leering at each other with dirty smiles.

The youth turned to look behind him and off to the right and off to the left. He experienced the joy of a man who at last finds leisure in which to look about him.

Underfoot there were a few ghastly forms motionless. They lay twisted in fantastic contortions. Arms were bent and heads were turned in incredible ways. It seemed that the dead men must have fallen from some great height to get into such positions. They looked to be dumped out upon the ground from the sky.

From a position in the rear of the grove, a battery was throwing shells over it. The flash of the guns startled the youth at first. He thought they were aimed directly at him. Through the trees he watched the black figures of the gunners as they worked swiftly and intently. Their labor seemed a complicated thing. He wondered how they could remember its formula in the midst of confusion.

The guns squatted in a row like savage chiefs. They argued with abrupt violence. It was a grim powwow. Their busy servants ran hither and thither.

A small procession of wounded men was going drearily toward the rear. It was a flow of blood from the torn body of the brigade.

To the right and to the left were the dark lines of other troops. Far in front he thought he could see lighter masses protruding in points from the forest. They were suggestive of unnumbered thousands.

Once he saw a tiny battery go dashing along the line of the horizon. The tiny riders were beating the tiny horses.

From a sloping hill came the sound of cheering and clashes. Smoke welled slowly through the leaves.

Batteries were speaking with thunderous oratorical effort. Here and there were flags, the red in the stripes dominating. They splashed bits of warm color upon the dark lines of troops.

The youth felt the old thrill at the sight of the emblem. They were like beautiful birds strangely undaunted in a storm.

As he listened to the din from the hillside, to a deep pulsating thunder that came from afar to the left, and to the lesser clamors which came from many directions, it occurred to him that they were fighting, too, over there, and over there, and over there. Heretofore he had supposed that all the battle was directly under his nose.

As he gazed around him, the youth felt a flash of astonishment at the blue, pure sky and the sun gleaming on the trees and fields. It was surprising that Nature had gone tranquilly on with her golden process in the midst of so much devilment.

BATTLEGROUND

1. Men act in different ways during a battle, depending on who they are, where they are, and with whom they are. How is this fact brought out in the story?

2. What were some of the hero's thoughts and feelings before the battle? during the battle? after the battle?

3. War has been described in different ways ranging from "dirty and degrading" to "heroic and noble." Describe this writer's attitude about war.

4. *The Red Badge of Courage,* from which this scene was taken, became a full-length movie. Imagine you had been assigned to produce this one scene. Whom would you have cast as the youth? What special photographic effects would you have sought? How many minutes in the total picture would this scene have taken? Give reasons for your decisions. Then, if you wish, check how the film was, in fact, made. It is described in the book *Picture* by Lillian Ross.

5. Write a paper on one of these topics:

> **a.** My First Taste of Danger
> **b.** I Was Paralyzed with Fear
> **c.** War—Then and Now

A WORD PICTURE

When Crane describes the youth's face as soiled "like that of a weeping urchin," he is using a comparison to help the reader see that the sweat that streamed down the youth's face dirtied it as tears dirty a child's. Other examples of Crane's use of comparison to make his descriptions vivid: A man's babbling seemed "soft and tender like the monologue of a babe." A highly irritated soldier sounds to the author "like a man who has mislaid his hat."

How many other comparisons can you find that help you gain a clearer view of the terror, the sadness, the danger, the excitement of war?

STEPHEN CRANE **503**

Crane disliked being called a poet. He was more interested in his ideas than in expressing them in any formal way. A rebel at heart, Crane opposed the conventions of poetry as he did the conventions of nineteenth-century society. Most of his poems do not rhyme, nor do they have a regular meter. Instead they have a fresh and original way of expressing an idea.

A Spirit Sped

A spirit sped
Through spaces of night;
And as he sped, he called,
"God! God!"
He went through valleys   5
Of black death-slime,
Ever calling,
"God! God!"
Their echoes
From crevice and cavern   10
Mocked him:
"God! God! God!"
Fleetly into the plains of space
He went, ever calling,
"God! God!"   15
Eventually, then, he screamed,
Mad in denial,
"Ah, there is no God!"
A swift hand,
A sword from the sky,   20
Smote him,
And he was dead.

The Blades of Grass

In heaven,
Some little blades of grass
Stood before God.
"What did you do?"
Then all save one of the little blades   5
Began eagerly to relate
The merits of their lives.
This one stayed a small way behind,
Ashamed:
Presently, God said,   10
"And what did you do?"
The little blade answered, "O my lord,
Memory is bitter in me,
For, if I did good deeds,
I know not of them."   15
Then God, in all His splendor,
Arose from His throne.
"O best little blade of grass!" He said.

STEPHEN CRANE   **505**

A Newspaper

A newspaper is a collection of half-injustices
Which, bawled by boys from mile to mile,
Spreads its curious opinion
To a million merciful and sneering men,
While families cuddle the joys of the fireside   5
When spurred by tale of dire lone agony.
A newspaper is a court
Where everyone is kindly and unfairly tried
By a squalor of honest men.
A newspaper is a market   10
Where wisdom sells its freedom
And melons are crowned by the crowd.
A newspaper is a game
Where his error scores the player victory
While another's skill wins death.   15
A newspaper is a symbol;
It is feckless life's chronicle,
A collection of loud tales
Concentrating eternal stupidities,
That in remote ages lived unhaltered,   20
Roaming through a fenceless world.

A Man Said to the Universe

A man said to the universe:
"Sir, I exist!"
"However," replied the universe,
"The fact has not created in me
A sense of obligation."   5

Love Met Me at Noonday

Love met me at noonday
—Reckless imp
To leave his shaded nights
And brave the glare—
And I saw him then plainly   5
For a bungler,
A stupid, simpering, eyeless bungler,
Breaking the hearts of brave people
As the sniveling idiot boy cracks his bowl,
And I cursed him,   10
Cursed him to and fro, back and forth,
Into all the silly mazes of his mind,
But in the end
He laughed and pointed to my breast,
Where a heart still beat for thee, beloved.   15

"FECKLESS LIFE'S CHRONICLE"

1. What do these poems tell you of Crane's ideas about humility, justice, God, truth, and love?

2. These poems have no rhyme or regular rhythm. This kind of poetry is called *free verse,* and it depends on the author's skill in painting pictures quickly and exactly in sounds and words. Is free verse suited to the ideas that Crane expresses?

3. Some of Crane's comparisons are unusual. Why does he compare a person to a blade of grass? Why does he call love "an eyeless bungler"?

4. In the poem "A Newspaper" what is the effect of joining opposite ideas such as "merciful and sneering" (line 4) and "kindly and unfairly" (line 8)? Crane defines a newspaper in several ways. Which definition do you think best fits today's papers?

THINKING ABOUT STEPHEN CRANE

1. Which of Crane's poems best states what you consider to be an important truth? Discuss.

2. *Versatile* is a word often used to describe Crane. What proof of his versatility have you found in your reading? What further proof can you find in your school or public library?

3. When Stephen Crane died, he was too young to sum up his own life or works. Suppose you were asked to suggest the message to be gained from the selections in this unit. What would it be?

4. Which of Crane's poems in this section has a theme that could best sustain a soldier going into battle? Defend your choice.

5. Vivid imagination and the power to project himself beyond his immediate environment are two basic qualities a writer must have. This is particularly well illustrated in "The First Taste of Battle": Crane had never been in battle before he wrote it! From war stories you have read by men who saw action, or from accounts you have heard from men who lived through war, or from what you imagine war is, how close to the "real thing" did Crane get in his account of "The First Taste of Battle"? Give specific illustrations from the selections.

UNIT EIGHT

Frost and Sandburg, Poets of the People

Robert Frost is considered a New England poet; yet he was born in San Francisco. He seems as American as pumpkin pie; yet his first book was published in England. Frost's life seems to be full of such contradictions. His poetry shows acute awareness of the kind of paradox we all live with. It was important to Robert Frost that, even when faced with obstacles, man usually has a choice and—as the poet shows in "The Road Not Taken"—what man does with that choice may determine the rest of his life.

Frost did not moralize in his poetry but tried to express his ideas in the plain language of the New England people among whom he lived. The rhythms and poetic speech he chose resemble the New England countryside—rocky, sometimes bleak, and hard to wrestle a crop from; yet with special qualities and pleasures to be savored by a man who has a taste for something biting and unpredictable.

Frost came to New England, his family's native ground, when he was a boy of eleven. Although he later taught for a living, he never cared much for formal education. He spent a few months at Dartmouth College and, some time later, less than two years at Harvard. No one showed any interest then in his poetry; to make a very difficult living he worked in a mill and a shoe factory, edited a country newspaper, tried for years to farm, and taught in village schools.

When you read his poetry, you will see that he was influenced by the work he did with his hands as well as by his close observation of the country, the people, and the ways of making a living in his part of the world. Frost knew that to do anything well, first of all you must care about it; and if you care about something, you want others to know about it.

Frost did care enough, through all his financial trouble and personal suffering, to persevere with his poetry. Poetry was the thing he cared about. A trip to England, strangely enough, resulted in the publication of Frost's first book. Since Robert Frost was a man who could always smile, he must have smiled at the thought that his intensely American writing should first have been published in the country from which we had separated ourselves by revolution.

Robert Frost once said that a poem "begins in delight and ends in wisdom." Carl Sandburg, in a similar vein, once defined a poem as "the synthesis of hyacinths and biscuits." Sandburg saw that a poem could be about beautiful things or homely things, and about both together. It was important for Sandburg to discover this because, like Walt Whitman, he wanted to break down poetic conventions so that he could find ways to express his views on America. At one time it was commonly accepted that only "genteel" words could be used in poetry and only "genteel" subjects be described, but Sandburg wanted to find language close to the simple people he loved.

In his search Carl Sandburg was helped by the circumstances of his daily life. The son of Swedish immigrants, he left home at nineteen to travel across America as a wandering worker. There was hardly any job to which he did not turn his hand—laborer, mill hand, dishwasher, trucker, pottery factory apprentice. The many different types of people he met delighted him, and he had a deep interest in the lives they led.

It took a long time for Sandburg to gain recognition as a poet. In 1914 an influential magazine in Chicago called *Poetry* published a few of his poems. Sandburg became associated with the "Chicago group," and slowly he began to make an impact on America. Many found his poetry shocking and brutal because it refused to confine itself to the genteel tradition, but Sandburg was expressing the rush, vigor, violence, even the coarseness of life in industrial, exploding America.

Two short poems show both Sandburg's modern slant and his wide range. The poem "Chicago" begins with the vigor and virility of the phrase "Hot Butcher for the World," while the poem "Fog" is musically soft and subtle: "The fog comes on little cat feet."

Carl Sandburg, like the minstrels of old and the youngsters of today, played the guitar and sang. From his earliest years he was deeply interested in folk music, which he saw as an expression of basic human emotions, of sadness, of triumph, often of frustration, sometimes of dreams. He was one of the first to realize that the blues were a basic expression of Negro life in America. One of his great contributions was a collection of folk music, *The American Songbag,* which included over one hundred folk songs never before written down.

Besides poetry, Sandburg contributed to American literature a six-volume biography of Abraham Lincoln, a massive work consulted by scholars and enjoyed by everyone. Sandburg, born in the Lincoln country of Illinois, was attracted to Lincoln as a reflection of the great simplicity and humanity of the American people. Today, both Carl Sandburg and Robert Frost stand as symbols of the strength of America.

"Old Enough to Know, Young Enough to Care"

MARK HARRIS

In 1961, Mark Harris, novelist of baseball and teacher of writing, determined to visit Robert Frost and Carl Sandburg, whom all America looked upon as "all-around wise men."

Between them, Robert Frost and Carl Sandburg have lived in esteem, sobriety, and good health 170 years.[1] By divergent roads, at different paces, and in different styles, they have arrived at eminences far beyond the privacy of literary effort. They have become national figures. In a country where no royal court exists to crown a single poet laureate, an amiable public has laureated both. Together they have become a much-prized national resource.

Indeed, Mr. Frost and Mr. Sandburg have so widely become objects of affection that distinctions between them have become blurred. In recent years, as their voices and their faces have become almost as familiar as their most familiar verse, they have popularly lost

[1] Harris was probably the last writer granted exclusive interviews by these two grand old men. Frost died in 1963 at the age of eighty-eight; Sandburg died in 1967 at the age of eighty-nine.

identity as poets and have been transformed into seers, all-around wise men. Whatever they say, profound, obscure, or simply teasing, is accepted as the truth and worthy of our undivided attention.

But surely, I have often told myself, this loving national lumping-together does a gross injustice to each man. Though each is venerable, each is gray, and each has written poetry upwards of a half-century, each is enormously different from the other. Each views the world at his own solitary angle from his own unique elevation. Like Jack Spratt and his wife, one is one thing, and one is another. Old enough to know, young enough to care, and free enough to speak as they please, they basically share not much more than their will to communicate. This, of course, they do in distinctive ways. Mr. Frost does it in measured, metered verses, from New England—that part of the country he has called the Upper Right Hand Corner. His emphasis is upon form, in the tradition of an intellectual life which is academic and aristocratic. Mr. Sandburg, on the other hand, is primarily associated with the Middle West, his guitar, free verse, and common folk.

Each is different. But is each really wise? If so, it might be well, I thought, to learn as quickly as I could the secrets of long life and survival. In the flagging days of a year of death and danger—Hemingway, Berlin, megatons, and bomb shelters—I decided I must hear for myself directly from each. I wrote letters to both men, asking them to see me.

Mr. Sandburg replied promptly and cordially from Beverly Hills, California, where he was writing a motion picture adapted from the late Fulton Oursler's best-selling book about Christ, *The Greatest Story Ever Told*. But Mr. Frost did not reply at all.

Mr. Sandburg's office was located in The Stars' Building on the Twentieth Century-Fox lot. He had at first been assigned Marilyn Monroe's vacated dressing room, but he had found it too splendid. Nevertheless, his present office, decorated in mint and lemon, with wall-to-wall carpeting, mirrors to the ceiling, and adjoining private bath, was by no means incommodious.

I found him entirely well, entirely robust. His stride was brisk and his figure slim. He was smartly dressed, meticulous, starched, and pressed. His face shone sunnily, as if he were still a young man struggling upward in the world. His countenance was gentle and eager, his voice deep and rich. Mr. Sandburg almost sings when he speaks, prolonging vowels not only for emphasis but also for the music of it, so that conversation is more than conversation —it is almost like a little concert. He speaks in a measured manner, with deliberation, attentive not only to whole words but to every syllable, with occasionally a distinctive, special, Sandburgian pronunciation all his own: *Ber*-lin for Ber-*lin* in the downstate Illinois way; *nostalya* for *nostalgia*. Mr. Sandburg was born in Galesburg, Illinois, of immigrant Swedish parentage. His father was a blacksmith's helper for the Chicago, Burlington & Quincy Railroad at 14 cents an hour.

He opened our conversation in a way which somewhat surprised me. "Have you seen any of my TV shows?" he asked. I said I had seen him once on *Person to Person*. "I was on *Person to Person* twice," he said, "and then I did *Wisdom* with NBC." Did a poet enjoy working with TV people? "So far it's worked out pretty good," he replied.

How about with movie people? Did a poet feel out of place in these luxurious surroundings? "Well, considering what goes with it." Producer George Stevens "is the only man who could have lured me out here—his four pictures that he made since he came back from the war. He would have been a general if the war had lasted, he has such ability as a commander and executive officer.

"There's poetry in all of Stevens' pictures," Mr. Sandburg said. "The picture *Giant* is more important as something for teaching American youth than any of Shakespeare's plays. George Stevens is a great artist. I call him the Michelangelo of the cinema. *Giant*—what money can do to men, what a lot of land can do to a man. There's a parable of Jesus about a man so proud of his lands, and he's gonna have *more* lands, and then he dies."

Mr. Sandburg gave me one of his poems, It read:

> Jesus had a way of talking soft and outside of a few bankers and higher-ups among the con men of Jerusalem everybody liked to have this Jesus around because he never made any fake passes and everything he said went and he helped the sick and gave the people hope.

Mr. Sandburg pointed to President Kennedy's Inauguration Address, posted near the map of Palestine. "That's the best inaugural address since Lincoln," Mr. Sandburg said. Mr. Sandburg had made four campaign speeches for Mr. Kennedy.

When I asked Mr. Sandburg for his rules of health, he gave me these: "The first, to eat regular and digest it. The second, to be out of jail. Third, to get what I write printed if I want it printed. That time has arrived with me. Last of all, love in the home and something like affection and esteem outside. When I wrote *The War Years* (four of the six volumes of his Lincoln biography), I used to work sixteen, eighteen hours a day, and there were times when pains used to crash through my head, and I used to

say, 'Could that be the preamble to a brain hemorrhage? Pain like that?' And I had an oath like some old-timer in the Old Testament: 'Oh, Lord, if Thou willst permit me to finish this task, Thou mayst ha-a-a-ve me.' I was willing to bargain with God: 'Strike me dead when I have read the last page *proof* of this book.'"

"Then, hard work has kept you in health," I said.

"Yes, and I have had a rare bird of a helpmate," he added.

"And you are still hard at work, aren't you?"

"I have something like three hundred poems I'm working on," he replied.

During the writing of *The War Years*, Mr. Sandburg had lived intimately with Lincoln. Had he, in any way, as biographers often do, actually assumed a resemblance to his subject? Mr. Sandburg humbly thought not. "I'm sure that I go along with Lincoln's sense of humor," he confessed, "but in a certain—oh, keen mentality, or relentless logic, he surpasses me."

"The logic of a poet is different," I offered.

"Well, I wouldn't say exactly that. I rather think, though, that he had the gift of reading character. I may have something of that now, and across my seventies, but across his forties and fifties he had an ability of reading people that I didn't have at that age. He was smarter sooner."

"It's been said," I said, turning to a subject which proved to be a sore spot, "that your work lacks form."

He had been digging out souvenirs for me from the drawers of his great desk, but now he stopped, and with a trace of irritation, he replied, "Well, I'm not some sort of an *addict* for form." He paused, rallying his argument. "But if I lack *form*, all the proverbs of Solomon, all the psalms of David, the book of

Ecclesiastes, and the Old Testament—they are all lacking form." Mr. Sandburg's laughter returned, and he dismissed the subject. He resumed his search of his desk, finding for me two poems written about him by admirers in the Middle West.

I felt it appropriate in this time of tension to ask Mr. Sandburg whether I ought to build a bomb shelter. He had not given the problem any thought, but he thought about it now. He replied slowly. "If I build a bomb shelter, it will be on account of my children and grandchildren. I have two of the loveliest grandchildren that ever walked the earth. The boy is nineteen, the girl is eighteen. He's already far gone on the guitar; *she* writes poems. When you're eighty-four, you don't give a damn whether your end comes an hour from now or ten years from now."

"But *me*," I implored. "Shall *I* build a bomb shelter?"

"Toss a coin," said Mr. Sandburg. "Toss a coin."

More than a decade ago, in lines from *The Unknown War*, the poet had made his peace with the bleakest possibility:

Be calm, collected, easy.
In the face of the next war to come, be calm.
In the faint light and smoke of the flash and the mushroom of the first bomb blast of the Third World War, keep your wits collected.
At the information to be given out, after the few days of the fast moving next war, take it easy, be calm and collected, and say to yourself, First things come first and after this world comes another.

His secretary served us coffee, and Mr. Sandburg drank two cups, black.

Then I bade him farewell, and returned to my home in San Francisco, hoping a reply would be awaiting me from Mr. Frost.

Lamentably, there was none. Now I tried the telephone, and it was costly. I did not reach Mr. Frost, but I did reach his secretary, Mrs. Kathleen Morrison. "Shall I, or shall I not, come?" I asked, to which she replied, "It's entirely up to you," the implication being, or so I felt, it's a free country and I might cross it if I wished. And yet, she added, relenting just a little, if I insisted, she would not entirely thwart me. She would reserve a room for me at the local inn.

From the inn in Vermont, I once again telephoned Mrs. Morrison, who directed me: through the village of Ripton, I must go, then up along the Middlebury River, past several houses, to a silver mailbox, and finally half a mile on an unpaved road. Mr. Frost, Mrs. Morrison said, would see me (to decide, so to speak, whether to see me), and she directed me to his cabin—uphill fifty yards or so. The cabin is concealed until a visitor has all but reached it. Its exterior is cedar slabs; inside it is knotty pine. Mr. Frost was there and I went in.

The poet wore unpressed slacks and a clean white shirt, collar open, no tie. His face—handsome and rugged—struck me as massive, except that his eyes were narrow, and I had the feeling that I was being spied upon. Behind his eyes Mr. Frost was hiding. This general sensation of remoteness was sharpened by the fact that Mr. Frost reclines, or slouches, in his chair, drawing away into himself, into his thoughts. Between our chairs two schnauzers lay.

Mr. Frost asked me how I had come, and I said mostly by train, rather than by air. "I don't *like* planes," he said, "but I feel a little more successful when I get off one than when I get off a train. It was bumpy in landing in Tel Aviv last time. I thought, if I got back, I'd go on with my career."

He was at work, then? Yes, he hoped to have a new book "of quite a lot of poems" ready for publication soon, possibly in the spring.

I mentioned baseball. Until two years ago he had played softball summers but "a very hot liner" convinced him he was "not as sure as I used to be." Had he caught the liner? Oh, yes, he'd *caught* it.

Was he sizing me up? If so, he was employing for the purpose two pairs of eyeglasses. One pair, equipped with a hearing aid, he called his "hearing glasses," the other his "seeing glasses," and he alternated between them as the moment demanded. In part, it was the glasses that had caused him so much trouble on Inauguration Day when, unable to read his new poem, *The Preface,* he had had to abandon it. "Yes, the glasses," he said, "and the wind and the sun and the cold, nothing was right. I went home thinking I'd made a mess of it, very depressed, and feeling kind of sick at heart. Then everybody began to say I did wonders. Some said, 'I bet you did all that on purpose'; it was a show I'd put on. I hadn't thought of that."

Wouldn't it be well if we had more poets in Washington, I asked—for poets to be more influential in affairs of state? to have more *power?*

"I want influence without pressin' it," he said. "I didn't expect ever to be an influence." What were his politics? He was, he said, a "Madisonian Washingtonian Jeffersonian Democrat." He had once named Lincoln and Emerson, too, as men he particularly admired. Did he have any additions to that list? No. "I don't want to diminish the Washington Monument by having one for everybody down there; it'll get to be like a graveyard."

We walked briefly out-of-doors. It was his more natural place. Indoors he

slouched, but here he stood erect and alert. He moved surely and busily. I asked him if I might snap his picture, and he paused, as the quick way to get it over with, staring past me into the lowering sun, and he said, "I never pointed a camera or a gun at anybody. Never owned a gun." But he confessed that he had had to electrify his fences against coons. "I live in a fortified garden," he said.

How large was the farm? Two hundred acres. Corn, peas, potatoes. "Once I met a lady on a train—mistook me for a farmer. I said I'd rather be mistaken for a farmer above all things except a baseball pitcher. I never called myself a poet till I was over forty. I thought it was a praise word—*a poet*—and I'm very shy about it now."

He was examining a little tree. He bent, stooping a little, as if he were shaking a child's hand. "I wrote a poem once," he said, "beginning *The birch begins to crack its outer sheath.*"

"Yes, yes," I eagerly said. " 'A Young Birch,' a tree so beautiful that even people bent on efficiency knew it wasn't to be cut down. 'The most efficient help you ever hired/Would know that it was there to be admired.' "

He was by no means displeased that I had remembered the poem, and he tore a bit of the cracking sheath and gave it to me, as my reward. He showed me three other small trees he had recently planted—a birch, a beech, and a shad. He said, "I saw a black bear on the road the other day," leading me downhill now, near the road, and I had the feeling he might be dismissing me, leading me toward my car. But no, we were only parting for a little while, to give him time, I think, to think me over. "I never got happy about driving a car," he said. Then he said I might return that night and *see* him.

It was dark, and no moon. Mrs. Morrison lent me a flashlight, and I walked up alone to Mr. Frost's cabin. The schnauzers barked, but when they quieted, all was silence, and I asked Mr. Frost if he listened to the radio. "Not much," he said. "It's an old radio and it makes a queer, streaky noise."

How, then, did he receive news of the world?

"From people I know," he said.

But didn't he read newspapers? Yes, the Rutland *Herald*, New York *Herald-Tribune*, the New York *Times*, Boston *Globe*. "Whatever I am, I'll take a little walk and get one. But I'm nurtured on books. I'll be reading books after everyone else has stopped."

He asked me about San Francisco. He was born there, eighty-seven years ago, lived there as a boy, and he can still name the order of the streets in the neighborhood of Leavenworth and Washington.

Might we talk about literature? Oh, yes, but there were certain questions he had heard too often. "When Hemingway went down in the plane in Africa, I imagined he'd be walking through the jungles when out jumped tourists from behind the trees— 'Mr. Hemingway, what do you think of symbolism?' "

But the whole body of Mr. Frost's work is a vast symbolic structure. Isn't it? "I suppose," he confessed, "I'm always saying something that's just the edge of something more. Symbols are what fly off everything. A little goes a long way. I don't wallow in it. We hate slop, however eloquent."

Of his work he said, "Every phrase, every poem, every whole speech is a dip for depth. I've been playing *only* to score, *only* to win."

"I don't like to talk about myself," he said. "I'd rather hold myself off from myself, in rhyme and meter. That's as near as I want to come to talking about myself. People say to me, 'I know what you mean,' but what they want to know

is what's eating me. I don't always know. Sometimes it's a hate, somebody I hate, somebody I've argued with makes me write a poem. It's in the poetry I'm always struggling to say it better. It's a kind of gratification that I'm after. This," he said—a book, *Complete Poems of Robert Frost*, he meant, his life's labor—"this isn't just amateur apprentice work that I've been writing. With all its imperfections I'll never write any better. I never had this divine dissatisfaction that they brag about so much. I'm modestly satisfied. I've gotten my truth of feeling in." But he appeared inclined to talk just a little of himself after all.

"I've been a teacher all my life," he said, "just the same as I'm a Democrat, but I've been a dissatisfied teacher. I can't leave it alone. I'm like some monkeys Darwin tells about. Somebody showed them some snakes, and they screamed and ran away, but they kept coming back. I'm that way about education. I've taught every darn year from kindergarten to graduate school, Latin, English, mathematics, history, algebra, philosophy, and one year psychology. Well, it was *called* psychology, but what I mainly taught 'em was that it was no good to 'em. It's all nonsense. I have friends that think everybody ought to be psychoanalyzed. I know someone that's had their child psychoanalyzed ever since it was five years old. My self-respect wouldn't let me do it. I wouldn't surrender. I can take somebody on, but I wouldn't be *taken* on."

Still slouching, still peering, he was firm, but never cross, never hostile. There were truths of which he felt certain, but in a quiet voice, his tone somewhat humbly resigned to the probability that regardless of what he said there was little hope of anyone's learning except as he had learned: by living it over the spread of the years.

"Never give a child a choice," he

said. "Don't give him a choice of believing in God or not. He can start having choices when he goes to college: they have the elective system there, you know. There's so many courses now where everything you say is right enough—Sociology, Psychology, Contemporary Civilization.

"I'm at large, and I'm a civilized man, but school is for *discipline*. A student is an orange pip between my fingers: if I pinch him, he'll go far. I'm not violent, but I'm going for the whole damn system. Discipline. Tightness. Firmness. Crispness. Sternness. And sternness in our lives. Life is tons of discipline. Your first discipline is your vocabulary; then your grammar and your punctuation, you see. Then, in your exuberance and bounding energy you say you're going to add to that. Then you add rhyme and meter. And your delight is in *that* power."

It was power I had begun asking him about. This was his answer, was it? Discipline produced power? Discipline in teaching, in writing, in all of life? Form? "It might be something like that," he said.

I asked him if he would sign my copy of the *Complete Poems*, and he took it now and inscribed it, and I inquired— since Mr. Sandburg had left me doubtful—"Shall I build a bomb shelter?"

He returned the book and capped the pen. "You shouldn't if I don't," he said. "I hadn't thought about it. Whatever becomes compulsory, I'll probably do. If we all die together, we'll be in good company. On the other side we'll brush the dust off and say, 'Wasn't that something!'"

"That's very depressing," I said, "to think we might not have any future to believe in."

He rose and went into another room. In a few moments he returned with four poems I had never seen. "The Founding Fathers didn't believe in the future,"

he said, sitting again. "They believed it *in*. You're always believing ahead of your evidence. What was the evidence I could write a poem?" He had been almost forty years old when his first book was published. "I just believed it. The most creative thing in us is to believe a thing in, in love, in all else. You believe yourself into existence. You believe your marriage into existence, you believe in each other, you believe that it's worthwhile going on, or you'd commit suicide, wouldn't you?

"And the ultimate one is the belief in the future of the world. I believe the future *in*. It's coming in by my believing it. You might as well call that a belief in God. This word *God* is not an often-used word with me, but once in a while it arrives there."

"That's much more cheerful than what you said before," I said.

"I contain opposites," he said. "I can hold a lot. I can get up a phrase to handle almost everything that happens."

We left the cabin. The schnauzers followed. Mr. Frost lighted my way down the slope. He said he'd been thinking of buying a telescope, but it cost a thousand dollars, so he was going to get some good advice before he plunged. I recalled some lines of Robert Frost:

I knew a man who failing as a farmer
Burned down his farmhouse for the
    fire insurance,
And spent the proceeds on a telescope
To satisfy a life-long curiosity
About our place among the infinities.
And how was that for other-worldli-
    ness?

Near the road, I told him I'd promised to return the flashlight to Mrs. Morrison. He offered to do it himself. In the morning I telephoned her to say good-by, and I asked her if he'd returned it to her, and she said he had.

FIVE POEMS

ROBERT FROST

Stopping by Woods on a Snowy Evening

Whose woods these are I think I know.
His house is in the village though;
He will not see me stopping here
To watch his woods fill up with snow.

My little horse must think it queer   5
To stop without a farmhouse near
Between the woods and frozen lake
The darkest evening of the year.

He gives his harness bells a shake
To ask if there is some mistake.   10
The only other sound's the sweep
Of easy wind and downy flake.

The woods are lovely, dark, and deep.
But I have promises to keep,
And miles to go before I sleep,   15
And miles to go before I sleep.

A Minor Bird

I have wished a bird would fly away,
And not sing by my house all day;

Have clapped my hands at him from the door
When it seemed as if I could bear no more.

The fault must partly have been in me.   5
The bird was not to blame for his key.

And of course there must be something wrong
In wanting to silence any song.

The Impulse

It was too lonely for her there,
   And too wild,
And since there were but two of them,
   And no child,

And work was little in the house,   5
   She was free,
And followed where he furrowed field,
   Or felled tree.

She rested on a log and tossed
   The fresh chips,   10
With a song only to herself
   On her lips.

And once she went to break a bough
   Of black alder.
She strayed so far she scarcely heard   15
   When he called her—

And didn't answer—didn't speak—
   Or return.
She stood, and then she ran and hid
   In the fern.   20

He never found her, though he looked
   Everywhere,
And he asked at her mother's house
   Was she there.

Sudden and swift and light as that   25
   The ties gave,
And he learned of finalities
   Besides the grave.

A Considerable Speck

A speck that would have been beneath my sight
On any but a paper sheet so white
Set off across what I had written there.
And I had idly poised my pen in air
To stop it with a period of ink   5
When something strange about it made me think.
This was no dust speck by my breathing blown,
But unmistakably a living mite
With inclinations it could call its own.
It paused as with suspicion of my pen,   10
And then came racing wildly on again
To where my manuscript was not yet dry;
Then paused again and either drank or smelt—
With loathing, for again it turned to fly.
Plainly with an intelligence I dealt.   15
It seemed too tiny to have room for feet,
Yet must have had a set of them complete
To express how much it didn't want to die.
It ran with terror and with cunning crept.
It faltered; I could see it hesitate;   20
Then in the middle of the open sheet
Cower down in desperation to accept
Whatever I accorded it of fate.
I have none of the tenderer-than-thou
Collectivistic regimenting love   25
With which the modern world is being swept.
But this poor microscopic item now!
Since it was nothing I knew evil of
I let it lie there till I hope it slept.

I have a mind myself and recognize   30
Mind when I meet with it in any guise.
No one can know how glad I am to find
On any sheet the least display of mind.

Stopping by Woods on a Snowy Evening

1. Write two or three sentences carefully describing the setting of this poem.

2. In lines 9–12 there is appeal to the sense of hearing. What sounds are heard? What is the value of choosing these particular sounds?

3. What idea do you find in the last stanza? Why does the poet leave the reader guessing as to "promises to keep"? Why does he repeat "And miles to go before I sleep"? What special meaning might "sleep" have?

A Minor Bird

1. What does "minor" mean in the title of this poem?

2. Why did the poet try to drive away the bird?

3. In the last stanza the poet finds meaning in the incident described. What is the meaning? What other "songs" of life should not be silenced?

The Impulse

1. What is an impulse? Describe the impulse in this poem.

2. In line 11 the wife sang "a song only to herself." Why? What quality in her character is suggested?

3. What do you think she did after she ran away?

4. In line 26 we read that "The ties gave." What "ties"? Explain what happens in this line.

5. Write several careful sentences describing the wife and indicating her attitude toward life.

A Considerable Speck

1. What actions by the "speck" lead the poet to say in line 15, "Plainly with an intelligence I dealt"? What does this sentence mean? Refer to several lines which support your opinion.

2. What attitude toward the insect does the poet express in lines 27–31? What quality in the poet's nature is suggested by these lines?

3. State the meaning of the last two lines. How does the word *Considerable* in the title contribute to an understanding of these lines?

This poem tells the story of Silas, a hired man on a small New England farm. After years of work for the farmer, Silas went away; but one evening he returned "home." The poem begins at this point—with Warren arriving from the market and with Mary, his wife, waiting to tell him that Silas is back. Watch the quotation marks closely in reading this poem, for the story of Silas is told through the conversation of Mary and Warren.

The Death of the Hired Man

ROBERT FROST

Mary sat musing on the lamp flame at the table,
Waiting for Warren. When she heard his step,
She ran on tiptoe down the darkened passage
To meet him in the doorway with the news
And put him on his guard. "Silas is back."   5
She pushed him outward with her through the door
And shut it after her. "Be kind," she said.
She took the market things from Warren's arms
And set them on the porch, then drew him down
To sit beside her on the wooden steps.   10

"When was I ever anything but kind to him?
But I'll not have the fellow back," he said.
"I told him so last haying, didn't I?
'If he left then,' I said, 'that ended it.'
What good is he? Who else will harbor him   15
At his age for the little he can do?
What help he is there's no depending on.
Off he goes always when I need him most.
'He thinks he ought to earn a little pay,
Enough at least to buy tobacco with,   20
So he won't have to beg and be beholden.'

'All right,' I say, 'I can't afford to pay
Any fixed wages, though I wish I could.'
'Someone else can.' 'Then someone else will have to.'
I shouldn't mind his bettering himself   25
If that was what it was. You can be certain,
When he begins like that, there's someone at him
Trying to coax him off with pocket money—
In haying time, when any help is scarce.
In winter he comes back to us. I'm done."   30

"Sh! not so loud: he'll hear you," Mary said.

"I want him to: he'll have to soon or late."

"He's worn out. He's asleep beside the stove.
When I came up from Rowe's I found him here,
Huddled against the barn door fast asleep,   35
A miserable sight, and frightening, too—
You needn't smile—I didn't recognize him—
I wasn't looking for him—and he's changed.
Wait till you see."

                    "Where did you say he'd been?"

"He didn't say. I dragged him to the house,   40
And gave him tea, and tried to make him smoke.
I tried to make him talk about his travels.
Nothing would do: he just kept nodding off."

"What did he say? Did he say anything?"

"But little."

                    "Anything? Mary, confess   45
He said he'd come to ditch the meadow for me."

"Warren!"

                    "But did he? I just want to know."

"Of course he did. What would you have him say?
Surely you wouldn't grudge the poor old man
Some humble way to save his self-respect.   50
He added, if you really care to know,
He meant to clear the upper pasture, too.
That sounds like something you have heard before?
Warren, I wish you could have heard the way
He jumbled everything. I stopped to look   55
Two or three times—he made me feel so queer—
To see if he was talking in his sleep.
He ran on Harold Wilson—you remember—
The boy you had in haying four years since.
He's finished school, and teaching in his college.   60
Silas declares you'll have to get him back.
He says they two will make a team for work:
Between them they will lay this farm as smooth!
The way he mixed that in with other things.
He thinks young Wilson a likely lad, though daft   65
On education—you know how they fought
All through July under the blazing sun,
Silas up on the cart to build the load,
Harold along beside to pitch it on."

"Yes, I took care to keep well out of earshot."   70

"Well, those days trouble Silas like a dream.
You wouldn't think they would. How some things linger!
Harold's young college boy's assurance piqued him.
After so many years he still keeps finding
Good arguments he sees he might have used.   75
I sympathize. I know just how it feels
To think of the right thing to say too late.
Harold's associated in his mind with Latin.
He asked me what I thought of Harold's saying
He studied Latin like the violin   80
Because he liked it—that an argument!
He said he couldn't make the boy believe
He could find water with a hazel prong—
Which showed how much good school had ever done him.

He wanted to go over that. But most of all   85
He thinks if he could have another chance
. To teach him how to build a load of hay—"

"I know, that's Silas' one accomplishment.
He bundles every forkful in its place,
And tags and numbers it for future reference,   90
So he can find and easily dislodge it
In the unloading. Silas does that well.
He takes it out in bunches like big birds' nests.
You never see him standing on the hay
He's trying to lift, straining to lift himself."   95

"He thinks if he could teach him that, he'd be
Some good perhaps to someone in the world.
He hates to see a boy the fool of books.
Poor Silas, so concerned for other folk,
And nothing to look backward to with pride,   100
And nothing to look forward to with hope,
So now and never any different."

Part of a moon was falling down the west,
Dragging the whole sky with it to the hills.
Its light poured softly in her lap. She saw   105
And spread her apron to it. She put out her hand
Among the harplike morning-glory strings,
Taut with the dew from garden bed to eaves,
As if she played unheard the tenderness
That wrought on him beside her in the night.   110
"Warren," she said, "he has come home to die:
You needn't be afraid he'll leave you this time."

"Home," he mocked gently.

                                          "Yes, what else but home?
It all depends on what you mean by home.
Of course he's nothing to us, any more   115
Than was the hound that came a stranger to us
Out of the woods, worn out upon the trail."

"Home is the place where, when you have to go there,
They have to take you in."

                      "I should have called it
Something you somehow haven't to deserve."   120

Warren leaned out and took a step or two,
Picked up a little stick, and brought it back
And broke it in his hand and tossed it by.
"Silas has better claim on us, you think,
Than on his brother? Thirteen little miles   125
As the road winds would bring him to his door.
Silas has walked that far no doubt today.
Why didn't he go there? His brother's rich,
A somebody—director in the bank."

"He never told us that."

                         "We know it though."   130

"I think his brother ought to help, of course.
I'll see to that if there is need. He ought of right
To take him in, and might be willing to—
He may be better than appearances.
But have some pity on Silas. Do you think   135
If he'd had any pride in claiming kin
Or anything he looked for from his brother,
He'd keep so still about him all this time?"

"I wonder what's between them."

                           "I can tell you.
Silas is what he is—we wouldn't mind him—   140
But just the kind that kinsfolk can't abide.
He never did a thing so very bad.
He don't know why he isn't quite as good
As anyone. He won't be made ashamed
To please his brother, worthless though he is."   145

"I can't think Si ever hurt anyone."

"No, but he hurt my heart the way he lay
And rolled his old head on that sharp-edged chair back.
He wouldn't let me put him on the lounge.
You must go in and see what you can do.   150
I made the bed up for him there tonight.
You'll be surprised at him—how much he's broken.
His working days are done; I'm sure of it."

"I'd not be in a hurry to say that."

"I haven't been. Go, look, see for yourself.   155
But, Warren, please remember how it is:
He's come to help you ditch the meadow.
He has a plan. You mustn't laugh at him.
He may not speak of it, and then he may.
I'll sit and see if that small sailing cloud   160
Will hit or miss the moon."

                                    It hit the moon.
Then there were three, making a dim row,
The moon, the little silver cloud, and she.
Warren returned—too soon, it seemed to her,
Slipped to her side, caught up her hand and waited.   165
"Warren?" she questioned.

                                    "Dead," was all he answered.

THE DEATH OF THE HIRED MAN

1. Silas is represented as an irresponsible, opinionated black sheep of a man. Select lines in the poem which support this statement. Do you think it is a fair statement?

2. Why is Silas so strongly critical of Harold Wilson? What quality in Silas' nature does this attitude suggest?

3. What are the two definitions of "home" in this poem? Which of the two is the more sympathetic? How does the second suggest the character of the speaker? Explain.

4. Write a carefully planned paragraph describing Mary or Warren as a person. Use two or three references to the poem to support your ideas.

5. Why was it appropriate that Silas should come to Warren's to die?

Sayings of Robert Frost

The following prose selections reveal glimpses

of the poetic insight, the homely philosophy, and the

rich wisdom of this great American.

1. The figure a poem makes. It begins in delight and ends in wisdom. . . . It begins in delight, it inclines to the impulse, it assumes direction with the first line laid down, it runs a course of lucky events, and ends in a clarification of life, . . . a momentary stay against confusion.

2. Poetry provides the one permissible way of saying one thing and meaning another.

3. The right reader of a good poem can tell the moment it strikes him that he has taken an immortal wound—that he will never get over it.

4. Nothing flatters me more than to have it assumed that I could write prose—unless it be to have it assumed that I once pitched baseball with distinction.

5. I hear people say the more they love anyone, the more they see his faults. Nonsense. Love is blind and should be left so.

6. We are all being marked by each other all the time, classified, ranked, put in our place, and I see no escape from that. I am no sentimentalist. You have got to mark, and you have got to mark, first of all, for accuracy, for correctness.

7. The most exciting movement in nature is not progress, advance, but expansion and contraction, the opening and shutting of the eye, the hand, the heart, the mind.

SAYINGS OF ROBERT FROST

1. Three of the seven "Sayings of Robert Frost" concern poetry. Which of the three do you think is most appreciative of poetry? Be prepared to explain your answer.

2. Which two "Sayings" show most clearly Frost's sense of humor?

3. What does the word *homely* mean when applied to Frost's philosophy? Where do you find evidence of his homely philosophy?

4. Which of these "Sayings" suggests most clearly Frost's simple but rich wisdom?

On the Road

CARL SANDBURG

Carl Sandburg, having decided he must break away from home, set out "on the road." The adventures of this Swedish youth from Galesburg, Illinois, may make you think about your own life.

I had my bitter and lonely hours moving out of boy years into a grown young man. But I had been moving too in a slow way to see that to all the best men and women I had known in my life and especially all the great ones I had read about, life wasn't easy, life had often its bitter and lonely hours, and when you grow with new strengths of body and mind, it is by struggle. . . . I believed there were lives far more bitter and lonely than mine and they had fixed stars, dreams, and moonsheens, hopes and mysteries, worth looking at during their struggles. I was groping.

I was nineteen years old, nearly a grown man. And I was restless. The jobs I'd had all seemed dead end with no future that called to me. Among the boys I could hold my own. With the girls I was bashful and couldn't think of what to say till after I left them, and then I wasn't sure. I had never found a "steady."

I read about the Spanish General Weyler and his cruelties with the people of Cuba who wanted independence and a republic. I read about Gomez, Garcia, Maceo, with their scrabbling little armies fighting against Weyler. They became heroes to me. I tried to figure a way to get down there and join one of those armies. I would have signed up with any recruiting agent who could have got me there. Nothing came of this hope.

What came over me in those years 1896 and 1897 wouldn't be easy to tell. I hated my home town and yet I loved it. And I hated and loved myself about the same as I did the town and the people. I came to see that my trouble was inside of myself more than it was in the town and the people.

I decided in June of 1897 to head west and work in the Kansas wheat harvest. I would beat my way on the railroads; I would be a hobo and a "gaycat." I had talked with hoboes enough to know there is the professional tramp who never works and the gaycat who hunts work and hopes to go on and get a job that suits him. I would take my chances on breaking away from my home town, where I knew every street and people in every block and farmers on every edge of town. . . .

The family didn't like the idea. Papa scowled. Mama kissed me, and her eyes had tears after dinner one noon when I walked out of the house with my hands free, no bag or bundle, wearing a black-sateen shirt, coat, vest, and pants, a slouch hat, good shoes and socks, no underwear. In my pockets were a small bar of soap, a razor, a comb, a pocket mirror, two handkerchiefs, a piece of string, needles and thread, a Waterbury watch, a knife, a pipe and a sack of tobacco, three dollars and twenty-five cents.

It was the last week in June, an after-noon bright and cool. A little west of the Santa Fe station stood a freight train waiting for orders. As the train started, I ran along and jumped into a boxcar. I stood at the open side door and watched the running miles of young corn. Crossing the long bridge over the Mississippi, my eyes swept over it with a sharp hunger that the grand old river satisfied. Except for my father, when riding to Kansas to buy land, no one of our family had seen the Father of Waters. As the train slowed down in Fort Madison, I jumped out.

I bought a nickel's worth of cheese and crackers and sat eating and looking across the Mississippi. The captain of a small steamboat said I could work passage to Keokuk unloading kegs of nails. I slept on the boat, had breakfast, sailed down the river watching fields and towns go by—at Burlington, Quincy, and Keokuk shouldering kegs of nails to the wharves. At Keokuk I spread newspapers on green grass near a canal and slept in the open. I washed my face and hands at the canal, using soap from my pocket and drying with a handkerchief. Then I met a fellow who said, "On the road?" When I said, "Yes," he led me to where he had been eating bread and meat unwrapped from a newspaper. "I got three lumps last night," he said, and handed me a lump. A lump was what you were handed if you got something to eat at a house where you asked for it. My new friend said, "I got a sit-down before I got the lumps." At one house he had been asked to sit at the kitchen table and eat. Then, because he wanted to have this day free to look at the canal and the blue sky, he went from house to house for lumps, hiding them under wooden sidewalks so his hands were empty. The lump he gave me had four slices of buttered bread and two thick cuts of roast beef. "This is breakfast and dinner for me," I said.

His face and hands were pudgy as though your fingers would sink into them if you touched them. He had come out of a Brooklyn orphan asylum, had taken to The Road, and said he had never done a day's work in his life. He was proud he had found a way to live without working. He named Cincinnati Slim and Chicago Red and other professional tramps he had traveled with, as though they were big names known to all tramps and I must have heard of them. He named towns where the jail food was good and how in winter he would get a two or three months' sentence for vagrancy in those jails. "Or I might go south for the cold weather," he said, "keeping away from the towns where they're horstyle." Now I had learned that where they are hostile, they are "horstyle" in tramp talk. He had a slick tongue and a fast way of talking, and soon I walked away, leaving him where he lay on the green grass looking at the blue sky. I would have felt sorry for him if he wasn't so sure he could take care of himself.

During a heavy rainstorm that night I slept in the dry cellar of a house the carpenters hadn't finished and I was up and out before they came to work. I had a fifteen-cent breakfast, found an old tomato can, bought a cheap brush, and had the can filled with asphaltum for a few nickels. Then I went from house to house in several blocks and got three jobs blacking stoves that were rusty, earning seventy-five cents, and two jobs where my pay was dinner and supper. I slept again in the house the carpenters hadn't finished and the next day went from house to house and got no jobs with pay brushing asphaltum on rusty stoves, though I did get breakfast, dinner, and supper for three jobs. The day after, I bought a refill of asphaltum, earned three meals and twenty-five cents. The following day was the same as the day before. I found that the housewives were much like those for whom I had poured milk in Galesburg. I found, too, that if I said I was hoping to earn money to go to college, they were ready to help me. The trouble was there were not enough rusty stoves.

The next day was the Fourth of July, with crowds pouring into Keokuk. I saw a sign "Waiter Wanted" in a small lunch counter near the end of Main Street. The owner was running the place by himself and said I could make myself useful at fifty cents a day and meals. He showed me the eggs, lard, and frying pan, the buns and ham for sandwiches, the doughnuts, and the coffeepot. At ten o'clock he went out, telling me I was in charge and to be polite serving customers. Three or four people drifted in before eleven-thirty, when he came back, feeling good, he said, and he would help through the noon rush. Five or six customers came in the next two hours and he sat in a quiet corner taking a sleep while I handled the trade. There were not more than two customers at any one time and I flourished around, got them what they called for on our plain and simple bill of fare. I felt important. Maybe after a while I might work up to be a partner in the business.

The owner woke up and went out saying he would be back soon. At three o'clock he came in feeling better than the last time. He had forgotten to eat at noon and I offered to fix him two fried eggs, which I served him with a bun and coffee. He went out again saying he would be back soon. At five o'clock he came back "stewed to the gills," slumped himself in a corner on the floor, and went to sleep. I fried myself three eggs and ate them with two buns and coffee. I fixed two sandwiches with thick cuts of ham, put them in my coat pockets along with two doughnuts, opened the money drawer and took out a half dollar. With my coat on one arm,

I closed the front door softly, and that night slept in a boxcar that took me halfway across the state of Missouri. For a poor boy seeking his fortune, I hadn't done so bad for one day.

Next was the railroad section gang at Bean Lake, Missouri. My Irish boss, Fay Connors, hired me at a dollar and twenty-five cents a day and I was to pay him three dollars a week for board and room in his four-room one-story house thirty feet from the railroad tracks. There were five of us in the gang and you would have known Connors was the boss. He liked his voice and his authority. At no time did he get mad and bawl out a man, but he had a frozen-faced way of letting men know he was once a section *hand* and was now a section *boss*. I tamped ties several days from seven till noon and from one till six. My muscles ached at night like they did when I worked in the ice harvest. Then came weed-cutting. We swung our scythes along the right of way; I had to train a new set of muscles and *they* ached at night.

At morning, noon, and evening, the meals at the Connors table were the same: fried side pork, fried potatoes, and coffee. Connors seemed to like it. So did his wife and three small children. At the end of two weeks, on a Sunday morning, I hopped a freight for Kansas City and left Boss Connors to collect for my board and room out of my paycheck.

In Kansas City, Mrs. Mullin had a sign in the window of her restaurant on Armour Avenue, "Dishwasher Wanted." She took the sign out when the Swede boy from Illinois made himself at home in the kitchen. Noontime was the rush hour of the workers from the meat-packing plants nearby. It was a fight in that dish trough to get enough dishes cleaned for serving the customers. I swept the eating room morning and afternoon and mopped it on Saturday.

My sleeping place was at the end of a hallway with my cot curtained off, and I washed and shaved, using my pocket mirror, at a sink in the hall.

I was up at six in the morning and had the eating room swept for customers who began coming at six-thirty when we opened. I worked every weekday till eight at night except for an hour or two in the afternoon. I had good times in that kitchen. The mulatto chef was fat, jolly, always cheerful, and would fix me three good meals a day. He would ask what I wanted as though he was an uncle of mine and nothing was too good for me. The one waiter was also a mulatto. George was handsome and gay, could sing either oldtime songs or late hits, and would sing special songs I called for. I had Sunday off and walked miles around Kansas City.

In a week or so the wheat harvest in western Kansas would be ready. Mrs. Mullin paid me my second week's pay of one dollar and fifty cents and I said good-by and saw the sign "Dishwasher Wanted" whisked back into the window. Saying good-by to George and the chef wasn't easy. They were goodhearted men who had made everything easier and brighter for me.

I slept two nights in a fifteen-cent second-floor "flophouse" where forty men in one room each had a cot about an arm's length apart. A near neighbor might be snoring, and at two or three in the morning, there might be a scream from a fellow waking out of a bad dream. Worst of all were the flat brown creepers who could bite into your skin so you were awake on the instant. They had homes in our blankets. We had no sheets.

Hopping freight trains on my way west, I had one bad afternoon. A shack (hobo for brakeman) had ordered me off an open coal car where I was crouched. When the train started, I got on again. The train was running full speed when he climbed down from the car ahead and another shack followed him. He put his face close to mine. "I told you to stay off this train. Now you'll come through with two bits or you'll take what you get." It was my first time with a shack of that kind. I had met brakemen who were not smalltime grafters, and one who spotted me in a boxcar corner said, "If you're going to ride, keep out of sight." I figured I might owe the railroad money for fare but the shack wasn't a passenger-fare collector. So I didn't come through with two bits. He outweighed me by about forty pounds and when his right fist landed on my left jaw and his left fist slammed into my mouth, I went to the floor. As I slowly sat up, he snarled, "Stay where you are or you'll get more." Then as he and his partner turned to go, he gave me a last look and laughed, "You can ride, you've earned it."

I stood up and watched the passing land. The trees were few; no such timber as in Illinois and Missouri. I had come to the Great Plains. I was traveling, though my handkerchief was splotched red from putting it to my mouth. When the train slowed down, I got off and found myself at a hobo jungle, two men leaving to catch the train I had quit, two more washing their shirts in a shallow creek shaded by three cottonwood trees. I washed my shirt, socks, and handkerchief. The two men were gaycats, said they had spent their last nickel for a loaf of bread and a half pound of Java and could I scrape the nickels for a few weenies? I said fair enough and went for the weenies and we ate well. I caught a freight that night that had me in Emporia, where I walked past the office of the *Emporia Gazette* but didn't have the nerve to step in and see the editor, William Allen White. After a big two-bit meal I went to the city park, where I lay on the grass for a sleep and then talked with two men who got me to singing for them. They were professional tramps and wanted me to go along with them. They were sure I could make money singing in saloons, and they had the idea we would all share in the money so made. It seemed a little queer to me.

That night a bright full moon was up in a clear sky, and out past the Sante Fe water tank waiting their chances to catch a freight train west was a gay bunch of eight men, most of them heading toward the wheat harvest.

In a windy rain I jumped out of the boxcar I caught in Emporia and found a sleeping place under a loading platform for stock cars. About seven in the morning, I read the station sign and learned I was in Hutchinson, Kansas. I had heard it was better not to hit the houses near the railroad; they had been hit too often by 'boes. I walked eight or ten blocks and hit two houses. "Have you got any work I can do for breakfast?" At each they took one look at me and shut the door. At the third house a woman sent her daughter to get me a saw, showed me a woodpile and a sawbuck. For an hour I kept the saw going, piled the wood, and went to the house. The smiling mother and daughter led me to the family table, set fried ham and potatoes, applesauce, bread and coffee before me. After I had eaten, they handed me a large lump. I thanked them, walked Main Street to see what Hutchinson was like, and went to my loading platform. Unwrapping the lump, I found fried chicken and bread that would make dinner and supper, along with two pocketfuls of apples that had come down in the wind and rain the night before.

Lindsborg, Kansas, was Swedish, and Pastor Swenson, the head of Bethany College there, was a Lutheran Synod leader I had heard preach in Galesburg. It was either hay or broomcorn harvest I worked in with other Swedes on a farm near Lindsborg. I stayed three days at a dollar a day and meals, sleeping in a barn hayloft. On my third and last morning I had been awake a few minutes when I heard voices down below. One voice came clear, a Swede saying, "Is that bum up yet?" I said to myself, "Am I a bum?" And I had to answer, "Yes, I am a bum." I had bummed my way to Lindsborg; I had no baggage nor bundle, and I expected to bum my way on a train out of Lindsborg. The first time in my life I heard myself referred to as a bum was among Swedes I had made a detour to see. I was getting no such hand of fellowship as from George and the chef in the Kansas City kitchen.

Newspapers said the country was pulling out of the Hard Times, yet there were many men still out of work, men who had left their homes hoping for jobs somewhere, riding the boxcars and sitting around the jungle hangouts. Some had learned hobo slang; some didn't care for it. There was always a small fraternity who knew each other at once by their slang. They were the professional tramps, who divided into panhandlers and petty thieves. Panhandlers talked about "how to work Main Street," what kind of faces to ask for a dime or a quarter. "Never mooch a goof wearing a red necktie," I heard. They would argue about the best kind of story to melt the heart of the citizen you walked along with. The longer you made your story, the more danger there was that the citizen would ask you questions and maybe while you were answering a cop would come along "and he sees you're a vag and jugs you." "I think I'll try the goat in this town," said one, and I learned the goat was the Catholic priest. "I had a good snooze in a knowledge box last night" meant the fellow had slept in a country schoolhouse.

The petty thieves did less talking. The only one who got confidential with me wore a good brown suit, a brown shirt with a brown necktie. His face and mustache were like the pictures of the hero in the *Family Story Paper*. His quiet words to me were, "I'm a second-story man. I could use you." He would have me stand on his shoulders and climb up on a porch, go through a window, and search for money and jewels we would split. He hadn't been doing so well lately but he had seen good times and they would come again. He had a soft voice, and he was polite. I told him I would think about it, but I managed to get away from him without telling him what I thought about it.

I was meeting fellow travelers and fellow Americans. What they were doing to my heart and mind, my personality, I couldn't say then or later and be certain. I was getting a deeper self-respect than I had had in Galesburg, so much I knew. I was getting to be a better storyteller. You can be loose and easy when from day to day you meet strangers you will know only an hour or a day or two. What girls I was meeting on a job or at a sit-down usually wanted to know where I was from, where I was going, what kind of a home and folks I had, and I was working out of my bashfulness. . . .

I saw Pikes Peak so I could say I saw it. At the Windsor, a first-class hotel in Denver, I washed dishes two weeks at a dollar and fifty cents a week, had a cubbyhole for a room, and meals as good as were served to the silk-hat guests. Then came the question, should I head for the West Coast or east to Galesburg? I admitted I was a little homesick. A passenger train was on slow speed out of the yards one night and I hopped on the steps of a Pullman vestibule. A conductor and porter ordered me off. I got off and saw the train slow to a stop. I climbed on top of a Pullman car, lay with my head toward the engine, and swore a solemn oath I wouldn't go to sleep. The car rocked and shook going

around curves and my hands held tight so I wouldn't slide off. It was a cool September night and the train speed made it cold. I still had no underwear. I buttoned my coat, turned the collar up, and tied a handkerchief around my neck. I went to sleep twice and coming out of it kept hitting and kicking myself to stay awake.

Daybreak came. An early farmer waved to me. I saw we were pulling in to a division point, McCook, Nebraska. I climbed down and started to walk out of the yards. A one-eyed man in plain clothes with a club and a star stood in my way. "Where did you come from?" His tone was "horstyle." "I just got off that train," I said. He gave me orders in a more horstyle tone: "We don't want the likes of you in this town. You get back on that train." There were no train-men in sight as I climbed back to where I had been riding. I had a daylight view of the Nebraska landscape for thirty miles from McCook to the next stop at Oxford. No one was waiting for me at Oxford. I went to a lunch counter, where they let me into the kitchen to wash off the cinders and soot. Then I ordered a monster thirty-five-cent break-fast of ham and eggs, fried potatoes, bread, coffee, and two pieces of pie.

Heading east I stopped three days in a jungle with five good fellows. Shirt, socks, and handkerchiefs got washed. We had several meals of corn we picked from fields nearby to roast or boil and sat around a fire talking after our sup-per. I caught a freight that landed me in Nebraska City. I chopped wood and picked apples for two sit-downs. At a large brick house where I chopped wood, the man of the house, a lawyer, seeing my suit of clothes somewhat ragged, asked me if I would like an old suit of his. He brought out an iron-gray, all-wool suit, better than any I had had in my life. I offered to chop more wood but he laughed and said I'd better be on

my way home. I found myself that night in a boxcar with four others. We spread newspapers under us, threw our coats over our shoulders, and tried for sleep. The night was clear and frosty. After a couple of hours, we were saying, "It's too cold to sleep here." The five of us marched to the city calaboose and asked the marshal to let us in. The cells had the expected stink, but we spread our newspapers on the stone floor, slept warm, and on leaving were told to get out of town that day.

I caught a freight for Omaha. In Omaha, as in Kansas City and Denver, I stood before the United States Army recruiting office and read many times the pay and conditions Uncle Sam of-fered his Regular Army boys. I came near enlisting. One year of service I could see, or maybe two years, but the required three years had me backing out. I would make my decision, walk away, and come back the next day, read the pay and conditions, and make the same decision that three years was too long.

The Hotel Mercer took me on as dishwasher at a dollar and fifty cents a week. The hotel was leased and run by a fancily dressed tall man who was known as Wink Taylor. I didn't notice him wink at any time but he probably had the name because he was quick as a wink. At the end of the first week, I didn't get my pay nor at the end of the second week. Then came word that the Hotel Mercer was foreclosed and Wink Taylor vanished, owing me three dol-lars and owing the chambermaids, the dining-room and kitchen hands, too.

I had one last sleep in the Mercer, crossed over to Council Bluffs, had breakfast, then caught one freight train after another till I came in sight of Galesburg the afternoon of October fif-teenth.

I walked along Berrien Street to the only house in the United States where

I could open a door without knocking and walk in for a kiss from the woman of the house. They gave me a sit-down, and as they had had only two or three letters from me, they asked questions about where I'd been. When I showed my father fifteen dollars and a few nickels, he said the money would come in handy and I should watch it. The clean bed sheets that night felt good.

Mart was suspicious of my fine suit of clothes. "I'll bet you didn't buy it new. If you bought it, it was a hock shop." So I told him how I got it. Mart said that along in August he had read in a newspaper about a hobo who fell off the bumpers in western Kansas and was mangled to death. The folks hadn't read it and he didn't tell them. "But I was afraid, Cully, that maybe it was you." Then I told him how in Colorado it could have been me.

What had the trip done to me? I couldn't say. It had changed me. I was easier about looking people in the eye. When questions came, I was quicker at answering them or turning them off. I had been a young stranger meeting many odd strangers and I had practiced at having answers. At home and among my old chums of the Dirty Dozen, they knew I had changed but they could no more tell how than I. Away deep in my heart, now I had hope as never before. Struggles lay ahead, I was sure, but whatever they were, I would not be afraid of them.

THE FACT IS—

1. How did Carl Sandburg feel about life when he was nineteen?
2. What is the "Father of Waters"?
3. What were some of the unusual places Sandburg slept in?
4. Why did the "hobo" fear a "shack"?
5. What was "the only house in the United States where I could open a door without knocking"?

ON THE BRINK OF MANHOOD

1. Carl said, "I hated my home town and yet I loved it. And I hated and loved myself about the same as I did the town and the people" (page 533). Explain these two sentences.

2. On one occasion Carl had to confess, "Yes, I am a bum." What did he mean by the term?

3. Carl writes, "I was meeting fellow travelers and fellow Americans" (page 537). In what ways did he benefit by these experiences? In what other ways might you benefit by "striking out on your own"? Do you think it is possible to set out today and live as Sandburg did?

4. Using the following topic sentence—A man must stand on his own two feet—write a well-planned paragraph.

FOUR POEMS

CARL SANDBURG

New Hampshire Again

I remember black winter waters,
I remember thin white birches,
I remember sleepy twilight hills,
I remember riding across New Hampshire lengthways.
I remember a station named "Halcyon," a brakeman calling to
   passengers "Halcyon!! Halcyon!!"
I remember having heard the gold diggers dig out only enough for
   wedding rings.
I remember a stately child telling me her father gets letters
   addressed "Robert Frost, New Hampshire."
I remember an old Irish saying, "His face is like a fiddle and
   everyone who sees him must love him."
I have one remember, two remembers, ten remembers; I have a
   little handkerchief bundle of remembers.

One early evening star just over a cradle moon,
One dark river with a spatter of later stars caught,
One funnel of a motorcar headlight up a hill,
One team of horses hauling a bobsled load of wood,
One boy on skis picking himself up after a tumble—
I remember one and a one and a one riding across New Hamp-
   shire lengthways: I have a little handkerchief bundle of
   remembers.

Elm Buds

Elm buds are out.
Yesterday morning, last night, they crept out.
They are the mice of early spring air.

To the north is the gray sky.
Winter hung it gray for the gray elm to stand dark against.
Now the branches all end with the yellow and gold mice of early
    spring air.
They are moving mice creeping out with leaf and leaf.

Anywhere and Everywhere People

There are people so near nothing they are everywhere without
being seen.

There are people so eager to be seen they nearly always manage to
be seen.

There are people who want to be everywhere at once and they seem
to get nowhere.

There are people who have never been anywhere and they are less
anxious about it than those who have been everywhere.

Could it be there are people so near to nothing they might be so
humble as to say, "We go everywhere without being seen and it
comes right easy on us"?

Could it be there are people who have never been seen anywhere
and they ask people who have been seen everywhere, "How
does it feel to be seen everywhere?"

Arithmetic

Arithmetic is where numbers fly like pigeons in and out of your
head.

Arithmetic tells you how many you lose or win if you know how
many you had before you lost or won.

Arithmetic is seven eleven all good children go to heaven—or five
six bundle of sticks.

Arithmetic is numbers you squeeze from your head to your hand to
your pencil to your paper till you get the answer.

Arithmetic is where the answer is right and everything is nice and
you can look out of the window and see the blue sky—or the
answer is wrong and you have to start all over and try again and
see how it comes out this time.

FROST AND SANDBURG

543

If you take a number and double it and double it again and then
double it a few more times, the number gets bigger and bigger
and goes higher and higher and only arithmetic can tell you
what the number is when you decide to quit doubling.

Arithmetic is where you have to multiply—and you carry the
multiplication table in your head and hope you won't lose it.

If you have two animal crackers, one good and one bad, and you eat
one and a striped zebra with streaks all over him eats the other,
how many animal crackers will you have if somebody offers you
five six seven and you say No no no and you say Nay nay nay and
you say Nix nix nix?

If you ask your mother for one fried egg for breakfast and she gives
you two fried eggs and you eat both of them, who is better in
arithmetic, you or your mother?

A LOVER OF NATURE AND PEOPLE

New Hampshire Again

1. The first three lines of this poem offer a good example of imagery.
Why do you suppose Sandburg chose each of these particular details
rather than other details?

2. In two places in the poem the word *lengthways* is used. Why is it
more effective to use this adverb than a noun like *highways* or *railroads?*

3. The poet mentions a station called "Halcyon." What does *halcyon*
mean? How does this word describe life in New Hampshire?

4. The second stanza offers a series of impressions (images). Which two
or three appeal to you particularly? Explain why.

5. In the last line Sandburg repeats "a little handkerchief bundle of
remembers." This repetition determines the poet's feeling for New
Hampshire and the mood of the poem. Explain.

Elm Buds

1. In the first stanza there is a strong metaphor, or implied comparison. What unlike things are compared? Explain how.

2. In the second stanza the poet uses the adjective *gray* in two lines. Why does he repeat this word? What is the image? Explain.

3. The last line—"They are moving mice creeping out with leaf and leaf"—completes the metaphor introduced in the first stanza. What characteristic of "mice" is emphasized? Explain the completed comparison.

Anywhere and Everywhere People

1. The title of this poem suggests the poet's general attitude toward people. What is his attitude? Explain by quoting lines from the poem.

2. In the line "There are people who want to be everywhere at once and they seem to get nowhere," the poet indicates one type of person. What is he like? Explain and, if you can, illustrate from your own experience.

3. Read again the question at the end. What type of person would be asked this question? What do you think is his chief characteristic?

4. Do you share Sandburg's attitude toward "people"? In two or three sentences, express your own ideas.

Arithmetic

1. In the first line of this poem, Sandburg uses a simile. What two things are being compared? In two or three sentences, show how this simile suggests the poet's attitude toward arithmetic.

2. How does the poet's references to childhood rhymes help you to understand his feeling about arithmetic?

3. The question at the end gives you a final impression of the poet's purpose. What is it?

4. Do you consider "Arithmetic" a poem? Write a paragraph to explain why, or why not.

THINKING ABOUT ROBERT FROST AND CARL SANDBURG

1. Frost has said: "Poetry has got to have 'beat.'" Do his poems have a beat, or rhythm? If so, which one or two poems offer most evidence of beat? How does the beat make the poem more effective?

2. Identify by title each of the following lines from Frost's poems:

a. "The fault must partly have been in me."

b. "And he learned of finalities / Besides the grave."

c. "Part of a moon was falling down the west, / Dragging the whole sky with it to the hills."

d. "But I have promises to keep, / And miles to go before I sleep."

    (1) Which quotation impresses you as being most poetic?

    (2) Which quotation shows the poet in a humble mood?

    (3) Which quotation might apply to anyone faced with an important decision?

    (4) Which quotation shows the poet in the most serious mood?

3. In "On the Road" Sandburg writes about human nature. Which one of his poems deals with this subject? Do any people in the poem resemble Sandburg in "On the Road"? Write a careful paragraph showing what these two selections have in common.

4. Sandburg writes "free verse." What is "free" about this poet's verse? Which two of these poems best illustrate this type of poetry? Explain your answer.

5. In "New Hampshire Again" Sandburg recalls pleasantly and thoughtfully his memories of New Hampshire. Which one of Frost's poems is most similar to this one by Sandburg? Justify your choice.

6. Both Frost and Sandburg show deep feeling and understanding of nature. Select one poem by Frost and one by Sandburg which illustrate this statement. Write a carefully planned paragraph comparing these two poems. In your paragraph, show similarities and differences in *what* the poets say, in *how* they say it, and in their feeling for nature.

John Steinbeck: The Dignity of Man

We seem to be running in all directions at once—but we are running. And I believe that our history, our experience in America, has endowed us for the change that is coming. We have never sat still for long; we have never been content with a place, a building, or with ourselves. Americans do not lack places to go and new things to find.

—AMERICA AND THE AMERICANS

John Steinbeck, who died in 1968, was no stranger to America's "places to go and new things to find." His most successful nonfiction book, *Travels with Charley*, is a warm, funny, and delightful account of a cross-country camping trip he made, accompanied only by his poodle, Charley.

Steinbeck was born and raised in California, where he attended Stanford University. Later he moved to New York. During his travels about the country, often in the early years doing all kinds of work, he has formed a deep affection for America.

In common with famous American writers of earlier days—Twain, Sandburg, Frost, Melville, and Stephen Crane—Steinbeck shares not only a wanderlust but also an interest in the simple, hardworking, average American. John Steinbeck would have been equally at home with Mark Twain's roustabouts and Sandburg's farm workers. In *Travels with Charley*, Steinbeck wrote of his wanderlust:

When I was very young and the urge to be someplace else was on me, I was assured by mature people that maturity would cure this itch. When years described me as mature, the remedy prescribed was middle age. In middle age I was assured that greater age would calm my fever, and now that I am fifty-eight, perhaps senility will do the job. Nothing has worked. Four hoarse blasts of a ship's whistle still raise the hair on my neck and set my feet to tapping. The sound of a jet, an engine warming up, even the clopping of shod hooves on pavement brings on the ancient shudder, the dry mouth and vacant eye. . . .

John Steinbeck's best-known novel, *The Grapes of Wrath*, is about the travels of the Joad family. The Joads were "Okies," farmers fleeing from Oklahoma where dust storms and erosion had ruined the land. It is probably because of Steinbeck's sensitive treatment of these migrant workers on their way to California in the late thirties that the word *Okie* and the problems of the Okie had such wide currency and understanding all over the country.

Steinbeck is usually classified as a realistic, even "hardboiled," writer. There is some truth in this, but it is not the whole truth. In just as many ways, Steinbeck is a romantic, even sentimental, writer. His subject matter is usually tough and naturalistic, but his love for people and for the country always shines through, giving his work a specially appealing and attractive quality. Steinbeck's hallmark may be versatility. In *Of Mice and Men*—the story of the powerful but weak-minded Lennie and his faithful protector, George—Steinbeck created a successful short novel and play. *The Cup of Gold* is historical romance. *The Moon is Down* is a well-balanced drama of wartime occupation, presumably of the Nazis in Norway. *The Sea of Cortez* is a scientific account of marine biology exploration. *The Short Reign of Pippin IV* is political satire. He once wrote to his editor, "I do not think all the things in my books are good but all things in my books are me."

In spite of the wide range of his writing, Steinbeck is often remembered chiefly for his great indignation at the miseries, misfortunes, and deprivations of the poor. But perhaps above all, Steinbeck is a great storyteller. With his love of exaggeration and rich sense of humor, he reminds one of the wandering minstrel performing in the great hall of a medieval castle, taking as much enjoy-ment from the entertainment as he gives.

In 1962 he received the Nobel Prize in literature for the "long career of writing in which Steinbeck produced both realistic and imaginative work, distinguished by social perception and sympathetic humor." For all the bitter realism of his subject matter, Steinbeck is fundamentally an affirmative man. In his speech accepting the Nobel Prize, he said: "The writer is delegated to declare and to celebrate man's proven capacity for greatness of heart and spirit —for gallantry in defeat—for courage, compassion, and love. . . . I hold that a writer who does not passionately believe in the perfectability of man has no dedication nor any membership in literature."

Flight

"Peanut," his mother called him at first—"foolish chicken." But sooner than he ever dreamed, he would have to prove he was neither "peanut" nor "chicken" . . . but a man.

About fifteen miles below Monterey, on the wild coast, the Torres family had their farm, a few sloping acres above a cliff that dropped to the brown reefs and to the hissing white waters of the ocean. Behind the farm the stone mountains stood up against the sky. The farm buildings huddled like the clinging aphids on the mountain skirts, crouched low to the ground as though the wind might blow them into the sea. The little shack, the rattling, rotting barn were gray-bitten with sea salt, beaten by the damp wind until they had taken on the color of the granite hills. Two horses, a red cow and a red calf, half a dozen pigs, and a flock of lean, multicolored chickens stocked the place.

A little corn was raised on the sterile slope, and it grew short and thick under the wind, and all the cobs formed on the landward sides of the stalks.

Mama Torres, a lean, dry woman with ancient eyes, had ruled the farm for ten years, ever since her husband tripped over a stone in the field one day and fell full length on a rattlesnake. When one is bitten on the chest, there is not much that can be done.

Mama Torres had three children, two undersized black ones of twelve and fourteen, Emilio [1] and Rosy, whom Mama kept fishing on the rocks below the farm when the sea was kind and when the truant officer was in some distant part of Monterey County. And there was Pepé, the tall smiling son of nineteen, a gentle, affectionate boy, but very lazy. Pepé had a tall head, pointed at the top, and from its peak coarse black hair grew down like a thatch all around. Over his smiling little eyes Mama cut a straight bang so he could see. Pepé had sharp Indian cheekbones and an eagle nose, but his mouth was as sweet and shapely as a girl's mouth, and his chin was fragile and chiseled. He was loose and gangling, all legs and feet and wrists, and he was very lazy. Mama thought him fine and brave, but she never told him so. She said, "Some lazy cow must have got into thy father's family, else how could I have a son like thee?" And she said, "When I carried thee, a sneaking lazy coyote came out of the brush and looked at me one day. That must have made thee so."

Pepé smiled sheepishly and stabbed at the ground with his knife to keep the blade sharp and free from rust. It was his inheritance, that knife, his father's knife. The long, heavy blade folded back into the black handle. There was a button on the handle. When Pepé pressed

the button, the blade leaped out ready for use. The knife was with Pepé always, for it had been his father's knife.

One sunny morning when the sea below the cliff was glinting and blue and the white surf creamed on the reef, when even the stone mountains looked kindly, Mama Torres called out the door of the shack, "Pepé, I have a labor for thee."

There was no answer. Mama listened. From behind the barn she heard a burst of laughter. She lifted her full long skirt and walked in the direction of the noise.

Pepé was sitting on the ground with his back against a box. His white teeth glistened. On either side of him stood the two black ones, tense and expectant. Fifteen feet away a redwood post was set in the ground. Pepé's right hand lay limply in his lap, and in the palm the big black knife rested. The blade was closed back into the handle. Pepé looked smiling at the sky.

Suddenly Emilio cried, "Ya!"

Pepé's wrist flicked like the head of a snake. The blade seemed to fly open in midair, and with a thump the point dug into the redwood post, and the black handle quivered. The three burst into excited laughter. Rosy ran to the post and pulled out the knife and brought it back to Pepé. He closed the blade and settled the knife carefully in his listless palm again. He grinned self-consciously at the sky.

"Ya!"

The heavy knife lanced out and sunk into the post again. Mama moved forward like a ship and scattered the play.

"All day you do foolish things with the knife, like a toy baby," she stormed. "Get up on thy huge feet that eat up shoes. Get up!" She took him by one loose shoulder and hoisted at him. Pepé grinned sheepishly and came halfheartedly to his feet. "Look!" Mama cried.

JOHN STEINBECK   **551**

"Big lazy, you must catch the horse and put on him thy father's saddle. You must ride to Monterey. The medicine bottle is empty. There is no salt. Go thou now, Peanut! Catch the horse."

A revolution took place in the relaxed figure of Pepé. "To Monterey, me? Alone? *Sí*, Mama."

She scowled at him. "Do not think, big sheep, that you will buy candy. No, I will give you only enough for the medicine and the salt."

Pepé smiled. "Mama, you will put the hatband on the hat?"

She relented then. "Yes, Pepé. You may wear the hatband."

His voice grew insinuating. "And the green handkerchief, Mama?"

"Yes, if you go quickly and return with no trouble, the silk green handkerchief will go. If you make sure to take off the handkerchief when you eat, so no spot may fall on it."

"*Sí*, Mama. I will be careful. I am a man."

"Thou? A man? Thou art a peanut."

He went into the rickety barn and brought out a rope, and he walked agilely enough up the hill to catch the horse.

When he was ready and mounted before the door, mounted on his father's saddle that was so old that the oaken frame showed through torn leather in many places, then Mama brought out the round black hat with the tooled leather band, and she reached up and knotted the green silk handkerchief about his neck. Pepé's blue denim coat was much darker than his jeans, for it had been washed much less often.

Mama handed up the big medicine bottle and the silver coins. "That for the medicine," she said, "and that for the salt. That for a candle to burn for the papa. That for *dulces* [1] for the little ones. Our friend Mrs. Rodriguez will give you dinner and maybe a bed for the night. When you go to the church, say only ten paternosters and only twenty-five Ave Marias. [2] Oh! I know, big coyote. You would sit there flapping your mouth over Aves all day while you looked at the candles and the holy pictures. That is not good devotion to stare at the pretty things."

The black hat, covering the high pointed head and black thatched hair of Pepé, gave him dignity and age. He sat the rangy horse well. Mama thought how handsome he was, dark and lean and tall. "I would not send thee now alone, thou little one, except for the medicine," she said softly. "It is not good to have no medicine, for who knows when the toothache will come, or the sadness of the stomach. These things are."

"*Adiós*, Mama," Pepé cried. "I will come back soon. You may send me often alone. I am a man."

"Thou art a foolish chicken."

He straightened his shoulders, flipped the reins against the horse's shoulder, and rode away. He turned once and saw that they still watched him, Emilio and Rosy and Mama. Pepé grinned with pride and gladness, and lifted the tough buckskin horse to a trot.

When he had dropped out of sight over a little dip in the road, Mama turned to the black ones, but she spoke to herself. "He is nearly a man now," she said. "It will be a nice thing to have a man in the house again." Her eyes sharpened on the children. "Go to the rocks now. The tide is going out. There will be abalones to be found." She put the iron hooks into their hands and saw them down the steep trail to the reefs. She brought the smooth stone metate

---

[1] *dulces* (DOOL·sayss): sweets, candy.

[2] **paternosters** (PAY·ter·NAHS·terz) and ...
Ave Marias (AH·vay ma·REE·ahz): prayers.

to the doorway and sat grinding her corn to flour and looking occasionally at the road over which Pepé had gone. The noonday came and then the afternoon, when the little ones beat the abalones on a rock to make them tender and Mama patted the *tortillas* to make them thin. They ate their dinner as the red sun was plunging down toward the ocean. They sat on the doorsteps and watched a big white moon come over the mountaintops.

Mama said, "He is now at the house of our friend Mrs. Rodriguez. She will give him nice things to eat and maybe a present."

Emilio said, "Someday I, too, will ride to Monterey for medicine. Did Pepé come to be a man today?"

Mama said wisely, "A boy gets to be a man when a man is needed. Remember this thing. I have known boys forty years old because there was no need for a man."

Soon afterward they retired, Mama in her big oak bed on one side of the room, Emilio and Rosy in their boxes full of straw and sheepskins on the other side of the room.

The moon went over the sky, and the surf roared on the rocks. The roosters crowed the first call. The surf subsided to a whispering surge against the reef. The moon dropped toward the sea. The roosters crowed again.

The moon was near down to the water when Pepé rode on a winded horse to his home flat. His dog bounced out and circled the horse yelping with pleasure. Pepé slid off the saddle to the ground. The weathered little shack was silver in the moonlight, and the square shadow of it was black to the north and east. Against the east the piling mountains were misty with light; their tops melted into the sky.

Pepé walked wearily up the three steps and into the house. It was dark inside. There was a rustle in the corner.

Mama cried out from her bed. "Who comes? Pepé, is it thou?"

"*Si*, Mama."

"Did you get the medicine?"

"*Si*, Mama."

"Well, go to sleep, then. I thought you would be sleeping at the house of Mrs. Rodriguez." Pepé stood silently in the dark room. "Why do you stand there, Pepé? Did you drink wine?"

"*Si*, Mama."

"Well, go to bed then and sleep out the wine."

His voice was tired and patient, but very firm. "Light the candle, Mama. I must go away into the mountains."

"What is this, Pepé? You are crazy." Mama struck a sulfur match and held the little blue burr until the flame spread up the stick. She set light to the candle on the floor beside her bed. "Now, Pepé, what is this you say?" She looked anxiously into his face.

He was changed. The fragile quality seemed to have gone from his chin. His mouth was less full than it had been, the lines of the lips were straighter, but in his eyes the greatest change had taken place. There was no laughter in them any more, nor any bashfulness. They were sharp and bright and purposeful.

He told her in a tired monotone, told her everything just as it had happened. A few people came into the kitchen of Mrs. Rodriguez. There was wine to drink. Pepé drank wine. The little quarrel—the man started toward Pepé and then the knife—it went almost by itself. It flew, it darted before Pepé knew it. As he talked, Mama's face grew stern, and it seemed to grow more lean. Pepé finished. "I am a man now, Mama. The man said names to me I could not allow."

Mama nodded. "Yes, thou art a man, my poor little Pepé. Thou art a man. I have seen it coming on thee. I have watched you throwing the knife into the post, and I have been afraid." For a moment her face had softened, but now it grew stern again. "Come! We must get you ready. Go. Awaken Emilio and Rosy. Go quickly."

Pepé stepped over to the corner where his brother and sister slept among the sheepskins. He leaned down and shook them gently. "Come, Rosy! Come, Emilio! The Mama says you must arise."

The little black ones sat up and rubbed their eyes in the candlelight. Mama was out of bed now, her long black skirt over her nightgown. "Emilio," she cried. "Go up and catch the other horse for Pepé. Quickly, now! Quickly." Emilio put his legs in his overalls and stumbled sleepily out the door.

"You heard no one behind you on the road?" Mama demanded.

"No, Mama. I listened carefully. No one was on the road."

Mama darted like a bird about the room. From a nail on the wall, she took a canvas water bag and threw it on the floor. She stripped a blanket from her bed and rolled it into a tight tube and tied the ends with string. From a box beside the stove, she lifted a flour sack half-full of black stringy jerky.[1] "Your father's black coat, Pepé. Here, put it on."

Pepé stood in the middle of the floor watching her activity. She reached behind the door and brought out the rifle, a long 38–56, worn shiny the whole length of the barrel. Pepé took it from her and held it in the crook of his elbow. Mama brought a little leather bag and counted the cartridges into his hand. "Only ten left," she warned. "You must not waste them."

[1] **jerky:** dried meat.

Emilio put his head in the door. "*'Qui 'st 'l caballo,*[2] Mama."

"Put on the saddle from the other horse. Tie on the blanket. Here, tie the jerky to the saddle horn."

Still Pepé stood silently watching his mother's frantic activity. His chin looked hard, and his sweet mouth was drawn and thin. His little eyes followed Mama about the room almost suspiciously.

Rosy asked softly, "Where goes Pepé?"

Mama's eyes were fierce. "Pepé goes on a journey. Pepé is a man now. He has a man's thing to do."

Pepé straightened his shoulders. His mouth changed until he looked very much like Mama.

At last the preparation was finished. The loaded horse stood outside the door. The water bag dripped a line of moisture down the bay shoulder.

The moonlight was being thinned by the dawn, and the big white moon was near down to the sea. The family stood by the shack. Mama confronted Pepé. "Look, my son! Do not stop until it is dark again. Do not sleep even though you are tired. Take care of the horse in order that he may not stop of weariness. Remember to be careful with the bullets—there are only ten. Do not fill thy stomach with jerky or it will make thee sick. Eat a little jerky and fill thy stomach with grass. When thou comest to the high mountains, if thou seest any of the dark watching men, go not near to them nor try to speak to them. And forget not thy prayers." She put her lean hands on Pepé's shoulders, stood on her toes, and kissed him formally on both cheeks, and Pepé kissed her on both cheeks. Then he went to Emilio and Rosy and kissed both of their cheeks.

Pepé turned back to Mama. He

[2] *'Qui 'st 'l caballo* (KEEST'l ka·BAH·yo): Here is the horse.

seemed to look for a little softness, a little weakness in her. His eyes were searching, but Mama's face remained fierce. "Go now," she said. "Do not wait to be caught like a chicken."

Pepé pulled himself into the saddle. "I am a man," he said.

It was the first dawn when he rode up the hill toward the little canyon which let a trail into the mountains. Moonlight and daylight fought with each other, and the two warring qualities made it difficult to see. Before Pepé had gone a hundred yards, the outlines of his figure were misty; and long before he entered the canyon, he had become a gray, indefinite shadow.

Mama stood stiffly in front of her doorstep, and on either side of her stood Emilio and Rosy. They cast furtive glances at Mama now and then.

When the gray shape of Pepé melted into the hillside and disappeared, Mama relaxed. She began the high, whining keen of the death wail. "Our beautiful —our brave," she cried. "Our protector, our son is gone." Emilio and Rosy moaned beside her. "Our beautiful— our brave, he is gone." It was the formal wail. It rose to a high, piercing whine and subsided to a moan. Mama raised it three times and then she turned and went into the house and shut the door.

Emilio and Rosy stood wondering in the dawn. They heard Mama whimpering in the house. They went out to sit on the cliff above the ocean. They touched shoulders. "When did Pepé come to be a man?" Emilio asked.

"Last night," said Rosy. "Last night in Monterey." The ocean clouds turned red with the sun that was behind the mountains.

"We will have no breakfast," said Emilio. "Mama will not want to cook." Rosy did not answer him. "Where is Pepé gone?" he asked.

Rosy looked around at him. She drew her knowledge from the quiet air. "He has gone on a journey. He will never come back."

"Is he dead? Do you think he is dead?"

Rosy looked back at the ocean again. A little steamer, drawing a line of smoke, sat on the edge of the horizon. "He is not dead," Rosy explained. "Not yet."

Pepé rested the big rifle across the saddle in front of him. He let the horse walk up the hill and he didn't look back. The stony slope took on a coat of short brush so that Pepé found the entrance to a trail and entered it.

When he came to the canyon opening, he swung once in his saddle and looked back, but the houses were swallowed in the misty light. Pepé jerked forward again. The high shoulder of the canyon closed in on him. His horse stretched out its neck and sighed and settled to the trail.

It was a well-worn path, dark, soft leaf-mold earth strewn with broken pieces of sandstone. The trail rounded the shoulder of the canyon and dropped steeply into the bed of the stream. In the shallows the water ran smoothly, glinting in the first morning sun. Small round stones on the bottom were as brown as rust with sun moss. In the sand along the edges of the stream, the tall, rich wild mint grew, while in the water itself the cress, old and tough, had gone to heavy seed.

The path went into the stream and emerged on the other side. The horse sloshed into the water and stopped. Pepé dropped his bridle and let the beast drink of the running water.

Soon the canyon sides became steep and the first giant sentinel redwoods guarded the trail, great round red trunks bearing foliage as green and lacy as ferns. Once Pepé was among the trees, the sun was lost. A perfumed and purple light lay in the pale green of the underbrush. Gooseberry bushes and blackberries and tall ferns lined the stream, and overhead the branches of the redwoods met and cut off the sky.

Pepé drank from the water bag, and he reached into the flour sack and brought out a black string of jerky. His white teeth gnawed at the string until the tough meat parted. He chewed slowly and drank occasionally from the water bag. His little eyes were slumberous and tired, but the muscles of his face were hardset. The earth of the trail was black now. It gave up a hollow sound under the walking hoofbeats.

The stream fell more sharply. Little waterfalls splashed on the stones. Five-fingered ferns hung over the water and dripped spray from their finger tips. Pepé rode half over his saddle, dangling one leg loosely. He picked a bay leaf from a tree beside the way and put it into his mouth for a moment to flavor the dry jerky. He held the gun loosely across the pommel.

Suddenly he squared in his saddle, swung the horse from the trail, and kicked it hurriedly up behind a big redwood tree. He pulled up the reins tight against the bit to keep the horse from whinnying. His face was intent and his nostrils quivered a little.

A hollow pounding came down the trail, and a horseman rode by, a fat man with red cheeks and a white stubble beard. His horse put down his head and blubbered at the trail when it came to the place where Pepé had turned off. "Hold up!" said the man, and he pulled up his horse's head.

When the last sound of the hoofs died away, Pepé came back into the trail again. He did not relax in the saddle any more. He lifted the big rifle and swung the lever to throw a shell into the chamber, and then he let down the hammer to half cock.

The trail grew very steep. Now the redwood trees were smaller and their tops were dead, bitten dead where the wind reached them. The horse plodded on; the sun went slowly overhead and started down toward the afternoon.

Where the stream came out of a side canyon, the trail left it. Pepé dismounted and watered his horse and filled up his water bag. As soon as the trail had parted from the stream, the trees were gone and only the thick brittle sage and manzanita and chaparral edged the trail. And the soft black earth was gone, too, leaving only the light tan broken rock for the trail bed. Lizards scampered away into the brush as the horse rattled over the little stones.

Pepé turned in his saddle and looked back. He was in the open now: he could be seen from a distance. As he ascended the trail, the country grew more rough and terrible and dry. The way wound about the bases of great square rocks. Little gray rabbits skittered in the brush. A bird made a monotonous high creaking. Eastward the bare rock mountaintops were pale and powder-dry under the dropping sun. The horse plodded up and up the trail toward a little V in the ridge which was the pass.

Pepé looked suspiciously back every minute or so, and his eyes sought the tops of the ridges ahead. Once, on a white barren spur, he saw a black figure for a moment; but he looked quickly away, for it was one of the dark watchers. No one knew who the watchers were, nor where they lived, but it was better to ignore them and never to show interest in them. They did not bother one who stayed on the trail and minded his own business.

The air was parched and full of light dust blown by the breeze from the eroding mountains. Pepé drank sparingly from his bag and corked it tightly and hung it on the horn again. The trail moved up the dry shale hillside, avoiding rocks, dropping under clefts, climbing in and out of old water scars. When he arrived at the little pass, he stopped and looked back for a long time. No dark watchers were to be seen now. The trail behind was empty. Only the high tops of the redwoods indicated where the stream flowed.

Pepé rode on through the pass. His little eyes were nearly closed with weariness, but his face was stern, relentless, and manly. The high mountain wind coasted sighing through the pass and whistled on the edges of the big blocks of broken granite. In the air, a red-tailed hawk sailed over close to the ridge and screamed angrily. Pepé went slowly through the broken jagged pass and looked down on the other side.

The trail dropped quickly, staggering among broken rock. At the bottom of the slope, there was a dark crease, thick with brush, and on the other side of the crease, a little flat, in which a grove of oak trees grew. A scar of green grass cut across the flat. And behind the flat another mountain rose, desolate with dead rocks and starving little black bushes. Pepé drank from the bag again, for the air was so dry that it encrusted his nostrils and burned his lips. He put the horse down the trail. The hoofs slipped and struggled on the steep way, starting little stones that rolled off into the brush. The sun was gone behind the westward mountain now, but still it glowed brilliantly on the oaks and on the grassy flat. The rocks and the hillsides still sent up waves of the heat they had gathered from the day's sun.

Pepé looked up to the top of the next dry withered ridge. He saw a dark form against the sky, a man's figure standing on top of a rock, and he glanced away quickly not to appear curious. When a moment later he looked up again, the figure was gone.

Downward the trail was quickly covered. Sometimes the horse floundered for footing, sometimes set his feet and slid a little way. They came at last to the bottom, where the dark chaparral was higher than Pepé's head. He held up his rifle on one side and his arm on the other to shield his face from the sharp, brittle fingers of the brush.

Up and out of the crease he rode, and up a little cliff. The grassy flat was before him, and the round, comfortable oaks. For a moment he studied the trail down which he had come, but there was no movement and no sound from it. Finally he rode out over the flat, to the green streak, and at the upper end of the damp, he found a little spring welling out of the earth and dropping into a dug basin before it seeped out over the flat.

Pepé filled his bag first, and then he let the thirsty horse drink out of the pool. He led the horse to the clump of oaks, and in the middle of the grove, fairly protected from sight on all sides, he took off the saddle and the bridle and laid them on the ground. The horse stretched his jaws sideways and yawned. Pepé knotted the lead rope about the horse's neck and tied him to a sapling among the oaks, where he could graze in a fairly large circle.

When the horse was gnawing hungrily at the dry grass, Pepé went to the saddle and took a black string of jerky from the sack and strolled to an oak tree on the edge of the grove, from under which he could watch the trail. He sat down in the crisp, dry oak leaves and automatically felt for his big black knife to cut the jerky, but he had no knife. He leaned back on his elbow and gnawed at the tough strong meat. His face was blank, but it was a man's face.

The bright evening light washed the eastern ridge, but the valley was darkening. Doves flew down from the hills to the spring, and the quail came running out of the brush and joined them, calling clearly to one another.

Out of the corner of his eye, Pepé saw a shadow grow out of the bushy crease. He turned his head slowly. A big spotted wildcat was creeping toward the spring, belly to the ground, moving like thought.

Pepé cocked his rifle and edged the muzzle slowly around. Then he looked apprehensively up the trail and dropped the hammer again. From the ground beside him, he picked an oak twig and threw it toward the spring. The quail flew up with a roar and the doves whistled away. The big cat stood up: for a long moment he looked at Pepé with cold yellow eyes, and then fearlessly walked back into the gulch.

The dusk gathered quickly in the deep valley. Pepé muttered his prayers, put his head down on his arm, and went instantly to sleep.

The moon came up and filled the valley with cold blue light, and the wind swept rustling down from the peaks. The owls worked up and down the slopes looking for rabbits. Down in the brush of the gulch, a coyote gabbled. The oak trees whispered softly in the night breeze.

Pepé started up, listening. His horse had whinnied. The moon was just slipping behind the western ridge, leaving the valley in darkness behind it. Pepé sat tensely gripping his rifle. From far up the trail, he heard an answering whinny and the crash of shod hoofs on the broken rock. He jumped to his feet, ran to his horse, and led it under the trees. He threw on the saddle and cinched it tight for the steep trail, caught the unwilling head and forced the bit into the mouth. He felt the saddle to make sure the water bag and the sack of jerky were there. Then he mounted and turned up the hill.

It was velvet-dark. The horse found the entrance to the trail where it left the flat, and started up, stumbling and slipping on the rocks. Pepé's hand rose up to his head. His hat was gone. He had left it under the oak tree.

The horse had struggled far up the trail when the first change of dawn came into the air, a steel grayness as light mixed thoroughly with dark. Gradually the sharp, snaggled edge of the ridge stood out above them, rotten granite tortured and eaten by the winds of time. Pepé had dropped his reins on the horn, leaving direction to the horse. The brush grabbed at his legs in the dark until one knee of his jeans was ripped.

Gradually the light flowed down over the ridge. The starved brush and rocks stood out in the half-light, strange and lonely in high perspective. Then there came warmth into the light. Pepé drew up and looked back, but he could see nothing in the darker valley below. The sky turned blue over the coming sun. In the waste of the mountainside, the poor dry brush grew only three feet high. Here and there, big outcroppings of unrotted granite stood up like moldering houses. Pepé relaxed a little. He drank from his water bag and bit off a piece of jerky. A single eagle flew over, high in the light.

Without warning, Pepé's horse screamed and fell on its side. He was almost down before the rifle crash echoed up from the valley. From a hole behind the struggling shoulder, a stream of bright crimson blood pumped and stopped and pumped and stopped. The hoofs threshed on the ground. Pepé lay half-stunned beside the horse. He looked slowly down the hill. A piece of sage clipped off beside his head and another crash echoed up from side to side of the canyon. Pepé flung himself frantically behind a bush.

He crawled up the hill on his knees and one hand. His right hand held the

rifle up off the ground and pushed it
ahead of him. He moved with the in-
stinctive care of an animal. Rapidly he
wormed his way toward one of the big
outcroppings of granite on the hill
above him. Where the brush was high,
he doubled up and ran; but where the
cover was slight, he wriggled forward on
his stomach, pushing the rifle ahead of
him. In the last little distance there was
no cover at all. Pepé poised and then he
darted across the space and flashed
around the corner of the rock.

He leaned panting against the stone.
When his breath came easier, he moved
along behind the big rock until he came
to a narrow split that offered a thin section of vision down the hill. Pepé lay
on his stomach and pushed the rifle
barrel through the slit and waited.

The sun reddened the western ridges
now. Already the buzzards were settling down toward the place where the
horse lay. A small brown bird scratched
in the dead sage leaves directly in front

of the rifle muzzle. The coasting eagle
flew back toward the rising sun.

Pepé saw a little movement in the
brush far below. His grip tightened on
the gun. A little brown doe stepped
daintily out on the trail and crossed it
and disappeared into the brush again.
For a long time Pepé waited. Far below
he could see the little flat and the oak
trees and the slash of green. Suddenly
his eyes flashed back at the trail again.
A quarter of a mile down, there had
been a quick movement in the chaparral. The rifle swung over. The front
sight nestled in the V of the rear sight.
Pepé studied for a moment and then
raised the rear sight a notch. The little
movement in the brush came again. The
sight settled on it. Pepé squeezed the
trigger. The explosion crashed down the
mountain and up the other side, and
came rattling back. The whole side of
the slope grew still. No more movement. And then a white streak cut into
the granite of the slit and a bullet

whined away and a crash sounded up from below. Pepé felt a sharp pain in his right hand. A sliver of granite was sticking out from between his first and second knuckles and the point protruded from his palm. Carefully he pulled out the sliver of stone. The wound bled evenly and gently. No vein or artery was cut.

Pepé looked into a little dusty cave in the rock and gathered a handful of spider web, and he pressed the mass into the cut, plastering the soft web into the blood. The flow stopped almost at once.

The rifle was on the ground. Pepé picked it up, levered a new shell into the chamber. And then he slid into the brush on his stomach. Far to the right he crawled, and then up the hill, moving slowly and carefully, crawling to cover and resting and then crawling again.

In the mountains the sun is high in its arc before it penetrates the gorges. The hot face looked over the hill and brought instant heat with it. The white light beat on the rocks and reflected from them and rose up quivering from the earth again, and the rocks and bushes seemed to quiver behind the air.

Pepé crawled in the general direction of the ridge peak, zigzagging for cover. The deep cut between his knuckles began to throb. He crawled close to a rattlesnake before he saw it, and when it raised its dry head and made a soft beginning whir, he backed up and took another way. The quick gray lizards flashed in front of him, raising a tiny line of dust. He found another mass of spider web and pressed it against his throbbing hand.

Pepé was pushing the rifle with his left hand now. Little drops of sweat ran to the ends of his coarse black hair and rolled down his cheeks. His lips and tongue were growing thick and heavy. His lips writhed to draw saliva into his mouth. His little dark eyes were uneasy and suspicious. Once when a gray lizard paused in front of him on the parched ground and turned its head sideways, he crushed it flat with a stone.

When the sun slid past noon, he had not gone a mile. He crawled exhaustedly a last hundred yards to a patch of high, sharp manzanita, crawled desperately, and when the patch was reached, he wriggled in among the tough, gnarly trunks and dropped his head on his left arm. There was little shade in the meager brush, but there was cover and safety. Pepé went to sleep as he lay and the sun beat on his back. A few little birds hopped close to him and peered and hopped away. Pepé squirmed in his sleep and he raised and dropped his wounded hand again and again.

The sun went down behind the peaks and the cool evening came, and then the dark. A coyote yelled from the hillside. Pepé started awake and looked about with misty eyes. His hand was swollen and heavy; a little thread of pain ran up the inside of his arm and settled in a pocket in his armpit. He peered about and then stood up, for the mountains were black and the moon had not yet risen. Pepé stood up in the dark. The coat of his father pressed on his arm. His tongue was swollen until it nearly filled his mouth. He wriggled out of the coat and dropped it in the brush, and then he struggled up the hill, falling over rocks and tearing his way through the brush. The rifle knocked against stones as he went. Little dry avalanches of gravel and shattered stone went whispering down the hill behind him.

After a while the old moon came up and showed the jagged ridgetop ahead of him. By moonlight Pepé traveled more easily. He bent forward so that his throbbing arm hung away from his body. The journey uphill was made in dashes and rests, a frantic rush up a few yards and then a rest. The wind coasted down the slope rattling the dry stems of the bushes.

The moon was at meridian when Pepé came at last to the sharp backbone of the ridgetop. On the last hundred yards of the rise, no soil had clung under the wearing winds. The way was on solid rock. He clambered to the top and looked down on the other side. There was a draw like the last below him, misty with moonlight, brushed with dry, struggling sage and chaparral. On the other side the hill rose up sharply and at the top the jagged rotten teeth of the mountain showed against the sky. At the bottom of the cut, the brush was thick and dark.

Pepé stumbled down the hill. His throat was almost closed with thirst. At first he tried to run, but immediately he fell and rolled. After that he went more carefully. The moon was just disappearing behind the mountains when he came to the bottom. He crawled into the heavy brush, feeling with his fingers for water. There was no water in the bed of the stream, only damp earth. Pepé laid his gun down and scooped up a handful of mud and put it in his mouth, and then he spluttered and scraped the earth from his tongue with his finger, for the mud drew at his mouth like a poultice. He dug a hole in the stream bed with his fingers, dug a little basin to catch water; but before it was very deep, his head fell forward on the damp ground and he slept.

The dawn came and the heat of the day fell on the earth, and still Pepé slept. Late in the afternoon his head jerked up. He looked slowly around. His eyes were slits of weariness. Twenty feet away in the heavy brush a big tawny mountain lion stood looking at him. Its long thick tail waved gracefully; its ears were erect with interest, not laid back dangerously. The lion squatted down on its stomach and watched him.

Pepé looked at the hole he had dug in the earth. A half inch of muddy water had collected in the bottom. He tore the sleeve from his hurt arm, with his teeth ripped out a little square, soaked it in the water, and put it in his mouth. Over and over he filled the cloth and sucked it.

Still the lion sat and watched him. The evening came down but there was no movement on the hills. No birds visited the dry bottom of the cut. Pepé looked occasionally at the lion. The eyes of the yellow beast drooped as though he were about to sleep. He yawned and his long thin red tongue curled out. Suddenly his head jerked around and his nostrils quivered. His big tail lashed. He stood up and slunk like a tawny shadow into the thick brush.

A moment later Pepé heard the sound, a faint, far crash of horses' hoofs on gravel. And he heard something else, a high whining yelp of a dog.

Pepé took his rifle in his left hand and he glided into the brush almost as quietly as the lion had. In the darkening evening he crouched up the hill toward the next ridge. Only when the dark came did he stand up. His energy was short. Once it was dark, he fell over the rocks and slipped to his knees on the steep slope, but he moved on and on up the hill, climbing and scrambling over the broken hillside.

When he was far up toward the top, he lay down and slept for a little while. The withered moon, shining on his face, awakened him. He stood up and moved up the hill. Fifty yards away he stopped and turned back, for he had forgotten his rifle. He walked heavily down and poked about in the brush, but he could not find his gun. At last he lay down to rest. The pocket of pain in his armpit had grown more sharp. His arm seemed to swell out and fall with every heartbeat. There was no position lying down where the heavy arm did not press against his armpit.

With the effort of a hurt beast, Pepé got up and moved again toward the top of the ridge. He held his swollen arm away from his body with his left hand. Up the steep hill he dragged himself, a few steps and a rest, and a few more steps. At last he was nearing the top. The moon showed the uneven sharp back of it against the sky.

Pepé's brain spun in a big spiral up and away from him. He slumped to the ground and lay still. The rock ridgetop was only a hundred feet above him.

The moon moved over the sky. Pepé half turned on his back. His tongue tried to make words, but only a thick hissing came from between his lips.

When the dawn came, Pepé pulled himself up. His eyes were sane again. He drew his great puffed arm in front of him and looked at the angry wound. The black line ran up from his wrist to his armpit. Automatically he reached in his pocket for the big black knife, but it was not there. His eyes searched the ground. He picked up a sharp blade of stone and scraped at the wound, sawed at the proud flesh and then squeezed the green juice out in big drops. Instantly he threw back his head and whined like a dog. His whole right side shuddered at the pain, but the pain cleared his head.

In the gray light he struggled up the last slope to the ridge and crawled over and lay down behind a line of rocks. Below him lay a deep canyon exactly like the last, waterless and desolate. There was no flat, no oak trees, not even heavy brush in the bottom of it. And on the other side a sharp ridge stood up, thinly brushed with starving sage, littered with broken granite. Strewn over the hill there were giant outcroppings, and on the top the granite teeth stood out against the sky.

The new day was light now. The flame of the sun came over the ridge and fell on Pepé where he lay on the ground. His coarse black hair was littered with twigs and bits of spider web. His eyes had retreated back into his head. Between his lips the tip of his black tongue showed.

He sat up and dragged his great arm into his lap and nursed it, rocking his body and moaning in his throat. He threw back his head and looked up into the pale sky. A big black bird circled nearly out of sight, and far to the left another was sailing near.

He lifted his head to listen, for a familiar sound had come to him from the valley he had climbed out of; it was the crying yelp of hounds, excited and feverish, on a trail.

Pepé bowed his head quickly. He tried to speak rapid words but only a thick hiss came from his lips. He drew a shaky cross on his breast with his left hand. It was a long struggle to get to his feet. He crawled slowly and mechanically to the top of a big rock on the ridge peak. Once there, he arose slowly, swaying to his feet, and stood erect. Far below he could see the dark brush where he had slept. He braced his feet and stood there, black against the morning sky.

There came a ripping sound at his feet. A piece of stone flew up and a bullet droned off into the next gorge. The hollow crash echoed up from below. Pepé looked down for a moment and then pulled himself straight again.

His body jarred back. His left hand fluttered helplessly toward his breast. The second crash sounded from below. Pepé swung forward and toppled from the rock. His body struck and rolled over and over, starting a little avalanche. And when at last he stopped against a bush, the avalanche slid slowly down and covered up his head.

THE FACT IS—

1. Why did Pepé have to visit the city?
2. What happened to Pepé in the city?
3. In what ways did Pepé change after his experience in the city?
4. How many people did Pepé see in the mountains? What were the first signs of danger?
5. How did Pepé die? Who killed him?

CORNERED

1. Do you approve or disapprove of Mama Torres's approach to making a man of Pepé? What circumstances impelled her suddenly to shelter him less and expose him more to the realities of life?

2. Imagine what might have happened between Pepé and his adversary in Mrs. Rodriguez's kitchen. Write a brief dialogue that the two might have engaged in.

3. Which do you think was the more manly thing for Pepé to do—stay and face a murder trial, or follow his mother's advice: "Do not wait to be caught like a chicken"?

4. Notice how vividly the author has described the farm and the changing scenery in the mountains. Point out some descriptive passages that you think are especially good. How is the changing landscape in the mountains related to Pepé's chances of escape? Describe the setting in which Pepé is killed.

5. Foreshadowing is a technique writers use to give readers a hint of what may yet come. Mama's reluctance to send Pepé alone to Monterey foreshadows his trouble in the city. Where is Pepé's impulse to defend himself by knife foreshadowed? Where is Pepé's death foreshadowed?

Italy

In war, as in games, you have to know

when to bluff and when the other fellow is bluffing.

December 10, 1943—The lieutenant walked slowly up the hill toward the German positions. He carried his white flag over his head, and his white flag was a bath towel. As he walked, he thought what a fool he was. He had really stuck his neck out. Last night when he had argued for the privilege of going up and trying to kid the jerry into surrender, he hadn't known it would be like this. He hadn't known how lonely and exposed he would be.

Forty paratroopers against eighty-seven jerries, but jerry didn't know that. The lieutenant also hoped jerry wouldn't know his guts were turned to water. His feet sounded loud on the path. It was early in the morning, and the sun was not up yet. He hoped they could see his white flag. Maybe it would be invisible in this light. He kept in the open as much as possible as he climbed the hill.

He knew that the forty paratroopers were crawling and squirming behind him, keeping cover, getting into position so that if anything should go wrong, they might attack and stand some chance of surprising the jerry. He knew the field glasses of the captain would be on the German position, waiting for something to happen.

"If they shoot at you, flop and lie still," the captain had said. "We'll try to cover you and get you out."

The lieutenant knew that if he were hit and not killed, he would hear the shot after he was hit, but if he were hit in the head, he wouldn't hear or feel anything. He hoped, if it happened, it would happen that way. His feet seemed very heavy and clumsy. He looked down and saw the little stones on the path, and he wished he could get down on his knees to see what kind of stones they were. He had a positive hunger to get down out of line. His chest tingled almost as if he were preparing to receive the bullet. And his throat was as tight as it had been once when he tried to make a speech in college.

Step by step he drew nearer, and there was no sign from jerry. The lieutenant wanted to look back to see whether any of the paratroopers were in sight, but he knew the Germans would have their field glasses on him, and they were close enough so that they could even see his expression.

It happened finally, quickly, and naturally. He was passing a pile of rocks when a deep voice shouted an order to him. There were three Germans, young-looking men, and they had their rifles trained on his stomach. He stopped and stared at them and they stared back. He wondered whether his eyes were as wide as theirs. They paused, and then a hoarse voice called from up ahead. The jerries stood up and they glanced quickly down the hill before they came out to him. And then the four marched on. It seemed a little silly to the lieutenant, like little boys marching up an alley to attack Connor's woodshed. And his bath towel on a stick seemed silly, too. He thought, well, anyway, if they bump me, our boys will get these three. In his mind's eye he could see helmeted Americans watching the little procession through their rifle sights.

Ahead was a small white stone building, but jerry was too smart to be in the building. A trench started behind the building and led down to a hole almost like a shell hole.

Three officers faced him in the hole. They were dressed in dusty blue and they wore the beautiful high caps of the Luftwaffe, with silver eagles and swastikas. They were electronics engineers, a ground service for the German Air Force. They faced him without speaking, and his throat was so tight that for a moment he could not begin. All he could think of was a green table; jerry had three deuces showing and the lieutenant, a pair of treys. He knew they had no more, but they didn't know what his hole card was. He only hoped they wouldn't know, because all he had was that pair of treys.

The *Oberleutnant* regarded him closely and said nothing.

"Do you speak English?" the lieutenant asked.

"Yes."

The lieutenant took a deep breath and spoke the piece he had memorized. "The colonel's compliments, sir. I am ordered to demand your surrender. At the end of twenty minutes, the cruisers will move up and open fire unless ordered otherwise following your surrender." He noticed the *Oberleutnant's* eyes involuntarily move toward the sea. The lieutenant lapsed out of his formality, as he had planned. "What's the good?" he said. "We'll just kill you all. We've got six hundred men ashore and the cruisers are aching to take a shot at you. What's the good of it? You'd kill some of us and we'd kill all of you. Why don't you just stack your arms and come in?"

The *Oberleutnant* stared into his eyes. He had seen the same look over the green table. That what's-in-the-hole look. The look balanced: call or toss in, call or toss in. The pause was centuries long, and then at last, "What treatment will we receive?" the *Oberleutnant* asked.

"Prisoners of war under Convention of The Hague." The lieutenant was trying desperately to show nothing in his face. There was another long pause. The German breathed in deeply and his breath whistled in his nose.

"It is no dishonor to surrender to superior forces," he said.

When the lieutenant went up to the Germans with his bath towel for a white flag, the captain of the paratroopers, peering through a crack between two buildings, watched him go. The men hidden below saw the lieutenant challenged, and then they saw him led behind the white stone building. The watching men hardly breathed then. They were waiting for the crack of a rifle shot that would mean the plan for kidding the Germans into surrender had failed. The time went slowly. Actually, it was only about fifteen minutes. Then the lieutenant appeared again, and this time he was accompanied by three German officers.

The watchers saw him walk down to a clear place in the path and there pause and point to the ground. Then two of the officers retired behind the white building again. But in a moment they reappeared, and behind them came the German soldiers. They straggled down the path and, at the place that had been indicated, they piled their arms, their rifles and machine guns, and even their pistols. The captain, lying behind his stones, watched and counted. He tallied the whole eighty-seven men who were supposed to be there. He said to his lieutenant, "By God, he pulled it off!"

And now a little pageant developed. As the Germans marched down the path, American paratroopers materialized out of the ground beside them, until they were closely surrounded by an honor guard of about thirty men. The whole group swung down the path and into the little white town that stood so high above the harbor of Ventotene.

Since Ventotene had been for hundreds of years an Italian prison island, there was no lack of place to put the prisoners. The top floor of what we would call a city hall was a big roomy jail, with four or five big cells. The column marched up the steps of the city hall and on up to the third floor, and then the Germans were split into three groups and one group was put into each of three cells, while the fourth cell was reserved for the officers. Then guards with tommy guns were posted at the doors of the cells, and the conquest was over.

The lieutenant who had carried the white flag sat down on the steps of the city hall a little shakily. The captain sat down beside him. "Any trouble?" the captain asked.

"No. It was too easy. I don't believe it yet." He lighted a cigarette, and his shaking hand nearly put out the match.

"Wonderful job," the captain said. "But what are we going to do with them?"

"Won't the ships be back tonight?"

"I hope so, but suppose they don't get back. We can't let anybody get any sleep until we get rid of these babies."

A trooper lounged near. "These jerry officers are raising hell," he said. "They want to see the commanding officer, sir."

The captain stood up. "Better come with me," he told the lieutenant. "How many men did you tell them we had?"

"Six hundred," the lieutenant said, "and I forget how many cruisers offshore."

The captain laughed. "One time I heard about an officer who marched fifteen men around a house until they looked like an army. Maybe we better do that with our forty."

At the door of the officers' cell, the captain took out his pistol and handed it to one of the guards. "Leave the door open and keep your eye on us all the time. If they make a suspicious move, shoot them!"

"Yes, sir," said the guard, and he unlocked and opened the heavy door.

The German officers were at the barred window, looking down on the deserted streets of the little town. They could see two lonely sentries in front of the building. The German *Oberleutnant* turned as the captain entered. "I demand to see the colonel," he said.

The captain swallowed. "Er—the colonel? Well, he is engaged."

For a long moment the German stared into the captain's eyes. Finally he said, "You are the commanding officer, aren't you?"

"Yes, I am," the captain said.

"How many men have you?"

"We do not answer questions," the captain said stiffly.

The German's face was hard and disappointed. He said, "I don't think you have six hundred men. I think you have only a few more than thirty men."

The captain nodded solemnly. He said, "We've mined the building. If there is any trouble—any trouble at all —we'll blow the whole mess of you. . . ." He turned to leave the cell. "You'll be taken aboard ship soon now," he said over his shoulder.

Going down the stairs, the lieutenant said, "Have you really mined the building?"

The captain grinned at him. "Have we really got six hundred men?" he asked. And then he said, "Lord, I hope the destroyer gets in tonight to take these babies out. None of us is going to get any sleep until then."

THE FACT IS—

1. There is a difference between how the lieutenant feels before, during, and after the capture. Describe his different moods.

2. What "little white lies" are used to outwit the enemy?

3. The contest between the Americans and the Germans is compared to a game of cards. Why? Who held the deuces? the treys? Who held the "hole card"?

THE BIG BLUFF

1. It has been said that "all's fair in love and war." Explain why you agree or disagree with this saying.

2. Would you have volunteered for the lieutenant's assignment? Why?

3. Visit a library to find and report on one of these:

> **a.** A book by a war correspondent about his war experiences.
>
> **b.** A book about war heroes behind enemy lines. See, for example, James Dean Sanderson's *Behind Enemy Lines*.
>
> **c.** A book about some outstanding event in World War II. Cornelius Ryan's *The Longest Day* and John Toland's *The Last Hundred Days* are such books.

4. Imagine the conversation at the German headquarters when it was learned how the *Oberleutnant's* men were captured.

5. Interview someone in your community who has had war experiences. Write the substance of your interview in question-and-answer form.

JOHN STEINBECK   **567**

Jalopies
I Have Cursed
and Loved

If your radiator leaked, you used cornmeal; if your rear end

knocked, sawdust. Small wonder that when selling your car,

"the trick was to trade [it] in just before it exploded. . . ."

ecently I drove from Garrison-on-Hudson to New York on a Sunday afternoon, one unit in a creeping parade of metal, miles and miles of shiny paint and chrome inching along bumper to bumper. There were no old rust heaps, no jalopies. Every so often we passed a car pulled off the road with motor trouble, its driver and passengers waiting patiently for a tow car or a mechanic. Not one of the drivers seemed even to consider fixing the difficulty. I doubted that anyone knew what the trouble was.

On this funereal tour I began to think of old times and old cars. Understand, I don't want to go back to those old dogs. Any more than I want to go back to that old poverty. I love the fine efficient car

I have. But at least I remembered. I remembered a time when you fixed your own car or you didn't go anyplace. I remembered cars I had owned and cursed and hated and loved.

The first car I remember in the little town where I was born was, I think, a Reo with a chain drive and a steering bar. It was owned by a veterinary who got himself a bad name in Salinas for owning it. He seemed disloyal to horses. We didn't like that car. We shouted insults at it as it splashed by on Stone Street. Then, gradually, more automobiles came into town owned by the very rich. We didn't have a car for many years. My parents never accepted the time-payment plan. To them it was a debt like any other debt, and to them debt was a sin. And a car cost a lot of money all in one piece.

Now, it took a long time for a car to get in a condition where I could afford it, roughly about fifteen years. I had an uncle who ran a Ford agency but he didn't give free samples to his relatives. He got rich selling Fords and himself drove a Stutz Bearcat—four cylinders, sixteen valves. Those were proud times when he roared up in front of our house with his cutout open, sounding like a rolling barrage. But this was dream stuff and not for us.

My first two cars were Model T's, strange beings. They never got so beat up that you couldn't somehow make them run. The first one was a touring car. Chickens had roosted on its steering wheel, and I never got their marks off. The steering wheel was cracked so that if you put any weight on it, it pinched your fingers when you let up. The back seat was for tools, wire, and spare tires. . . . I had it a long time. It never saw shelter or a mechanic. I remember how it used to shudder and sigh when I cranked it and how its crank would kick back viciously. It was a mean car. It loved no one, it ran in spurts and seemed to be as much influenced by magic as by mechanics.

My second Model T was a sedan. The back seat had a high ceiling and was designed to look like a small drawing room. It had lace curtains and cut-glass vases on the sides for flowers. It needed only a coal grate and a sampler to make it a perfect Victorian living room. . . . There were gray-silk roller shades you could pull down to make it cozy and private. But ladylike as this car was, it had also the indestructibility of ladies. Once in the mountains I stalled in a snowstorm a quarter of a mile from my cabin; I drained the water from the radiator and abandoned the car for the winter. From my window I could see it hub-deep in the snow. For some reason now forgotten, when friends visited me, we used to shoot at that car trying not to hit the glass. At a range of a quarter of a mile with a thirty–thirty, this was pretty hard. In the spring I dug it out. It was full of bullet holes but by some accident we had missed the gas tank. A kettle of hot water in the radiator, and that rolling parlor started right off. It ran all summer.

Model T's created a habit pattern very difficult to break. I have told the following story to the Ford Company to prove their excellence. The cooling system of the Model T was based on the law that warm water rises and cool water sinks. It doesn't do this very fast, but then Model T's didn't run very fast. Now when a Model T sprung a radiator leak, the remedy was a handful of corn-meal in the radiator. The hot water cooked the meal to mush, and it plugged the leak. A little bag of meal was standard equipment in the tool kit.

In time, as was inevitable, I graduated to grander vehicles. I bought an open Chevrolet which looked like a black bathtub on wheels, a noble car full of innovations. I was living in Los Angeles at the time and my mother was coming to visit me. I was to meet her at the station, roughly thirty-five miles from where I lived. I washed the car and noticed that the radiator was leaking. Instinctively I went to the kitchen and found we had no cornmeal, but there was oatmeal which is even better because it is more gooey. I put a cup of it in the radiator and started for the station.

Now, the Chevrolet had a water pump to circulate the water faster. I had forgotten this. The trip to the station must have cooked the oatmeal thoroughly.

My mother arrived beautifully dressed. I remember she wore a hat with many flowers. She sat proudly beside me in the front seat and we started for home. Suddenly there was an explosion —a wall of oatmeal rose into the air, cleared the windshield, splashed on my mother's hat, and ran down her face. And it didn't stop there. We went through Los Angeles traffic exploding oatmeal in short bursts. I didn't dare stop for fear my mother would kill me in the street. We arrived home practically in flames because the water system was clogged and the limping car gave off clouds of smoke that smelled like burned oatmeal, and was. It took a long time to scrape my mother. She had never really believed in automobiles and this didn't help.

In the days of my nonsensical youth, there were all kinds of standard practices which were normal then but now seem just plain nuts. A friend of mine had a Model T coupé. . . . It rested in a lot behind his house and after a while he became convinced that someone was stealing his gasoline. The tank was under the front seat and could ordinarily be protected by locking the doors. But this car had no locks. First he left notes on the seat begging people not to steal his gasoline, and when this didn't work, he rigged an elaborate trap. He was very angry, you see. He designed his snare so that if anyone opened the car door, the horn would blow and a shotgun would fire.

Now, how it happened, we don't know. Perhaps a drop of water, perhaps a slight earthquake. Anyway, in the middle of the night, the horn went off. My friend leaped from bed, put on a bathrobe and a hat, I don't know why, raced out the back door shouting "Got you!"—yanked open the car door and the shotgun blew his hat to bits. It was his best hat too.

Well, about this time the depression came along and only increased the complications. Gasoline was hard to come by. One of my friends, wishing to impress his date, would drive into a filling station, extend two fingers out the window, out of the girl's sight, and say, "Fill her up." Then, with two gallons in the tank he would drive grandly away. . . .

With the depression came an era of automotive nonsense. It was no longer possible to buy a small car cheaply. Everyone wanted the Fords and Chevrolets. On the other hand, Cadillacs and Lincolns could be had for a song. There were two reasons for this. First, the big cars cost too much to run and, second, the relief committees took a sour view of anyone with a big expensive-looking car. Here is a story somewhat in point.

A friend of mine found himself in a condition of embarrassment which was pretty general and, to him, almost permanent. An old school friend, rich and retired, was going to Europe and suggested that George live in his great house in Pebble Beach in California. He could be a kind of caretaker. It would give him shelter and he could look after the house. Now, the house was completely equipped, even to a Rolls Royce in the garage. There was everything there but food. George moved in and in a first flush of joy drove the Rolls to Monterey for an evening, exhausting the tank. During the next week he ate the dry cereals left in the kitchen and set traps for rabbits in the garden. At the end of ten days, he was in a starving condition. He took to staying in bed in luxury to conserve his energy. One morning, when the pangs of hunger were eating at him, the doorbell rang. George arose weakly, stumbled across the huge drawing room, across the great hall carpeted in white, and opened the baronial door. An efficient-looking woman stood on the porch. "I'm from the Red Cross," she said, holding out a pledge card.

George gave a cry of pleasure, "Thank heavens you've come," he said.

It was all crazy like that. It was so long since George had eaten they had to give him weak soup for quite a while.

At this time, I had an old, four-cylinder Dodge. It was a very desirable car—twelve-volt battery, continental gearshift, low-compression engine, supposed to run forever. It didn't matter how much oil it pumped. It ran. But gradually I detected symptoms of demise in it. We had developed an instinct for this. The trick was to trade your car in just before it exploded. I wanted something small but that I couldn't have. For my Dodge and ten dollars I got a Marmon, a great, low, racy car with aluminum body and aluminum crankcase—a beautiful thing with a deep purring roar and a top speed of nearly a hundred miles an hour. In those days we didn't look at the car first. We inspected the rubber. No one could afford new tires. The tires on the Marmon were smooth but no fabric showed, so I bought it. And it was a beautiful car—the best I had ever owned. The only trouble was that it got about eight miles to the gallon of gasoline. We took to walking a good deal, saving gasoline for emergencies.

One day there was a disturbing click in the rear end and then a crash. Now, anyone in those days knew what had happened. A tooth had broken in the ring gear of the rear end. This makes a heartbreaking noise. A new ring gear and pinions installed would come to ninety-five dollars or, roughly, three times what I had paid for the whole car.

It was obviously a home job, and it went this way. With a hand jack, I raised the rear end onto concrete blocks. Then I placed the jack on blocks and raised again until finally the Marmon stuck its rear end up in the air like an anopheles mosquito. Now it started to rain. I stretched a piece of oilcloth to make a tent. I drained the rear end, removed the covers. Heavy, black grease ran up my sleeve and into my hair. I had no special tools, only a wrench, pliers, and a screwdriver. Special tools were made by hammering out nails on a brick. The ring gear had sheared three teeth. The pinions seemed all right, but since they must be fitted, I had to discard them. Then I walked to a wrecking yard three miles away. They had no Marmons. It took a week to find a Marmon of my vintage. There were two days of bargaining. I finally got the price down to six dollars. I had to remove the ring gear and pinions myself, but the yard generously loaned tools. This took two days. Then, with my treasures back at my house, I spent several days more lying on my back fitting the new parts. The ground was muddy and a slow drip of grease on my face and arms picked up the mud and held it. I don't ever remember being dirtier or more uncomfortable. There was endless filing and fitting. Kids from as far as six blocks away gathered to give satiric advice.... Finally, all was in place. Now I had to make new gaskets out of cardboard and tighten everything all around. I put in new grease, let the rear end gently down. There was no use in trying to get myself clean—that would take weeks of scrubbing with steel wool.

Now, word got around that the job was done. There was a large and friendly delegation to see the trial run—neighbors, kids, dogs, skeptics, well-wishers, critics. A parrot next door kept saying "Nuts!" in a loud squawking voice.

I started the engine. It sounded wonderful; it always sounded wonderful. I put the car in gear and crept out to the street, shifted gears, and got half a block before the rear end disintegrated with a crash like the unloading of a gravel car. Even the housing of the rear end was shattered. I don't know what I did wrong but what I did was final. I sold the Marmon as it stood for twelve dollars. The junkman from whom I had bought the ring gear hauled it away—aluminum body, aluminum crankcase, great engine, silver-gray paint job, top speed a hundred miles an hour, and pretty good rubber too. Oh, well—that's the way it was.

In those days of the depression, one of the centers of social life was the used-car dealer's lot. I got to know one of these men of genius and he taught me quite a bit about this business which had become a fine art. I learned how to detect sawdust in the crankcase. If a car was really beat up, a few handfuls of sawdust made it very quiet for about five miles. All the wiles and techniques of horse-trading learned over a thousand years found their way into the used-car business. There were ways of making tires look strong and new, ways of gentling a motor so that it purred like a kitten, polishes to blind the buyer's eyes, seat covers that concealed the fact that the springs were coming through the upholstery. To watch and listen to a good used-car man was a delight, for the razzle-dazzle was triumphant. It was a dog-eat-dog contest and the customer who didn't beware was simply unfortunate. For no guarantee went beyond the curb.

My friend in the used-car business offered a free radio in every car sold for one week. Now, a customer came in who hated radios. My friend was pained at this. The customer said, "All right, how much will that car be without a radio?"

My friend wrote some figures on a pad. "Well," he said, "I can let you have it for ten dollars extra—but I don't want to make a practice of it."

And the customer cheerfully paid.

It's all different now. Everything is chrome and shiny paint. A car used to be as close and known and troublesome and dear as a wife. Now we drive about in strangers. It's more comfortable, sure, but something has been lost. I hope I never get it back.

BUYER BEWARE

1. The author compares the cars he drove as a young man with the cars he drives today. What is the difference between today's cars (and their owners) and those of the past?

2. Explain the title. Does it mean that Mr. Steinbeck liked some of his jalopies and hated others? Or does it mean that he liked all his jalopies, even those that troubled him?

3. What does the writer mean by the last line: "I hope I never get it back"?

4. Write your own essay about "A Jalopy (Hot Rod, Sports Car, Stock Car) I Have Loved (Cursed, Hated)"; "A Machine I Have Cursed (Loved)."

5. *Highway Robbery,* by Sam Crowther and Irwin Winehouse (Stein & Day, Publishers) is but one of many books aimed at educating the public about how to buy, maintain, insure, keep safe the car of their choice. Read and report on one such book.

From The Grapes of Wrath

Migrant People

The following two selections from *The Grapes of Wrath* a novel about poor migrant farmers, show how it was to move from one barren hope to another in the Depression America of the thirties.

The cars of the migrant people crawled out of the side roads onto the great cross-country highway, and they took the migrant way to the West. In the daylight they scuttled like bugs to the westward; and as the dark caught them, they clustered like bugs near to shelter and to water. And because they were lonely and perplexed, because they had all come from a place of sadness and worry and defeat, and because they were all going to a new mysterious place, they huddled together; they talked together; they shared their lives, their food, and the things they hoped for in the new country. Thus it might be that one family camped near a spring, and another camped for the spring and for company, and a third because two families had pioneered the place and found it good. And when the sun went down, perhaps twenty families and twenty cars were there.

In the evening a strange thing happened: the twenty families became one family, the children were the children of all. The loss of home became one loss, and the golden time in the West was one dream. And it might be that a sick child threw despair into the hearts of twenty families, of a hundred people; that a birth there in a tent kept a hundred people quiet and awestruck through the night and filled a hundred people with the birth-joy in the morning. A family which the night before had been lost and fearful might search its goods to find a present for a new baby. In the evening, sitting about the fires, the twenty were one. They grew to be units of the camps, units of the evenings and the nights. A guitar unwrapped from a blanket and tuned—and the songs, which were all of the people, were sung in the nights. Men sang the words, and women hummed the tunes.

Every night a world created, complete with furniture—friends made and enemies established; a world complete with braggarts and with cowards, with quiet men, with humble men, with kindly men. Every night relationships that make a world, established; and every morning the world torn down like a circus.

At first the families were timid in the building and tumbling worlds, but gradually the technique of building worlds became their technique. Then leaders emerged, then laws were made, then codes came into being. And as the worlds moved westward, they were more complete and better furnished, for their builders were more experienced in building them.

The families learned what rights must be observed—the right of privacy in the tent; the right to keep the past black hidden in the heart; the right to talk and to listen; the right to refuse help or to accept, to offer help or to decline it; the right of son to court and daughter to be courted; the right of the hungry to be fed; the rights of the pregnant and the sick to transcend all other rights.

And the families learned, although no one told them, what rights are monstrous and must be destroyed: the right to intrude upon privacy, the right to be noisy while the camp slept, the right of seduction or rape, the right of adultery and theft and murder. These rights were crushed, because the little worlds could not exist for even a night with such rights alive.

And as the worlds moved westward, rules became laws, although no one told the families. It is unlawful to foul near the camp; it is unlawful in any way to foul the drinking water; it is unlawful to eat good rich food near one who is hungry, unless he is asked to share.

And with the laws, the punishments —and there were only two—a quick and murderous fight or ostracism; and ostracism was the worst. For if one broke the laws, his name and face went with him, and he had no place in any world, no matter where created.

In the worlds, social conduct became fixed and rigid, so that a man must say "Good morning" when asked for it; so that a man might have a willing girl if he stayed with her, if he fathered her children and protected them. But a man might not have one girl one night and another the next, for this would endanger the worlds.

The families moved westward, and the technique of building the worlds improved so that the people could be safe in their worlds; and the form was so fixed that a family acting in the rules knew it was safe in the rules.

There grew up government in the worlds, with leaders, with elders. A man who was wise found that his wisdom was needed in every camp; a man who was a fool could not change his folly with his world. And a kind of insurance developed in these nights. A man with food fed a hungry man, and thus insured himself against hunger. And when a baby died, a pile of silver coins grew at the door flap, for a baby must be well buried, since it had had nothing else of life. An old man may be left in a potter's field, but not a baby.

A certain physical pattern is needed for the building of a world—water, a riverbank, a stream, a spring, or even a faucet unguarded. And there is needed enough flat land to pitch the tents, a little brush or wood to build the fires. If there is a garbage dump not too far off, all the better; for there can be found equipment—stove tops, a curved fender to shelter the fire, and cans to cook in and to eat from.

And the worlds were built in the evening. The people, moving in from the highways, made them with their tents and their hearts and their brains.

In the morning the tents came down, the canvas was folded, the tent poles tied along the running board, the beds put in place on the cars, the pots in their places. And as the families moved westward, the technique of building up a home in the evening and tearing it down with the morning light became fixed; so that the folded tent was packed in one place, the cooking pots counted in their box. And as the cars moved westward, each member of the family grew into his proper place, grew into his duties; so that each member, old and young, had his place in the car; so that in the weary, hot evenings, when the cars pulled into the camping places, each member had his duty and went to it without instruction: children to gather wood, to carry water; men to pitch the tents and bring down the beds; women to cook the supper and to watch while the family fed. And this was done without command. The families, which had been units of which the boundaries were a house at night, a farm by day, changed their boundaries. In the long hot light, they were silent in the cars moving slowly westward; but at night they integrated with any group they found.

Thus they changed their social life— changed as in the whole universe only man can change. They were not farm men any more, but migrant men. And the thought, the planning, the long staring silence that had gone out to the fields, went now to the roads, to the distance, to the West. That man whose mind had been bound with acres lived with narrow concrete miles. And his thought and his worry were not any more with rainfall, with wind and dust, with the thrust of the crops. Eyes watched the tires, ears listened to the clattering motors, and minds struggled with oil, with gasoline, with the thinning rubber between air and road. Then a broken gear was tragedy. Then water in the evening was the yearning, and food over the fire. Then health to go on was the need and strength to go on, and spirit to go on. The wills thrust westward ahead of them, and fears that had once apprehended drought or flood now lingered with anything that might stop the westward crawling.

The camps became fixed—each a short day's journey from the last.

And on the road the panic overcame some of the families, so that they drove night and day, stopped to sleep in the cars, and drove on to the West, flying from the road, flying from movement. And these lusted so greatly to be settled that they set their faces into the West and drove toward it, forcing the clashing engines over the roads.

But most of the families changed and grew quickly into the new life. And when the sun went down—

Time to look out for a place to stop.

And—there's some tents ahead.

The car pulled off the road and stopped, and because others were there first, certain courtesies were necessary. And the man, the leader of the family, leaned from the car.

Can we pull up here an' sleep?

Why, sure, be proud to have you. What state you from?

Come all the way from Arkansas.

They's Arkansas people down that fourth tent.

That so?

And the great question, How's the water?

Well, she don't taste so good, but they's plenty.

Well, thank ya.

No thanks to me.

But the courtesies had to be. The car lumbered over the ground to the end tent, and stopped. Then down from the car the weary people climbed, and stretched stiff bodies. Then the new tent sprang up; the children went for water and the older boys cut brush or wood. The fires started and supper was put on to boil or to fry. Early comers moved over, and states were exchanged, and friends and sometimes relatives discovered.

Oklahoma, huh? What county?

Cherokee.

Why, I got folks there. Know the Allens? They's Allens all over Cherokee. Know the Willises?

Why, sure.

And a new unit was formed. The dusk came, but before the dark was down, the new family was of the camp. A word had been passed with every family. They were known people—good people.

I knowed the Allens all my life. Simon Allen, ol' Simon, had trouble with his first wife. She was part Cherokee. Purty as—as a black colt.

Sure, an' young Simon, he married a Rudolph, didn' he? That's what I thought. They went to live in Enid an' done well—real well.

Only Allen that ever done well. Got a garage.

When the water was carried and the wood cut, the children walked shyly, cautiously among the tents. And they made elaborate acquaintanceship gestures. A boy stopped near another boy and studied a stone, picked it up, examined it closely, spat on it, and rubbed it clean and inspected it until he forced the other to demand, What you got there?

And casually, Nothin'. Jus' a rock.

Well, what you lookin' at it like that for?

Thought I seen gold in it.

How'd you know? Gold ain't gold, it's black in a rock.

Sure, ever'body knows that.

I bet it's fool's gold, an' you figgered it was gold.

That ain't so, 'cause Pa, he's foun' lots a gold an' he tol' me how to look.

How'd you like to pick up a big ol' piece a gold?

Sa-a-ay! I'd git the bigges' old piece a candy you ever seen.

Me too. Le's go to the spring.

And young girls found each other and boasted shyly of their popularity and their prospects. The women worked over the fire, hurrying to get food to the stomachs of the family—pork if there was money in plenty, pork and potatoes and onions. Dutch-oven biscuits or cornbread, and plenty of gravy to go over it. Side meat or chops and a can of boiled tea, black and bitter. Fried dough in drippings if money was slim, dough fried crisp and brown and the drippings poured over it.

Those families which were very rich or very foolish with their money ate canned beans and canned peaches and packaged bread and bakery cake; but they ate secretly, in their tents, for it would not have been good to eat such fine things openly. Even so, children eating their fried dough smelled the warming beans and were unhappy about it.

When supper was over and the dishes dipped and wiped, the dark had come, and then the men squatted down to talk.

And they talked of the land behind them. I don't know what it's coming to, they said. The country's spoilt.

It'll come back though, on'y we won't be there.

Maybe, they thought, maybe we sinned some way we didn't know about.

Fella says to me, gov'ment fella, an' he says, she's gullied up on ya. Gov'ment fella. He says, if ya plowed 'cross the contour, she won't gully. Never did have no chance to try her. An' the new super' ain't plowin' 'cross the contour. Runnin' a furrow four miles long that ain't stoppin' or goin' aroun' Jesus Christ Hisself.

And they spoke softly of their homes: They was a little coolhouse under the win'mill. Use' ta keep milk in there ta cream up, an' watermelons. Go in there midday when she was hotter'n a heifer, an' she'd be jus' as cool, as cool as you'd want. Cut open a melon in there an' she'd hurt your mouth, she was so cool. Water drippin' down from the tank.

They spoke of their tragedies: Had a brother Charley, hair as yella as corn, an' him a growed man. Played the 'cordeen nice too. He was harrowin' one day an' he went up to clear his lines. Well, a rattlesnake buzzed an' them horses bolted an' the harrow went over Charley, an' the points dug into his guts an' his stomach, an' they pulled his face off an'—

They spoke of the future: Wonder what it's like out there?

Well, the pitchers sure do look nice. I seen one where it's hot an' fine, an' walnut trees an' berries; an' right behind they's a tall up mountain covered with snow. That was a pretty thing to see.

If we can get work, it'll be fine. Won't have no cold in the winter. Kids won't freeze on the way to school. I'm gonna take care my kids don't miss no more school. I can read good, but it ain't no pleasure to me like with a fella that's used to it.

And perhaps a man brought out his guitar to the front of his tent. And he sat on a box to play, and everyone in the camp moved slowly in toward him, drawn in toward him. Many men can chord a guitar, but perhaps this man was a picker. There you have something —the deep chords beating, beating, while the melody runs on the strings like little footsteps. Heavy, hard fingers marching on the frets. The man played and the people moved slowly in on him until the circle was closed and tight, and then he sang "Ten-Cent Cotton and Forty-Cent Meat." And the circle sang softly with him. And he sang "Why Do You Cut Your Hair, Girls?" And the circle sang. He wailed the song, "I'm Leaving Old Texas," that eerie song that was sung before the Spaniards came, only the words were Indian then.

And now the group was welded to one thing, one unit, so that in the dark the eyes of the people were inward, and their minds played in other times, and their sadness was like rest, like sleep. He sang the "McAlester Blues" and then, to make up for it to the older people, he sang "Jesus Calls Me to His Side." The children drowsed with the music and went into the tents to sleep, and the singing came into their dreams.

And after a while the man with the guitar stood up and yawned. Good night, folks, he said.

And they murmured, Good night to you.

And each wished he could pick a guitar, because it is a gracious thing. Then the people went to their beds, and the camp was quiet. And the owls coasted overhead, and the coyotes gabbled in the distance, and into the camp skunks walked, looking for bits of food—waddling, arrogant skunks, afraid of nothing.

The night passed, and with the first streak of dawn, the women came out of the tents, built up the fires, and put the coffee to boil. And the men came out and talked softly in the dawn.

When you cross the Colorado river, there's the desert, they say. Look out for the desert. See you don't get hung up. Take plenty water, case you get hung up.

I'm gonna take her at night.

Me too.

The families ate quickly, and the dishes were dipped and wiped. The tents came down. There was a rush to go. And when the sun arose, the camping place was vacant, only a little litter left by the people. And the camping place was ready for a new world in a new night.

But along the highway the cars of the migrant people crawled out like bugs, and the narrow concrete miles stretched ahead.

Flood

Over the high coast mountains and over the valleys, the gray clouds marched in from the ocean. The wind blew fiercely and silently, high in the air, and it swished in the brush, and it roared in the forests. The clouds came in brokenly, in puffs, in folds, in gray crags; and they piled in together and settled low over the west. And then the wind stopped and left the clouds deep and solid. The rain began with gusty showers, pauses, and downpours; and then gradually it settled to a single tempo, small drops and a steady beat, rain that was gray to see through, rain that cut midday light to evening. And at first the dry earth sucked the moisture down and blackened. For two days the earth drank the rain, until the earth was full. Then puddles formed, and in the low places little lakes formed in the fields. The muddy lakes rose higher, and the steady rain whipped the shining water. At last the mountains were full, and the hillsides spilled into the streams, built them to freshets, and sent them roaring down the canyons into the valleys. The rain beat on steadily. And the streams and the little rivers edged up to the banksides and worked at willows and tree roots, bent the willows deep in the current, cut out the roots of cottonwoods, and brought down the trees. The muddy water whirled along the banksides and crept up the banks until at last it spilled over, into the fields, into the orchards, into the cotton patches where the black stems stood. Level fields became lakes, broad and gray, and the rain whipped up the surfaces. Then the water poured over the highways, and cars moved slowly, cutting the water ahead, and leaving a boiling, muddy wake behind. The earth whispered under the beat of the rain, and the streams thundered under the churning freshets.

When the first rain started, the migrant people huddled in their tents, saying, It'll soon be over, and asking, How long's it likely to go on?

And when the puddles formed, the

men went out in the rain with shovels and built little dikes around the tents. The beating rain worked at the canvas until it penetrated and sent streams down. And then the little dikes washed out and the water came inside, and the streams wet the beds and the blankets. The people sat in wet clothes. They set up boxes and put planks on the boxes. Then, day and night, they sat on the planks.

Beside the tents the old cars stood, and water fouled the ignition wires and water fouled the carburetors. The little gray tents stood in lakes. And at last the people had to move. Then the cars wouldn't start because the wires were shorted; and if the engines would run, deep mud engulfed the wheels. And the people waded away, carrying their wet blankets in their arms. They splashed along, carrying the children, carrying the very old, in their arms. And if a barn stood on high ground, it was filled with people, shivering and hopeless.

Then some went to the relief offices, and they came sadly back to their own people.

They's rules—you got to be here a year before you can git relief. They say the gov'ment is gonna help. They don' know when.

And gradually the greatest terror of all came along.

They ain't gonna be no kinda work for three months.

In the barns, the people sat huddled together; and the terror came over them, and their faces were gray with terror. The children cried with hunger, and there was no food.

Then the sickness came, pneumonia, and measles that went to the eyes and to the mastoids.

And the rain fell steadily, and the water flowed over the highways, for the culverts could not carry the water.

Then from the tents, from the crowded barns, groups of sodden men went out, their clothes slopping rags, their shoes muddy pulp. They splashed out through the water, to the towns, to the country stores, to the relief offices, to beg for food, to cringe and beg for food, to beg for relief, to try to steal, to lie. And under the begging, and under the cringing, a hopeless anger began to smolder. And in the little towns pity for the sodden men changed to anger, and anger at the hungry people changed to fear of them. Then sheriffs swore in deputies in droves, and orders were rushed for rifles, for tear gas, for ammunition. Then the hungry men crowded the alleys behind the stores to beg for bread, to beg for rotting vegetables, to steal when they could.

Frantic men pounded on the doors of the doctors; and the doctors were busy. And sad men left word at country stores for the coroner to send a car. The coroners were not too busy. The coroners' wagons backed up through the mud and took out the dead.

And the rain pattered relentlessly down, and the streams broke their banks and spread out over the country.

Huddled under sheds, lying in wet hay, the hunger and the fear bred anger. Then boys went out, not to beg, but to steal; and men went out weakly, to try to steal.

The sheriffs swore in new deputies and ordered new rifles; and the comfortable people in tight houses felt pity at first, and then distaste, and finally hatred for the migrant people.

In the wet hay of leaking barns, babies were born to women who panted with pneumonia. And old people curled up in corners and died that way, so that the coroners could not straighten them. At night the frantic men walked boldly to hen roosts and carried off the squawking chickens. If they were shot at, they did not run, but splashed sullenly away;

and if they were hit, they sank tiredly in the mud.

The rain stopped. On the fields the water stood, reflecting the gray sky, and the land whispered with moving water. And the men came out of the barns, out of the sheds. They squatted on their hams and looked out over the flooded land. And they were silent. And sometimes they talked very quietly.

No work till spring. No work.

And if no work—no money, no food.

Fella had a team of horses, had to use 'em to plow an' cultivate an' mow, wouldn' think a turnin' 'em out to starve when they wasn't workin'.

Them's horses—we're men.

The women watched the men, watched to see whether the break had come at last. The women stood silently and watched. And where a number of men gathered together, the fear went from their faces, and anger took its place. And the women sighed with relief, for they knew it was all right—the break had not come; and the break would never come as long as fear could turn to wrath.

Tiny points of grass came through the earth, and in a few days the hills were pale green with the beginning year.

ONE FAMILY

1. Is it appropriate for Steinbeck to compare the migrant convoys of cars with bugs? Why?

2. The poor are sometimes accused of a loose and disorganized way of life, with no leadership, direction, or goal. After reading these two sections from *The Grapes of Wrath*, do you agree?

3. Life on the road was sharply contrasted with life in camp. What was the difference?

4. Note the changing moods of the townspeople, the longer the migrants remain. What are these changes? Why do they occur? Where in our own time are situations arising where townspeople and strangers are in conflict? What resemblances do you see between these modern instances and those in Steinbeck's novel? What differences?

5. *The Grapes of Wrath* was read by millions; the motion picture version was seen by more millions. As *Uncle Tom's Cabin* solidified antislavery sentiment before the Civil War, *The Grapes of Wrath* crystallized public indignation into Federal legislation to protect people without place or property. Pretend that you are a newspaperman of the 1930's, traveling with the migrant workers; write a column expressing your opinion of their situation and treatment.

6. Assume that you had been assigned the task of shooting "still" photographs to help advertise *The Grapes of Wrath* movie. Confine yourself to these two excerpts and indicate which three photographs you'd take based on description or incidents in this section.

America and the Americans

Life, liberty, and the pursuit of happiness are among

the goals for which Americans have striven since

the beginning of their history. Have they succeeded

entirely? One man has his doubts . . . and his hopes.

It is customary (indeed, at high-school graduations it is a requirement) for speakers to refer to America as a "precious inheritance"—our heritage, a gift proffered like a sandwich wrapped in plastic on a plastic tray. Our ancestors, so it is implied, gathered to the invitation of a golden land and accepted the sacrament of milk and honey.

This is not so. In the beginning we crept, scuttled, escaped, were driven out of the safe and settled corners of the earth, to the fringes of a strange and hostile wilderness, a nameless and hostile continent. Far from welcoming us, it resisted us. This land was no gift. The firstlings worked for it, fought for it, and died for it. They stole and cheated and double-crossed for it, and when they had taken a little piece, the way a fierce-hearted man ropes a wild mustang, they had then to gentle it and smooth it to make it habitable at all.

We built America, and the process made us Americans—a new breed, rooted in all races, stained and tinted with all colors, a seeming ethnic anarchy. Then in a little, little time, we became more alike than we were different —a new society; not great, but fitted by our very faults for greatness: *E Pluribus Unum.*

The whole thing is crazy. Every single man in our emerging country was out for himself against all others—for his safety, his profit, his future. When his family grew up about him, he set it against all other families. When communities arose, each one defended itself against other communities. The surges of the new restless, needy, and strong— grudgingly brought in for purposes of hard labor and cheap wages—were resisted, resented, and only accepted when a new and different wave came in.

All that was required to release the mechanism of oppression and sadism was that the newcomers be meek, poor, weak in numbers, and unprotected—although it helped if their skin, hair, eyes were different, and if they spoke some language other than English, or worshiped in some church other than Protestant. The Pilgrim Fathers took out after the Catholics, and both clobbered the Jews; the Germans clotted for self-defense until the Irish took the resented place; the Irish became "Americans" against the Poles; the Slavs against the Italians. On the West Coast the Chinese ceased to be enemies only when the Japanese arrived; and they, in the face of the invasions of Hindus, Filipinos, and Mexicans.

JOHN STEINBECK **581**

It occurs to me that this very cruelty toward newcomers might go far toward explaining the speed with which the ethnic and national strangers merged with the "Americans." In spite of all the pressure the old people could bring to bear, the children of each ethnic group denied their background and their ancestral language. Despite the anger, the contempt, the jealousy, the self-imposed ghettos and segregation, something was loose in this land called America. The new generations wanted to be Americans more than they wanted to be Poles, or Germans, or Hungarians, or Italians, or British. And in one or two, certainly not more than three generations, each ethnic group has clicked into place in the union without losing the *pluribus.* When we read the lineup of a University of Notre Dame football team, called "The Fighting Irish," we do not find it ridiculous that the names are Polish, Slovak, Italian—or Fiji, for that matter. They *are* The Fighting Irish.

One of the characteristics most puzzling to a foreign observer is the strong and imperishable dream the American carries. On inspection, it is found that the dream has little to do with reality in American life. Consider the dream and the hunger for home. The very word can reduce nearly all of my compatriots to tears. Builders and developers never build houses—they build homes. The dream home is either in a small town or in a suburban area where grass and trees simulate the country. This dream home is a permanent seat, not rented but owned. It is a center where a man and his wife grow graciously old, warmed by the radiance of well-washed children and grandchildren. Many thousands of these homes are built every year; built, planted, advertised, and sold—and yet the American family rarely stays in one place for more than five years.

The dreams of a people either create folk literature or find their way into it; and folk literature, again, is always based on something that happened. Our most persistent folktales—constantly retold in books, movies, and television shows—concern cowboys, gunslinging sheriffs, and Indian fighters. These folk figures existed—perhaps not quite as they are recalled nor in the numbers indicated, but they did exist; and this dream persists. Even businessmen in Texas wear the highheeled boots and big hats, though they ride in air-conditioned cars and have forgotten the reason for the high heel. All of our children play cowboy and Indian. The brave and honest sheriff who with courage and a six-gun brings law and order and civic virtue to a Western community is perhaps our most familiar hero, no doubt descended from the brave, mailed knight of chivalry who battled and overcame evil with lance and sword. Even the recognition signals are the same: white hat, white armor—black hat, black shield. And in these moral tales, so deepset in us, virtue does not arise out of reason or orderly process of law—it is imposed by violence and maintained by the threat of violence. I wonder whether this folk wisdom is the story of our capability. Are these stories permanent because we know within ourselves that only the threat of violence makes it possible for us to live together in peace?

A national dream need not, indeed may not, be clear-cut and exact. For Americans it is called "The American Way of Life." No one can define it or point to any one person or group who lives it, but it is very real nevertheless.

I have often wondered at the savagery and thoughtlessness with which our early settlers approached this rich continent. They came at it as though it were an enemy, which of course it was.

They burned the forests, they swept the buffalo from the plains, blasted the streams, and ran a reckless scythe through the virgin and noble timber. Perhaps they felt that the land could never be exhausted, that a man could move on to new wonders endlessly. They pillaged the country as though they hated it, as though they held it temporarily and might be driven off at any time.

This tendency toward irresponsibility persists in very many of us today—our rivers are poisoned by reckless dumping of sewage and toxic industrial wastes, the air of our cities is filthy and dangerous to breathe from the belching of uncontrolled products from combustion of coal, coke, oil and gasoline. Our towns are girdled with wreckage and the debris of our toys—our automobiles and our packaged pleasures.

Through our uninhibited spraying against one enemy, we have destroyed the natural balances our survival requires. All of these evils can and must be overcome if America and the Americans are to survive; but a great many of us still conduct ourselves as our ancestors did, stealing from the future for our clear and present profit.

Since the river-polluters, the air-poisoners are not criminal or even bad people, we must presume that they are heirs to the early conviction that sky and water are unowned and that they are limitless. In the light of our practices here at home, it is interesting to read of the care taken with the carriers of our probes into space, to make utterly sure that they are free of pollution of any kind. We would not think of doing to the moon what we do every day to our own country.

When the first settlers came to America and dug in on the coast, they huddled in defending villages hemmed in by the sea on one side and by endless forests on the other, by Red Indians and, most frightening, the mystery of an unknown land extending nobody knew how far. And for a time very few cared or dared to find out.

Later, however, brave and forest-wise men drifted westward to hunt, to trap, and eventually to bargain for the furs which were the first negotiable wealth America produced for trade and export. Then trading posts were set up as centers of collection, and the exploring men moved up and down the rivers and crossed the mountains, made friends for mutual profit with the Indians, learned the wilderness techniques, so that these explorer-traders soon dressed, ate, and generally acted like the indigenous people around them.

For a goodly time the Americans were travelers moving about the country collecting its valuables, but with little idea of permanence; their roots and their hearts were in the towns and the growing cities along the eastern edge. Then the population began to move westward. The newcomers were of peasant stock, and they had their roots in a Europe where they had been landless, for the possession of land was the requirement for and the proof of a higher social class than they had known. In America they found beautiful and boundless land for the taking—and they took it. They cut and burned the forests to make room for crops, and when they had cropped out a piece, they moved on, raping the country like invaders. The topsoil, held by roots and freshened by leaf-fall, was left helpless to the spring freshets, stripped and eroded with the naked bones of clay and rock exposed.

One thing Americans did discover earlier than most of the world was that ability had nothing to do with birth. Of course we have to some extent overdone this, as we do most things. For a long period we felt that a man of birth and background was automatically bad. But here again our paradoxical tendency took charge: we had learned to distrust inherited position, property and money; but we proceeded to admire the same things if self-acquired. When we revolted against the old country and set up our own stalls, we were careful to eliminate the hated symbols of aristocracy—titles, honors, inherited perquisites. But since every man wants admiration and some even want envy, we had only money and possessions to admire and envy. The rich in America of the middle period may have been cursed and disparaged, but they had chosen the one way to be noticed.

I find I have been putting off writing about the most serious problem Americans are faced with, both as a people and as individuals. We discuss it constantly, and yet there is not even a name for it. Immorality does not describe it, nor does lack of integrity, nor does dishonesty. Many people, not able to face the universal spread and danger of the cancerous growth, split off a fragment of the whole to worry about or to try to cure. But I begin to think that the evil is one thing, not many, that racial unrest, the emotional crazy quilt that drives our people in panic to the couches of the psychoanalysts, the fallout, dropout, copout insurgency of our children and young people, the rush to stimulant as well as hypnotic drugs, the rise of narrow, ugly, and vengeful cults of all kinds, the distrust and revolt against all authority, political, religious, or military, the awful and universal sense of apprehension and even terror—and this in a time of plenty such as has never been known —I think all of these are manifestations of one single cause.

Perhaps we will have to inspect mankind as a species, not with our usual awe at how wonderful we are but with the cool and neutral attitude we reserve for all things save ourselves. Man is indeed wonderful, and it may be that his gaudiest achievement has been to survive his paradoxes. But what has happened to us now? Something deep and controlling and necessary.

I'm not going to preach about any good old days. By our standards of comfort, they were pretty awful. What did they have then that we are losing or have lost? Well, for one thing they had rules—rules concerning life, limb, and property, rules governing deportment, manners, conduct, and finally rules defining dishonesty, dishonor, misconduct, and crime. The rules were not always obeyed, but they were believed in, and a breaking of the rules was savagely punished.

But now we have food and shelter and transportation and the more terrible hazard of leisure. I strongly suspect that our moral and spiritual disintegration grows out of our lack of experience with plenty. Once, in a novel, I wrote about a woman who said she didn't want a lot of money. She wanted just enough. To which her husband replied that "just enough" doesn't exist. There is no money or not enough money. Even a billionaire hasn't enough money.

But we are also poisoned with things. Having many things seems to create a desire for more things, more clothes, houses, automobiles. Think of the pure horror of Christmases when children tear open package after package and then, when the floor is heaped with wrappings and presents, say—"Is that all?" And two days later the smashed and abandoned "things" are added to our national trash pile, and perhaps the child, having got in trouble, explains, "I didn't have anything to do." And he means exactly that—nothing to do, nowhere to go, no direction, no purpose, and worst of all, no needs. Wants he has, yes, but for more bright and breakable "things." We are trapped and entangled in things.

In my great-grandmother's time things were important. I know, because I have read her will, and the things she found important enough to bequeath by legal instrument we would have thrown away—such things as four pewter spoons, one broken in the handle, the square of black cotton lace. I had from Grandmama the little box of leaves from the Mount of Olives, a small bowl carved from one piece of onyx and beautiful to see, twelve books, and eight sheets of music. These were valuable things.

It is probable that the want of things and the need of things have been the two greatest stimulants toward the change and complication we call progress. And surely we Americans, most of us starting with nothing, have contributed our share of wanting. Wanting is probably a valuable human trait. It is the means of getting that can be dangerous.

When students cheat in examinations, it may be bad for them as individuals, but for the community it means that the graduate is traveling with false papers and very shortly the papers—in this case the college degree—lose their value. When military cadets cheat, it is a kind of treason, for it means they have not learned to do the things they will be assigned to do. John Kennedy said his famous lines, "Ask not what your country can do for you; ask what you can do for your country," and the listening nation nodded and smiled in agreement. But he did not say it because it might happen, but because it *is* happening, and in increasing volume. And it is historically true that a nation whose people take out more than they put in will collapse and disappear.

The evil that threatens us came quickly and quietly, came from many directions and was the more dangerous because it wore the face of good. Almost unlimited new power took the place of straining muscles and bent backs. Machinery took the heavy burden from our shoulders. Medicine and hygiene cut down infant mortality almost to the vanishing point, and at the same time extended our life span. Automation began to replace our workers. Whereas the majority of our people used to work the land, new developments in machines and chemistry enabled a precious few to produce more food than we needed or could possibly use. Leisure, which again had been the property of heaven, came to us before we knew what to do with it, and all of these good things falling on us unprepared constitute calamity.

We have the things and we have not had time to develop a way of thinking about them. We struggle with our lives in the present and our practices in the long and well-learned past. We had a million years to get used to the idea of fire and only twenty to prepare ourselves for the productive-destructive tidal wave of atomic fission. We have more food than we can use and no way to distribute it. Our babies live, and we have no work for their hands. We retire men and women at the age of their best service for no other reason than that we need their jobs for younger people. To allow ourselves the illusion of usefulness, we have standby crews for functions which no longer exist.

And finally we can come back to the subject of morals.

Ethics, morals, codes of conduct are the stern rules which in the past we needed in order to survive—as individuals, as groups, as nations. Now, although we give lip service to survival, we are embarrassed and beginning to be smothered by our own numbers. Americans, who are makers and lovers of statistics, are usually puzzled and irritated when it is suggested that we are a statistic. But neither the sleeping pill, the Church, nor the psychiatrist can long hide from us the fact that economic laws apply to ourselves, that increased supply causes a drop in value; that we already have too many people and are in process of producing *far* too many.

Could it be that below the level of thought, our people sense the danger of the swarming, crowding invasion of America by Americans? Starvation, pestilence, plague, which once cut us down, are no longer possible. And war? Well, during the *last* war, with all its slaughter, the world's population increased. Are people genuinely afraid of the bomb, or do they look to it to do the job we have eliminated from nature?

It is probable that here is where morals—integrity, ethics, even charity—have gone. The rules allowed us to survive, to live together, and to increase. In our written, remembered, and sensed history, there has always been more work than we could ever do. Our needs were greater than their possible fulfillment. But if our will to survive is weakened; if our love of life, our memories of a gallant past and faith in a shining future are removed—what need is there for morals or rules?

Why are we on this verge of moral and hence nervous collapse? I believe it is because we have reached the end of a road and have discovered no new path to take, no duty to carry out, and no purpose to fulfill. I think we will find a path to the future, but its direction may be unthinkable to us now. When it does appear, however, and we move on, the path must have direction, it must have purpose—and the journey must be filled with a joy of anticipation, for the boy today, hating the world, creates a hateful world and then tries to destroy it and sometimes himself as well.

Something happened in America to create the Americans. Now we face the danger which in the past has been most destructive to the human: success; plenty, comfort, and ever-increasing leisure. No dynamic people has ever survived these dangers. If the anesthetic of self-satisfaction were added to our hazards, we would not have a chance of survival—as Americans.

If I inspect my people and study them and criticize them, I must love them if I have any self-love, since I can never be separate from them and no more objective about them than I am about myself. I am not young, and yet I wonder about my tomorrow. How much more, then, must my wonder be about the tomorrow of my people, which is a young people. My questioning is compounded of some fear, more hope, and great confidence.

I have named the destroyers of nations: comfort, plenty, and security—out of which grow a bored and slothful cynicism, in which rebellion against the world as it is, and myself as I am, is submerged in listless self-satisfaction. A dying people tolerates the present, rejects the future, and finds its satisfactions in past greatness and half-remembered glory. A dying people arms itself with defensive weapons and with mercenaries against change. When greatness recedes, so does belief in greatness. A dying poet invariably concedes that poetry has gone, that beauty has withered away. Then mountains do not rise up as they once did against the sky, and girls are not as pretty. Ecstasy fades to toleration, and agony subsides to a dull aching. Vision dims like the house lights in a theater—and the world is finished. As it is with a poet, so it is with a people.

It is in the American negation of these symptoms of extinction that my hope and confidence lie. We are not satisfied. Our restlessness, perhaps inherited from the hungry immigrants of our ancestry, is still with us. Young Americans are rebellious, angry, searching like terriers near a rat's nest. The energy pours out in rumbles, in strikes, and causes, even in crime; but it is energy. Wasted energy is only a little problem, compared with the lack of it.

The world is open as it has never been before, and for the first time in human experience, we have the tools to work with. Three fifths of the world and perhaps four fifths of the world's wealth lie under the sea, and we can get to it. The sky is open at last, and we have the means to rise into it. Revolt is in the air—in the violence of the long, hot summer; in the resentment against injustice and inequality, and against cynical cruelty. There is blind anger against delay, against the long preparation for the long journey—perhaps the longest, darkest journey of all, with the greatest light at the end of it.

We are in the perplexing period of change. We seem to be running in all directions at once—but we are running. And I believe that our history, our ex-perience in America, has endowed us for the change that is coming. We have never sat still for long; we have never been content with a place, a building— or with ourselves. Americans do not lack places to go and new things to find. We have cut ourselves off from the self-abuse of war by raising it from a sin to an extinction. Far larger experiences are open to our restlessness—the fascinating unknown is everywhere.

How will the Americans act and re-act to a new set of circumstances for which new rules must be made? We know from our past some of the things we will do. We will make mistakes; we always have. But from our beginning, in hindsight at least, our social direction is clear. We have moved to become one people out of many. We have failed sometimes, taken wrong paths, paused for renewal, filled our bellies, and licked our wounds; but we have never slipped back—never.

ONLY IN AMERICA

1. List the positive qualities Steinbeck sees in the American society; the negative qualities.

2. In what sense does Steinbeck recall "the good old days" as better than modern times? Worse?

3. From your own reading of history, where do you think Steinbeck is right? Wrong? What doubts, if any, has he raised in your mind?

4. What fact (or opinion) shocked, surprised, angered, or delighted you?

5. Our late President John F. Kennedy is quoted. What is the quotation? What point is Steinbeck illustrating through it?

6. Writers are sometimes invited to serve as presidential advisors. If Steinbeck were an advisor, what proposals for improvement might he offer?

7. Portraits of the American scene have been written by dozens of writers, foreign and native. Select one such writer, and compare his (or her) views with those of Steinbeck.

8. Assume that you have been invited to serve on a TV panel on which Steinbeck is the guest. What questions would you want to ask him about this particular essay?

9. Write one of the following:

    a. A letter in answer to Mr. Steinbeck.

    b. A talk you'd like to give at a school assembly celebrating "I Am an American" day or some other important day honoring our past.

    c. An essay entitled "What Is America to Me."

10. Suppose a pen pal from a foreign land asked you to send an essay on your country that would help him (or her) better understand it. Why would (or wouldn't) you send this essay by Mr. Steinbeck?

THINKING ABOUT JOHN STEINBECK

1. Steinbeck's interests cover a wide range, as his prolific output proves.

a. Examine *Reader's Guide to Periodical Literature* for the past five years (or more). Select five Steinbeck article titles that suggest the breadth of his interests; read and report on one article of your choice.

b. Examine the card catalogue in your school or public library. In addition to the books from which selections in this section were taken, list five other Steinbeck book titles; read and report on one.

2. Adlai Stevenson once defined real patriots as "those who love America as she is, but who want the beloved to be more lovable." By this definition, would you consider Mr. Steinbeck patriotic? Explain.

3. Through both his fiction (*The Grapes of Wrath, Cannery Row*) and his nonfiction ("America and the Americans," *Travels with Charley*), Mr. Steinbeck has been a close observer and a vigorous critic of the American scene. Through which of these literary forms in this section has he succeeded in making his most telling points about the American scene?

4. From the days of his "jalopy" youth to his "shiny-paint-and-chrome" present, from the depression of the thirties to the boom of the sixties, Mr. Steinbeck has lived and written about strikingly contrasting periods in our history. What are some of these contrasts? Despite these, what has remained essentially unchanged? What are some aspects of life in our past that Steinbeck is glad to see gone? Which does he very badly miss?

5. In this unit Steinbeck has concerned himself with many themes: the struggle for survival, particularly of the poor; outwitting an enemy; the joys and pangs of owning a jalopy; the problems and promise in America. What other writers in this book have concerned themselves with similar themes? Who among them has views similar to Steinbeck's? different from Steinbeck's? Explain.

A SUPPLEMENTARY PROGRAM

READING SKILLS SUPPLEMENT

INTRODUCTION

We all know how important it is to be able to read. We read hundreds of things every day, sometimes without being aware that we are reading at all—newspapers, road signs, package labels, addresses, posters, direction signs, maps, box covers, TV commercials, price tags, and so forth.

Some people read only well enough to get by, but to do better in your school, business, and social life, you must be able to read better. Each year your reading requirements will increase. Unless you master effective reading skills now, you will not be prepared to handle the material.

There is much reading to be done before you graduate from high school. Since you are mainly concerned with required reading at the moment, this Reading Skills Supplement is aimed at helping you acquire skills directed at getting the most from your high school reading assignments. When possible, exercises and explanatory material are taken from the textbook.

This Supplement is divided into four main units with four primary objectives:

1. *Vocabulary Building.* The biggest problem for most students learning to read is building a vocabulary. In order to read, you must understand the words. There are many ways to build your vocabulary, but there are a few simple methods of finding out word meanings without taking time to go to the dictionary. This unit explores these various techniques.

2. *Comprehension Skills.* It is possible to know the meaning of every word and still not understand the sentence, paragraph, or article. The way a sentence or paragraph is constructed helps you to get meaning from it. You can learn to be alert for words that signal changes in meanings and thought. You must be able to read "between the lines" and to make inferences from the author's words, style, and organization. The comprehension skills discussed in this unit are essential if you are to get meaning from your reading.

3. *Increased Reading Rate.* The skilled reader is always at the controls. He is able to shift speeds to match his purpose in reading and the difficulty of the material. He has a slow rate for complex course assignments, a fast rate for certain simple, low-vocabulary prose, and a medium rate for other reading. He is able to choose his reading rate according to the material at hand. He can skip and skim to find facts.

Some of the faster reading skills discussed in this unit will be new to you, and some may review skills you already have. In either case, they are skills you *must* have in order to keep up in your required reading assignments.

4. *Better Study Habits.* The most important thing to you right now is the reading you do for schoolwork. Your understanding and retention of the material for examinations may concern you more than anything else. Your grades depend upon your ability to study well. A passing grade may have been thought sufficient at one time, but now it is necessary to be in the upper third or fourth of the class in order to qualify for admission to many colleges. The unit on study skills contains techniques that you can put to use immediately to make your studying easier and more productive.

In summary, this Supplement gives you tools to use in all reading. Some of the techniques we discuss may already be familiar to you and will simply serve the purpose of review; others will be new skills that you will need to practice and try out for yourself. *All* of them are included for one purpose: to help you become a skilled reader who is able to read all material quickly and with understanding.

UNIT ONE

BUILDING YOUR VOCABULARY

Why is vocabulary building regarded as such a terrible chore? First of all, it is only natural to dislike something totally new and strange; secondly, the attempt to get to know a new word is time-consuming and not always satisfactory. It is irritating to be reading along rapidly with a great deal of interest only to be stopped short by a new, unfamiliar word. You know that to stop and look up the word is going to break your train of thought, ruin your concentration, and disrupt your whole reading pattern. Your inclination may be to ignore the word and to struggle along without finding out its meaning.

This is not the right decision for several reasons. The author used the word because he meant it to be understood; if he could have left it out without hurting the overall meaning, he probably would have. Also, there is a good possibility that the word will reappear in the same selection. You are bound to run into the word some other time when it may be even more important to know it.

Don't be the person who says, "I wish I had" or "I

wish I did." Find out the meaning of a new word the first time you meet it. Vocabulary tests are used by employment agencies, on college entrance exams, in civil service tests, and on armed forces placement exams. Teachers, employers, the government—everyone you meet that can offer you some sort of help in education or employment—will be interested in your word power!

Even in conversation, it is best to stop the person who is talking to you to ask the meaning of a word you do not understand. You may remember the story about Roberto Clemente (page 284), who was playing baseball in Montreal in 1954. He understood practically no English at the time. A player whom he had robbed of an extra-base hit called him a name. Roberto, assuming he was being complimented on the catch, replied, "Sank you." This is not as unusual an example as it might seem. It is not a sign of ignorance or stupidity not to know the meaning of a word, but it can often be embarrassing not to find out.

Since you are familiar with looking words up in the dictionary, we will concentrate on ways of getting at a word's meaning *without the dictionary*. There are two ways to do this: (1) break the word up into parts (called *morphemes*) and from the meaning of its parts deduce the meaning of the whole word, or (2) determine the meaning of a word by its use in context. That is, determine its meaning by the words and sentences which surround it.

We will start with the smallest meaningful unit in the English language, the morpheme. It is from morphemes that words are made. In fact, some words are already morphemes. In the first section you will learn what they are and how they can help you to discover the meanings of words without using the dictionary.

Step 1. Word Structure: Morphemes

A morpheme is the smallest unit of meaning in our language. It may be a complete word or it may be a part added to a word or even buried inside a word. *Child* is a morpheme (it is a meaningful unit). *Children* is made up of two morphemes: *child* + plural. *Child's* is also made up of two morphemes: *child* + possessive. If this is the case, how many morphemes are there in the word *children's?* If you said three, you are right. *Children's* = *child* + plural + possessive. A morpheme is not necessarily a syllable. There are two syllables in the word *woman*; however, there is only one morpheme.

A prefix (*un–*, *contra–*, *pro–*, *sub–*, for example) is a morpheme; a suffix (*–ion*, *–able*, *–ly*) is a morpheme. How many morphemes are there in the words *subtract* and *workable?* How many in *unbelievable?*

Most endings added to words are morphemes: *–ish* and *–an* (Engl*ish* and Europe*an*); *–ly* and *–ness* (main*ly*, sad*ly*, rich*ness*, full*ness*); verb endings (wait*s*, wait*ed*, wait*ing*); and so forth. Remember that every word starts as only one morpheme. Every time we add a unit of meaning to that word (as *–ed* to *wait* to indicate past time or *–'s* to *child* to indicate possession), we are adding another morpheme.

Here are some other examples to show how words are formed from morphemes:

> ponies'—3 morphemes (*pony* + plural + possessive)
>   try—1 morpheme
>   tried—2 morphemes (*try* + past tense)
> welder—2 morphemes (*weld* + *–er*, suffix meaning "one who does"); one who welds
>   prefix—2 morphemes (*pre-*, prefix meaning "come before," + *fix*, root word meaning "to place"); to place before.

The word *morpheme* will be used frequently in the following pages. Be sure you understand its meaning before you continue. The following exercise will give you practice in recognizing morphemes.

- Try your skill at telling how many morphemes there are in each of the following words. Remember, any word part that has meaning by itself is a separate morpheme. Sometimes what may seem to be a single morpheme, because no morpheme has been added before or after the root word, may contain two morphemes, as the word *geese,* in which the plural is formed within the word rather than by adding *–s* (*goose* + plural = *geese*).

  1. piglet   **5.** fight   **8.** unkind
  2. Japanese   **6.** pair   **9.** painful
  3. stylish   **7.** peaceable **10.** kite
  4. bought

- *Follow-up.* Think about the number of morphemes in some of the words you use and see in the next few days. Make up legitimate words containing as many morphemes as possible by using plurals, prefixes, and suffixes. Here is one for a start—*unpredictability*—with five morphemes!

Step 2.   Recognizing Word Roots

Prefixes and suffixes are morphemes; they are meaningful units by themselves. However they are dependent upon the main morpheme, the *word root,* to complete their meaning in a form we can use.

The root of a word is that morpheme which carries the basic meaning.

Sometimes it is also called a *base* or a *stem*. Words having the same root are related in meaning. For this reason they are sometimes called *word families.*

These word families branch out from word roots, usually borrowed from another language. Latin and Classical Greek have probably contributed the most. You do not have to study either Latin or Greek to learn the Latin and Greek roots that will unlock the meaning to a very large number of otherwise unfamiliar English words.

Suppose in your reading you come across the sentence: "This seems to be an interminable task." You should be able to analyze the word and arrive at the meaning without the use of the dictionary. You recognize that the word has a prefix *in–,* meaning "not." You have seen the ending *–able* frequently in other words. You can guess that it is a suffix and that it means "able to." So far you have "not able to." You are left with *termin,* which must be the base or root of the word. Looking more closely at *termin,* you may recall other words in which this root is used, *terminate, terminal, termination.* All of these words have something to do with ending or finishing. When something *terminates,* it ends. A *terminal* is a limit or an end point, such as a bus *terminal.* The *termination* of a project is the ending or finishing of it. The word *interminable,* then, is made like this: *in–* (not) + *termin* (end) + *–able* (able to). An interminable task is one that never will end.

● Study each of the following word roots. In your notebook, write the answers to the practice exercises. Remember that the four word roots we have chosen barely touch upon the large number of word roots in the English language. As in the other steps, this exercise is only an introduction to the subject being discussed. The way to build your vocabulary is to use this method outside of this class.

Grad (gress) means "to step," or "to go." For example, *progress* means "to go ahead."

● In your notebook, write the word or word part based on the root *grad* that completes each of the following sentences.

1. I will _____ from high school soon.

2. What was your _____ on the last English test?

3. To go backward is to re_____.

4. You will have to use low gear to get up that steep _____.

5. Although the changes were made very _____, the differences were soon evident.

Secut (sequ) means "to follow." For example, a *sequel* is something that follows after.

- In your notebook, write the letter of the phrase in Column B that defines each word in Column A.

Column A	*Column B*
6. consecutive	**(a)** to pursue, to follow to the end
7. consequently	**(b)** the order in which events occur
8. sequence	**(c)** following in order, without interruption
9. second	**(d)** following as a result
10. prosecute	**(e)** following the first

Mag (or *magn*) means "great" or "large." For example, the lens *magnified* the object ten times. *Maj* means "greater" or "larger." A *major* operation is greater than a minor operation. *Max* means "greatest," or "largest." The *maximum* number of people allowed in the auditorium was 200.

- In your notebook, write one of the following words to complete each of the sentences. Each word will be used only once.

magnificent	major	magnitude
majority	maximum	magnanimous

11. John's portrayal of Hamlet was _____.

12. The bright stars in the sky have a greater _____ than the ones we cannot see so well.

13. A _____ of the entertainment committee voted to have ice cream and cake at the party.

14. Although he could have punished us severely, he was _____ and let us go with only a scolding.

15. My uncle was a _____ in the United States Army.

16. Forty pounds was the _____ weight allowed for each passenger's baggage on the airplane.

The root *crit* means "to judge." For example, John *criticized* the essay that had been read aloud to the class.

- Supply a word using the root *crit* to complete the following sentences.

17. Will you please stop being so _____ of the way I dress.

18. He was a music _____ for the Sunday newspaper.

19. A standard for judging things is called a _____.

20. I will listen to any _____ that will help me to improve my writing.

Step 3. Using Prefix Clues

As we have said, one way to discover the meaning of an unfamiliar word is to look at its parts. If you recognize the prefix—the morpheme that comes before the main part of the word and changes its meaning—you have a clue to the meaning of the word.

For example, you know what the word *use* means. Do you know that the prefix *dis–* means "the opposite of," or "the absence of"? If you do, you know that *disuse* means "not in use." You also know what *dislocate, disapprove, disagree,* and *disorganized* mean.

Inter– means "between" or "among." For example, *international* news refers to events that take place among nations.

● Choose one of the following words to complete each sentence.

intercept   intervene   interval
intermission   interrupt   intermediate

1. After he ate, David waited a short _____ before he went in swimming.

2. The two young boys fought so ferociously that one of the older boys had to _____ to stop the fight.

3. After each act of the school play, there was a short _____.

4. Jenny was neither a beginning nor advanced swimmer. She joined the _____ swimming class.

5. "How can I finish my homework if you continue to _____ me?"

6. "No, I never received your note. Did someone _____ it?"

Post– means "after" or "behind." For example, a *postscript* is something written after the main part of a letter. Caution: *post* at the beginning of a word is not always a prefix. *Postage* and *postal* refer to the word *post,* which means mail, and not to the prefix *post–.*

● In your notebook, answer briefly each of the following questions.

7. If a man began his army service during the *postwar* period, would he have fought in the war? Why?

8. If a *prelude* is music played before a religious service, what is a *postlude?*

9. Why does P.M. (post meridiem) mean afternoon?

10. A student is taking *postgraduate* work at a college. Has he already graduated from college? How do you know?

The prefix *syn–* or *sym–* means "along with," "together," "like."

For example, a *synthesis* is a putting together of parts to form a whole (from *syn–* plus *thesis*, "to place").

- Choose one of the following words to complete each of the sentences.

  sympathy   symphony   symmetrical
  synonym   synchronize

11. When we _____ our watches, we will make sure we arrive at the same time.

12. A design in which both sides are alike is called _____.

13. The word *precise* is a _____ for the word *exact*.

14. In a _____, the orchestra plays many sounds at the same time, or in harmony.

15. If *pathos* means suffering, _____ is a sharing of someone else's suffering or feelings.

The prefix *semi–* means "half," "partly," or "occurring twice." For example, a visit that is made *semiweekly* is made twice a week.

- Complete each of the following sentences with a word containing *semi–*.

16. A bill that is paid twice a month is paid _____.

17. The contest just before the final round is called the _____.

18. A turquoise is a _____ gem, not a precious stone like a diamond.

19. A half circle is a _____.

20. If a workman has not completely mastered a skill, he may be called _____.

The prefix *auto–* means self. For example, a robot is called an *automaton,* which means "a machine that acts by itself."

- Complete each sentence below with a word starting with *auto–*.

21. An _____ toaster is one that is self-acting.

22. An _____ is a biography written by a person about himself.

23. Since *mobile* means "moving," an _____ is a self-moving machine.

24. Mary asked the movie star to _____ his picture for her collection.

The prefix *ante–* means "before." An *antecedent* is something that comes before or precedes something else.

- Write the word that completes each sentence.

25. The abbreviation A.M. refers to _____ meridiem, or before noon.

26. A waiting room is called an _____.

27. Since *bellum* means "war," a prewar period is referred to as _____.

The prefix *anti–* means "against," or "opposite." For example, an *antiaircraft* gun is one that is used against airplanes. What kind of person is *antisocial?* Would you say he enjoyed parties or preferred to be alone?

● Complete each sentence below with a word beginning with *anti–*.

28. A substance that prevents freezing is called an _____.

29. To counteract the effects of a poison, one uses an _____.

30. Laws passed against big businesses called trusts are _____ laws.

Step 4. Using Suffix Clues

A *suffix* is a morpheme added to the end of a word to change its meaning or to make a new word. Some suffixes that you know are *–ion*, *–ish*, *–ment*, and *–tion*.

If you learn the meaning of some common suffixes, you will have a clue to the meaning of many new words. In your notebook, write the answers to the practice questions.

The suffix *–fy* means "to make" or "to cause to be." For example, *simplify* means "to make something simple." He *simplified* the problem for the younger children. All words ending in the suffix *–fy* are verbs.

● Below are definitions of six words that end in the suffix *–fy*. What are the six words? Be sure you spell each correctly.

1. To make something liquid

2. To cause terror

3. To make something beautiful

4. To cause something to have dignity

5. To make something clear

6. To cause horror

The suffix *–ish* means "belong to," as in the word *British;* "like" as in *babyish;* and "somewhat" as in *sweetish.*

● Add the suffix *–ish* to each of the following words. Many of the words will change spelling when the suffix is added. For example, *Denmark* becomes *Danish.*

7. mule   **8.** Scotland   **9.** red

10. white	**14.** late	**18.** fiend
11. Turkey	**15.** Spain	**19.** cool
12. green	**16.** boy	**20.** England
13. Ireland	**17.** child	

The suffix *–age* forms nouns that show an act or condition. For example, *marriage* is the condition of being married.

● Add the suffix *–age* to each of the following words. Then write a short sentence using each word.

Example: wreck—wreckage. We found a piece of the ship's wreckage.

| **21.** pass | **23.** parent | **25.** seep |
| **22.** use | **24.** shrink | **26.** front |

The suffix *–cy* forms nouns that show rank, office, quality, or state of being. For example, the office of captain may be called the *captaincy.*

● Add the suffix *–cy* to each of the following words. Be sure to spell the new words correctly.

Example: expectant—expectancy.

| **27.** bankrupt | **29.** president | **30.** pirate |
| **28.** occupant | | |

Step 5.   Synonyms and Antonyms: Clues to Meaning

In this lesson you are going to study two kinds of context clues. One kind of context clue occurs in words having the same or a similar meaning to an unfamiliar word. A word that has the same meaning as another word is called a *synonym.* For example, suppose you read the following sentence: *Tony's laugh was harsh and raucous.* You might guess, from reading the sentence, that *harsh* and *raucous* had similar meanings. You would be correct, for *raucous* means "hoarse" or "disagreeably harsh."

Another context clue is found in words or phrases that have the opposite meaning of the unfamiliar word. Such an opposite is called an *antonym.* If you know that a word means the opposite of a familiar word, you can guess its meaning.

Words such as *not, but, although, however, on the other hand, either,* and *or* often indicate an opposite or contrasting idea. For example, look at the following sentence: *Jean is a giddy, frivolous person, not serious like her sister Maryellen.* In this sentence Jean and Maryellen are contrasted. The word *not* tells you that Jean's personality is different from Maryellen's. *Serious* and *frivolous* are antonyms. If you did not know the meaning of *giddy* and *frivolous,* you would have the clue that they mean the opposite of *serious.*

● Read the following sentences. In your notebook, write the word that is closest in meaning to the word in italics.

1. Although Mr. Kraft had tried to train him to be orderly, Donald always worked in a *haphazard* manner.
(**a**) orderly, (**b**) disorderly, (**c**) careful, (**d**) happy

2. The new restaurant closed because it was losing so much money. It had a two-thousand-dollar *deficit.*
(**a**) shortage, (**b**) defeat, (**c**) profit, (**d**) surplus

3. The ability to read, write, and speak are not *innate,* but must be learned by all men.
(**a**) inborn, (**b**) intelligent, (**c**) acquired, (**d**) easy

4. Although he had never made a tool before, the farmer was able to *contrive* a hammer out of some old parts.
(**a**) find, (**b**) buy, (**c**) design, (**d**) use

5. When you write, try to say things in an original way instead of being *trite.*
(**a**) fresh, (**b**) commonplace, (**c**) foreign, (**d**) unusual

6. The sounds in the house seemed *ominous,* and Nancy was frightened. She wished that she were not alone.
(**a**) threatening, (**b**) loud, (**c**) unusual, (**d**) ordinary

7. Patty liked simple not *ornate* furniture.
(**a**) antique, (**b**) ordinary, (**c**) carved, (**d**) highly decorated

8. When he was happy, Jim was *demonstrative,* never hiding his feelings from other people.
(**a**) sad, (**b**) quiet, (**c**) noisy, (**d**) displaying feelings

9. Although we tried every day to trap the young fox, it always managed to *elude* us.
(**a**) detect, (**b**) smell, (**c**) see, (**d**) escape

10. Charles tried to change his lengthy answers to *concise* ones.
(**a**) correct, (**b**) practical, (**c**) brief, (**d**) decisive

11. Chicken pox, no longer a rare disease, is *prevalent* among children all over the world.
(**a**) uncommon, (**b**) harmful, (**c**) common, (**d**) harmless

12. Steve was always *prudent* about making big decisions. He considered all the possibilities carefully.
(**a**) wise, (**b**) hesitant, (**c**) firm, (**d**) active

13. Instead of making an *exhaustive* search for her little brother, Sally went directly to his favorite hiding place.
(a) thorough, (b) delayed, (c) sincere, (d) pretended

14. Although everyone in the courtroom expected the witness to *denounce* his employer, the man praised him.
(a) talk about, (b) argue with, (c) condemn, (d) describe

15. In selecting the furnishings for the drawing room, she tended to lean toward *contemporary* designs rather than the early American style preferred by her sister.
(a) old, (b) good, (c) present day, (d) plain

Step 6. Finding Indirect Context Clues

Sometimes the meaning of a word can be guessed only by reading the whole paragraph. Always read a sentence or two before and after a new word for context clues. An indirect clue might repeat the idea of the new word, or establish the mood of the paragraph in a way that makes the meaning of the word clear. For example, read the following paragraph, looking for a clue to the meaning of the word *premonition*.

Suddenly there came to him a *premonition* of danger. It seemed a shadow had fallen upon him. But there was no shadow. His heart had given a great jump into his throat.

Did you guess that *premonition* means "foreboding"; "a warning of something that is about to happen"? A synonym for *premonition* is the word *forewarning*. You know from the third sentence that there was no shadow, although there seemed to be one. This sentence tells you that although the man sensed that danger was near, he could not see it.

- Read the following paragraphs carefully. In your notebook, write the word which is closest in meaning to each word in italics.

At last, all the crew being on board, word was passed to go to dinner fore and aft, an order that made my heart jump with delight, for now my long *fast* would be broken. But though the sailors, *surfeited* with eating and drinking ashore, did not then touch the salt beef and potatoes which the black cook handed down into the forecastle, and though this left the whole allowance to me, to my surprise I found that I could eat little or nothing, for now I only felt deadly faint, but not hungry. ("He Is Initiated," page 407)

1. *Fast* means (a) run, (b) period without food, (c) period without sleep, (d) kind of meal.

2. *Surfeited* means (a) satisfied, (b) hungry, (c) unhappy, (d) covered.

The *upshot* of this business was that before I went to sleep that night, I felt well satisfied that it was not customary for sailors to call on the captain in the cabin, and I began to have an *inkling* of the fact that I had acted like a fool; but it all arose from my ignorance of sea usages. ("He Calls on the Captain," page 411)

3. *Upshot* means (a) ammunition, (b) outcome, (c) oddity, (d) beginning.

4. *Inkling* means (a) black fluid, (b) ill feeling, (c) vague idea, (d) dream.

Then to Springfield, Illinois, the old home town, the Sangamon nearby, the New Salem hilltop nearby, for the final rest of cherished dust. Thus the route and the ceremonial rites *in epitome.* The weather was April and May but the smoke and haze was October and the feeling of the hour silent snow on the January earth of a hard winter. ("A Tree Is Best Measured When It's Down," page 457)

5. (a) in order, (b) at the right time, (c) in brief, (d) in the proper place

These rocks and boulders were more difficult to walk on than those in the glacier valley, which had been dry, though much larger. Here his feet slipped on the slimy surfaces, back a step for every two forward. The *hindrance* was maddening, and anxiety shortened his breath. Once he almost fell.

6. (a) path, (b) obstacle, (c) wetness, (d) pace

The voice was calm and *resolute.* It was a good voice. The self-possession of that man had somehow induced a corresponding change in myself.

7. (a) uncertain, (b) unconvincing, (c) shy, (d) firm

Stifling my indignation at his rudeness, which by this time I found was my only plan, I replied that that was not so good a place for the shavings as that which I myself had selected, and asked him to tell me why he wanted me to put them in the place he designated. Upon this, he flew into a terrible rage, and without explanation *reiterated* his order like a clap of thunder. ("He Is Initiated," page 409)

8. (a) withdrew, (b) repeated, (c) whispered, (d) commanded

Step 7. Words in Context: The Specialized Vocabulary

Words and expressions are often adopted by a particular group of people to mean something specific in their type of work, entertainment, or simply their daily routine. There is often a similarity between the original meaning of the word and its meaning in the new context, but it *must be read in context in order to be properly understood.*

Take the common word *strike,* for instance. In Alaska to *strike* it rich means "to find gold." If a fisherman on Rangeley Lake were to get a *strike,* it would mean a rainbow trout had nibbled at the bait. If the coal miners in Illinois were to *strike,* it would mean they had walked off the job until negotiations for a new contract had been settled. If a new joke *strikes* a friend of yours as funny, then he is very much amused. If you *strike* up a friendship with a new girl in town, you may be working toward a future date. If an editor *strikes* some copy in the first edition, he takes it out. If you *strike* an umpire over the head with the bat, then you're on your way to the showers. Is it any wonder the foreigner is bewildered when he comes to the United States armed with his book entitled *Conversational English?* Probably the definition in his book would read: *strike*—"to hit."

A good dictionary will give most of the definitions above, but unless you understand how the word has been used, and in what context, the dictionary will not be much help. You may not even need to use a dictionary if you can associate the meaning the word had originally with its probable meaning in the new context.

Baseball is one area of entertainment in which countless common words have special meaning. In the story "Aches and Pains and Three Batting Titles" by Myron Cope, you will find many such words.

● Ten sentences have been taken from this story about Roberto Clemente. Each one contains a common word (or words) that has its own meaning when used in a baseball context. Write two definitions for each word: (a) its meaning in the context here, and (b) its meaning as you usually think of it.

1. "If I *struck* out, I stay in the line-up," he says.

2. "If I played well, I'm *benched.*"

3. "Much of the time I was used only as a *pinch* runner or for defense."

4. He . . . *favors* the basket catch made famous by Mays.

5. He often underhands the ball to second base in a great, looping arc instead of *pegging* it on the line.

6. They were *gunning for* a third straight pennant.

7. Walter O'Malley's brain trust . . . told the Montreal manager, Max Macon, to hide him—that is, play him sparingly lest enemy *bird dogs* take a fancy to him.

8. Groat *sparked* the team.

9. He has urged his teammates to set their *sights* high.

10. Paige *fanned* the first man.

ANSWER KEY TO UNIT ONE

Step 1

1. 2 morphemes (*pig* + *–let*, meaning "small")   2. 2 morphemes (*Japan* + *–ese*, meaning "native of")   3. 2 morphemes (*style* + *–ish*, meaning "having the quality of")   4. 2 morphemes (*buy* + past tense)   5. 1 morpheme   6. 1 morpheme   7. 2 morphemes (*peace* + *–able*, meaning "inclined toward")   8. 2 morphemes (*un–*, meaning "not," + *kind*)   9. 2 morphemes (*pain* + *–ful*, meaning "full of")   10. 1 morpheme

Step 2

1. graduate   2. grade   3. regress   4. grade   5. gradually   6. (c)   7. (d)   8. (b)   9. (e)   10. (a)   11. magnificent   12. magnitude   13. majority   14. magnanimous   15. major   16. maximum   17. critical   18. critic   19. criterion   20. criticism

Step 3

1. interval   2. intervene   3. intermission   4. intermediate   5. interrupt   6. intercept   7. No, *postwar* means "after the war."   8. music played at the end of a service   9. post (after) meridiem (noon)   10. Yes, post- (after) graduating   11. synchronize   12. symmetrical   13. synonym   14. symphony   15. sympathy   16. semimonthly   17. semifinals   18. semiprecious   19. semicircle   20. semiskilled   21. automatic   22. autobiography   23. automobile   24. autograph   25. ante   26. anteroom   27. antebellum   28. antifreeze   29. antidote   30. antitrust

Step 4

1. liquefy   2. terrify   3. beautify   4. dignify   5. clarify   6. horrify   7. mulish   8. Scottish   9. reddish   10. whitish   11. Turkish   12. greenish   13. Irish   14. latish   15. Spanish   16. boyish   17. childish   18. fiendish   19. coolish   20. English   21. passage   22. usage   23. parentage   24. shrinkage   25. seepage   26. frontage   27. bankruptcy   28. occupancy   29. presidency   30. piracy

Step 5

1. (b) disorderly   2. (a) shortage   3. (a) inborn   4. (c) design   5. (b) commonplace   6. (a) threatening   7. (d) highly decorated   8. (d) displaying feeling   9. (d) escape   10. (c) brief   11. (c) common   12. (a) wise   13. (a) thorough   14. (c) condemn   15. (c) present day

Step 6

1. (b) period without food   2. (a) satisfied   3. (b) outcome   4. (c) vague idea   5. (c) in brief   6. (b) obstacle   7. (d) firm   8. (b) repeated

Step 7

1. (a) missed three strikes in baseball
   (b) hit something or someone
2. (a) put on the bench and not permitted to play
   (b) furnished with benches
3. (a) used to run only when nobody else was available
   (b) squeeze tightly
4. (a) uses the same or similar method (as Mays)
   (b) does something for someone
5. (a) throwing a ball directly
   (b) pounding pegs into something
6. (a) seeking
   (b) shooting
7. (a) baseball scouts
   (b) dogs used in hunting birds
8. (a) encouraged or livened up
   (b) fired
9. (a) aims, objectives
   (b) device used on a gun for zeroing in on a target
10. (a) caused the man to strike out
    (b) stirred or cooled the air with a fan

UNIT TWO

COMPREHENSION SKILLS

A. Intonation

When we first learn to read, we read aloud to the teacher, plodding slowly along from one word to the next, carefully sounding out each individual letter or word. Each letter and each word is given the same monotonous stress. If you listened to a first-grade reading class, you might be reminded of a droning beehive. Occasionally some adventurous child will read in a singsong pattern that will separate him from the others, but that can be even more monotonous.

Unfortunately, many people still read like first graders. It isn't necessary to read aloud to be monotonous; you can bore yourself by reading silently in the same way. Reading may be intolerably dull and difficult for many people for just this reason. When faced with the written word, many people are strangely taken by an impulse to revert back to first grade and to pound out every single word with no variation. The sight of a question mark may give rise to a slight upward inflection at the end of the sentence, but other than that, every word is identical in stress and pitch level.

Thankfully, in normal conversation we do not say everything in the same monotonous fashion. Our friends would dwindle away if we did. We use inflections, place greater stress on certain words than on others, raise and lower our voice pitch, and insert appropriate pauses to indicate changes in thought. This whole process is called *intonation*.

Intonation is a necessary part of reading as well as speaking, because it is a means of bringing reading to life. The writer has many ways to help us arrive at a duplicate of the spoken word. Sentence structure, sentence and paragraph separation, and punctuation are the commonest methods.

The process of intonation is divided into three parts: *stress*, *pitch*, and *juncture*.

Step 8. Stress

Stress is the accent we place on a particular word or word part to change its meaning. To put it another way, it is the force with which we say a syllable.

Example: *object*

1. I ob**JECT** to your use of that word.
   (*Object* is used here as a verb.)
2. The **OB**ject of my affections is Fido.
   (*Object* in this instance is used as a noun.)

Notice that when the stress or accent shifts in a word, the result is often a new word that is a different part of speech and has a different meaning from the original word. As another example, consider the following pair of sentences:

1. You will need a driver's **PER**mit in order to learn to drive.
2. It may be more difficult to get your parents to per**MIT** you to drive.

In the first sentence the stress on **PER** (the first syllable) tells you that the word *permit* is a noun meaning a legal piece of paper allowing you to take driving lessons. In the second sentence the shift in stress to **MIT** tells you that *permit* is now a verb meaning to allow something to happen. Since you cannot hear stress when you read silently, you must be able to recognize stress from written signals such as word order and punctuation. The stress you give particular words shows your understanding of the meaning of the sentence you read.

Generally, only one word in a sentence receives the maximum stress or accent. When too many words in a sentence receive heavy stress, it is apparent that the reader is reading as he did in the first grade and is probably not getting the meaning as a whole.

● In each set of three sentences below, the first sentence contains a word printed in capital letters. This word can be stressed in two different ways, but only one of these two ways gives the correct meaning. Number from 1 to 5 in your notebook; after each number, write *a* or *b* to indicate the sentence that means the same as the first sentence in the group.

1. There seemed to be some DRAWBACK about joining the team.

a. He didn't explain why he wanted to draw back from joining the team.

b. There was a disadvantage to joining the team.

2. Gerald expected a CUTBACK in salary, but nothing like this!

a. Gerald had expected to cut back on some of his expenses.

b. From now on Gerald's wallet was going to be thinner than he had expected.

3. With disgust, the other students watched the principal PRESENT Harry the award.

a. The other students felt the award was a present for Harry.

b. The other students felt that Harry had not earned the award.

4. Phyllis deserves an INCREASE in salary if anyone does!

a. Phyllis is increasing her efforts for a higher salary.

b. Phyllis should get a raise before anyone else does.

5. Someone threw a rock through the glass in the GREENHOUSE.

a. Someone probably threw a rock through a window.

b. Someone probably hit some plants when he threw a rock.

Step 9. Pitch

Pitch is the rising or falling tone of voice that we use to place greater emphasis on a word or word part to change its meaning. Variation in pitch can give different meanings to the same sentence:

1. Who do you think you *are?* (Simple question.)

2. *Who* do you think you *are?* (Question showing anger.)

3. *Who* do you think *you* are? (Question showing sarcasm.)

Stress and pitch are linked together very closely. Pitch, unlike stress, depends on tone rather than loudness. To get a different pitch, we raise or lower our voice in tone. There are three important pitch levels: high, medium, and low. We will use numbers to symbolize the three levels of pitch: 3 for high, 2 for medium, 1 for low.

Most simple sentences begin with medium pitch, rise briefly to the high pitch, and then fall to the low pitch.

Example:

$$\text{I like} / \overset{3}{\text{ice}} \backslash \text{cream.}$$
(2 ———— I like / ice \ cream ———— 1)

We use a graph line to make it easier to visualize this rise and fall of pitch. Medium pitch (2) has a line directly under the word, high pitch (3) rises to a line above the word, and low pitch (1) falls to a line below the word.

Example:

$$\text{John saw a} / \overset{3}{\text{mouse.}}$$
(2 ———— John saw a / mouse \ ———— 1)

Notice how the pitch will sometimes drop in the middle of a word.

To read accurately you need to supply the proper pitch silently to the words in a sentence. The wrong pitch gives the wrong meaning. Notice the wide difference in meaning between the sample sentence we used at the beginning of this step. Say each of these three sentences aloud, using the graph line as a guide to variations in pitch from line to line.

Examples:

Who do you think you / are?

Who ⌐ do you think you ¬ are?

Who ⌐ do you think ⌐ you ¬ are?

There is still another way in which this sentence might be spoken. Draw a graph line to show how it would be spoken if you wanted to emphasize the first *you*.

Who do you think you are?

● Say the following statements to yourself and listen with your "inner ear" to the rise and fall of pitch. What happens to the pitch when the statements are changed to questions? What are the differences in meaning when the pitch changes?

1. That was a good play.

2. Don't be difficult.

3. Smile and the world smiles with you.

4. That was a great class trip.

5. We'll stand in line to see that movie.

The best practice with pitch is to read sentences aloud and then silently, listening for the intonation that gives the clearest meaning.

Step 10. Juncture

Juncture is a pause. It is generally thought of as a way of breaking or stopping the flow of speech. In conversation, juncture is no problem, because we simply pause, stop, and start without thinking much about it. In writing, juncture must usually be indicated by some form of punctuation. The purpose of juncture is, of course, to add to or to clarify the meaning of the speaker or writer. Sometimes misplaced or unclear juncture can cause confusing and embarrassing mistakes in meaning.

1. Don't fire Pamela until I give the signal.
(Pamela may be out of her job.)

2. Don't fire, Pamela, until I give the signal.
(Pamela should wait for the signal before firing.)

Both sentences have the same number of words and syllables, but notice the striking change in meaning when we pause after "fire" and after "Pamela" in the second sentence. The voice can easily insert the necessary junctures, or pauses; in writing these must be indicated by punctuation marks. To make the necessary junctures, we convert punctuation marks to pauses. In silent reading we must be conscious of these junctures when they are signaled by punctuation marks. Otherwise we may get a totally different meaning than the writer intended.

● Read the following pairs of sentences, supplying the juncture indicated by the punctuation marks to get the proper meaning. Answer the question following each pair, and give a reason for your answer.

1. a. How long have you taught Mrs. Filibuster?

b. How long have you taught, Mrs. Filibuster?

In which case is someone else teaching Mrs. Filibuster?

2. a. How about giving me some honey?

b. How about giving me some, honey?

Which speaker seems more affectionate?

3. a. Alice, the quarterback threw a touchdown pass.

b. Alice, the quarterback, threw a touchdown pass.

Which Alice knows very little about football?

4. a. Roger put a lot of time into the examination.

    b. Roger, put a lot of time into the examination.

In which case has Roger probably already taken the exam?

5. a. We all watched the bull fight Clara.

    b. We all watched the bullfight, Clara.

Which Clara is in a dangerous spot?

● Now that you can see what might happen if you ignore signs of juncture, read the following sentences. In your notebook, write the words after which a juncture is absolutely needed to clarify the meaning.

Example: Hold up Mary until we catch up with you.

Explanation: A pause must be taken after "up" and after "Mary" to make it clear that we don't want Mary suspended in the air.

6. As we walked along the snake began to rattle.

7. Will you are an ignoramus.

8. On your way down the flagpole is on the right.

9. No matter how much you kick Florence is going to the circus.

10. Today June is May first.

Remember, juncture guides you to meaning by use of punctuation marks.

B. The Paragraph

A paragraph stands out on a page: the first sentence is indented and the last sentence usually stops short of the right margin. However, paragraphs are not indented only to break up a page of writing; they are indented to show the reader that each one contains a new idea or moves on to a new phase of an earlier subject. A paragraph is a group of sentences that work together to make clear one central idea. Sentences that work together to make this one idea clear to the reader belong together in a paragraph. (Since the paragraph is a basic unit in writing as well as in reading, there is also a section on paragraphs in the Composition Skills Supplement, pages 645–55. You will notice, however, that there is a different emphasis in the composition section.)

A skilled reader is prepared for a variety of paragraph styles depending upon the subject matter, the author, and the general organization of the book chapter or article. Some paragraphs have topic sentences and some don't; some authors very neatly use the same method of paragraph development throughout an article and some don't; paragraphs in expository prose such as this will differ from those in fiction. So you see, there are any number of paragraph variations, but just as it is easier to drive several different automobile models if you are able to drive one of them, you are better prepared to handle all paragraphs more quickly and effectively if you can discover how the thought is developed in one or two.

Let's look at some paragraphs that do have topic sentences. Paragraphs with topic sentences are usually typical of expository prose, the reading you will do in most of your courses such as social studies and science.

Step 11. Paragraphs with Topic Sentences

Sometimes the main idea of a paragraph is stated in one sentence called the *topic sentence.* If you can find the topic sentence, you will discover the main idea of the paragraph.

All of the sentences in a well-written paragraph of factual writing help to develop one main idea. The topic sentence in a paragraph states that idea. The other sentences in the paragraph develop the idea by explaining it or by adding details or examples. These other sentences add information about the main idea.

A topic sentence may be anywhere in a paragraph—at the beginning, the middle, or the end. Often it is the first sentence in a paragraph. This placement enables the reader to understand the main idea right away. When a topic sentence is the last sentence in a paragraph, it sums up all the subordinate details that have come before it.

Read the following paragraph carefully. What is the main idea? Can you find the topic sentence?

[1]"Accuracy" is the watchword of the scientist. [2]A slight error may result in the failure of a big project. [3]Architects and builders are very careful with all measurements. [4]Tall chimneys and skyscrapers would be very unsafe if the measurement at the base were even slightly wrong. [5]And you know how an error by an engineer who is helping build a bridge might result in loss of life.

The topic sentence of this paragraph is the first: *"Accuracy" is the watchword of the scientist.* This means that scientists must be very accurate. The other sentences in the paragraph give examples of the main idea.

● Read the following paragraphs carefully. As you read, look for the topic sentence and the main idea. In your notebook, write the answers to the questions that follow each paragraph.

¹Whales are the largest animals that exist or have ever existed in this world. ²No fossilized creature of equal size has ever been found. ³A full-grown blue whale often measures over ninety feet in length; the cachalot, or blunt-headed sperm whale, may attain over seventy feet. ⁴But the statement that an animal is ninety feet long is mere information. ⁵The shock of realizing what it means can be experienced only by seeing the creature. ⁶A blue whale is four times the length of a bus. ⁷If you stood on its back, you could enter the second-floor window of a house. ⁸The tongue weighs as much as a full-grown elephant. ⁹The skeleton weighs twenty-two tons, the meat of the body fifty, and the fat twenty-five. ¹⁰The total weight of the animal, calculated by adding its parts together, amounts to 286,000 pounds. ¹¹If the creature could be hoisted onto one of a pair of scales long enough for the purpose, it could be balanced only by placing on the other scale thirty-six elephants or the population of a town of twenty-five hundred inhabitants.

1. The topic sentence is the (**a**) first, (**b**) second, (**c**) third, (**d**) eleventh.

2. The main idea of this paragraph is that (**a**) whales achieve a fantastic size, (**b**) no animal that we know anything about is as large as the whale, (**c**) a whale weighs 286,000 pounds, (**d**) one whale is equal to thirty-six elephants.

¹Man is probably the most naked, the most fragile, and the most unprotected being in creation. ²Compare him with one of the lower forms of animal life. ³The insect, for example, is formidably equipped for attack. ⁴If you doubt that, think of the last time you were stung by a hornet or bee. ⁵Like the most modern tank or plane, many insects have their own armor-plating for defense. ⁶Think also of the strength of the ant, which can lift a thousand times the weight of its body. ⁷Consider the cockroach and its strength and abilities in comparison to its size. ⁸It can run, swim, and even fly, as well as fight. ⁹Man cannot match this.

3. The topic sentence is the (**a**) first, (**b**) fourth, (**c**) sixth, (**d**) eighth.

4. The main idea of this paragraph is that (**a**) insects are superior to men, (**b**) the ant is stronger than a man, (**c**) man is less well equipped defensively and offensively than lower forms of animal life, (**d**) man has no reason to feel superior to many forms of animal life.

¹Americans love adventure. ²The men who discovered America were adventurers. ³The colonists who bravely built the first American settlements, the frontiersmen who fought their way across the continent, the miners and mountain men, the hunters and trappers, the cowboys and sod-busting farmers, the

hardy immigrants and restless New Englanders—all of these men were adventurers. ⁴Sometimes they sought adventure for money; sometimes to find a place to settle their families; sometimes just because they craved adventure. (Stories of Action, page 4)

5. The topic sentence is the (**a**) first, (**b**) second, (**c**) third, (**d**) fourth.

6. The main idea of this paragraph is that (**a**) restless New Englanders were adventurers, (**b**) Americans craved adventure, (**c**) many types of men symbolize America's spirit of adventure, (**d**) America would not have been discovered without adventurers.

¹What John F. Kennedy left us was most of all an attitude. ²To put it in the simplest terms, he looked ahead. ³He knew no more than anyone else what the future was going to be like, but he did know that that was where we ought to be looking. ⁴Only to a limited extent are we prisoners of the past. ⁵The future sets us free. ⁶It is our escape hatch. ⁷We can shape it to our liking, and we had better start thinking about how we would like it. (Introduction to *Four Days*, page 64)

7. The topic sentence is the (**a**) first, (**b**) second, (**c**) fourth, (**d**) fifth.

8. The main idea of this paragraph is that (**a**) John F. Kennedy looked ahead, (**b**) the future depends on the past, (**c**) our attitude should be to plan the future, (**d**) we should forget the past.

Step 12. Paragraphs Without Topic Sentences

It is easy to spot the main idea of a paragraph when it is summarized for you in a single topic sentence. But not all paragraphs have topic sentences. Most paragraphs in fiction (short stories and novels) have no topic sentences. Many paragraphs in nonfiction do not have topic sentences. Instead, each sentence adds something to the main idea. A statement of the paragraph's main idea may include a fact or detail from each sentence.

As you read the following paragraph, ask yourself: What is the main idea? What is the paragraph about? You may have to change your guess slightly as you read each sentence.

¹In the fifteenth century, Columbus had to prove to the king and queen of Spain that the earth was not flat before they would give him ships and sailors for his voyage. ²He felt that he had good proof when he explained that he saw the masts of the incoming ship before he saw the hull of the ship. ³But you have one proof that Columbus did not have—a proof that only those can show who look down on the earth from a great height. ⁴Pictures taken from a rocket at a

height of sixty to one hundred miles above the earth show that the surface of the earth curves.

Did you find a topic sentence in this paragraph? There is none. The first sentence introduces several topics that the paragraph might be about: Columbus and his voyage, the king and queen of Spain, the fifteenth century, and the idea that the earth is not flat. The second sentence narrows the topic by explaining Columbus's proof that the earth is round. You may have guessed that the rest of the paragraph would be about Columbus's idea. The third sentence introduces a new idea—a modern proof that the earth curves; and the last sentence tells what that modern proof is. This paragraph presents two proofs that the earth is round: Columbus's very old proof based on the way approaching ships are seen, and the modern proof of rocket photographs.

● In your notebook, write the exact word or phrase from the paragraph that completes the sentences following each paragraph.

The people who live around the Mediterranean Sea learned long ago how to farm the steep slopes of their countryside. They do it on terraces. A terrace is a level plot of land on the side of a hill or mountain. There are quite a few natural terraces on the slopes around the Mediterranean, and on these terraces men have been farming for many centuries. But Mediterranean farmers also learned long ago to build artificial terraces. They have done this by cutting away the earth of a slope in one place and moving the earth to another place. In each place they have leveled off the soil, making two fields where there were none before.

1. The main idea of this paragraph is that Mediterranean _____ use natural _____ or build manmade ones to farm the steep _____ of their land.

2. A terrace is a _____ stretch of land on the side of a _____ or _____.

The principal cause of most accidents is not the condition of the automobile, the road, or the weather. Most accidents occur when the weather is clear; only about one out of six fatal accidents takes place in rain, snow, or fog. It is easy to put the blame on the other fellow or to say the cause was a defective car, poor roads, or poor lights. The evidence puts the blame on the driver in the great majority of cases. Figures of the National Safety Council show that of all the drivers involved in fatal accidents, nearly one third were driving at excessive speeds. Other driver violations most often cited in motor vehicle deaths were: failure to have or to yield right of way, driving on wrong side of road, disregarding signs or officers, and improper passing.

3. The main idea of this paragraph is that most _____ automobile accidents are caused by driver _____.

4. The violation that caused nearly _____ of the fatal accidents is driving at excessive _____.

5. Four other driver violations are _____, _____, _____, _____.

Senator Jim Lane of Kansas had been a "conservative" Republican sympathetic to Johnson's plans to carry out Lincoln's reconstruction policies. But his frontier state was one of the most "radical" in the Union. When Lane voted to uphold Johnson's veto of the Civil Rights Bill of 1866 and introduced the administration's bill for recognition of the new state government of Arkansas, Kansas had arisen in outraged heat. A mass meeting at Lawrence had vilified the Senator and speedily reported resolutions sharply condemning his position. Humiliated, mentally ailing, broken in health, and laboring under charges of financial irregularities, Jim Lane took his own life on July 1, 1866. ("I . . . Looked Down into My Open Grave," page 69)

6. The main idea of this paragraph is to show that Jim Lane felt forced to take his own life because of the pressures brought to bear upon him by the _____ of his state.

7. The mass meeting in Lawrence succeeded in _____ the Senator.

8. The two things Lane did that brought down the wrath of the people in his state were _____.

Step 13. Methods of Paragraph Development

All of the sentences in a paragraph are related to the main idea. The way the author relates these sentences to the main idea and to each other may be your best clue to paragraph meaning.

Following are some ways by which an author may develop the main idea of the paragraph:

Comparison and Contrast. A comparison tells how things are alike; a contrast tells how things are different. A paragraph of comparison might begin, "The United States and Canada are similar in many ways. Both have vast areas, an abundance of natural resources . . ."

Description. A description gives details about something, often about the appearance of a person, place, or thing. For example, "The old, red house was kept in good condition. Its windows sparkled, framed by newly painted white trim. On the porch were . . ."

Argument. In this kind of paragraph, the writer tries to persuade or convince the reader. For example, "Everyone should vote for the new amendment to the Constitution. It is necessary because . . ."

Examples. Sometimes a topic sentence will make a statement, and the rest of the paragraph will give examples. "Some foods are made almost entirely of water and have no food value. Celery is one such food, and lettuce another . . ."

Definition. When a paragraph defines an idea, it attempts to pin down the meaning as exactly as possible. Here is the beginning of a definition paragraph. "Beauty is something that means different things to many people. Almost everyone will agree that something beautiful is pleasing to the eye, but . . ."

● Read the following paragraphs, paying special attention to the method of paragraph development. In your notebook, write the answer to each of the questions that follow.

> For the chosen few who come along at the right time with the right talent and luck, show business is a quick, glamorous road to fame and money and power. For others, like Bob Hope and Ethel Waters and Danny Kaye, tremendous success was preceded by long years of knocking at the gates, of dreary one-night stands in drab towns, of monotonous meals and miserable hotels. For most, it has been a lifetime of waiting for calls that never came.

1. The paragraph above is developed by (**a**) definition, (**b**) comparison or contrast, (**c**) argument, (**d**) example.

2. This introductory paragraph is probably introducing a story about show business (**a**) failure, (**b**) success, (**c**) glamor, (**d**) stars.

> The Junior prom. Boys on one side. Callous, unfunny jokes. Girls on the other. Nervous giggles and shy glances. A three-piece combo blaring away. The sax too loud. The piano untuned. Discordant sounds bouncing off the empty, hard wood floor.

3. The paragraph above is developed by (**a**) definition, (**b**) comparison or contrast, (**c**) description, (**d**) examples.

4. Judging by this one paragraph, the story is probably (**a**) humorous, (**b**) serious, (**c**) melodramatic, (**d**) tragic.

5. The author uses sentence fragments intentionally to give the effect of (**a**) static nervousness, (**b**) enjoyment, (**c**) optimism, (**d**) mystery.

> The crisis was on us. Even if I had been safely anchored, my cramped position would have kept me from helping him much

more. I felt helpless. In a few seconds I would reach the physical breaking point and Doug would go hurtling off the cliff. I did not see how I could keep him from slipping through and yet maintain my own balance. ("Two Boys on a Mountain," page 201)

6. The paragraph above begins with (**a**) a theoretical statement, (**b**) a statement of fact, (**c**) an argument, (**d**) an opinion.

7. The paragraph is developed by (**a**) definition, (**b**) comparison or contrast, (**c**) description, (**d**) examples.

8. Judging from this paragraph, the story is one of (**a**) mystery, (**b**) suspense, (**c**) humor, (**d**) information.

An emotion is a feeling that stirs you up in some way. Fear, anger, and love are emotions you have felt. Emotions may make you feel fine, as when you are happy. Or they may upset you, as when you are angry. There is nothing that shows that you are growing up quite so much as the way you handle your emotions. Everyone is angry or afraid or jealous or happy or sad at times. But some of us perhaps get too angry or too fearful or too jealous. Some of us may be "moody"—happy for a while and then blue and downhearted.

9. This paragraph begins with (**a**) detail, (**b**) definition, (**c**) comparison, (**d**) argument.

10. The second sentence gives three (**a**) examples, (**b**) details, (**c**) comparisons, (**d**) definitions.

Step 14. Paragraphs in Fiction

As we have noted, paragraphs in fiction are different from nonfiction (factual) paragraphs. Nonfiction is generally read for information as well as enjoyment; fiction is generally read solely for enjoyment. Paragraphs in fiction are usually more descriptive and may contain dialogue. Often they do not have topic sentences and do not necessarily follow any pattern of paragraph development.

Some people feel that it is easier to read fiction than nonfiction. This may be so, but even if you read fiction only for pleasure, you can still use comprehension and concentration skills. You want to understand the setting, the plot, and the characters. The setting is the place and time of the story's action. For example, the setting of a story about Abraham Lincoln might be Illinois in the 1840's. The story's plot is the series of events or actions that make up the story. Most careful readers have little trouble with setting and plot, but sometimes it is hard to understand the characters in fiction—what they do, what they are like, and why they act the way they do.

In reading fiction, you must often read between the lines; that is, you are often expected to make an inference, or guess, about things that are hinted at but not actually written down. Just as in conversation, it is sometimes the things that are left unsaid that are the most important. Take the following paragraph for example:

> It was the only house he had seen in three days; it nestled just at the base of the foothills which led to the Mexican border. For a long time he sat in the brush and wondered whether he should chance it. His throat was so dry he couldn't swallow, his mouth and lips were sore from lack of water, and he felt that if he didn't get some kind of food in his stomach soon, it wouldn't make any difference whether he made the border or not. ("The Returning," page 5)

It is obvious from what we have read that the man is hungry and thirsty. We also know that the story is going to take place somewhere near the Mexican border. Our past associations with other stories and movies tell us that this probably would be a rather hot, dusty climate. The man is trying to reach the border and has been traveling for three days; he is considering the house as a haven for food and water but wondering if he should chance it. From these facts we can infer that the man is trying to escape someone or something. The author has not told us any of these things in so many words; he has established a setting and described it in such a way that, by reading between the lines, we can make certain assumptions. In the very first paragraph the author has "set us up" for what is to follow.

● Read each of the following fiction paragraphs. In each, decide what the author has told you without actually saying it. Read between the lines, and in your notebook, write the letter of the best answer to each of the questions.

> The ghost that got into our house on the night of November 17, 1915, raised such a hullabaloo of misunderstanding that I am sorry I didn't just let it keep on walking, and go to bed. Its advent caused my mother to throw a shoe through a window of the house next door and ended up with my grandfather shooting a patrolman. I am sorry, therefore, as I have said, that I ever paid any attention to the footsteps. ("The Night the Ghost Got In," page 33)

1. We can infer from this first paragraph of a story that the story will be (**a**) tragic, (**b**) full of suspense, (**c**) humorous, (**d**) serious.

2. The thing that gives us the best clue as to the nature of the story is (a) the author's style, (b) the incidents discussed, (c) the unusual words, (d) the characters.

Chris allowed the dog to sniff long and thoroughly at his fingers. In the course of this, he forgot all the human eyes upon him. At the moment Puli was more important to him than anyone else. After a while the shaggy animal wagged his stubby tail as if to say that as far as he was concerned, there was no objection to Christoph's staying on the ranch. Then he curled up again on the warm stone.

3. From this paragraph, we can infer that Chris has just (a) found a lost dog named Puli, (b) been found in the desert by a rescue party, (c) arrived at a ranch which is to be his new home, (d) decided to leave the ranch.

4. The action takes place on a (a) rainy day, (b) warm day, (c) cold, winter day, (d) cold, stormy day.

5. Chris probably (a) is afraid of dogs, (b) likes dogs, (c) is a dog trainer, (d) is cruel to animals.

The two pairs of eyes met. Jenny's were clear and dark blue; Lars's were steel gray and clouding up with every second that passed. Had they been alone, a long discussion would have en-sued—agitated on one side, and calm, but firm on the other. But as it was now, the battle was confined to the eyes.

6. Lars and Jenny (a) were not alone, (b) were alone, (c) were having dinner, (d) never argued.

7. The person who was agitated was (a) Jenny, (b) Lars, (c) a stranger, (d) not with Lars and Jenny.

Baird reached for the throttles, jerked them wide open. The boat began to vibrate and a cross-breeze whipped icy water on Sue's face as the bow wave rose higher. Ken glanced at Sue, as if for a sign, but she kept staring straight ahead. If Baird was in a rage because a person who knew more about motors than he did had tried to tell him something, he'd have to deal with the situation he'd created. She summoned her new philosophy and decided to stay out of it.

8. The action takes place (a) near a lake, (b) in a sailboat, (c) in a garage, (d) in a motorboat.

9. Before this paragraph, there had probably been an argument between (a) Sue and Baird, (b) Sue and Ken, (c) Baird and Ken, (d) strangers.

10. The argument had probably been about (a) the way Baird was driving the boat, (b) Sue, (c) where to go, (d) how to steer the boat.

ANSWER KEY TO UNIT TWO

A. INTONATION

Step 8

1. b   2. b   3. b   4. b   5. b

Step 9

1. That was a good play. That was a good play?   2. Don't be difficult. Don't be difficult?   3. Smile and the world smiles with you. Smile and the world smiles with you?   4. That was a great class trip. That was a great class trip?   5. We'll stand in line to see that movie. We'll stand in line to see that movie?

Step 10

1. a   2. b   3. a   4. a   5. a   6. along,   7. Will,   8. down,   9. kick,
10. Today, June,

B. THE PARAGRAPH

Step 11

1. (a)   2. (b)   3. (a)   4. (c)   5. (a)   6. (c)   7. (a) and/or (d)   8. (c)

Step 12

1. farmers, terraces, slopes   2. level, hill, mountain   3. fatal, violations
4. one third, speeds   5. not yielding right of way, driving on wrong side of road, disregarding signs, improper passing   6. people   7. condemning
8. supporting Johnson's veto of the Civil Rights Bill of 1866 and introducing a bill for recognition of the new state government of Arkansas

Step 13

1. (b)   2. (a)   3. (c)   4. (b)   5. (a)   6. (b)   7. (c)   8. (b)   9. (b)
10. (a)

Step 14

1. (c)   2. (a)   3. (c)   4. (b)   5. (b)   6. (a)   7. (b)   8. (d)   9. (c)
10. (a)

UNIT THREE

INCREASED READING RATE

SPEED READING: FACT OR FICTION?

For the past several years there has been a lot of excitement about "speed reading." Unfortunately, advertising claims were so unbelievable that many people threw up their hands in despair and decided that there could be nothing to speed reading. People who spent an evening reading the newspaper didn't believe that they could toss it off in ten minutes; those who struggled for a month to plow through a book didn't believe they could whip through three novels in an evening.

Still, it is true that President Kennedy could read over a thousand words a minute. It is true that the average person can read faster— probably much faster—than he does. But as Adlai Stevenson said, "There are no gains without pains." It takes a great deal of practice to acquire effective reading skills. In some ways it takes more practice than any other learning process: not only must you learn new skills; you must shake off poor reading habits that have become established over many years of reading.

There are other qualifications to the assumption that "anyone can read over 1,000 words per minute." This skill depends upon the nature of the material being read and the capacity of the person doing the reading. President Kennedy had a marvelous ability to absorb and understand. But it was not inborn; it was acquired.

Comprehension and retention techniques may be learned by the average reader. We can only touch upon those skills here. To benefit from them, you should practice them whenever you can, both on your assignments and on your leisure reading. Before you learn more about the process of faster reading, check yourself on the following list of poor reading habits. How many of them do you have now?

1. Do you read word by word? If your lips move as you read or your larynx is vibrating in your throat, then you are reading word by word. This is perhaps the poorest reading habit of all.

2. Do you move your finger or pencil along the line of print as you read? If so, then your concentration is poor; you find it necessary to keep your place constantly to avoid having to reread. Your mind is not fully occupied with the reading and you are unsure of yourself.

3. Do you read everything from beginning to end without getting an overview or planning the reading beforehand? If you do, then you are reading many things you do not have to read at all. You are reading without any real purpose.

4. Do you read "words" rather than thoughts or ideas? If so, even though you may be reading every word, you are missing the important ideas.

5. Do you reread, that is, do you find yourself going back over the same line two or three times? If so, then your concentration is probably poor; you are not an involved reader.

6. Do you take hours to get through a reading assignment and then wonder if you will remember the important details that may be asked on a test? If so, you are not reading selectively; you need to clarify your purpose in reading.

In Step 15, you will read about two of the most important techniques to increase your reading rate—phrase reading and indenting. Remember, a faster reading rate is not possible on all reading material. An assignment in a technical subject such as biology may require not only word-by-word reading, but much rereading as well. Shakespeare is to be read slowly so that you can savor the words and language as well as grasp the content. Poetry, which depends on sound and intonation, is written to be read aloud and should never be read quickly. You will learn how to pace your reading rate to suit your purpose in reading and the difficulty of the material.

Now, break some of those poor reading habits by using these two faster reading techniques.

Step 15. Phrase Reading and Indenting

Phrase Reading

The most important new reading skill to help you develop a faster reading rate is called *phrase reading*. Even though phrase reading is the most important faster reading skill, remember that all faster reading skills are related to each other and none operate as well without the use of the others.

Do you remember how you first learned to read in grade school? If you were like many others, you first learned to recognize letters of the alphabet and the sounds of the letters. Next you read aloud to the teacher from a primer, going slowly from word to word, even reading word parts rather than word by word. If a word had more than one syllable, or even if it had only one syllable, you slowly sounded out the letters; suddenly the word emerged complete, and you were triumphant at your new discovery. This was a long process, but necessary. In the next few grades you were still asked to read aloud. Though you read words more quickly, you probably droned them out in a flat, meaningless monotone, giving each word equal stress. Chances are you treated silent reading the same way; maybe you even used your finger or a pencil to guide yourself from word to word. Suddenly special time devoted to reading stopped, and so did your reading training. You continued to use grade school reading habits, but all of your other classes became more involved and complex. Reading demands became greater.

What is the reading process? Contrary to common belief, your eyes do not move across the line of print in one smooth swing back and forth from left to right. Your eyes actually stop and start several times so that they may fixate (stop) on whatever it is you are reading. Your eyes see and register information to send to the brain only when they are stopped. Perhaps you have noticed people's eyes on a fast-moving subway or bus looking at something out of the window. The eyes make a whole series of jerky movements in an attempt to take in the scene outside the window. Think of the eye movements as movie film. We see the film as a smooth, continuous movement; however the film itself is a series of frames which move so quickly through the projector that we are not aware of the many "fixations."

Experiment #1. To see how your eyes work when you read, take a newspaper and punch a small pencil hole in the middle of it. Have a friend read the paper while you stand on the opposite side and watch his eye movements through the hole. You will see his eyes stop and start several times across each line of print, then swing back and repeat the performance on the next line. Take this newspaper and make a series of circles around word groups (two or three words in each group). Ask him to read again, only this time tell him to permit his eyes to stop only at each circled group, not at each word. Notice how much more quickly his eyes move as they stop and start from group to group.

Normally we read more quickly and effectively if we look slightly above the line of print rather than directly at it. The spaces between the words tend to stop us and prevent a smooth movement of the eye from left to right. In other words, we are almost forced to read word by word. By looking slightly above the line of print, we can see more of the words at one fixation, and we are not stopped or distracted by the normal word breakup of spaces. This is sometimes called "Space Reading."

Experiment #2. Look at an object on your desk—a pencil, cup, book, or something else. Now look slightly above the desk. You can still see the object just as easily, but in addition you are able to see more objects which surround it.

Read the sentence printed below as you would normally read.

The sensible man in the black frock coat is hungrily eating a peanut butter sandwich.

Now read this same sentence permitting your eyes to focus only once on each dot above each of the phrases.

The sensible man · in the black frock coat · is hungrily eating a peanut butter sandwich.

The first time you read this, your eyes may have stopped and started as many as fifteen times in order to take in all of the words. By reading in word groups and focusing slightly above the line, you were able to take in the same information in only four stops and starts. In terms of reading rate, you were able to read the same information in one quarter the length of time it took you the first time. Think of the time you would save if you could cut by three quarters other reading—articles, chapters, or complete books!

What is phrase reading? Phrase reading is simply reading by phrases, or word groups. These need not be grammatical phrases. They may be any logical groupings of words that go together. You can begin with phrases of three or four words. As you become familiar with phrase reading, you may be able to read larger phrase groups.

● Following is a brief paragraph written with the word groups separated by wider spaces. Read it first as you would normally, word by word. Read it again, phrase-by-phrase. Alternate these methods several times until you "get the feel" of reading in word groups. Remember to look slightly above the center of each word group.

If you read   word by word   you are wasting   valuable time; however,   if you read   phrase by phrase   you can cut your reading time   to less than half   the time you spend   reading by   the longer method.

Phrase reading is an effective skill for almost any nontechnical reading matter. Naturally, it is dependent on a good vocabulary and concentration. Practice this skill by circling phrases in a magazine article, or in some other dispensable reading material. Circle a few phrases, and then skip a paragraph to circle some more. Try to read the noncircled phrase paragraphs in the same way to help your eyes lose their dependence on guides.

Indenting

This reading technique is sometimes the breakthrough to faster reading habits. Even without phrase reading, it can greatly increase your reading rate.

Since it is possible to take in several words at one fixation, there is no point in starting to read a line at the very beginning or waiting to stop until the very end. There is nothing to read in the white margins on either side; eye movement to the margin is wasted movement. You can use a faster-reading technique called *"indenting."*

A paragraph is indented to show its separation from the rest of the text. In other words, the first sentence starts a few spaces in from the margin. If the other end of the sentence were indented, it would stop a few spaces before the right margin. To use the "indenting" technique in reading, start reading each line about one-fourth inch in from the left margin and stop one-fourth inch short of the right margin. Guide lines have been placed on the following paragraph to show where your eyes should start and stop on each line. Read this paragraph "phrase by phrase," using the indenting technique.

Americans are not very good listeners in face-to-face groups, although hardy enough in front of microwaves. In general, they talk more than they listen. Competition in our culture puts a premium on self-expression, even if the individual has nothing to express. What he lacks in knowledge he can make up for by talking fast or by pounding the table. He takes a course in personality development, hoping to learn to "sell himself." How many of us while ostensibly silent are inwardly preparing a statement to stun the company when we get the floor—and so are not listening at all? Yet it really is not difficult to learn to listen, just unusual.

Notice how your eyes almost zigzag down the paragraph from line to line.

● In the following reading selection, guidelines have been placed on the first few pages. Read this selection as quickly as possible using the phrase-reading and indenting techniques. When the guide lines stop, continue indenting just as if they were there. Make a note of your reading rate when you have completed the selection, and then answer the ten comprehension questions which follow it. For practice, reread the passage several times until your eyes become accustomed to this new method of reading.

"Off to a Good Start" from Kon-Tiki

THOR HEYERDAHL

*Starting Time*_____

There was a bustle in Callao Harbor the day the *Kon-Tiki* was to be towed out to sea. The minister of marine had ordered the naval tug *Guardian Rios* to tow us out of the bay and cast us off clear of the coastal traffic, out where in times gone by the Indians used to lie fishing from their rafts. The papers had published the news under both red and black headlines, and there was a crowd of people down on the quays from early in the morning of April 28.

We six who were to assemble on board all had little things to do at the eleventh hour, and, when I came down to the quay, only Herman was there keeping guard over the raft. I intentionally stopped the car a long way off and walked the whole length of the mole to stretch my legs thoroughly for the last time for no one knew how long. I jumped on board the raft, which looked an utter chaos of banana clusters, fruit baskets, and sacks which had been hurled on board at the very last moment and were to be stowed and made fast. In the middle of the heap, Herman sat resignedly holding on to a cage with a green parrot in it, a farewell present from a friendly soul in Lima.

"Look after the parrot a minute," said Herman. "I must go ashore and have a last glass of beer. The tug won't be here for hours."

He had hardly disappeared among the swarm on the quay when people began to point and wave. And round the point at full speed came the tug *Guardian Rios*. She dropped anchor on the farther side of a waving forest of masts which blocked the way in to the *Kon-Tiki* and sent in a large motorboat to tow us out between the sailing craft. She was packed full of seamen, officers, and movie photographers, and, while orders rang out and cameras clicked, a stout towrope was made fast to the raft's bow.

"*Un momento*," I shouted in despair from where I sat with the parrot. "It's too early; we must wait for the others—*los expedicionarios*," I explained and pointed toward the city.

But nobody understood. The officers only smiled politely, and the knot at our bow was made fast in more than exemplary manner. I cast off the rope and flung it overboard with all manner of signs and gesticulations. The parrot utilized the opportunity afforded by all the confusion to stick its beak out of the cage and turn the knob of the door, and when I turned round it was strutting cheerfully about the bamboo deck. I tried to catch it, but it shrieked rudely in Spanish and fluttered away over the banana clusters. With one eye on the sailors who were trying to cast a rope over the bow, I started a wild chase after the parrot. It fled shrieking into the bamboo cabin, where I got it into a corner and caught it by one leg as it tried to flutter over me. When I came out again and stuffed my flapping trophy into its cage, the sailors on land had cast off the raft's moorings, and we were dancing helplessly in and out with the backwash of the long swell that came rolling in over the mole. In despair I seized a paddle and vainly tried to parry a violent bump as the raft was flung against the wooden piles of the quay. Then the motorboat started, and with a jerk the *Kon-Tiki* began her long voyage.

My only companion was a Spanish-speaking parrot which sat glaring sulkily in a cage. People on shore cheered and waved, and the swarthy movie photographers in the motorboat almost jumped into the sea in their eagerness to catch every detail of the expedition's dramatic start from Peru. Despairing and alone, I stood on the raft looking out for my lost companions, but none appeared. So we came out to the *Guardian Rios*, which was lying with steam up ready to lift anchor and start. I was up the rope ladder in a twinkling and made so much row on board that the start was postponed and a boat sent back to the quay. It was away a good while, and then it came back full of pretty *señoritas* but without a single one of the *Kon-Tiki*'s missing men. This was all very well but it did not solve my problems, and, while the raft swarmed with charming *señoritas*, the boat went back on a fresh search for *los expedicionarios noruegos*.

Meanwhile Erik and Bengt came sauntering down to the quay with their arms full of reading matter and odds and ends. They met the whole stream of people on its way home and were finally stopped at a police barrier by a kindly official who told them there was nothing more to see. Bengt told the officer, with an airy gesture of his cigar, that they had not come to see anything; they themselves were going with the raft.

"It's no use," the officer said indulgently. "The *Kon-Tiki* sailed an hour ago."

"Impossible," said Erik, producing a parcel. "Here's the lantern!"

"And there's the navigator," said Bengt, "and I'm the steward."

They forced their way past, but the raft had gone. They trotted desperately to and fro along the mole, where they met the rest of the party, who also were searching eagerly for the vanished raft. Then they caught sight of the boat coming in, and so we were all six finally united and the water was foaming round the raft as the *Guardian Rios* towed us out to sea.

It had been late in the afternoon when at last we started, and the *Guardian Rios* would not cast us off till we were clear of the coastal traffic next morning. Directly we were clear of the mole, we met a bit of a head sea, and all the small boats which were accompanying us turned back one by one. Only a few big yachts came with us out to the entrance to the bay to see how things would go out there.

The *Kon-Tiki* followed the tug like an angry billy goat on a rope, and she butted her bow into the head sea so that the water rushed on board. This did not look very promising, for this was a calm sea compared with what we had to expect. In the middle of the bay, the towrope broke, and our end of it sank peacefully to the bottom while the tug steamed ahead. We flung ourselves down along the side of the raft to fish for the end of the rope, while the yachts went on and tried to stop the tug. Stinging jellyfish as thick as washtubs splashed up and down with the seas alongside the raft and covered all the ropes with a slippery, stinging coating of jelly. When the raft rolled one way, we hung flat over the side waving our arms down toward the surface of the water, until our fingers just touched the slimy towrope. Then the raft rolled back again, and we all stuck our heads deep down into the sea, while salt water and giant jellyfish poured over our backs. We spat and cursed and pulled jellyfish fibers out of our hair, but when the tug came back, the rope end was up and ready for splicing.

*Finishing Time*_____

● In your notebook, write the letter of the correct answer.

1. The *Kon-Tiki* started its journey from Callao Harbor in (**a**) April, (**b**) May, (**c**) July, (**d**) August.

2. The crew became separated because (**a**) some of them arrived late, (**b**) the towline broke, (**c**) Heyerdahl didn't speak Spanish, (**d**) the newsmen couldn't wait for them all.

3. The *Kon-Tiki* carried a crew of (**a**) four, (**b**) six, (**c**) eight, (**d**) three.

4. The *Guardian Rios* was a (**a**) yacht, (**b**) naval tug, (**c**) coast guard cutter, (**d**) Spanish sloop.

5. The parrot spoke (**a**) English, (**b**) Portuguese, (**c**) Spanish, (**d**) Spanish and English.

6. Callao Harbor is in (**a**) Tahiti, (**b**) Chile, (**c**) Peru, (**d**) Spain.

7. It would seem that most of the raft was constructed of (**a**) bamboo, (**b**) wooden piles, (**c**) driftwood, (**d**) metal.

8. *Kon-Tiki*'s missing men were prevented from going onto the quay by (**a**) señoritas, (**b**) a policeman, (**c**) newsmen, (**d**) naval officials.

9. The parrot is important to the story because (**a**) Heyerdahl was busy chasing it when the men released the raft from shore, (**b**) it would be company for the long voyage, (**c**) it escaped by itself, (**d**) Herman had owned it for a long time.

10. The men stuck their heads in the water (**a**) to look for the towrope, (**b**) accidentally, because of the roll of the raft, (**c**) to look for jellyfish, (**d**) to keep the raft right side up.

Step 16. Self-Pacing

The most important thing to know about faster reading skills once you have learned *how* to use them is *when* to use them. As we said earlier, you would not read a Shakespearean play or poetry at your fastest or even middle reading rate; you would read it slowly word-by-word to savor the words and to absorb the implied and unfamiliar meanings. On the other hand, you would not read a light mystery at your slowest word-by-word reading rate; you would read it quickly, looking for key words and phrases, your purpose being to pick up the setting, characters, and developing plot. Two things will determine the reading rate you bring to bear on the material you have at hand: purpose and difficulty.

Purpose. If you are reading for relaxation and need only to understand what is happening at the moment, you may read at a fast reading rate. If your purpose in reading is to prepare for an examination in a certain subject or to gather facts for a book report, you will read more slowly and carefully, possibly even making notes as you go along. Determine what your purpose is before you start.

Difficulty. If you are reading a simple article or book which does not contain hidden meanings, complicated writing, or a difficult vocabulary, again you may read quickly. If you are reading a complicated text which is difficult to understand, you have to read slowly. If you do not know how difficult a piece of material is going to be, preview-read it first. That is, read the first couple of paragraphs thoroughly, the first or topic sentences of several more paragraphs, and then the summary two or three paragraphs at the end. From this preview you should be able to decide what reading rate to use for the entire article or book.

● Following is another article designed to give you practice with rapid-reading skills. As you read the article, focus slightly above the line, not directly on it, remember to indent, and let your eyes move from word group to word group. Push yourself to a faster reading rate than you used before. Jot down the time when you begin reading and when you finish. Figure your reading rate on the chart at the end, and compare it with your earlier rate. Since comprehension is most important, carefully answer the ten questions which follow the article. Seven out of ten answers correct is considered adequate.

**Harmless
or
Deadly?**

OSMOND P. BRELAND

Starting Time――――

Many persons are intensely afraid of all spiders. Actually there are not many that are dangerous to human life, although the bites of several may cause local pain. The two spiders in the United States with the most evil reputation are the black widow and the tarantula. As for the big, hairy, fearsome-looking trantulas, a bite from one of them has never, so far as is known, caused death to a human being. People who have been bitten describe the effects as being comparable to those suffered from a bee sting.

But the black widow is a different matter, and there have been authentic cases of death from the bite of this spider. Black widow spiders have been reported from all the states of the United States, and their relatives, most of which are dangerous, occur in many other parts of the world. Old people and young children are most likely to die from the bite, but even healthy young adults must look upon these creatures with respect.

The black widow is easy to identify. It is of medium size with a coal-black body and a red or orange spot on its tummy shaped like an hourglass. It builds its web under rocks and in piles of wood, and it may sometimes be found in outhouses. It is not an aggressive creature, and most of its bites occur when a person accidentally bumps into the web. The spider feels the web vibrate, rushes out to capture an insect, and bites the first thing it encounters.

There is also a spider in Australia whose bite has been known to cause death. This is a large black species called a funnel-web spider. One or two other spiders of South America and certain other areas are rated dangerous by some scientists. But even on a worldwide basis, the number of spiders that are dangerous to human life is very small as compared with the number of kinds of spiders known.

The stinging apparatus of a scorpion is at the end of its elongated abdomen or tail. The scorpion uses it to kill insects for food, and with proper provocation, the creature is not adverse to testing its penetrating power on human anatomy. The most feared scorpion in the Western Hemisphere is the infamous Durango scorpion found in the state of Durango, Mexico, and adjacent areas. Its evil reputation is well earned. A young, healthy grown person has been known to die within less than an hour from the sting of one of these scorpions. Approximately 1,600 deaths in Durango over a period of some 35 years have been ascribed to these creatures. A dangerous species of scorpions also occurs in Trinidad, North Africa, Malaya, India, and other tropical regions. One of the most dangerous is an Egyptian form, which is reported to have a mortality of over 50 percent among young children.

Southern Arizona is the only region in the United States where deadly scorpions can be encountered in normal routine. Here some two dozen deaths have been recorded; all the victims were young children. These scorpions are relatives of the still more deadly Durango species, and we can be thankful that the creatures have not spread throughout the country. The sting of most scorpions in the United States is usually no more serious than that of a bee or wasp. Yet in 1945 a man in central Texas was killed by a scorpion sting. He was attended by a reputable physician, and there is no reason to doubt this report. This man must have been especially susceptible to the venom, and the case illustrates the dangers of minimizing the possible effects of even supposedly harmless species.

Centipedes are long, many-legged creatures that run with considerable rapidity. Under the head is a pair of strong jaws connected with poison glands. Tropical species are said sometimes to exceed a foot in length, and in the southwestern United States there is a big blue fellow with yellow legs and an orange-colored head that attains a length of 8 inches. There are probably more old wives' tales about centipedes than about any of the other creatures we have discussed. Favorite ones include the belief that the bite is invariably fatal and the report that the flesh will drop from the spot over which a centipede crawled. There has never been an authentic case of death from centipede bite. The bite of some species is painful, and there are some reports of hospitalization for centipede bites, but established fatalities are absent.

Many bites and stings from spiders, centipedes, and scorpions occur when the creatures creep into shoes and clothing that are not being worn. It is a wise man in tropical and subtropical areas who develops the habit of thoroughly shaking his shoes and clothing before putting them on.

A consideration of creatures that bite and sting would hardly be complete without a brief reference to a few stinging insects such as ants, bees, and wasps. Some authorities have estimated that it would require approximately 500 honeybee stings to cause death to a person not especially susceptible to the venom. But some people are far more sensitive than this. In fact, instances are known of death from a single honeybee sting. This is the result of an allergic reaction and is exceedingly rare. A particularly potent hornet hails from Thailand and adjacent regions. One physician states that a patient of his collapsed from from three stings, and five stings are said to be usually fatal.

The lethal properties of a marching horde of African army

ants are well known. When native villages are invaded, the inhabitants simply move out until the ants have cleaned out the vermin population and gone elsewhere. Many ants have very painful bites and stings, but first place should probably be awarded to a large black fellow, an inch and a half long, found in Central and South America. The insects are quite pugnacious and not at all hesitant about attacking anything that disturbs them, no matter how large. Deaths from the stings of these ants have not been noted, but in a person especially sensitive to the venom, the results could be quite serious and possibly fatal.

Finishing Time _____

● In your notebook, write the letter of the correct answer.

1. The name of the most deadly scorpion is (**a**) Albuquerque, (**b**) Deadwood, (**c**) Durango, (**d**) Gonzales.

2. The number of deaths recorded from the bite of a tarantula is (**a**) 5, (**b**) 10, (**c**) 15, (**d**) none.

3. When army ants invade a village in Africa, the natives (**a**) poison them, (**b**) move out until they leave, (**c**) eat them, (**d**) fight them furiously.

4. Although the average person would require about 500 honeybee stings to cause death, cases are on record where human beings have died from as few as (**a**) a few stings, (**b**) a dozen stings, (**c**) a hundred stings, (**d**) one sting.

5. The black widow has been found in (**a**) 20 states, (**b**) all the United States, (**c**) 30 states, (**d**) 5 states.

6. How many people have died in 35 years from the bite of the most deadly scorpion? (**a**) 10,050, (**b**) 1,600, (**c**) 2,400, (**d**) 5,500.

7. The scorpion is dangerous because of its (**a**) bite, (**b**) sting, (**c**) poison flesh, (**d**) spines.

8. Some centipedes in the tropics grow to a length of (**a**) a foot, (**b**) 6 inches, (**c**) 2 feet, (**d**) 3 inches.

9. Normally, in what state are scorpions most likely to be met? (**a**) Colorado, (**b**) Texas, (**c**) New Mexico, (**d**) Arizona.

10. In this selection the author seems to be most concerned with (**a**) giving facts about poisonous creatures, (**b**) stirring up fear in the reader, (**c**) telling stories that are not true, (**d**) doing all of the above.

● *Follow-up.* Every day or two, pick up an easy book or magazine article and read a few pages at your top reading rate for exactly ten minutes. Take an average word count of one page (multiply the average number of words in a line by the number of lines on the page), multiply it by the number of pages read, and divide by 10. This is your reading speed. Practice is the key. Practice!

ANSWER KEY TO UNIT THREE

Step 15

1. (a)   2. (c)   3. (b)   4. (b)   5. (c)   6. (c)   7. (a)   8. (b)   9. (a)
10. (b)

Step 16

1. (c)   2. (d)   3. (b)   4. (d)   5. (b)   6. (b)   7. (b)   8. (a)   9. (d)
10. (a)

UNIT FOUR

STUDY SKILLS

IMPROVING STUDY HABITS

The most important reading you do now is for your school assignments. How well you read them, how much you understand them, and how long you remember them are dependent on efficient study habits.

Organization of study time is of primary importance. It should be easy to determine how much time each assignment will take by using the preview reading technique discussed in this last unit. Also you will gauge your time according to your purpose in studying—for review, for an exam, for research, and so forth.

The following steps will help you get more out of your study time by showing you how to survey your assignments. They will show you how to ask questions, how to anticipate answers, how to determine your purpose; in short, they will help you to become a more involved reader, *an active reader.* An active reader reads more effectively, comprehends more easily, retains material longer, and is able to recite information more readily. All of these skills dovetail to make you a more effective student.

Step 17.   Preview Reading

Preview reading is as important as looking at a road map before taking a trip or figuring out probable expenses before beginning a vacation. Planning is part of your everyday life; you do it all the time. When you get up in the morning, you plan some sort of routine for the day. You divide your time into rough segments for eating, getting dressed, watching TV, studying, and sleeping. When you plan your study time, you decide how much time to give to each subject by estimating the amount of work it requires. Why, then, shouldn't you plan your reading time by looking ahead, by determining your purpose and foreseeing probable difficulties?

Preview reading serves two purposes: it saves time and it prepares you so that unexpected snags don't take you by surprise.

It saves time by telling you when an article is

1. no help and may be skipped.

2. some help and may be skimmed rather than read.

3. too technical or difficult and may require further background reading.

4. very helpful and should be read thoroughly. (In the last case the survey has prepared you to understand and read the article more quickly.)

It protects you from surprises by

1. showing you exactly how difficult the reading will be.

2. raising questions in your mind that you can expect to answer by reading.

3. helping you to become involved, thus improving your concentration.

You can use the preview reading technique on an article, a chapter, or even a complete book. It is especially useful when applied to your required school assignments.

Here are the four steps to preview reading:

1. Read the chapter or article heading and all subheads.

2. Read the first paragraph (or two) which introduces the subject.

3. Read the first sentence (more if you think necessary) of all other paragraphs.

4. Read the final one or two summary paragraphs.

If you are using your other reading skills, this procedure should not take you more than two or three minutes for most articles or chapters. After you have made your preview, decide what your purpose is in reading the article and how difficult the material is going to be. This will help you to determine how fast you are going to read.

Ask questions of the article or chapter as you read it. Sometimes it is possible to turn the first sentence of a paragraph into a question. Jot down some of the questions that occur to you: Who are the characters? What is the point of this article? What am I going to be expected to learn from it? Why did the author write it? What is he trying to prove? Is this article based mainly on fact or on the author's opinion? When you read the article thoroughly, you will find that you are more involved because you are looking for the answers to these questions. You will be able to concentrate better because you are an active reader!

● The following nonfiction article has been set up especially for preview reading. Everything that is put in boldface type (dark type) is to be read as part of the surveying method outlined above. Read the headings and boldface type as quickly as possible. It should not take you more than sixty seconds. Following the exercise are four general questions which you would normally ask yourself after surveying an article of this type. Quickly write the correct answers in your notebook and then reread the article thoroughly. When you have finished the second reading, record your reading rate (it should be faster than previous exercises because you have the advantage of the survey), and answer the more detailed comprehension questions (5–10).

"Safety from Fire" from You and Science

PAUL BRANDWEIN AND OTHERS

If it is important to make your home a comfortable place in which to live, it is even more important to make it a safe place in which to live. There are many hazards to safety in a house, but the most dangerous is fire. Let us see how fire protection can be built into a house.

Building in fire protection

The framework for the walls of houses is usually studs, which are pieces of wood 2 x 4 inches placed upright 12 to 16 inches apart. To the outer side of the studding, the boards of the outside wall are nailed. The material of which the inner wall is made is nailed to the inner side of the studs. This leaves an air space between the inside and outside walls. This space may be left empty or filled with insulating material. Why will filling this space with a material like rock wool, which will not burn, keep a fire from spreading quickly? Brick or poured concrete fire stops at each floor level also slow or stop the spread of fire from one floor to another.

As good as it is to prevent a fire from spreading rapidly, it is even better to prevent it from starting. This can be done by getting rid of the fire hazards in your home.

Getting rid of fire hazards

Strange as it may seem, many people burn down their houses while trying to keep the house warm. Of course, they do not mean to do so when they start a fire in a fireplace or furnace. Any fireplace or furnace is supposed to burn fuels safely. However, chimneys, flues, and furnaces may have cracks that need repairs. Sparks from burning fuel may reach parts of the house that will burn. Before a furnace or fireplace is used, chimneys should be inspected, and cleaned if necessary. Sometimes people forget to put a fire screen around a fire in a fireplace, and sparks perhaps pop out on a wooden floor, rugs, or a sofa. These sparks may smolder for some time and then suddenly burst into flame.

Sometimes furnaces and stoves are placed too close to walls that will burn if they become overheated. A sheet of metal placed upright behind the hot stove is helpful. It will carry away enough of the heat and give protection to the walls.

Cleaning cloths, newspapers, and curtains should be kept away from gas heaters, oil burners, electric heaters, and stoves. Matches should be kept out of reach of children. Have you checked all the places in your home where a fire might start or spread quickly? If not, let that be your job for tonight. Do something about any conditions which need correcting.

Fires which start themselves

Sometimes fires start without anyone's lighting them. Such fires are caused by *spontaneous combustion* or *spontaneous ignition*. In spontaneous combustion, a material suddenly bursts into flame. How does this happen? The answer lies in knowing the causes of fire.

A fire must have fuel, oxygen, and heat. The fuel may be anything that will burn. The oxygen is in the air. You may think that if there is no flame or heat nearby there cannot be a fire. This is not true. Some things, like damp hay, a pile of damp newspapers, drying paint rags, or oilsoaked rags, combine slowly with the oxygen of the air and in so doing become warm enough to start burning. This slow oxidation is especially dangerous if materials are stored where air does not circulate. The heat of slow oxidation builds up, and the materials start to burn. Carelessness in storing materials of this kind causes much property damage and loss of lives every year.

Putting out a fire at home

Even with the best of care, you may be unable to prevent a fire in your home. To be safe, you and your family must be ready to act quickly. If the fire is small, you may be able to put it out before it can spread.

You have learned there are three things a fire needs. And there are three ways to put out a fire. First, you can separate the fuel from the fire. For example, you might throw a burning pillow out of the window so it could not set fire to anything else in the house.

Second, you can shut off the oxygen supply. This would happen if you dropped a pot cover onto a pan of burning fat. Third, you can lower the temperature of the fuel below its *kindling temperature*. The kindling temperature is the lowest point at which a fuel will burn. Pouring water on most fuels will do this. Water will also shut off the supply of oxygen. **To put out a fire you need to do only one of these three things: remove the fuel, remove the oxygen, or lower the temperature. A fire extinguisher does one or more of these things. It is well to have one at home. Keep it where you can easily get at it if you need it.**

1. A rapid survey of this article shows that it is about (**a**) how to prevent forest fires, (**b**) the fire department, (**c**) fire prevention and safety in the home, (**d**) fire prevention and safety in schools.

2. One way to *prevent* fires is to (**a**) use spontaneous combustion, (**b**) get rid of fire hazards, (**c**) use fire extinguishers, (**d**) shut off the oxygen supply.

3. If you were going to read this article for the first time for a five-minute quiz, you would (**a**) scan it, (**b**) read it five times, (**c**) read one word at a time, (**d**) read it slowly and carefully.

4. From your preview reading, which one of the following questions will not be answered in this article? (**a**) How are fire extinguishers made? (**b**) What is spontaneous combustion? (**c**) How can fires at home be put out? (**d**) What are some common fire hazards?

● Go back and read the article carefully. In your notebook, write the exact words that complete each statement.

5. Many fires start in a _____ or _____ while people are trying to heat their homes.

6. _____ must be kept out of the reach of children.

7. Fires that start without anybody's lighting them are caused by _____.

8. In order to burn, a fire needs three things: _____, _____, and _____.

9. Three ways to put out a fire are: separate the _____ from the fire; shut off the _____ supply; lower the _____ of the fuel.

10. The _____ is the lowest temperature at which a fuel will burn.

Step 18. The Three R's

Rereading, Recitation, and Review

In the last step you were shown how to survey any new article or book chapter, how to ask questions to help you concentrate better and to become more involved, and how to determine a reading rate suitable to your reading purpose. Although all of these techniques are necessary if you are going to get the most from your reading, you need other skills if you are going to *retain* the important information for examinations.

Rereading. Repetition is still the best way to set something in your mind—*if* you concentrate and are selective about it. It is very seldom necessary to reread everything, yet many students waste hours rereading what they already know or what they will not need. Rereading to set facts, dates, or ideas in your mind for a test should depend on what you have discovered in the first survey and thorough reading. Probably you have already read the important points twice if you have followed the survey technique carefully; still there are often details and ideas which occur in the body of the article that are important.

If you know that the material you are reading is important for a test, keep a pencil handy. Devise your own method of marking points which you should go back to reread. A couple of vertical lines next to important sentences or paragraphs is one method. You may carry this system further by drawing a single line or making a check mark next to less important passages that should be reread. Even if the book is not yours, light pencil marks that can easily be erased will be enough to lead you back to important points in a rereading.

Reread quickly, *skipping* all of the irrelevant passages that you know are of no importance. The inclination is to read everything to play it safe. Nine times out of ten, your original hunch will be right, so skip what you feel is unimportant.

Read again those passages you have marked off. The best way to remember them is to copy them into your notebook *in your own words*. The process of rephrasing what the author has written into other words helps you to remember a great deal more than if you simply copy word-for-word what the author has said.

Recitation. Recitation, whether oral or written, should be clear, concise, and to the point. This section is not supposed to give hints for better writing habits, but if you read well and note only the most important ideas, you should be able to recall them when they are needed. Long, wordy answers to questions regarding what you have read do not deceive the instructor. Usually he has had years of experience and knows that wordy answers often cover up insecure knowledge of the subject matter.

Another aid to recitation is to stop from time to time in your rereading to make your own mental summary of the author's words. It helps both your retention of the material and your ability to further consolidate what the author may take too many words to say.

Review. Besides rereading, which is a form of review, there are many other worthwhile ways to review for a test.

1. Keep all tests and, immediately after you get them back, write in the correct answers of questions which you missed.

2. Look over the tests to check your retention of questions that may be asked again.

3. Review your notes, but don't waste time reviewing notes you know you know! Concentrate on sections you are still unsure of.

4. Review all text material with emphasis on marginal notes and signals of important passages. Again reread *only* those highlighted passages.

5. Plan your review time. Don't wait until the night before the test. Before reading a new chapter in your text, review the important passages in the preceding chapter or chapters. Divide your final review days for a test into easy sections, saving the final night for a combination review of all sections.

If you follow these easy steps and concentrate *only* on what you do *not* know or are unsure of, you will be able to approach the examination with confidence.

There is no specific exercise for this step. Put these suggestions to use when studying any or all of your subjects. Start now to develop confidence in yourself by previewing, questioning, rereading, reciting, and reviewing. If you do all of these things well, you will be able to study more effectively in less time.

In Summary

In the last few pages you have read about and practiced a variety of skills intended to help you understand more of what you read in less time and to make more effective use of your study time.

You will have noticed that all of these skills are interrelated in one way or another. Faster reading techniques help you to understand and concentrate better; comprehension techniques help you to read faster.

It is a good feeling to be in control in any situation. A basketball player feels this control when he has the other team sized up, knows the court, gauges the weaknesses and strengths of his own team, and can move in strongly with confidence and enjoyment in the game. An actor knows no greater pleasure than to be on stage in a good play with a good cast and a responsive audience all working together to make a powerful theatrical experience. A skilled reader can enjoy reading, because he has streamlined reading techniques at his fingertips. He knows when to read fast and when to read more slowly; how to get the meaning from words, sentences, paragraphs, and full articles with a minimum of effort and time; how to study without overstudying; and how to simply sit back and enjoy reading for its own sake.

We hope that the skills you have studied in these pages will have started you on the way to becoming this kind of reader. If so, you have a lifetime of pleasure ahead of you, because there is a lifetime of reading awaiting you. The important thing is not to let these skills stop here. Continue to practice them on all of your reading until they become firmly established habits.

ANSWER KEY TO UNIT FOUR

Step 17

1. (c) 2. (b) 3. (a) 4. (a) 5. fireplace, furnace 6. Matches 7. spontaneous combustion 8. fuel, oxygen, heat 9. fuel, oxygen, temperature 10. kindling temperature

COMPOSITION SKILLS SUPPLEMENT

Reading, speaking, listening, and writing are the four communication skills. You have read in this volume many stories, essays, excerpts from biographies, and poems. Perhaps you have talked about them, sharing your reactions with your classmates. At first you have probably liked some of them very much; others may not have appealed to you. If you have expressed your opinions freely and have listened attentively to the ideas of your teacher and classmates, you have a basis for arriving at a final judgment. It might be interesting to consider *why* you as an individual like or dislike what you read or hear.

Of the four communication skills, writing is the most demanding, since what one sees in writing is more likely to be criticized than what one hears in speaking. Only through frequent practice will you gain skill in putting your ideas across. Doing the exercises in the following units should develop your ability to write.

There is no direct relationship between the units in this Composition Skills Supplement and the units in the main text of this book. Although quotations are taken from various selections throughout the book, it is not necessary to have read any particular selection or unit in the book before tackling any unit in the Supplement. Units in the Composition Skills Supplement, however, must be taken in order, as they constitute a closely integrated program.

UNIT ONE

A TRIAL RUN

Personal experience provides a good springboard for expressing yourself in writing. Most of you occasionally go to the movies, see TV programs, listen to music, and engage in sports, either as members of a team or as spectators. Perhaps one of these activities appeals to you more than the others. Some of you may have been impressed by a character in a story that you have read in this book or by a person you have met in real life.

● Practice. Try your hand at writing a short theme, using one of the topics listed below:

A Good Movie Is Not a Waste of Time
Watching TV Is Educational
Baseball (or Football) Is Boring
Modern Music Does Make Sense
Meeting _____ Was an Exciting Experience

Before you start writing, *think* of what you know about each of these topics. Which one of them offers you the best opportunity to write easily? Remember that every piece of writing—paragraph, short theme, long essay—should have a *b*eginning, a *d*evelopment, and an *e*nd (BDE). After you have finished this first short theme, read it carefully to see that you have followed these simple suggestions.

UNIT TWO

ORIGINAL, VIVID SENTENCES

The first unit gave you a chance to write a short theme using one of several suggested topics. It gave both you and your teacher an opportunity to see what you can do—to judge where you stand.

To improve your themes, first consider sentences. Of course, words together make sentences, which can be dull and unappealing or vivid and lively, depending on how carefully you compose them. You should recognize that although nouns are important, verbs, adjectives, and adverbs are generally the successful writer's chief concern. A strong, clear, effective sentence is a fine achievement; you can learn to write such sentences.

Lesson 1. Effective Sentences

The opening paragraph of Daniel de Paola's "The Returning" (page 5) illustrates how effectively both words and sentences can be used to capture the interest of the reader.

It was the only house he had seen in three days; it nestled at the base of the foothills which led to the Mexican border. For a long time he sat in the brush and wondered whether he should chance it. His throat was so dry he couldn't swallow, his mouth and lips were sore from lack of water, and he felt that if he didn't get some kind of food in his stomach soon, it wouldn't make any difference whether he made the border or not.

• Practice A.

1. What in the first sentence tells us that the man has been traveling? What tells us that he is in sparsely settled territory? What suggests that he is heading for Mexico?

2. What tells us that it might be dangerous for the man to go to the house he has seen?

3. What words does the author use to let us know that the man is thirsty? that he is hungry? that he is close to death?

The author of "The Returning" tries to capture our interest by showing us a man in trouble and making us wonder whether he will make it to safety. James Thurber, in "The Night the Ghost Got In" (page 33) uses a different approach:

> The ghost that got into our house on the night of November 17, 1915, raised such a hullabaloo of misunderstanding that I am sorry I didn't just let it keep on walking, and go to bed. Its advent caused my mother to throw a shoe through a window of the house next door and ended up with my grandfather shooting a patrolman. I am sorry, therefore, as I have said, that I ever paid any attention to the footsteps.

● Practice B.

1. A ghost is usually imagined to arouse terror in the people who see it. What phrase in the first sentence suggests that Thurber's attitude toward ghosts is unusual?

2. Some writers create suspense by making you wonder what is going to happen. In this story, however, Thurber tells you at least two things that are going to happen—his mother is going to throw a shoe through someone's window, and his grandfather is going to shoot a patrolman. How does this create suspense?

3. In the third sentence of this paragraph, Thurber repeats a remark he had already made in the first sentence. Is this a violation of the principle that a good writer uses as few words as possible?

● Practice C. Thurber invites his reader's attention by promising to amuse him. The opening of "The Returning" is an invitation to adventure and possible danger. Thurber holds the reader, as you have seen, by telling him what will happen; de Paola holds the reader by making him want to know what will happen.

1. In an effective opening sentence the author often tells the reader where and when the action occurs. How does Thurber do this? How does de Paola do it? Keeping in mind the kind of story each author is telling, why do you think each chooses the method he does?

2. In both passages a house is mentioned. Neither house is described in much detail until later in the story. Why? What details does each author add in his first paragraph?

3. In fiction the author usually tries to establish sympathy for the main character early in his story. If the reader doesn't care what happens to that character, he probably won't finish the story. Choose one of these opening paragraphs, and explain why you do or do not feel sympathy for the character introduced.

Lesson 2. Strong Sentences

As we have seen, well-constructed sentences are composed of words so skillfully chosen that they convey vivid impressions.

● Practice A. In each of the following sentences, select the *one* of the three words in parentheses which is the best choice to make these sentences strong and colorful.

1. A (fine, pretty, glittering) (bunch, array, group) of jewels was (displayed, placed, seen) in the shop window.

2. (Quickly, Suddenly, Eagerly) the thief (looked at, inspected, explored) them.

3. (Turning, Looking, Peering) quickly to right and left, he (damaged, broke, smashed) the glass and reached in.

4. Without considering the consequences, he (took, grabbed, caught) a handful and (put, pressed, stuffed) them into his pocket.

5. Then he felt a gun (shoved, placed, pushed) against his back, as a (weak, harsh, thin) voice (stated, said, shouted), "(Drop, Release, Reject) them and (lift, stick up, elevate) your hands."

Now that you have chosen the most appropriate words, copy these completed sentences. Compare your sentences with your classmates' and discuss them with the class and your teacher.

● Practice B. The following paragraph from Alex Gaby's story "Terror on the Highway" (page 11) is an example of how the use of sentence variety expresses changing action. Note how the author uses strong words and strong sentences to bring the story to a highly charged climax. Good writers are sensitive to strong words—words that express the exact shade of meaning and feeling they want to convey. The are also sensitive to the rhythm of a paragraph. They carefully pace the action by combining direct simple sentences with more involved complex sentences.

> The red car. He saw that the hood of it was wrenched loose, and he yanked it open. There it was—the bright chrome of the air scoops, the special milled head, the four-barrel carburetors— all of it that gave the red car its special life. He began to hammer at these things with the jack handle until it was a jagged, broken mess under the hood, and the jack handle was bent in his hand, and then the rest of the anger left him. (page 23)

1. The first sentence is, technically, not a sentence at all, as there is no verb. What is the effect of the words "The red car" standing by themselves?

2. The second sentence is compound-complex. What are the subject and predicate of the two main clauses?

3. Notice how carefully the author of this paragraph chooses his words. For example, in the second sentence he could have said, "He saw that the hood of it was loose and he opened it." What words does he use to add force to the sentence?

4. How does the author use specific concrete detail throughout the paragraph to make the scene real for the reader?

● Practice C. Now you are ready to try writing your own sentences. Arrange them in logical order with each one following naturally after the other. Choose your words carefully and vary your sentences in both length and arrangement. Use as a model the sentences we have just examined in the paragraph above.

1. Use the following sentences as a point of departure for writing several *original,* complete sentences—simple, compound, and complex.

"Oh, that was a day! Never will I have such another."

2. The quotation above is taken from Dorothy Canfield Fisher's story, "The Heyday of the Blood." Turn to page 327 to see how she uses sentences to make a paragraph. Compare your own work with her writing and with that of your classmates.

UNIT THREE

PARAGRAPHS

In the last practice of the unit on sentences (Practice C), you were actually writing a short paragraph. What is a paragraph?

A paragraph is a group of related sentences developing *one* topic or *one* point of view. Like all good pieces of writing, the conventional paragraph has a *beginning,* a *development,* and a logical *end* (BDE), the end frequently taking the form of a concluding or summary sentence.

Lesson 1. The Topic Sentence

The topic sentence states or strongly implies the subject of the paragraph. Often it is the first sentence. Study the following paragraph taken from "Sam Houston: Lone Star" (page 95)

All but unexplored, this realm of "Tejas" was larger than any European country except Russia. One flank of it was washed by the Gulf, where the commerce of the world would come, another by the coiling snake of the Rio Grande; with one outstretched arm it touched the sea-voiced resinous pine belt in the east, and with the other reached to the ultimate desert ranges. Carpeted with blue-bonnets, arched over by a taut sky, this seems a land designed from Creation for hoof-beats and flying-fields, for longhorns and long trains calling a cry like homesickness for Texas, as they bear away the cotton and the corn, the lumber or the fruit, the cattle and the wheat, from the Blacklands and the Redlands, the Big Thicket or the Big Bend, the Panhandle or the Valley, the Grand Prairie or the Cross Timbers. Not yet did any man guess what Texas was to bring America, with the greatest oil fields in the world, superabundance of natural gas, and nearly half the world's output of helium, with un-tapped supplies of coal, deposits of sulfur, iron, asphalt, potash, copper, silver, lead, mercury, tungsten, uranium, and titanium. But to Texas came at last a man big enough for her.

● Practice A.

1. What *one* point of view does the opening sentence establish?

2. What *details* are used to develop the topic sentence? List several.

3. How does the final or end sentence play an important part in determining the effectiveness of this paragraph? Explain.

● Practice B. You may have noticed that the paragraph above is de-veloped by using details or examples. Select *one* of the following topic sentences and develop it by details or examples.

1. My home town is a pleasant place to live.

2. My girl friend (or boy friend) is a real doll (or a great guy).

3. My mother doesn't appreciate my friends.

4. Some dogs think they are human.

Lesson 2. Coherence

According to the dictionary, coherence concerns a logical arrange-ment of ideas—"a sticking together." You may make a paragraph co-herent by using carefully chosen words or phrases to connect sentences. Here are several groups of words used to connect.

To emphasize or to supply an additional idea:

also	in addition to	moreover
and	in fact	similarly

To contrast an idea to another already expressed:

although	however	on the contrary
but	nevertheless	yet

To express time:

| afterwards | eventually | sometimes |
| at length | meanwhile | usually |

To introduce a strong conclusion:

| as a result | finally | therefore |
| consequently | hence | thus |

● Practice A. Read carefully this paragraph from "John Paul Jones" (page 81).

> Although Jones was more than willing to fight, even he (quite rightly) insisted on his share of the prize money when he did happen to capture merchant ships. In fact, as Morison relates, he spent a large part of his time ashore trying to collect what was coming to him and his crew. Usually it took him a long time to get it. Histories of the Continental Navy are full of disputes over prize money, which was the main motivating force for seafaring men in those days.

1. How many of the sentences begin with a connecting word or phrase?

2. Explain the purpose of each connecting word or phrase.

3. Substitute other connectives for those used in the paragraph above. Are they equally good?

● Practice B. Now that you are familiar with the use of connecting words, consider how you can improve the paragraph you wrote for Lesson 1, Practice B, by introducing connectives.

Lesson 3. The Narrative

The paragraphs we have discussed so far have been developed by *detail* or *example*. A paragraph may also be developed from a topic sentence by telling an anecdote, which is a short *narrative* of an interesting or entertaining nature. Read carefully the following illustration taken from "Leontyne Price" (page 301):

> I also remember something that was funny. Wait till you hear this. I remember I had everything thought out in *Aïda*. I said to myself, "I can't go wrong. This'll be the first time I've ever been out on a stage for this kind of thing," and let's face it, my skin was in my favor for a change. "I got that made, I can't lose! There's nothing to worry about. OK, fine: Molinari-Pradelli is not a heavy-handed conductor; I will be heard. The only thing I don't know is exactly— well—if I get on the wrong side of the stage, I *get* on the wrong side

of the stage. I can't go wrong. When the Ethiopian slaves come in, I will just go where they go; and with Robert Merrill, the Amonasro, I'll just go with him." But I couldn't figure out where the tomb was going to be. So I kept walking up to the director, during the night, you know, between the acts, and I kept saying, "Maestro, where . . .?" but he acted as if he wasn't listening and said, "You were wonderful, you are beautiful tonight, and you just go change the costume and it's going to be fine." Finally I said, "I have a question to ask you: Where is the tomb? Where am I going to die? I don't have the slightest idea where I am going to die!" And he broke up with laughter. Well, I did find the tomb.

- Practice A.

   1. Which one of the first three sentences really presents the topic? Why do you choose this particular sentence?

   2. How many connecting words do you find in this paragraph? List them.

   3. If you find this anecdote "funny," try to explain why it is entertaining. The chatty style in which it is written contributes humor. What else makes it amusing?

   4. Is the last sentence effective as a conclusion? Why, or why not?

- Practice B. Write an original paragraph which illustrates this method of narration. Don't overlook connecting words or phrases. You might use one of the following topics, or you may prefer to create your own in writing a topic sentence for an anecdote:

   > The Day I Just Missed the Bus
   > The Class Joker
   > A Freak Accident
   > How I Got My Revenge
   > The Hazards of School Politics

   Don't forget a concluding sentence.

Lesson 4. The Argument

A third way to develop a paragraph is to supply arguments or reasons for doing something. The following paragraph from "The First Inaugural Address," by Abraham Lincoln, illustrates this method (page 454).

Note: This selection is an excerpt from Lincoln's plea for national unity (March 4, 1861) at the time when the Southern states were threatening to secede and form their own Confederacy.

My countrymen, one and all, think calmly and well upon this whole subject. Nothing valuable can be lost by taking time. If there be an object to hurry any of you in hot haste to a step which you would never take deliberately, that object will be frustrated by taking time; but no good object can be frustrated by it. Such of you as are now dissatisfied still have the old Constitution unimpaired, and on the sensitive point, the laws of your own framing under it; while the new administration will have no immediate power, if it would, to change either. If it were admitted that you who are dissatisfied hold the right side in this dispute, there is still no single good reason for precipitate action. Intelligence, patriotism, Christianity, and a firm reliance on Him who has never yet forsaken this favored land are still competent to adjust in the best way all our present difficulty. In your hands, my dissatisfied fellow countrymen, and not in mine, are the momentous issues of civil war. The government will not assail you. You can have no conflict without being yourselves the aggressors. You have no oath registered in heaven to destroy the government, while I shall have the most solemn one to "preserve, protect, and defend" it.

● Practice A.

1. What one reason does Lincoln emphasize in the first half of this paragraph? Find at least three sentences in which this reason appears.

2. What other reasons does he give in the second half of this paragraph as to why his countrymen should "think calmly and well upon this whole subject"?

3. What relationship do you find between the topic sentence and the last sentence? Is the concluding sentence a logical end to the reasoning in this paragraph? Explain.

● Practice B. Write an original paragraph in which you argue for or against some question important to you. Try to arrange your ideas so that they will have increasing value in arriving at a conclusion. The following subjects may be helpful as a basis for writing your own topic sentence:

> How to Show School Loyalty
> A Man's Obligation to Serve His Country
> Too Much Homework
> The Need for School Athletic Teams
> Your Own Choice

Lesson 5. Comparison and Contrast

A fourth method of developing a paragraph is to use comparison or contrast. You should remember that comparison sometimes includes like ideas as well as different ideas, although contrast involves only *un*like ideas.

Study carefully the following paragraphs from "The Undelivered Speech," by John F. Kennedy (page 66). Obviously they are closely related.

America today is stronger than ever before. Our adversaries have not abandoned their ambitions—our dangers have not diminished—our vigilance cannot be relaxed. But now we have the military, the scientific, and the economic strength to do whatever must be done for the preservation and promotion of freedom.

That strength will never be used in pursuit of aggressive ambitions—it will always be used in pursuit of peace. It will never be used to promote provocations—it will always be used to promote the peaceful settlement of disputes.

We in this country, in this generation, are—by destiny rather than choice—the watchmen on the walls of world freedom. We ask, therefore, that we may be worthy of our power and responsibility—that we may exercise our strength with wisdom and restraint—and that we may achieve in our time and for all time the ancient vision of peace on earth, good will toward men. That must always be our goal—and the righteousness of our cause must always underlie our strength. For as was written long ago: "Except the Lord keep the city, the watchman waketh but in vain."

- Practice A.

1. Where do you find similar or comparative ideas expressed? List them.

2. Where do you find *dis*similar or contrasting ideas? Explain.

3. Contrasting ideas are sometimes emphasized by using balanced statements rather than connecting words—statements which offset each other. Select and copy examples of this device.

4. Do you find in the last paragraph any evidence of comparison or contrast? If so, copy the sentence or sentences involved.

5. How does the final quotation—"Except the Lord keep the city, the watchman waketh but in vain"—contribute to the effectiveness of these paragraphs? Explain.

- Practice B. Here are the first and final paragraphs of a long theme written by a high school student. The subject was "A Comparative Study of Characters in Several Plays."

Anderson's purpose in writing *Mary of Scotland* and Sherwood's purpose in writing *Abe Lincoln in Illinois* are closely allied. Basically, both authors attempt to create a realistic picture of historical figures. However, rather than studying these characters in terms of their roles in history, Anderson and Sherwood reveal them as human beings. Besier's purpose in writing *The Barretts of Wimpole Street* is dissimilar to Anderson's and

Sherwood's purpose. Besier aims to present an exciting, dramatic love story, emphasizing the characters of those people most deeply involved in the romance.

Robert Sherwood achieves his purpose more effectively than either Besier or Anderson. His portrait of Abe Lincoln is one of lasting human value. Although Abe Lincoln, as a leader in history, might always appear to be strong, clear-headed, and self-assured, he is also, as Sherwood shows, a human being who fears, who questions, and who doubts. Abe does not leave Illinois happily, as the conquering hero, to go to Washington. Instead he is sad. After all, he is only a man—a man who will miss all his friends, for he realizes the worth both of these simple people and of friendship. His reactions are very human. Furthermore, through the portrait which Sherwood paints, Abe becomes a universal figure. Sherwood's purpose is close to being fully achieved as the historical Abe Lincoln becomes a highly realistic person.

1. Read these opening and concluding paragraphs carefully to find examples of comparison and/or contrast.

2. List the similar and dissimilar ideas in the first paragraph.

3. Look at the final paragraph. Does the student use either comparison or contrast to reach a conclusion? Explain it in your own words.

4. Reexamine these paragraphs to find connecting words and phrases. What are they and how do they contribute?

Practice C. Now you are ready to try your hand at writing a paragraph expressing comparison or contrast. The following topic sentences may give you ideas:

1. Napoleon and Hitler had several qualities in common.

2. Although Tom and Jim look alike, they are very different in character.

3. Both basketball and hockey require speed, but (one—whichever you choose) is more steadily demanding than (the other).

4. The two short stories _____ are similar in setting but dissimilar in plot.

Review what you have written to be sure that every sentence refers to the topic sentence and that each leads logically to the concluding sentence.

Lesson 6. Methods Combined

Paragraphs may be developed by using two or more methods illustrated above. On such an occasion the topic sentence may occur at the beginning, in the development, or at the end. However, it will still suggest or establish the point of view of the writer. Here are two closely related paragraphs taken from "Everything Happened to Sam," by Mark Twain (page 474). Read them carefully to recognize the method or methods used in the development of each paragraph.

My mother had a good deal of trouble with me, but I think she enjoyed it. She had none at all with my brother Henry, who was two years younger than I, and I think that the unbroken monotony of his goodness and truthfulness and obedience would have been a burden to her but for the relief and variety which I furnished in the other direction. I was a tonic. I was valuable to her. I never thought of it before but now I see it. I never knew Henry to do a vicious thing toward me or toward anyone else—but he frequently did righteous ones that cost me as heavily. It was his duty to report me, when I needed reporting and neglected to do it myself, and he was very faithful in discharging that duty. He is Sid in *Tom Sawyer*. But Sid was not Henry. Henry was a very much finer and better boy than Sid ever was.

It was Henry who called my mother's attention to the fact that the thread with which she had sewed my collar together to keep me from going in swimming had changed color. My mother would not have discovered it but for that, and she was manifestly piqued when she recognized that that prominent bit of circumstantial evidence had escaped her sharp eye. That detail probably added a detail to my punishment. It is human. We generally visit our shortcomings on somebody else when there is a possible excuse for it—but no matter. I took it out of Henry. There is always compensation for such as are unjustly used. I often took it out of him—sometimes as an advance payment for something which I hadn't yet done. These were occasions when the opportunity was too strong a temptation, and I had to draw on the future. I did not need to copy this idea from my mother and probably didn't. It is most likely that I invented it for myself. Still, she wrought upon that principle upon occasion.

● Practice A.

1. What is the topic sentence of the first paragraph? Copy it on a sheet of paper.

2. What is the topic sentence of the second paragraph? Look carefully, then copy it on the same sheet of paper.

3. What is the relationship between the two topic sentences you have chosen? Explain.

4. In the first paragraph what method or methods of development does the author use? Justify your choice.

5. In the second paragraph what method or methods are illustrated? State it or them clearly.

6. What is the function of the concluding sentence to the second paragraph? Explain briefly but clearly.

● Practice B. Now that you are familiar with four different methods of paragraph development (by details or examples, by narrative, by argument or reasons, by comparison and/or contrast), you can try your hand at writing one or two closely related paragraphs which use a variety of methods. Choose your topic sentence wisely. Here are several suggestions:

1. Life can be exciting (or dull).

2. My parents expect too much (or too little) of me.

3. Participation in any major sport is worthwhile but time-consuming.

4. _____ is a great place to visit (but I wouldn't want to live there).

5. We learn through experience.

Lesson 7. Dialogue

To complete your understanding of the paragraph, you should be familiar with how it is used in dialogue—conversation between two or more characters.

You should remember to establish a situation in a first sentence or brief paragraph and to start a new paragraph whenever the speaker changes. Also, you must use quotation marks and other punctuation marks carefully.

In the following excerpt from "You've Got to Learn," by Robert Murphy (page 125), young Andy Gates is telling his father that his dog Nicky has just been killed by an otter.

His father saw him and waited with his hands tucked into the top of his levis. Gates was a kindly and unhurried man; he looked at the boy's face and didn't mention the chores that he'd done himself.

"Trouble, Andy?" he asked.

The boy's chin trembled. "Nicky," he said. "There was an otter—" He couldn't go on. He began to cry again, and suddenly went to his father as he hadn't done for years, and leaned against him, crying. "He went after the little one," he said, shaking with sobs, "and the big one drowned him. And Joe—" He couldn't talk about Joe.

"Joe would understand it, boy," his father said, sliding an arm around him. "Joe would know you couldn't help it."

"I was keeping him for Joe," Andy said. "Joe left him with me. He was Joe's and mine." He began to cry violently again. "Joe's and mine," he repeated, remembering Joe at the gate, going away. "I'll kill him!" he burst out, thumping his father's broad chest. "I'll find him and kill him!"

The man started to speak and checked himself, realizing the futility of words. The boy was extraordinarily moved; it was useless to talk against an emotion so deep that he could only guess at it. Time would have to smooth it out—time and what patient understanding he could give. The man was silent for a long time, holding the boy in the crook of his arm.

"Supper, Andy," he said finally. "Get ready for supper, boy."

"I don't want any supper, Dad," Andy said. "I—I couldn't eat any supper."

"All right," Gates said. "Go along up to your room, then. Go up the front stairs. I'll tell Mother you won't be down."

● Practice A.

1. In one original sentence, summarize the opening situation.

2. Notice how the comma, period, question mark, exclamation mark, and dash are used. Where do they occur in relation to the closing quotation mark?

3. When would the question mark appear outside the closing quotation mark?
Example: Did you say to me, "You can't hold me responsible"?

4. Notice that toward the end of the conversation there is a paragraph without quotation marks, beginning "The man started to speak." What is its purpose?

5. Of what importance is the father's last remark to his son?

6. What kind of man is the father as revealed in this short excerpt? In a single sentence, describe him.

● Practice B. From a short story in this book, choose an incident or a situation described and rewrite it, using dialogue. Before you begin, look again to the information given in Practice A above. You must use your imagination.

Select *one* from these suggestions:

1. The following two paragraphs are taken from "The Ledge," by Laurence Hall (page 49). Read them carefully to be sure you know exactly what happens in them. Then rewrite them, making use of dialogue wherever you can.

The boys fondled their new guns, sighted along the barrels, worked the mechanisms, compared notes, boasted, and gave each other contradictory advice. The fisherman got their attention once and pointed at the horizon. They peered through the windows and saw what looked like a black scum floating on top of gently agitated water. It wheeled and tilted, rippled, curled, then rose, strung itself out, and became a huge raft of ducks escaping over the sea. A good sign.

The boys rushed out and leaned over the washboards in the wind and spray to see the flock curl below the horizon. Then they went and hovered around the hot engine, bewailing their lot. If only they had been already set out and waiting. Maybe these ducks would be crazy enough to return later and be slaughtered. Ducks were known to be foolish.

2. In "Trapped in the Desert," by Gary Beeman (page 223), you will find another good possibility for using dialogue to tell an incident:

The food revived us, and we discussed whether to try walking out. Jim felt too weak for such a long trek, and I rated my own chances a bare 50–50. We decided to keep working on the car. I didn't really grasp, even then, that we were in desperate danger. I knew that unwary motorists had died of thirst in the desert; not long before, in Death Valley, just thirty miles to the north, the dried-out corpses of two young men had been found close beside their stalled car. But somehow I felt it couldn't happen to us.

My memories of that second night are blurred. It was all we could do to jack up the car and run it back a few feet until it slipped off the disintegrating ties. We kept resting, I remember, and half-dozing. About four o'clock we fell asleep.

The dialogue will involve Jim and "I," the narrator. Notice that only a part of this excerpt can be told in dialogue.

3. Create your own situation involving an incident and develop it by using dialogue. You may write your paper completely in dialogue or you may use a combination of dialogue and narrative. Use more than two characters if you wish. Be sure to watch punctuation carefully.

UNIT FOUR

THE OUTLINE

Before writing a composition, you should plan it carefully. This same practice is wise procedure if you are arranging your ideas for an oral theme. An outline showing the subdivisions is always desirable.

Lesson 1. Preparing to Make an Outline

Before attempting to organize an outline, you might jot down at random a number of ideas which pertain to the subject you have chosen.

Example: The Value of an Education Today (your subject)
    The need for at least a high school diploma
    Education beyond high school
    Advantages from some sort of education
    Training for a profession
    Training for leisure time
    A training program in industry or in the armed forces
    Training to work with your hands
    Social benefits
    Money
    Education and happiness

● Practice. Following the directions given above, decide on a topic which interests you and about which you have something to say. Then jot down your thoughts and ideas. You may use one of the subjects below or another of your own choosing.

    A Career in Auto Mechanics
    A Work-Study Program
    Programing for Computers
    High School Clubs as Training Grounds
    Part-time Jobs with a Future
    Hobbies and Earning a Living

Lesson 2. Suggestions for Outlining

Several reminders may be helpful:

1. The title of the composition is not part of the outline itself.
2. Avoid using the words "Introduction," "Body," and "Conclusion."
3. Use Roman numerals to identify main headings.
4. Let all main topics and subtopics be similarly expressed.

A. Study the following pattern. Notice the use of Roman numerals, capital and small letters, numbers, and indentation.

    I. (It is preferable to use a complete sentence.)
      A. (Short sentence or phrase)
        1. (Phrase or word)
        2. (Phrase or word)
          a. (Word only)
          b. (Word only)

　　　　B.
　　　　　1.
　　　　　　　a.
　　　　　　　b.
　　　　　2.
　　II.
　　　　A.
　　　　　1.
　　　　　2.
　　　　B.
　　　　　1.
　　　　　2.
　　　　C.
　　　　　1.
　　　　　2.
　III.
　　　　A.
　　　　B.
　　　　C.

Note: Do not use one subtopic alone. Use two or more, or none. Wherever there is a 1, there must be a 2; wherever there is an *a*, there must be a *b*.

B. Consider the following sample outline to see how the pattern just described is used.

The Elizabethan Age in England

I. The drama during this period flourished.
　A. Queen Elizabeth supported it.
　　1. Many playwrights
　　　a. Shakespeare
　　　b. Marlowe
　　　c. Jonson
　　2. Several theaters
　　　a. Globe
　　　b. Swan
　　　c. Rose
　B. Companies of actors appeared.
　　1. Lord Chamberlain's
　　2. Lord Admiral's
　　3. Queen's Players
II. There were other forms of entertainment.
　A. Some Englishmen enjoyed the arts.
　　1. Interest in painting
　　2. Interest in sculpture
　　3. Traveling minstrels

4. Small orchestras
B. Pageants were popular.
   1. Delighted Queen Elizabeth
   2. Enjoyed by courtiers
III. The politics of the time gave evidence of a revolutionary spirit.
A. Continuing struggle for the throne
   1. Queen Elizabeth of England
   2. Queen Mary of Scotland
B. Scheming among the nobles
   1. Many for Elizabeth
   2. Some for Mary
IV. This was a period of exploration and discovery for men who sought fame and fortune.
A. Martin and Frobisher
B. Sir Francis Drake
C. Sir Walter Raleigh

Lesson 3. Making Your Own Outline

In this unit you have had information on the purpose of an outline, suggestions for organizing your ideas, information on a desirable pattern to follow, and a sample outline. You are now ready to write your own outline. You might like to use one of the subjects proposed in Lesson 1, or use your own original subject, or select one from the following:

> The Benefits of a Strong Physical Education Program
> Driver Education
> John Steinbeck, Famous Novelist (or some other familiar author)
> Abraham Lincoln, a Great American

UNIT FIVE

THE COMPOSITION OR THEME

A careful outline is sound preparation for writing a good composition. Of course, you may occasionally be asked to write in class a paragraph or even a short theme which has not been announced, but the longer composition will probably be preceded by an outline.

There are five steps which may be helpful when you are asked to write a theme of several well-developed paragraphs:

1. Careful selection of a subject
2. Preparation of an outline
3. Writing the first draft (perhaps in class)
4. The composition itself (a revision of your first draft)
5. Rewriting after your theme has been corrected

Lesson 1.   Unity, Coherence, and Emphasis in Your Composition

In the unit on the paragraph, you learned that every sentence in a paragraph must be directly related to the topic sentence of the paragraph (oneness of idea—*unity*). You also learned that sentences within the paragraph should be arranged in a systematic manner (orderly development of ideas—*coherence*). Similarly, paragraphs in a composition must have oneness (unity) and order (coherence); that is, each paragraph must have direct bearing on the title of your theme, and paragraphs should follow one another in an orderly manner. Likewise, sentences in a paragraph and paragraphs in a composition should be arranged for *emphasis:* the beginning and the end are the most important positions. If you begin your composition effectively, you will attract the attention of the reader; if you have a strong ending, you will leave an impression on the reader.

● Practice A. Study carefully the following selection from "Aches and Pains and Three Batting Titles" (page 284). Notice how well unity, coherence, and emphasis are illustrated in these three introductory paragraphs to a short biographical sketch of the great Roberto Clemente.

> The batting champion of the major leagues lowered himself to the pea-green carpet of his 48-foot living room and sprawled on his right side, flinging his left leg over his right leg. He wore gold Oriental pajama tops, tan slacks, battered bedroom slippers, and—for purposes of the demonstration he was conducting—a tortured grimace. "Like dis!" he cried, and then dug his fingers into his flesh, just above his upraised left hip. Roberto Clemente, the Pittsburgh Pirates' marvelous right fielder and their steadiest customer of the medical profession, was showing how he must greet each new day in his life. He has a disk in his back that insists on wandering, so when he awakens, he must cross those legs, dig at that flesh, and listen for the sound of the disk popping back where it belongs.
>
> Around the room necks were craned and ears alerted for the successful conclusion of the demonstration. "No, you cannot hear the disk now," shouted Roberto. "It is in place now. But every morning you can hear it from here to there, in the whole room. *Boop!*"

Boop? Certainly, boop. Not only one boop but two, for there is another disk running around up in the vicinity of Roberto's neck. For that one he must have someone manipulate his neck muscles until the sound of the boop is heard.

Answer these questions:

1. What one idea catches the reader's attention at once?

2. How is this idea emphasized in the first paragraph?

3. How does the writer maintain coherence in this first paragraph?

4. In the second and third paragraphs unity is apparent as the composition (or essay) moves ahead. How is this unity achieved?

5. Is the last paragraph emphatic, particularly the last sentence? Why, or why not?

- Practice B. You may wish to examine a longer piece of writing. Turn to page 64 and read or reread the selection "Introduction" by Bruce Catton, which also illustrates unity, coherence, and emphasis. Then consider the following questions:

1. The author achieves unity by focusing on a certain attitude of President Kennedy's. What is this attitude? How is it related to the topic of each paragraph?

2. An author achieves coherence by his smooth transition from one idea to another. What word in the first sentence of the second paragraph relates this paragraph to the one that precedes it? How does the author show the relationship of each of the following paragraphs with the paragraph that precedes it?

3. One means of achieving emphasis is by the repetition of certain key words or phrases; another is by the repetition of certain sentence patterns, with the key words changed. Give examples of the use of both techniques in Bruce Catton's "Introduction."

Lesson 2. Writing a Composition

You should now be ready to write your own carefully planned composition. Unit Four, The Outline, provides you with a variety of topics. (See Lesson 1, page 656, and Lesson 3, page 658.) Perhaps you prefer to write on one of these additional topics:

The Appeal of Television
A Biographical Sketch
Preparing for a Career in Art (or Music)
Popular Music
The Fascination of the Theater
Present-day Movies
Women's Changing Fashions
A Memorable Character

Reminders:
>Make full use of your outline.
>Revise your first draft.
>Go over your theme for correct paragraphing.
>Observe unity, coherence, and emphasis.
>Be sure to write complete sentences.
>Check capitalization, punctuation, and spelling.
>Proofread for grammatical errors.
>Finally, let your finished theme be neat and clear.

UNIT SIX

THE RIGHT WORD

Although this final unit deals with single words, it is a capstone for the entire Composition Skills Supplement. Once a writer becomes competent in handling sentences, paragraphs, and longer connected writing, he must return his attention to the point it never really left—the single word. The importance of the exact word, the right word in the right place at the right time, cannot be overestimated. It is no accident that prose writers measure their output as so many words (a 500-word essay, a 5,000-word short story, a 100,000-word novel, and so forth) and that poets examine and turn over and reexamine every word with tender loving care. Prose writers as well as poets search for the exact word; some search more carefully than many poets. John Updike said that the reader of a printed story cannot see "the labor, the decisions, and the agony of indecision that went into it." Lafcadio Hearn told of rewriting a single paragraph seventeen times to achieve his effect. Christopher Morley said that he sometimes sweated for hours to come up with the one right word. "How forcible are right words!" says the Bible.

Lesson 1. Lightning or the Lightning Bug?

"The difference between the right word and the almost right word," wrote Mark Twain, "is the difference between lightning and lightning bug."

We should search for the lightning word in every area of our speech and writing. Writers seek the simple but distinctive word rather than the clumsy invention or overflowing verbiage. We can see this search in its best and worst aspects on the daily sports page, where writers rack their brains to come up with fanciful names like "The Sultan of Swat," "El

Goofo," "The Lip," "Two-Ton Tony," and "Champagne Tony." Apt names stick; they gather their own associations and tend sometimes to throw their owners into the shade. Forty years ago Grantland Rice coined the term "The Four Horsemen." Probably for every person who can tell you the names of the four men—Layden, Crowley, Miller, and Stuhldreyer—there are a thousand who can tell you that the phrase refers to a certain Notre Dame backfield.

● Practice. Below are pairs of nicknames given to sports figures. From each pair, choose the one that seems closer to lightning and farther from the lightning bug. Give reasons for your choices.

1. The Splendid Splinter   Stan the Man
2. Jolting Joe   The San Francisco Flash
3. Tex   Night Train Lane
4. The Babe   The Wild Bull of the Pampas

Lesson 2.   Words to Fire the Imagination

American history—from "No taxation without representation!" to "The Great Society" and beyond—is filled with phrases that fired the American imagination. In nearly every generation, Americans have fought under rallying cries they perhaps only dimly understood but were willing to die for: "Give me liberty or give me death!" "Millions for defense but not one cent for tribute!" "54–40 or fight!" "Liberty and union now and forever, one and inseparable!" "Make the world safe for democracy!" "Remember the Alamo!" "Remember the Maine!" "Remember Pearl Harbor!"

● Practice. Select any two of the rallying cries listed above. Find out, if you can, who coined the expressions and what the historical background of the expression was. Which of the two expressions do you think was more successful in stirring people to action? Can you tell why it was?

Lesson 3.   Diction

Careful word choice, the search for the one word that lights up the imagination by striking at once both the exact sense and the right emotion, is called *diction*. In this lesson you will observe four phases of diction: *connotation, levels of usage, concreteness,* and *imagery*. Does all this sound difficult? It isn't really. When a woman is described as "pleasantly plump" rather than "fat," the writer is being careful of *connotation*. When she is called "Fatso," the writer is dropping to a lower *level of usage*. When he writes "That is a fat lady" rather than "Some people are fat," he is being concrete as opposed to abstract. To say "She eats like a hog" is to use *imagery.*

- Practice. Without necessarily referring to the four elements of diction given in this lesson, differentiate between the expressions in each of the following pairs. Which do you prefer? Why?

    1. Life is no bed of roses.
    Life is extremely difficult.
    2. A fresh difference arose between my brother and me.
    My brother cheated me.
    3. The American public is a great beast.
    There is good reason to distrust democracy.
    4. Prosperity is just around the corner.
    Economic indexes would seem to indicate a definite upward trend sometime in the near future.
    5. Hey, Stupid!
    Young man!

Lesson 4. Connotation

> Eighty-seven years ago our ancestors produced in North America a novel political autonomy, thought of in the absence of restraint, and set apart to further the purpose that human beings collectively and without exception are caused to come into existence having the same or similar rights or privileges.

Does that sentence sound familiar? Even though you never heard it stated that way before, you probably recognized the restatement of Lincoln's "Gettysburg Address": "Four score and seven years ago our fathers brought forth on this continent a new nation, conceived in liberty, and dedicated to the proposition that all men are created equal."

The restatement is awkward and harder to read than the original, but it says, or *denotes*, the same thing. The *denotation* may be the same; the *connotation* is wildly scrambled. Since "eighty-seven years ago" is clearer and easier than "four score and seven years ago," why isn't it better? Partly, we reject it because we are familiar with Lincoln's wording. But mainly our objection is based on connotation: Lincoln echoed the language of the Bible. This echo is pleasing to the listener, who associates the deep thoughts of the Bible with the deep thoughts of Lincoln's address. What other connotations are present in Lincoln's sentence? The reference to liberty and the clause "all men are created equal" come directly from the Declaration of Independence. To the spiritual connotations, Lincoln added historical connotations; these two threads run throughout the entire speech.

● Practice. In the last paragraph of "The Gettysburg Address" (page 455), find:

1. Three words or expressions that echo the language of the Bible.

2. Three words or expressions that recall our historic heritage.

Lesson 5. Kinds of Connotation

Good writers carefully choose the word with exactly the connotation they want. They know that there are many ways to present the same basic facts, the same denotation. One of the most obvious distinctions among words of the same denotation is that some have good connotations, some have fairly neutral connotations, and some have bad connotations.

He is a nut. You are eccentric. I am independent.

He looks old and wrinkled. You look mature. I look distinguished.

He flops in a run-down shack. You live in marginal housing. I reside in a home that needs some repair.

He is a garbage man. You are a trash collector. I am a sanitary engineer.

● Practice. In each quotation below, one word is in italics. Tell from the description whether the writer approves of the person or thing named, disapproves, shows no special feeling either way, or shows feelings both ways.

1. A *horseman* rode by, a fat man with red cheeks and a white stubble beard. —JOHN STEINBECK (page 556)

2. I never knew *Henry* to do a vicious thing toward me or toward anyone else—but he frequently did righteous ones that cost me as heavily. —MARK TWAIN (page 474)

3. He felt the subtle battle brotherhood more potent even than the cause for which they were fighting. It was a mysterious *fraternity* born of the smoke and danger of death.

—STEPHEN CRANE (page 500)

4. There was a *funeral*. . . . It was garish, vulgar, massive, bewildering, chaotic. Also it was simple, final, majestic, august. . . .

—CARL SANDBURG (page 458)

5. Why, who makes much of a *miracle?*
As to me I know of nothing else but miracles.

—WALT WHITMAN (page 423)

6. I have none of the tenderer-than-thou
Collectivistic regimenting *love*
With which the modern world is being swept.

—ROBERT FROST (page 522)

Lesson 6. Levels of Usage

Usage is like water. It finds its own level; and when it shifts suddenly from one level to another, there may be a calamity. In schools the usage most often taught is what linguists consider formal usage, appropriate speech for "polite society" and for most writing. Teachers generally regard knowledge of this kind of usage as a necessity for advancement in our society. Other authorities tend to disagree with this judgment; they point out that the sky doesn't fall on people who say "it's me" or "between you and I" or even "shaddup." They warn that formal usage, too, has its dangers. The worker on a building job who says "Please hand me that serrated-jawed Stillson wrench, young man" rather than "Hey Mack, gimme that wrench" may get something he isn't looking for.

Fortunately we don't have to settle this argument. But there are two points that you, as a writer, should remember: (1) you must decide how formal or informal you want to be in any particular piece of writing; and (2) unless you have good reason to do otherwise, you must stick to the level you've chosen.

The hardest question is still unanswered. How do you know how formal to be? That depends on many factors: your subject, your purpose, your audience. No one can tell you exactly how formal to be on all occasions, but there are certain generally accepted boundaries. There is a common standard, a sort of rock-bottom floor level, beneath which most careful writers do not go. Since there is an overlapping between formal and informal vocabularies, we cannot draw a distinct line between them. Most words you ordinarily use belong in both vocabularies. We can, however, recognize when an individual word or way of talking just won't do. What sort of thing won't do? Ungrammatical expressions ("him and me done it"), slang ("goof off" for "loaf," "greasy spoon" for a restaurant), profanity, local or dialect terms ("square" for a city block, "crick" for "creek"), shoptalk or trade jargon—in fact, any specialized language that is not accepted or understood by people in general.

● Practice A. In the George Bernard Shaw play *Pygmalion* and in its musical version, *My Fair Lady*, Professor Higgins manages to pass off an ignorant flower girl as a lady, mainly by teaching her to talk like a lady. Because she talks in a "superior" way, she is accepted as being superior. Here are some before-and-after samples of her talk. Which is which? Why is one speech in each pair "superior" to the other? Can you change the "inferior" speech into a "superior" one?

1. a. I ain't done nothing wrong by speaking to a gentleman.

   b. I was brought up to be just like him, unable to control myself.

2. a. I don't want no balmies teaching me.

   b. I should like you to call me Eliza now, if you would.

3. a. How do you do, Professor Higgins. Are you quite well?

    b. Oh, you are real good. Thank you, Captain.

4. a. I can be civil and kind to people, which is more than you can.

    b. You ought to be stuffed with nails, you ought.

● Practice B. Different levels of usage are sometimes carefully employed for a specific effect. On the same page a writer may shift from very formal to informal standard to below standard. The three passages below, taken from *The Red Badge of Courage* by Stephen Crane (pages 499–503), deal with an enemy attack and its repulse. Rank the italicized parts of the passages according to the following pattern: high level of usage, average level of usage, low level of usage. Explain your ranking. What does Stephen Crane achieve by using three levels of usage?

1. A hatless general pulled his dripping horse to a stand near the colonel of the 304th. He shook his fist in the other's face. *"You've got to hold 'em back!"* he shouted, savagely; *"you've got to hold 'em back!"*

2. At last an exultant yell went along the quivering line. The firing dwindled from an uproar to a last vindictive popping. *As the smoke slowly eddied away, the youth saw that the charge had been repulsed.*

3. A sentence with variations went up and down the line. *"Well, we've helt 'em back. We've helt 'em back; derned if we haven't."*

● Practice C. Often just one ill-chosen word, like the clinker by a concert artist, calls so much attention to itself that the entire performance is ruined. (Some authorities might consider *clinker* in the preceding sentence such a word!) In each sentence below there is at least one word that strikes the wrong note. Find the wrong words and replace them by words that ring true. Defend your choices.

1. Nobody knew that the heavyweight champion had suffered a jammed finger and busted ribs until after the fight.

2. The symphonic music being played on the stereo was drownded out by the jazz combination on the family room television set.

3. Since she was neither a Civil War buff nor a travel bug, his wife refused to make the long, strenuous auto trip to Virginia.

4. Foreigners who attend American basketball games are astounded to see a coach violate their precepts of good sportsmanship by constantly bellyaching to the officials.

5. Some preachy women marry good-natured slobs because they think they can upgrade their mode of conduct.

Lesson 7. Concreteness

One way to classify words is to call them *concrete* or *abstract*. Possibly you have been told always to choose concrete and specific words because such words make your descriptions clearer than abstract and general words do. This is a fine rule. A composition containing words like *tiger, man-eater, spit, snarl,* and *scratch* is usually much easier to read and understand than one loaded with words like *love, democracy, wisdom, ambition,* and *greed.* Good writers use both kinds of words, but are careful not to overwork abstractions. They make sure that their descriptions are full of vigorous concrete words in specific detail.

- Practice A. Read the following paragraph from John Steinbeck's essay, "Jalopies I Have Cursed and Loved" (page 569). List at least ten concrete terms Steinbeck uses.

> My first two cars were Model T's, strange beings. They never got so beat up that you couldn't somehow make them run. The first one was a touring car. Chickens had roosted on its steering wheel, and I never got their marks off. The steering wheel was cracked so that if you put any weight on it, it pinched your fingers when you let up. The back seat was for tools, wire, and spare tires. . . . I had it a long time. It never saw shelter or a mechanic. I remember how it used to shudder and sigh when I cranked it and how its crank would kick back viciously. It was a mean car. It loved no one, it ran in spurts and seemed to be as much influenced by magic as by mechanics.

- Practice B. After reading Herman Melville's description of fish-eating by the Typee natives, write a parallel description of your own. You should choose some habit or custom which fascinates you and which you think may fascinate your classmates. It may be as ordinary as your little brother taking a bath or as extraordinary as your little sister playing third base. Notice how Melville piles up concrete details as he describes the native custom. Try to get as much concreteness into your description.

> I grieve to state so distressing a fact, but the inhabitants of Typee were in the habit of devouring fish much in the same way that a civilized being would eat a radish, and without any more previous preparation. They eat it raw; scales, bones, gills, and all the inside. The fish is held by the tail, and the head being introduced into the mouth, the animal disappears with a rapidity that would at first nearly lead one to imagine it had been launched bodily down the throat.

Lesson 8. More or Less Concrete

Do you remember the first sentence under "Concreteness" (page 667)? Even though it is true that words may generally be classed as concrete or abstract, it is also true that some words are more concrete than others. *Collie* is a more concrete term than *dog*, which is more concrete than *mammal*, which is more concrete than *vertebrate*, which is more concrete than *being*. And the same word in different contexts will have different degrees of concreteness. "The family next door," for example, is more concrete than "the American family" or "the family of man." In writing descriptions, you not only should choose the most concrete word but also be sure that you are using that word in the most concrete sense your context calls for.

● Practice. Arrange each set of words or phrases in order from the least concrete to the most concrete.

1. structure   house   building   mansion

2. volume   grammar book   textbook   English textbook

3. land   garden   lot   plot

4. a local school   the school in Yorktown   Yorktown High School the modern American school   school   the school situation

Lesson 9. Imagery

Everyone today seems concerned with images. Presidents as well as comedians must take vocal lessons and use make-up for TV. An actor can be elected governor or senator of a great state; a senator can cut a best-selling record. Cigarettes and cars are sold by associating their image with youth, vigor, and beauty. Frozen foods are "sold" by a jolly green giant, canned fish by a talking tuna. Huge corporations symbolize themselves in homely terms by the use of Charlie Brown or Mr. Magoo or the Cartwrights of the Ponderosa. This form of imagery is familiar.

Imagery can give a lift to your writing like the lift it gives to public figures and name brand products. The two main tools for you to use are vivid description and striking comparison.

● Practice. Concrete words with strong connotations combined in imaginative ways produce vivid descriptions. In each pair of sentences below, one is a vivid description taken from a selection in this textbook; the other is a tame rephrasing. Which is which? Defend your answer by pointing out the vivid, picture-making words and expressions.

1. a. It was pleasant there, with the hay and bees all around, and the earth felt good.   **b.** It was pleasant there, with the smell of the hay and the drone of the bees, and the good, warm feeling of the earth.

2. a. A lot of people from different places in our large country came many miles because they could get an empty lot of ground without paying anything for it. But it was good ground! **b.** Thousands and thousands of people from all over this vast commonwealth of ours traveled hundreds of miles to get a bare piece of land for nothing. But what land!

3. a. It was a piece of empty ground—some little trees were out past the area of flat level ground and then there was a steep hill with some rocks on it. **b.** It was a lonely stretch—a few small trees beyond the small patch of prairie, and then the rocky slope leading up.

4. a. He was a huge, overly strong, coarse man, who liked during the winter to hunt for ducks that ate off the ocean ledges which were not covered by water when the tide was low. **b.** He was a big, raw man, with too much strength, whose delight in winter was to hunt the sea ducks that flew in to feed by the outer ledges, bare at low tide.

Lesson 10.   Striking Comparisons

The quickest and usually the best way to achieve striking comparisons is by using figurative language—metaphors and similes. Although you probably associate such language with poetry, plays by Shakespeare, and pretentiously written fiction, you should know that everyday language is also full of figures of speech. Metaphors based on parts of the body alone could easily fill a book this size. A few examples follow: eye of a needle, hand of cards, handful of people, thumbnail sketch, elbow-room, head man, headland, sweetheart, table leg, foot of the table, foot of the class, footbridge, foothill, footloose, footman, footnote.

Many of the sports nicknames discussed under "Lightning or the Lightning Bug?" (page 661) are metaphors. Notice how the men have been compared to things they resemble in one way or another: the Notre Dame backfield to four men on horseback; the slender Ted Williams to a splinter; Luis Firpo, the boxer, to a wild bull. Can you see that the title "Lightning or the Lightning Bug?" is also a metaphor? What is the right word compared to? What is the almost right word compared to?

● Practice. In each of the following excerpts from ads, what is being compared to what? Which statements are likely to interest the reader most?

1. Walking around without a trust fund is like skydiving without a parachute.

2. Then there's the familiar bug. While it's not as big as the other two Volkswagens, it has plenty of room for four people and a small dog.

3. Our popularity explosion.

4. No forms system is stronger than its weakest link.

5. Fuming with indignation, Robert Brown decided: "Chimneys let your fuel dollars go up in smoke."

6. We call our first-class service "chateau-in-the-sky."

7. Don't play mover's roulette! Call a reputable mover.

8. A good lawn is contagious. Before you know it, the entire neighborhood has caught on.

Lesson 11. A New Look at Old Scenes

Well-chosen figures of speech cause the reader to discover a new way of looking at one particular thing, or at things in general. In Walt Whitman's poem with the first line, "O Captain! my captain! our fearful trip is done," the reader "discovers" Abraham Lincoln as captain of a ship that has weathered a terrible journey. Carl Sandburg's description of Lincoln's birth ("Tom Lincoln and the moaning Nancy Hanks welcomed into a world of battle and blood, of whispering dreams and wistful dust, a new child, a boy") awakens in the reader a sense of Lincoln's hard life, his aims, and his struggles.

● Practice. Paraphrase each quotation in your own words.

1. Grandfather was fresh as a daisy and full of jokes at breakfast next morning.   —JAMES THURBER (page 37)

2. Part of a moon was falling down the west, / Dragging the whole sky with it to the hills.   —ROBERT FROST (page 528)

3. The sun would be shooting his golden spikes above the Happar mountain ere I threw aside my tapa robe.

—HERMAN MELVILLE (page 415)

4. But Sam looked higher than Indian politics; already he could faintly see his star shining in the blue.

—DONALD CULROSS PEATTIE (page 94)

5. And o'er his heart a shadow / Fell as he found / No spot of ground / That looked like Eldorado.   —EDGAR ALLAN POE (page 384)

6. She had the heart-free laugh of a girl. It came seldom, but when it broke upon the ear, it was as inspiring as music.

—MARK TWAIN (page 492)

7. Pepé had sharp Indian cheekbones and an eagle nose, but his mouth was as sweet and shapely as a girl's mouth, and his chin was fragile and chiseled.   —JOHN STEINBECK (page 551)

8. It filled the wells, it pleased the pools, / It warbled in the road, / It pulled the spigot from the hills / And let the floods abroad.

—EMILY DICKINSON (page 464)

GLOSSARY

This glossary gives pronunciations and meanings for many words throughout the book that are not explained in footnotes. Words that have more than one meaning are defined according to their use in the book, but the most common meaning of a word is also given if it is not well known. If a word appears in more than one form, the different forms are labeled as to part of speech, number, or tense.

A

abalone (ab·uh·LOH·nee). An edible shellfish.

abate (a·BAYT). To lessen or diminish.

abrasion (a·BRAY·zhun). Friction; scraping.

absolved (ab·SOLV'D). Released; freed.

abstemious (ab·STEE·mee·us). Eating and drinking sparingly.

acclivity (a·KLIV·ih·tee). An upward slope.

adapted (a·DAP·ted). Adjusted; conformed.

admonishing (ad·MON·ish·ing). Warning. *Noun:* **admonition** (ad·ma·NISH·un). Warning.

aeolian harps (ee·OH·lee·un). Stringed instruments which make musical sounds when exposed to the wind. **Aeolus.** The mythical god of wind.

affluent (AF·lu·ent). 1. Wealthy. 2. Abundant.

aggressive (uh·GRESS·iv). Ready to attack; full of vigor and action.

alacrity (a·LAK·rih·tee). Cheerful willingness; liveliness.

alkali (AL·kuh·ly). A mineral salt having a sharp, bitter taste.

allayed (a·LAYD). Layed to rest; calmed.

alleged (a·LEJ'D). So-called; said to be true without proof.

allusion (a·LOO·zhun). Indirect reference; suggestion.

aloe (AL·oh). A kind of plant sometimes used as a medicine.

amiable (AY·mee·a·bul). Friendly. *Adverb:* **amiably.**

amphibious (am·FIB·ih·us). Capable of living on land or in water.

anguish (ANG·gwish). Extreme mental or physical pain.

angular (ANG·gyoo·ler). Bony; gaunt.

animus (AN·ih·mus). Hostile feeling.

anomalous (a·NOM·a·lus). Abnormal; exceptional.

anonymous (uh·NAWN·uh·mus). Bearing no name; of unknown authorship.

antic (AN·tik). Unusual; fantastic.

apathetic (ap·uh·THET·ik). Indifferent; without emotion.

aphid (AY·fid). A small, juice-sucking insect, injurious to plants.

aphorisms (AF·oh·riz·umz). Proverbs; brief statements of a truth or principle.

apparition (ap·a·RISH·un). Ghost; phantom.

apprehension (ap·reh·HEN·shun). Fear or misgiving.

apprentice (uh·PREN·tiss). Beginner; someone learning a job.

apprise (a·PRYZ). Notify; inform.

approbation (ap·ruh·BAY·shun). Approval.

arbitrarily (ar·bih·TRAIR·ih·lee). Dictatorially; absolutely.

ardently (AHR·dunt·lee). Intensely; keenly; fiercely.

arduous (AR·joo·us). Involving great labor or hardship.

arrogantly (AR·a·gant·lee). Haughtily; unduly proud.

ascended (uh·SEND·id). Climbed; rose.

aspirations (as·pih·RAY·shunz). High ambitions.

aspiring (uh·SPYR·ing). Desiring something high or good.

assented (a·SENT·ed). Agreed; approved.

assimilating (a·SIM·ih·lay·ting). Absorbing or taking in.

assuage (a·SWAYJ). To soothe.

athwartships (a·THWART·ships). Across the boat.

attrition (a·TRIH·shun). A gradual wearing down or weakening.

audacious (aw·DAY·shus). Daring; bold.

audible (AW·dih·bul). Loud enough to be heard.

august (aw·GUST). Inspiring awe and admiration; imposing.

Ave Marias (AH·vay ma·REE·ahz). Prayers.

aversion (a·VERZH·un). Extreme dislike.

B

badgering (BAJ·er·ing). Teasing or annoying.

baffled (BAF·uld). Outwitted; foiled.

ballet (bal·LAY). A theatrical dance.

barnstormer. Person who tours rural areas giving shows, making speeches, and so forth.

baroque (ba·ROHK). Fantastic in style; grotesque.

bas-relief (bah·reh·LEEF). Sculpture in which the figures project slightly from the background.

bedight (beh·DYT). Dressed; adorned.

benevolent (beh·NEV·uh·lunt). Ready to do good; kind.

benign (beh·NYN). Gentle; mild; kindly.

beveled (BEV·uld). With edges sloped or slanted.

bivouac (BIV·oo·ak). A temporary encampment for soldiers in the field.

blackjacks. Scrub oaks.

blandishment (BLAN·dish·ment). Flattering speech or action.

blaspheming (blas·FEEM·ing). Swearing.

bluebonnets. Brilliant blue flowers; state flower of Texas.

bolstered (BOHL·sterd). Supported; propped up.

bristle (BRIS·ul). To show anger or irritation.

buoyant (BOY·unt). 1. Lighthearted; cheerful. 2. Floating on water or in air.

C

cadenced (KAY·dens't). Rhythmical; measured or regular.

calaboose (KAL·a·boos). Informal term for a jail.

calliope (ka·LY·oh·pee). A musical instrument made of whistles.

calumny (KAL·um·nee). False and malicious accusation.

candor (KAN·der). Frankness, sincerity.

canker (KANG·ker). A disease of trees, causing decay.

careen (kuh·REEN). To sway from side to side.

censured (SEN·shurd). Condemned; blamed.

ceremoniously (sehr·eh·MOH·nee·us·lee). Formally.

chaparral (chap·uh·RAL). A thicket of low thorny shrubs; dwarf oak.

chastising (chas·TYZ·ing). Punishing; restraining.

chimera (ka·MIR·a). An absurd creation of the imagination.

chiropractor (KY·ruh·prack·tur). Person who believes he can cure diseases by manipulating body structures, especially the spine.

cholera (KOL·er·a). An acute, infectious, epidemic disease.

chronic (KRON·ik). Habitual; continuing for a long time.

civic (SIV·ik). Of a city or a citizen.

civilly (SIV·ih·lee). Courteously; politely. *Noun:* **civility.** Courtesy; politeness.

clandestine (klan·DES·tin). Kept secret for a purpose.

clemency (KLEM·an·see). Leniency; mercy.

cockles (KOCK·uls). Wrinkles. **Cockles of his heart.** The depths of his feelings.

codger (KOD·jer). A strange man, usually an old one.

colleagues (KOLL·eegs). Associates; people working together in a profession or other special group.

colossus (ka·LOS·sus). Huge statue.

coma (KO·mah). Unconsciousness due to illness or injury.

comb (KOHM). The ridge of a roof.

commended (ka·MEND·ed). Recommended; approved.

commiserate (kuh·MIZ·uh·rayt). To feel sympathy for.

commissary (KOM·ih·sa·ree). A store selling food or equipment.

competence (KOM·peh·tens). Ability. *Adjective:* **competent.** Able; capable.

complacency (kom·PLAY·sen·see). A feeling of content; self-satisfaction; smugness.

con (kon). Confidence game; trick to deceive.

conceptions (kun·SEPP·shunz). Ideas.

concur (kon·KUR). Agree or approve.

condign (kon·DYN). Deserved.

confines (KON·fyns). Boundaries; limits; surroundings.

conformation (kon·for·MAY·shun). Structure or outline.

congenital (kun·JEN·uh·tul). Existing from birth.

conjointly (kon·JOINT·lee). Unitedly.

consecrated (KON·seh·kray·ted). Dedicated; devoted.

consigned (kun·SYND). 1. Sent. 2. Thought of as being (some certain place or thing).

consistency (kun·SIS·ten·see). 1. Agreement. 2. Staying the same.

constellation (kon·steh·LAY·shun). A group or cluster of stars.

consternation (kon·ster·NAY·shun). Dismay, fear.

consummate (KON·sum·ayt). To bring to completion.

consumption (kun·SUMP·shun). Use.

contours (KON·toorz). Outlines of figures or forms.

contrivance (kon·TRY·vans). 1. Mechanical device. 2. Thing planned. *Verb:* **contrive** (kon·TRYV). 1. Design; invent. 2. Plan cleverly.

contusions (kon·TOO·zhunz). Bruises.

convulsively (kon·VUL·siv·lee). In a violent and disturbed manner.

corporeal (kor·POR·ee·ul). Material; physical.

counseled (KOWN·seld). Gave advice.

counter (KOUN·ter). Oppose; contradict.

covert (KUV·ert). A shelter or hiding place; a covering.

covet (KUV·it). Long for.

cower (KOW·er). Crouch in fear; tremble.

credo (KREE·doh). A set of beliefs; a creed.

credulity (kreh·DYOO·lih·tee). Readiness to believe on slight evidence.

crevasse (kreh·VAS). A deep split, as in a glacier.

crevice (KREV·is). An opening formed by a crack.

cronies (KRO·neez). Friends.

cul-de-sac (kul·deh·SAK). 1. A passage open only at one end. 2. A blind alley; a trap.

culvert (KUL·vert). A drain under a road.

curator (kyoo·RAY·ter). The person in charge of a museum or art collection.

cynical (SIN·ik·ul). Showing a scornful distrust of men's good intentions or qualities.

D

dastardly (DAS·tard·lee). Base; cowardly.

dauntless (DAWNT·les). Fearless.

debauch (deh·BAWCH). 1. Dissipate. 2. Corrupt.

debilitation (de·bill·uh·TAY·shun). Weakening.

decanter (deh·KAN·ter). An ornamental bottle from which wine or water is served.

decorum (deh·KOR·um). Conformity to good taste in behavior or dress.

decrepit (dee·KREP·it). Worn out by old age or excessive use.

deference (DEF·er·ens). Respect; regard.

deficiency (dih·FISH·un·see). Lack.

deft. Skillful; clever.

degenerate (deh·JEN·a·rit). 1. Inferior. 2. Weakened physically, mentally, or morally.

dehydration (dee·hy·DRAY·shun). Loss of water; a drying up.

delirium (deh·LIR·ee·um). Wandering of the mind.

demarcation (dee·mar·KAY·shun). A boundary; a separating.

demeaned (de·MEEND). Degraded; lowered in reputation. *Noun:* **demeanor** (de·MEEN·er). Behavior; air.

demoniac (deh·MOH·nih·ak). Devilish. Also **demonic** (deh·MON·ic).

deploy (deh·PLOI). To place or position according to a plan.

deride (deh·RYD). To ridicule; to mock.

despondent (deh·SPON·dunt). Disheartened; without hope.

despotism (DES·pa·tiz·um). Unlimited authority.

detestable (deh·TEST·a·bul). Extremely hateful.

dictum (DIK·tum). A positive statement.

diffidently (DIF·ih·dent·lee). Shyly; timidly; lacking in self-confidence.

diffusion (dih·FYOO·zhun). Spreading abroad.

dignitary (DIG·nuh·teh·ree). One who holds high position.

dilapidated (dih·LAP·ih·day·ted). Fallen into decay; neglected.

diminuendo (dih·min·yoo·EN·do). Gradually lessening in volume of sound.

diphtheria (dif·THIR·ee·ah). An acute contagious disease of the throat.

direst (DYR·est). Most dreadful, terrible.

discompose (dis·kom·POHZ). To make uneasy; to disarrange.

discreet (dis·KREET). Wise; cautious.

discus (DIS·kus). Flat metal disk thrown for distance.

disintegrate (dis·IN·tu·grayt). Crumble; break apart.

disk. 1. Flat, circular plate. 2. Flat outgrowth between bones.

disreputable (dis·REP·yoo·ta·b'l). Not of good reputation; not esteemed.

dissever (dih·SEV·er). Separate; divide.

dissolution (dis·uh·LOO·shun). Breaking apart.

dissuade (dih·SWAYD). To advise against.

distention (dis·TEN·shun). Expansion; growing larger and less flexible.

distorted (dis·TOR·tid). Twisted.

diverged (dih·VERJ'D). Went in different directions.

diverse (dih·VERS). Different; unlike.

docility (do·SIL·ih·tee). State of being easily managed or taught.

dogged (DOG·id). Stubborn.

dominated (DOM·uh·nayt·id). Controlled; governed.

drollery (DROH·ler·ee). An amusing way of acting or talking.

E

eccentric (ek·SEN·trik). Unconventional in a conspicuous way.

eddy (ED·ih). A backward-circling current of water or air.

effaced (e·FAYS'D). Wiped out; canceled.

effrontery (ef·FRUN·ta·ree). Shameless boldness; impudence.

elite (ay·LEET). Favored people.

emaciation (ih·MAY·shee·AY·shun). Wasting away.

emancipated (eh·MAN·sih·payt·ed). Set free.

eminent (EM·ih·nent). Well-known; standing above others.

enigmatic (en·nig·MAT·ik). Puzzling.

entwined (in·TWYND). Twisted around or twisted together.

epic (EP·ik). A long narrative poem about a hero. *Adjective:* Of heroic character.

epitome (eh·PIT·o·mee). 1. A concise summary. 2. A person or thing which typifies a whole class.

epoch (EP·uk). An interval of time.

equivocal (eh·KWIV·a·kul). Questionable; dubious.

errata (ih·RAH·tuh). *Printing term:* Mistakes, errors.

esteemed (eh·STEEMD). 1. Highly regarded. 2. Rated.

etched (ECH'T). Outlined or sketched.

ethics (ETH·iks). The principles of right conduct.

ethnic (ETH·nik). Distinctive of a particular race or language group of mankind.

eulogy (YOO·lu·jee). Spoken or written high praise, especially when delivered publicly.

evade (ee·VAYD). Avoid by trickery; get around.

evince (eh·VINS). To indicate clearly.

exalted (egs·ZAWL·ted). Increased the intensity of; heightened; elevated.

excelsior (ek·SEL·si·or). Long, fine wood shavings used as stuffing or as packing material.

exchequer (eks·CHEK·er). The treasury of a state or nation; total financial funds.

excruciating (eks·KROO·shee·ayt·ing). Unbearable; very painful.

exertion (ig·ZUR·shun). 1. Strong action. 2. Work.

exhilaration (eks·zil·uh·RAY·shun). The state of being animated or gay.

expedient (eks·SPEE·dee·ent). A suitable means; something advisable.

expostulation (eks·pos·choo·LAY·shun). A firm but friendly protest.

exquisite (EKS·kwiz·it). Especially fine; delicate.

extemporary (eks·TEM·poh·rehr·ee). Sudden; unplanned.

extortion (eks·TOR·shun). The act of obtaining money by means of threats or violence.

exuberance (eg·ZOO·ba·rans). Abundance of high spirits.

exultation (eks·zul·TAY·shun). Joy over a success or victory.

F

fable (FAY·bul). A legend or myth; a foolish or improbable story.

fandango (fan·DANG·go). A lively Spanish dance.

feckless (FEK·lus). Feeble; listless; without energy or effectiveness.

feinted (FAYNT·id). Pretended; made a boxing move to throw an opponent off guard.

felicity (feh·LIS·ih·tee). Happiness.

felon (FEL·un). One who has committed a serious crime.

fervently (FER·vent·lee). Eagerly.

fey (FAY). Acting as if enchanted.

fiasco (fee·AS·ko). A complete or humiliating failure.

figment (FIG·munt). Something imagined.

filibusterers (fil·ih·BUS·ta·rerz). Soldiers of fortune; adventurers.

flambeaux (FLAM·bohz). Burning torches.

flawless. Absolutely perfect.

fluency (FLOO·un·see). Smoothness and readiness, especially of speech.

fodder (FOD·ur). Coarse feed for horses or cattle. **Cannon fodder.** Soldiers wounded or killed by artillery.

folklore (FOHK·lor). Traditions, customs, and stories preserved among the common people.

folly (FOL·ee). Foolishness.

forlornly (for·LORN·lee). Abandoned, deserted; cheerless.

fortissimo (for·TISS·uh·moh). 1. Very loud, in music. 2. High point.

founder (FOUN·der). To sink after filling with water.

freshet (FRESH·it). A sudden rise or overflow of a stream.

frets. A series of ridges fixed across the fingerboard of a stringed instrument to guide the fingers.

frivolous (FRIV·uh·lus). Petty; silly.

frontispiece (FRUN·tiss·pees). Picture facing the title page of a book.

fundamentals (fun·duh·MEN·tulz). Basic or essential points.

furtive (FUR·tiv). Sly; secret.

fusillade (fyoo·zih·LAYD). A quick succession of shots.

G

gait. Manner of walking or stepping.

gambol (GAM·bul). To skip about, as in dancing or playing.

gaping (GAY·ping). Staring with open-mouthed surprise.

garbles (GAR·bulz). Mixes up or confuses on purpose.

garish (GAIR·ish). Showy; harsh and glaring.

gauged (GAYJ'D). Estimated; judged.

gaunt (GAWNT). Haggard; thin.

gawk. To stare stupidly; gape.

genes (JEENS). Parts of cells through which characteristics and traits are passed from parent to child.

genesis (JEN·eh·sis). Origin; beginning.

genus (JEE·nus). A particular sort, kind, or class.

germination (jer·mih·NAY·shun). Sprouting; the beginning of growth.

ghouls (GOOLZ). Robbers of graves.

gibbet (JIB·it). Gallows.

gossamer (GOS·a·mer). Flimsy; unsubstantial.

grimaced (grih·MAYST). Made faces.

grisly (GRIZ·lee). Bloody; frightening.

grizzled (GRIZZ·uld). Having gray hair.

grueling (GROO·el·ing). Exhausting; very difficult.

guile (GILE). Treacherous cunning.

guise (GYZ). External appearance; dress.

gunwale (GUN·el). The part of a ship where the deck meets the outer sides.

gyration (jy·RAY·shun). A spiral or whirling motion.

H

halcyon (HAL·see·un). Calm; peaceful.

hapless (HAP·les). Unlucky; unfortunate.

harangues (ha·RANGZ). Long, loud, and vehement speeches; tirades.

heyday (HAY·day). 1. Period of highest success. 2. Joy.

hogsheads (HOGZ·hedz). Large barrels.

hombre (OM·breh). The Spanish word for "man."

hue (HYOO). Outcry.

hummock (HUM·uk). A low mound of earth.

husbanded (HUZ·band·ud). Conserved; spent wisely.

hybrid (HY·brid). Anything with a mixed origin or composition.

hyperbolically (hy·per·BOL·ih·kul·lee). In an exaggerated or overstated way, usually for humor or to make a point.

hypochondriac (hi·puh·KON·dree·ack). Person who thinks he is always sick.

hysterical (hiss·TER·ih·kul). Uncontrolled; violent.

I

idiom (ID·ih·um). 1. A way of expression. 2. An expression peculiar to a language.

ignoble (ig·NOH·bul). Inferior; degraded.

ignominious (ig·no·MIN·eh·us). Disgraceful; humiliating.

illusion (ih·LOO·zhun). A false or overly optimistic idea.

immobilized (ih·MOH·bih·lyzd). Immovable; fixed in place.

immortality (im·or·TAL·uh·tee). 1. Living forever. 2. Eternal fame.

impartiality (im·par·shee·AL·uh·tee). Complete fairness.

impeachment (im·PEECH·munt). The act of bringing charges against a public official and trying him before a proper tribunal.

impede (im·PEED). Hinder; stop the progress of.

impending (im·PEN·ding). Threatening to happen.

imperceptible (im·per·SEP·tih·bul). Not easily distinguishable.

imperious (im·PIR·ih·us). 1. Urgent; imperative. 2. Domineering; arrogant.

implacable (im·PLAY·ka·bul). Unrelenting; unappeasable.

imprecations (im·preh·KAY·shunz). Curses.

impropriety (im·proh·PRY·eh·tee). Action not conforming with standards of conduct or good taste.

incalculable (in·KAL·kyoo·la·bul). Not predictable.

incarnate (in·KAR·nit). 1. In human form. 2. Typified.

incomprehensible (in·kom·pree·HENS·a·bul). Not understandable.

inconclusive (in·kon·KLOO·siv). Without a final decision or result.

incredible (in·KRED·ih·bul). Unbelievable.

incredulous (in·KRED·yoo·lus). Not willing to believe; skeptical.

incumbrance (in·KUM·brans). Something burdensome; a hindrance. (Also spelled **encumbrance**.)

indenture (in·DEN·chur). An agreement between a master and an apprentice.

indicted (in·DYT·ed). Charged with a crime; accused. *Noun:* **indictment** (in·DYT·ment).

indigenous (in·DIJ·eh·nus). Native.

indiscreet (in·dis·KREET). Not wise and careful.

indolently (IN·doh·lent·lee). Lazily. *Adjective:* **indolent.**

indomitable (in·DOM·ih·tuh·bul). Not easily defeated.

indubitably (in·DOO·bih·tuh·blee). Certainly; undoubtedly.

induce (in·DOOS). To influence; to persuade.

ineffable (in·EF·a·bul). Too overpowering to be expressed in words.

ineffectual (in·ih·FECK·choo·ul). Not effective; not successful.

ineradicable (in·ih·RAD·uh·kuh·bul). Impossible to root out or remove.

inevitable (in·EV·ih·ta·bul). Bound to happen. *Adverb:* **inevitably.**

inexorably (in·EK·sa·ra·blee). Relentlessly; unyieldingly.

infamy (IN·fa·mee). Public disgrace; evil notoriety.

inferno (in·FER·noh). Any place comparable to hell; a hot place.

infidels (IN·fih·delz). Unbelievers.

ingenious (in·JEEN·ee·us). Clever; able to solve problems.

insatiable (in·SAY·shuh·bul). Extremely greedy; unable to be satisfied.

insidious (in·SID·ee·us). Treacherous; subtly deceitful.

insurgence (in·SUR·juns). Revolt; uprising.

insurrection (in·sa·REK·shun). An organized resistance to government.

intemperate (in·TEM·per·it). Lacking moderation; unrestrained.

intense (in·TENS). Earnest; eager. *Noun:* **intensity.**

interminable (in·TER·mih·na·bul). Unending; endless.

intervene (in·ter·VEEN). Interrupt; come between; stop.

intimation (in·tih·MAY·shun). A hint; an indirect suggestion or reference.

intravenous (in·truh·VEE·nus). In the veins.

intrigue (in·TREEG). Secret plotting.

intuitively (in·TOO·ih·tiv·lee). Instinctively.

inured (in·YOORD). Accustomed.

invariably (in·VAIR·ee·uh·blee). Unchangeably; constantly.

inveigle (in·VEE·gul). To flatter into doing something.

invincible (in·VIN·suh·bul). Unconquerable.

irascible (ih·RAS·ih·bul). Irritable; easily provoked to anger.

iridescent (ir·ih·DES·unt). Shining with many colors, as in soap bubbles or mother-of-pearl.

irrational (ih·RASH·un·ul). Senseless; contrary to reason.

irrevocable (ir·REV·a·ka·bul). Unalterable.

isolation (eye·soh·LAY·shun). Solitude; aloneness.

itinerant (eye·TIN·ur·ent). Wandering from place to place.

J

javelin (JAV·uh·lin). Long spear thrown for distance.

jeopardize (JEP·ar·dyz). Imperil; expose to injury.

judiciously (joo·DISH·us·lee). Wisely; in a careful manner.

K

kids (KIDZ). Gloves made of kidskin.

kinship. Relationship.

kinsman. A blood relation, such as a cousin or uncle.

knell (NEL). The tolling of a bell announcing a death; an omen of death.

L

languorous (LANG·ger·us). Not wanting to do anything; listless.

lassitude (LAS·ih·tyood). Weariness.

laudable (LAW·duh·bul). Deserving praise.

leviathan. (leh·VY·eh·thun). A gigantic water beast mentioned in the Bible.

libelling (LY·bel·ing). Publishing false and deliberately harmful statements.

lieu (LOO). Place. **In lieu of.** In the place of.

linguist (LING·gwist). 1. Person who knows several languages. 2. Person who specializes in any language.

literally (LIT·ur·uh·lee). Actually; really.

literate (LIT·er·at). Able to read and write.
ludicrous (LOO·da·krus). Absurd; ridiculous.
luminous (LOO·muh·nus). Shining.
lush. Covered with vigorous plants.

M

machete (muh·SHET·ee). Heavy knife used in tropical America.
magnitude (MAG·nuh·tood). Size, especially huge size.
mailed (MAYLD). Covered with defensive armor.
maim (MAYM). Disable; mutilate.
malevolence (ma·LEV·oh·lens). Act of wishing evil toward others.
malicious (ma·LISH·us). Spiteful.
malign (ma·LYN). Evil; ill disposed.
mandibles (MAN·dih·bulz). Jaws.
manifestation (man·uh·fess·TAY·shun). Sign; indication.
manila (ma·NIL·uh). 1. A fiber. 2. A type of paper.
mantis (**praying mantis**) (MAN·tis). An insect which eats other insects and assumes a prayerlike attitude while awaiting its prey.
meditative (MED·ih·tay·tiv). Thoughtful.
meerschaum (MIR·showm). A tobacco pipe made from a particular mineral.
menacing (MEN·us·ing). Threatening.
mettlesome (MET·ul·sum). Spirited; courageous.
milieux (mee·LYUR). French word for settings, environments.
mirage (mih·RAZH). Optical illusion; something that appears to be real but is not.
miscellany (MIS·uh·lay·nee). Assorted collection.
mode. Way; method; manner.
modulate (MOD·yoo·layt). Soften; modify.
morale (ma·RAL). State of mind.
morosely (muh·ROHS·lee). Sullenly; gloomily.
mortification (mor·ti·fuh·KAY·shun). Humiliation; shame.
muddle (MUD·ul). Stir or mix. **Muddle steel.** Work in a steel mill.
multitudinous (mull·tih·TOO·duh·nus). Numerous.
mundane (mun·DAYN). Worldly.
munificent (myoo·NIF·ih·sent). Generous.
murky (MUR·kee). Dark; hazy; obscure.
musculature (MUSS·kuh·luh·choor). Arrangement of muscles.
myriad (MIR·ee·ud). A vast, indefinite number.

N

navvy (NAV·ee). British word for "laborer."
negotiating (nih·GOH·shee·ayt·ing). Dealing (with someone).
nettled (NET·uld). Annoyed; provoked.
nonchalant (NON·shah·lant). 1. Lacking in enthusiasm or interest. 2. Casual. *Noun:* **nonchalance.**
nondescript (NON·de·skript). Not distinctive; ordinary.
nonpareil (non·pa·REL). One who has no equal.
notoriety (noh·ta·RY·eh·tee). The state of being widely known and generally disapproved of. *Adjective:* **notorious** (noh·TOR·ee·us).
nub. Point.

O

obnoxious (ob·NOCK·shus). Highly disagreeable; offensive.
obsession (ob·SESH·un). A persistent idea or feeling.
odious (OH·dee·us). Hateful; offensive.
omen (OH·men). An incident regarded as a prophetic sign.
ominous (OM·ih·nus). Threatening.
omnipotent (om·NIP·oh·tent). Almighty; unlimited in power.
oppressed (uh·PREST). Under a feeling of being weighed down.
opulence (OP·yoo·lens). Abundance; riches.
ordeal (or·DEEL). Severe hardship or suffering.
ornate (or·NAYT). Elaborately decorated; showy.
orthodox (OR·thuh·docks). Conventional; doing what most people do.
oscillating (OS·ih·lay·ting). Swinging back and forth like a pendulum.
ostracism (OS·tra·siz·um). Banishment; exclusion.
overprepossessing (oh·vur·PREE·puh·ZESS·ing). Especially attractive.
overwrought (oh·vur·RAWT). Strained from overwork.

P

palmy (PAH·mee). Prosperous.
palpable (PAL·puh·bul). Easily or plainly seen or heard; obvious.
palpitation (pal·pih·TAY·shun). Quivering; trembling.
paltry (POL·tree). Trifling; trivial.

pandemonium (pan·deh·MOH·nee·um). Complete confusion.

panorama (pan·oh·RAH·mah). A long-range, complete view of a region.

paradoxical (par·a·DOKS·ih·kul). Contradictory; absurd.

parsimonious (pahr·sih·MOH·nee·us). Stingy.

passivity (pa·SIV·ih·tee). Lack of resistance.

paternosters (pay·ter·NOS·terz). Prayers.

pathos (PAY·thaws). The arousing of pity or sorrow.

peevish (PEE·vish). Irritable; fretful; cross.

pelf. Money, especially if dishonestly acquired.

perceptibly (per·SEP·tih·blee). Noticeably. *Adjective:* **perceptible.**

percussion (per·KUSH·un). The shock or sound produced by one thing striking against another.

peremptorily (peh·REMP·ta·rih·lee). Dictatorially; in a decisive manner.

perfidy (PUR·fih·dee). Treachery, faithlessness.

perforce (per·FORS). By force of circumstances; of necessity.

perfunctory (per·FUNGK·toh·ree). Done merely as a duty; performed carelessly.

perpetually (per·PECH·yoo·uh·lee). Constantly; forever.

perplexity (per·PLEK·sa·tee). Bewilderment, confusion.

persistent (per·SIS·tent). Continuous.

pertinacity (per·tih·NAS·ih·tee). Obstinacy; stubbornness.

perverseness (per·VERS·ness). Contrariness.

pewter (PYOO·tur). An alloy, usually of tin and lead, formerly much used for tableware.

phantasm (FAN·taz·um). A mental image; an imaginary appearance.

phenomenon (feh·NOM·eh·non). A marvel; an unexplainable fact.

piercing (PEER·sing). Sharp; penetrating.

pinioned (PIN·yun'd). Bound; shackled.

piquant (PEE·kant). Interesting; tart.

piqued (PEEK'T). Irritated; annoyed.

pittances (PIT·ans·es). Small amounts of money.

pivotal (PIV·a·tul). Being the central point on which something turns.

plaintive (PLAYN·tiv). Mournful.

platoon system (pluh·TOON). In football, using one team on offense and another complete team on defense.

plausible (PLAW·sih·bul). Easy to believe.

poignant (POIN·yant). Piercing; penetrating.

pontifically (pon·TIF·ih·kul·lee). With the dignity of a bishop.

portent (POR·tent). An indication or sign of something which is about to happen.

posterity (pos·TERR·ih·tee). Future generations.

potentate (PO·ten·tayt). Powerful ruler or king.

practitioner (prack·TISH·un·er). Person who practices a profession.

precarious (preh·KAIR·ee·us). Uncertain; risky.

precept (PREE·sept). A rule prescribing a particular kind of conduct or action.

predatory (PRED·a·toh·ree). Robbing; plundering.

predestined (pree·DES·tin'd). Decided or decreed beforehand.

preliminaries (prih·LIM·uh·ner·eez). Happenings leading to the main event.

premature (pree·ma·TYOOR). Too early; untimely.

preternaturally (pree·ter·NACH·er·a·lee). Outside the natural order; supernaturally.

prismatic (priz·MAT·ik). Showing the colors of the rainbow.

proboscis (pro·BOS·is). A tubular feeding structure of certain insects, such as bees and mosquitoes.

prodigal (PROD·ih·gal). Lavish; too generous. *Adverb:* **prodigally.**

prodigious (proh·DIJ·us). 1. Vast; immense. 2. Amazing; marvelous.

prodigy (PRO·dih·jee). A person, especially a child, of great talent.

proffer (PROF·er). To offer for acceptance.

promontory (PROM·un·toh·ree). A high point of land projecting into water.

propitious (pro·PI·shus). Favorable.

propriety (proh·PRY·eh·tee). Established customs of polite behavior.

protégé (PROH·tuh·zhay). A person who is cared for by a more powerful person.

provincial (proh·VIN·shul). Belonging to a region; local.

provocations (prov·a·KAY·shunz). Acts of provoking; stirring up anger or resentment. *Verb:* **provoke.**

prowess (PROU·es). Strength; skill.

proximity (proks·IM·ih·tee). Nearness.

pulsating (PUL·say·ting). Vibrating; quivering.

puny (PYOO·nee). Small and feeble.

purgatory (PER·ga·toh·ree). A place or state of suffering; condition of misery.

purged (PURJ'D). Cleansed; purified.

Q

quavering (KWAY·ver·ing). Shaking; trembling.

quelled (KWELD). Overpowered; suppressed.

querulous (KWER·uh·lus). Complaining; whining.

quid (KWID) A pound sterling (British slang).

quizzically (KWIZ·ih·kah·lee). 1. Amusingly; teasingly. 2. Oddly. 3. Questioningly. *Adjective:* **quizzical.**

R

rabid (RAB·id). Furious; violently angry.

rampant (RAM·punt). Unrestrained; widespread.

rancors (RANG·kerz). Resentments.

ravaging (RAV·ij·ing). Destroying, usually by violent action.

rebuffed (rih·BUFFED). Rudely rejected.

recalcitrant (reh·KAL·sih·trant). Rebellious; not complying.

receded (reh·SEE·ded). Moved back; withdrew.

recoiled (reh·KOILD). Jumped back.

reconnoiter (ree·ko·NOI·tur). To examine or survey as for military or engineering purposes.

recreant (REK·ree·ant). A cowardly or faithless person.

recuperate (rih·KOO·puh·rayt). Gain back health or strength.

refractory (re·FRAK·toh·ree). Impossible to manage or control.

refrain (re·FRAYN). A verse which is repeated at intervals in a song or poem.

regale (re·GAYL). To entertain; to feast.

regalia (reh·GAYL·ya). Fine clothes; distinctive costume.

repose (rih·POHZ). Rest.

reprimand (REP·rih·mand). To reprove sharply; to scold.

repudiates (reh·PYOO·dee·ayts). Rejects.

repugnant (reh·PUG·nant). Distasteful. *Noun:* **repugnance.** A feeling of aversion and resistance.

respite (RES·pit). An interval of rest; a delay.

restrained (rih·STRAYND). Held back from acting.

retrieved (rih·TREEVD). Got back; restored.

retrogressed (reh·troh·GRES'T). Deteriorated; moved backward.

revelation (re·veh·LAY·shun). Disclosure; something made known.

revere (re·VEER). To respect; to admire.

reverie (REV·er·ee). Daydream.

ritual (RICH·oo·ul). Ceremony, rite; for a prescribed form for performing a religious ceremony.

rudiments (ROO·dih·ments). The first stages; that which is undeveloped or partially developed.

ruefully (ROO·fuh·lee). Sadly; mournfully.

ruminate (ROO·mih·nayt). To ponder; to think about something again and again. *Noun:* **ruminating.**

S

sadistic (sa·DIS·tik). Cruel.

saffron (SAF·run). 1. A deep yellow-orange color. 2. Part of a crocus used for coloring and for flavoring in cooking.

sagacious (sa·GAY·shus). Wise; having good judgment.

sallies (SAL·eez). Sudden rushes.

sardonically (sahr·DON·ih·kul·lee). Derisively; sneeringly.

satire (SAT·eyr). Ridicule.

satiric (sa·TIR·ik). Sarcastic; ironic.

saturnalia (sa·tur·NAY·lya). Riotous fun.

saunter (SAWN·tur). To walk leisurely; to stroll.

savoir-faire (sah·vwahr-FEHR). French expression meaning skill, dexterity, or know-how.

savoring (SAY·vu·ring). Relishing; tasting or enjoying with pleasure.

scanning. Looking over.

scoff (SKOF). To speak with contempt; jeer; mock.

scourge (SKURJ). 1. A widespread misfortune; suffering. 2. A punishment.

scrupulous (SKROO·pyoo·lus). Conscientious.

scurrying (SKUR·ih·ing). Moving hurriedly; scampering.

scuttle (SKUT·ul). Covered opening on a ship.

seer. A prophet; person who foretells events.

seines (SAYNS). Long fishnets with floats at the top and weights at the bottom.

sepulcher (SEP·ul·ker). A burial place; tomb.

seraph (SEHR·af). A celestial being.

serene (suh·REEN). Calm; peaceful; unworried.

serried (SEHR·eed). Pressed together in rows, as in military formations.

showboating. In sports, exaggerating to make a play look harder, or giving an action an extra flourish.

simper (SIM·pur). To smile in a silly, self-conscious manner.

sinewy (SIN·yoo·ee). Strong; vigorous.

sinister (SIN·iss·tur). Evil; attended by disaster.

sires (SYRZ). Male ancestors; forefathers.

skeptical (SKEP·tih·kul). Doubting; disbelieving.

slithered (SLITH·erd). Slid; glided.

slothful. Sluggish; lazy.

solace (SOL·is). Comfort.

solemnities (su·LEM·nih·teez). Ceremonious observances. *Verb:* **solemnize.** To celebrate.

solicited (so·LIS·ih·tud). Obtained by persuasion.

solicitous (soh·LIS·ih·tus). 1. Anxious or concerned. 2. Eager. *Noun:* solicitude.

somnolent (SOM·noh·lunt). Drowsy; not lively.

speculation (speh·kyoo·LAY·shun). A theory or conjecture.

sporadic (spo·RAD·ik). Occasional; occurring here and there.

staccato (sta·KAH·toh). Consisting of short, clearcut, disconnected tones or beats.

stalemate (STAYL·mayt). A deadlock.

stamina (STAM·uh·na). Ability to endure, to withstand hardship.

starboard (STAR·bord). The right-hand side of a vessel as one faces the front.

steerage (STEER·uj). Lower decks of passenger vessel, allotted to those paying lowest fares.

stipulate (STIP·yoo·layt). To require as an essential condition in making an agreement.

stolid (STOL·id). Showing little or no feeling.

stultified (STUL·tih·fyd). 1. Made worthless; nullified. 2. Made absurd or foolish.

stupefied (STOO·peh·fyd). Stunned; amazed; astounded.

stupendous (stoo·PEN·dus). Impressive; of great size.

subsequent (SUB·seh·kwent). Following.

subsided (sub·SY·ded). Quieted down; ceased. *Noun:* subsidence.

subsist (sub·SIST). To live.

substance (SUB·stuns). What anything is made of; reality; solidity.

succinctly (suk·SINGKT·lee). Briefly; concisely.

succumbed (sa·KUMD). Gave way; yielded.

summarily (SUM·a·rih·lee). Performed without delay; instantly.

supercilious (soo·per·SIL·ee·us). Arrogant; exhibiting haughty contempt.

superficial (soo·per·FISH·ul). Shallow; slight; not real or genuine.

superfluous (soo·PER·floo·us). Useless; more than is needed.

superlative (su·PER·luh·tiv). To the highest degree.

supersede (soo·per·SEED). To take the place of.

supersonic (soo·per·SON·ik). Faster than sound.

supple (SUP·ul). Easily bent; easily changed. *Noun:* suppleness.

supplicating (SUP·lih·kayt·ing). Earnestly asking.

surfeit (SUR·fit). To feed to fullness.

surmised (sur·MYZ'D). Guessed.

surreptitious (sur·up·TISH·us). Accomplished by secret means.

symbol (SIM·bul). Something which stands for something else, especially for a quality or an idea. *Verb:* symbolize.

synopses (sih·NOP·seez). Summaries; abridgements.

T

tacit (TAS·it). 1. Making no sound; silent. 2. Unexpressed.

taciturn (TAS·ih·turn). Silent; not talkative.

taint (TAYNT). Suspicion of dishonor.

tamped (TAMPT). Forced down by firm repeated blows.

tarried (TA·reed). Lingered; waited; stayed.

tawdry (TAW·dree). Showy and cheap; in poor taste.

tawny. Tan-colored; brownish-yellow.

tedious (TEE·dee·us). Tiresome; boring.

tenure (TEN·yur). A holding; the period during which something is held.

tersely (TERS·lee). Shortly and to the point. *Adjective:* terse.

tether. A rope or chain.

tiers (TEERZ). Levels or layers.

tinctured (TINGK·churd). Tinged; colored.

titillated (TI·tih·lay·tud). Pleasurably excited.

torrential (tu·REN·shul). Overpowering; resembling a turbulent stream of water.

tortuous (TOR·choo·us). Consisting of irregular bends or turns; twisting.

trammeled (TRAM·ul'd). Restricted; beaten down.

transcended (tran·SEND·ed). Rose above.

transgress (trans·GRES). To break a law.

traumatic (traw·MAT·ik). Causing an emotional or physical wound.

traversed (TRAV·erst). Passed over or across.

trebled (TREB·uld). Multiplied by three.

trek. A journey, especially a slow, difficult one.

tumultuous (too·MUL·tyoo·us). Disorderly; involving a commotion or disturbance.

turbulent (TUR·byoo·lent). Disturbed; disordered; excited.

turpitude (TUR·pih·tood). Inherent baseness; depravity; vileness.

U

uncanny (un·KAN·ee). Unnatural; strange.

undulating (UN·dyoo·lay·ting). Having the appearance of waves, *Noun:* undulation.

unique (yoo·NEEK). Only one of its kind.

unprecedented (un·PRES·ih·dent·id). Never done before.

unquenchable (un·KWENCH·uh·bul). Not able to be suppressed.

unregimented (un·REJ·uh·ment·id). Not able to act in groups or be fit into regular organizations.

untoward (un·TOHRD). Causing annoyance; vexatious; unseemly.

unwonted (un·WUN·tid). Not according to custom; unusual.

V

vacuity (va·KYOO·ih·tee). Emptiness; the state of being in a vacuum.

vagrancy (VAY·gran·see). The state of being a penniless wanderer. *Noun:* **vagrant.**

vanguard (VAN·gard). The front of an army; leaders in a movement, such as in art.

vanquished (VANG·kwisht). Defeated in battle.

vaunted (VAWN·ted). Spoken of boastfully.

veered (VEERD). Turned; changed direction.

venom (VEN·um). 1. A poisonous liquid secreted by certain snakes. 2. Spite; malice.

verve (VERV). Enthusiasm, spirit, vigor.

vex (VEKS). Irritate; annoy. *Noun:* **vexation.**

victuals (VIT·ulz). Food.

vigil (VIJ·ul). The act of staying awake in order to observe or protect; watch.

vilified (VIL·ih·fyd). Slandered; maligned; degraded.

vintage (VIN·tij). 1. A crop, usually of grapes. 2. Of a particular year.

vituperation (vy·too·pa·RAY·shun). Violent, wordy abuse.

vociferous (voh·SIF·er·us). Making a loud outcry; noisy. *Adverb:* **vociferously.**

vortex (VOR·teks). Whirlpool.

votive (VOH·tiv). Dedicated by a vow; given in fulfillment of a vow or promise.

vying (VEYE·ing). Contending; competing.

W

wan (WON). Pale; sickly.

warped (WORPD). 1. Turned from the proper course. 2. Twisted out of shape.

warren (WOR·un). 1. A crowded living place. 2. An enclosure for keeping small game (rabbits).

wary (WA·ri). Carefully watching and guarding.

windlass (WIND·lus). Any of several devices for hauling or lifting.

wistful (WIST·ful). Wishful; longing.

wrought (RAWT). Fashioned; formed; worked.

Y

yammer (YAM·mer). Whine, cry.

yaw (YOH). To steer a ship wildly or out of its course.

Z

zither (ZITH·er). A stringed instrument.

INDEX OF AUTHORS AND TITLES

F 1
G 2
H 3
I 4
J 5
K 6
L
M 7